INHALED PARTICLES
III

INHALED PARTICLES
III

Proceedings of an International Symposium
organized by the British Occupational Hygiene Society
in London, 14–23 September, 1970

Edited by
W. H. WALTON

VOLUME I

UNWIN BROTHERS LIMITED
THE GRESHAM PRESS, OLD WOKING, SURREY, ENGLAND

First printed and published 1971
by
Unwin Brothers Limited, The Gresham Press, Old Woking, Surrey, England

ORGANIZING COMMITTEE

Chairman: Dr. J. M. ROGAN, Chief Medical Officer, National Coal Board.

Dr. J. M. BARNES, Director, Toxicology Research Unit, Medical Research Council.

Dr. A. CRITCHLOW, Safety in Mines Research Establishment, Ministry of Technology.

Dr. J. C. GAGE, Director, Industrial Hygiene Laboratories, Imperial Chemical Industries.

Dr. J. C. GILSON, Director, Pneumoconiosis Research Unit, Medical Research Council.

Dr. J. GRAHAM JONES, Medical Service, British Steel Corporation.

Dr. J. S. McLINTOCK, Medical Service, National Coal Board.

Dr. S. A. ROACH, Department of Occupational Health, London School of Hygiene & Tropical Medicine.

Mr. W. H. WALTON, Institute of Occupational Medicine, Edinburgh.

Committee
Secretary: Mr. G. F. CORY, Pneumoconiosis Research Unit, Medical Research Council.

CONTENTS

VOLUME I

Contents—Vol. I

SECTION II. PULMONARY CLEARANCE

Contents—Vol. I

Contents—Vol. I

SECTION IV. BIOLOGICAL REACTIONS — ANCILLARY FACTORS

CONTENTS

VOLUME II

Contents—Vol. II

SECTION VIII. CHARACTERISTICS OF AIRBORNE DUSTS

SECTION IX. EPIDEMIOLOGICAL STUDIES

Contents—Vol. II

SECTION X. DUST SAMPLING AND STANDARDS

PREFACE

THESE two volumes record the Proceedings of the third International Symposium in a series organised at 5-year intervals by the British Occupational Hygiene Society. It was held at the Imperial College of Science and Technology London, from 16th to 23rd September, 1970.

When, some twelve years ago, I first suggested to the Society that it should sponsor a symposium on Inhaled Particles and Vapours, the basic mechanisms underlying health hazards from the inhalation of airborne contaminants were receiving increasing research attention and new ideas were beginning to lead to a reappraisal of some established practices, particularly in relation to the mineral dust diseases. It therefore seemed at that time that an attempt to bring together the results of the latest research would be useful to both the research workers and those responsible for practical measures of health protection. The 2nd and 3rd symposia have had similar aims. The continuing growth of interest in this field is indicated by the present 90 papers, as compared with 48 in 1965 and 38 in 1960; indeed, the large amount of material offered made it necessary on this occasion to restrict the scope to 'Inhaled Particles', leaving 'Vapours' for another meeting. Much of the work now reported has not been published elsewhere.

A vast amount of information is contained in these 91 papers; its assembly should do much to facilitate an appraisal of the complex subject as a whole and to guide further research towards important outstanding problems. The Discussions, too, though recorded in smaller print, will be found to contain ideas and information of great relevance.

Perusal of the contributions will reveal that substantial advances have been made since 1965. The picture of laminar reversible airflow in the smaller airways of the lungs has been shown to be too simple. Studies of particle inhalation and deposition have been extended to fibrous particles, and to humans with lung abnormalities. The mechanisms of pulmonary clearance by muco-ciliary transport in the upper airways and by alveolar macrophages from the respiratory region have been further studied: the alveolar macrophage is now considered by many to originate in the bone marrow, not from the alveolar epithelium (1960) or lymphoid tissue (1965). Considerable progress has been made in understanding the toxicity of quartz to alveolar macrophages and the protective action of various substances. Quartz and other minerals from different sources have variable activities and the protective effect of some constituents of mixed dusts may be only temporary; the importance of carrying out long term animal experiments using the actual dusts found in industry is therefore emphasised. The dust hazards in mining have again received considerable attention and important results are described from epidemiological studies of pneumoconiosis begun more than a decade ago in Britain, Germany and South Africa. These have led to the introduction of new dust standards for British and American coalmines. There appears to be good agreement between British and German results for the dose-response relationship in coalworkers simple pneumoconiosis, although the roles of different mineral constituents of the dust remain elusive. Chronic bronchitis has attracted increased attention and a relationship to dust exposure has been found in coalminers, after allowing for the much greater effect of tobacco smoking.

No doubt different aspects of the work will be singled out by other readers, according to their particular interests.

I wish to thank the many people who have helped me with my editorial duties, including Dr. J. C. Gilson and my colleagues Mr. J. Dodgson, Mr. R. Love, Dr. D. C. F. Muir, Dr. S. Rae, Dr. D. D. Walker and especially Dr. T. L. Ogden who, with his wife, prepared the subject index, Mrs. E. B. Duncan for work on the bibliographies, and my secretary Miss H. F. B. Anderson. Dr. A. C. Critchlow's earlier contribution as Secretary of the Programme Sub-Committee and in supervising the recording of the discussions must also be mentioned. I am most grateful to the Authors and to Messrs. Unwin Brothers Ltd. for their ready co-operation.

W. H. WALTON

Institute of Occupational Medicine,
Roxburgh Place, Edinburgh EH8 9SU

SECTION I
INHALATION AND DEPOSITION

NEW METHODS FOR THE GENERATION OF AEROSOLS OF INSOLUBLE PARTICLES FOR USE IN INHALATION STUDIES*

OTTO G. RAABE, GEORGE M. KANAPILLY and GEORGE J. NEWTON

*Lovelace Foundation for Medical Education and Research,
Albuquerque, New Mexico, U.S.A.*

Abstract — Advanced methods are described for the generation of aerosols of
well defined physical and chemical character that simulate occupational dusts.
Aerosols produced from various aqueous solutions and suspensions are altered in
chemical composition and physical shape under controlled conditions. Because of
their simplicity and reproducibility and because of the variety of aerosols of
insoluble particles in the respirable size range that are attainable, these techniques
are ideal for use in inhalation experiments. Aerosols both of toxic metal oxides
and of innocuous materials with incorporated radionuclides may be prepared. The
generation of monodisperse aerosols (coefficient of variation $< 1\%$) of insoluble
spherical particles with these methods is described.

The physical and chemical nature of aerosols produced by the methods described
have been investigated. Their physical characteristics were determined by electron-
microscopic studies, particle density measurements, and aerodynamic samples,
and their chemical properties by tracer and instrumental techniques.

INTRODUCTION

THE generation of respirable aerosols of "insoluble" forms with well defined physical
and chemical characteristics is an important aspect of inhalation studies. Methods
which have been used for producing aerosols of insoluble materials include dispersion
of dry powders and the atomization of solutions and suspensions. When dry powders
are dispersed the particles produced are usually irregular in shape and in a state of
aggregation. The production of reproducible concentrations or size distributions is
difficult and the standard deviation of the distribution is usually large. Aerosols of
insoluble materials can be produced by atomization of solutions such as plastics in
organic solvents, but the removal of the solvent vapor from the air is usually a problem.
Nebulization of an aqueous colloidal suspension forms insoluble particles of the
aggregates of the colloidal micelles and no organic solvents are required. If the micelles
are small and in high concentrations, the resultant particles will be nearly spherical
and their size distribution may be predicted from the droplet distribution assuming
the suspension behaves as a solution. If the micelles are large, many of the particles
may be aggregates. Unfortunately, aerosols produced from colloids may have in-

* Based upon work performed under Contract AT(29-2)-1013 between the United States Atomic
Energy Commission and the Lovelace Foundation for Medical Education and Research.

herent porosity because of the interstices between the micellular components, and the chemical character of these aerosols is usually doubtful.

In this report a general approach is described in which heat treatment of various aerosols generated from aqueous solutions and suspensions is used to create spherical aerosol particles of desirable chemical and physical forms. One application of the concept involves the production of spherical particles of insoluble metal oxides from aqueous solutions with heat treatment of the aerosols. Usually commercially available forms of metals such as oxalates, citrates, tartrates, etc. can be directly used. This procedure involves (a) nebulizing a solution of metal ions in chelated form, (b) drying the droplets, (c) passing the aerosol through a high-temperature heating column to produce the spherical oxide particles, and (d) cooling the aerosol with the addition of diluting air. Another example of aerosol alteration by heat treatment is the production of spherical aluminosilicate particles with incorporated radionuclides by heat fusion of clay aerosols. This method involves (a) ion exchange of desired radionuclide cation into clay in aqueous suspension and washing away of the unexchanged fraction, (b) nebulization of the clay suspension yielding a clay aerosol, (c) heat fusion of clay aerosol removing water and forming an aerosol of smooth solid spheres, and (d) cooling the aerosol with the addition of diluting air.

In inhalation experiments the use of spherical, or nearly spherical, particles provides many advantages including (1) ease of particle density determinations, (2) improved predictability of aerodynamic properties, (3) simplicity of the kinetic equations which describe dissolution (as in the lung) and other phenomena, and (4) ease of differentiating the experimental particles from extraneous particles.

EXPERIMENTAL DESIGN

Using the miniature Lovelace nebulizer (Figure 1), previously described by Newton et al. (1966) and Raabe (1970), aerosols of droplets are generated from aqueous solutions or suspensions. This nebulizer generates about 50 μl/min with a total air flow of $1 \cdot 6$ l/min; the droplet distribution has a volume median diameter of $5 \cdot 8$ μm and geometric standard deviation (σ_g) of $1 \cdot 8$. The solutions and suspensions normally used are in concentrations between 1 mg/ml and 10 mg/ml of the final aerosol product to yield aerosols in the respirable size range. These aerosols are passed directly through a heated tube at temperatures to 1150°C to effect the evaporation of water and the desired chemical and physical transformations. They are then passed through a metallic tube ($1 \cdot 2$ cm diameter $\times$ 45 cm) or small chamber for cooling. The aerosols are then mixed with diluting air (usually in a ratio of 20:1), and passed directly to the inhalation exposure equipment.

The heating column, a quartz tube wrapped with nichrome wire and covered with a fiberglass and cement insulation (Figure 2), is powered by a 60 Hz source with the potential adjustable from 50 to 120 volts to provide the desired operating temperature. These columns are about 45 cm long (only 30 cm of which is heated) and about $2 \cdot 5$ cm inside diameter. Temperature calibrations were performed with a platinum, platinum-rhodium thermocouple and an optical pyrometer.

The air containing the droplets passing through the column is heated to the column temperature at nearly constant pressure and expands to about five times its original volume at 1150°C. With about $1 \cdot 6$ l/min of aerosol which expands to about 8 l/min, the average exit speed is about 25 cm/s. Also, since thermophoresis causes the

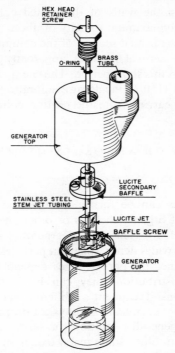

FIGURE 1. Lovelace nebulizer used in this study to generate aerosols of droplets of solutions and suspensions.

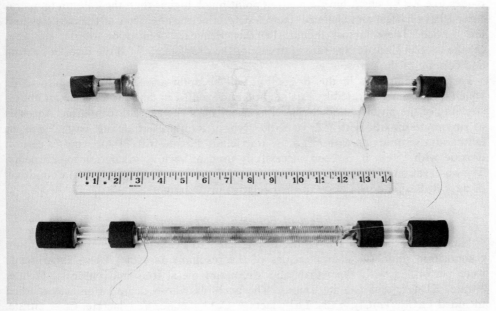

FIGURE 2. Construction of the quartz tube heating column used in this study to alter aerosol character and create insoluble forms showing (below) the quartz tube with carbon connectors and nichrome wire windings and (above) the completed column with insulation of fiberglass and cement. The ruler is marked in inches.

aerosol to move away from the walls of the heated column, most of the aerosol travels near the center at the maximum velocity of about 50 cm/s. The time required for the aerosol to traverse the heated section of the column was calculated to be near 0·6 s. As shown later, the aerosol particles apparently achieve temperatures near that of the heated column in this short period. The energy required to heat the aerosol droplets to a temperature of 1150°C, including evaporation of the water, is about 350 cal/l; therefore, the energy carried from the heating column by the aerosol is only about 40 watts.

PRODUCTION OF AEROSOLS OF METAL OXIDES

General

Aerosols of metal oxides can be formed in the heating column from droplets generated from solutions of organic chelates or other chemical forms of the chosen metals (KANAPILLY et al., 1970). This heat degradation of compounds to form the oxide in the aerosol state provides dense, spherical particles under the proper chemical and physical conditions. Since the particle sizes depend upon the solution concentration and the droplet distribution, they can be carefully controlled to avoid undesirable size distributions. Treatment at different degradation temperatures will produce aerosols of different chemical and physical properties.

The constituents of the generator solution (or suspension) are usually chosen on the basis of experimentation. Since some metal oxides such as PbO may reach their melting point in the column, dense spherical particles can be produced by degrading almost any organic complex of such metals. However, with aerosols of ceramic oxides like ZrO_2, which have a melting point much higher than the column temperature, other physical and chemical factors determine the character of the particles that are formed. These factors include (a) the chemical composition of the solution, (b) the droplet sizes, (c) the rate of drying of the droplets, and (d) the rates of heating and cooling of the aerosols.

Particular emphasis in this discussion will be upon aerosols of zirconium oxide which have been generated by this method and studied in detail to provide an understanding of the physical and chemical mechanism of the aerosol formation. Aerosols of zirconium dioxide with ^{95}Zr or with ^{95}Nb, of thulium sesquioxide with ^{171}Tm, of lanthanum sesquioxide with ^{140}La, of americium dioxide with ^{241}Am, and of cerium dioxide with ^{144}Ce, have been successfully used in various inhalation experiments. The observation of lung retention half-times for these particles measured in hundreds of days in Beagle dogs attests to their relative insolubility.

Effect of Solution Composition

Numerous experiments have been conducted to evaluate the effects of solution composition upon the characteristics of the resultant aerosols. These experiments were performed with rare earth and zirconium metal ions and chloride, lactate, citrate, EDTA, and oxalate anions. The aerosols whose degradation was studied included $LaCl_3$, $TmCl_3$, YCl_3, La^{3+} lactate, Ce^{3+} lactate, Y^{3+} lactate, Ce^{3+} citrate, Ce^{3+} EDTA, La^{3+} EDTA, Y^{3+} EDTA and Zr^{4+} oxalate. The aerosols of these solutions were passed through a heating column at 1150°C, cooled with diluting air, and sampled with an electrostatic precipitator for electron-microscopical examination.

The aerosols produced from chlorides were solid and spherical in appearance. This may be due to the melting of the aerosol particles as chlorides prior to decomposition. Aerosols from clear solutions containing chelating agents appeared as hollow bubbles and broken shells and those from cloudy solutions, which probably contained some colloidal micelles, yielded spherical and solid particles. Zirconium oxalate solutions with micellular components, provided spherical particles with extremely good characteristics (Figure 3). Other experiments have shown that hydroxide-EDTA complexes

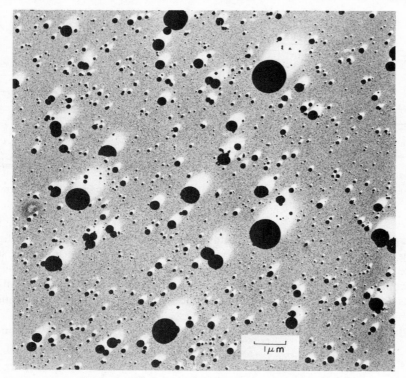

FIGURE 3. Electronmicrograph of a sample of an aerosol of zirconium oxide produced by degrading an aerosol of zirconium oxalate at 1100 °C.

of metal ion in a semi-colloidal suspension generally provide good particles after heat degradation. Studies with clear solutions of La³⁺ lactate showed that the formation of hollow shells was related to rapid entry of the droplets into the high temperature column. Low temperature predrying at about 50°C proved desirable for producing solid spherical particles in the heating column.

Effect of Temperature Upon Aerosol Properties

To quantitatively evaluate the degree of degradation of chelated materials at various temperatures and the chemical form of the resultant aerosol particles, two methods have been used: studies with ^{14}C tagged chelates, and evaluation of the infrared absorption spectra of collected aerosol particles. These two techniques were applied to studies of aerosols produced by the thermolysis of droplets of zirconium oxalate.

The composition of the solutions used to produce the zirconium aerosol was:

zirconium: $3 \text{ mg/ml} = 3 \cdot 3 \times 10^{-2}\text{M}$
oxalic acid: $22 \text{ mg/ml} = 0 \cdot 24 \text{ M}$
^{14}C (uniform label): $5 \mu\text{Ci/ml}$
pH: $0 \cdot 85$

The experimental setup for this study is shown schematically in Figure 4. It consists

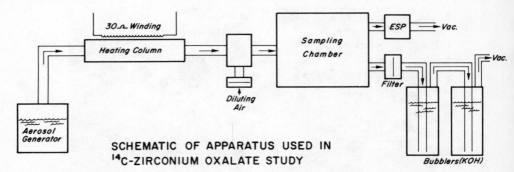

FIGURE 4. Schematic of the apparatus used in this study for the measurement of the thermolysis of ^{14}C zirconium oxalate aerosols.

of a Lovelace nebulizer, a heating column, a cooling and mixing chamber into which diluting air is supplied, a sampling chamber from which cascade impactor samples for size distribution analysis and electrostatic precipitator samples for electron-microscopic observation can be taken, and a filtration system for collection of the aerosols followed by two backup bubblers containing KOH solution to collect the CO_2 which is produced.

Standard liquid scintillation techniques were used to evaluate the ^{14}C content of

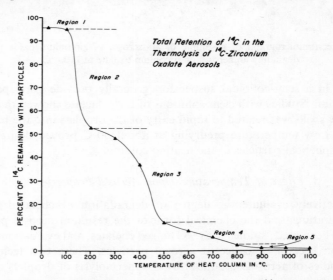

FIGURE 5. Retention of ^{14}C in the thermolysis of aerosols of ^{14}C zirconium oxalate.

the aerosols collected on the aerosol filter and the ^{14}C of the CO_2 collected by the bubblers. Filter samples were dissolved in 2-ethoxyethanol for addition to the cocktail. The ^{14}C remaining in the aerosol fraction provided a clear indication of the extent of degradation (Figure 5). These results suggest regions of temperature associated with four chemical states of the aerosol. The chemical nature of these regions can be tentatively described by comparing these results to thermogravimetric studies of the decomposition of metal oxalates such as the study of calcium oxalate by PELTIER & DUVAL (1947), the study of lanthanum oxalate by WENDLANDT (1958), and the study of plutonium oxalate by NISSEN (1967). Region 1 (Figure 5) consists of aerosols of droplets treated at temperatures less than 100°C; this region represents water evaporation from these droplets with only slight loss of oxalic acid. Region 2, which extends from about 100°C to 200°C, also involves droplets as observed on electron micrographs; the loss of ^{14}C in this region indicates evaporation of oxalic acid. Regions 3, 4, and 5 were all observed to involve aerosols of dense spherical particles. The range from about 200°C to 500°C is region 3 which shows a rapid loss of ^{14}C resulting from the degradation of zirconium oxalate to form zirconium carbonate. Region 4, which extends from about 500°C to about 800°C, involves the degradation of zirconium carbonate and zirconium oxycarbonate and formation of zirconium oxide. Region 5 above 800°C, yields particles which are primarily the oxide. The relative quantities of the intermediate products predicted on the basis of the ^{14}C content at various column temperatures are shown in Figure 6. The temperature values used were those

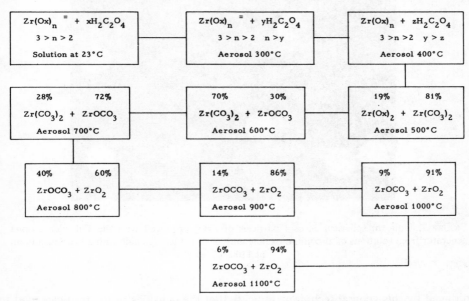

FIGURE 6. Species of zirconium compounds formed at various temperatures in the thermolysis of zirconium oxalate aerosols.

associated with the air in the heating column. The consistency of these data with static thermogravimetric studies described in the literature, strongly suggests that the aerosol particles themselves do attain temperatures close to the column temperature. Identification of the chemical constituents of aerosols produced from zirconium oxalate solutions at various temperatures were also made by infrared absorption spectral analyses.* Four samples were prepared from aerosolized solutions of the same type as used in the ^{14}C study. These were passed through heating columns at temperatures of 1100°C, 900°C, 650°C, and 200°C, which yielded samples A, B, C, and D, respectively. The spectra of these aerosols after collection on filters were studied with respect to spectra of known compounds which have been reported. The results indicated that sample A was mostly ZrO_2 with oxycarbonate as a trace impurity. Water was observed to be only negligible. Samples B and C contained more oxycarbonate and water than did sample A. There is a corresponding decrease in ZrO_2 content A > B > C. Sample D contains mostly oxalate with some carbonate. The results obtained from this study are consistent with the results of the ^{14}C-oxalate study of the thermolysis of zirconium oxalate aerosols.

Studies with the Millikan apparatus indicated that the density of the zirconium oxide particles was $3 \cdot 3 \pm 0 \cdot 5$ as compared with the accepted value of $5 \cdot 6$ for monoclinic zirconium oxide. Studies of the densities of other refractory metal oxide aerosols

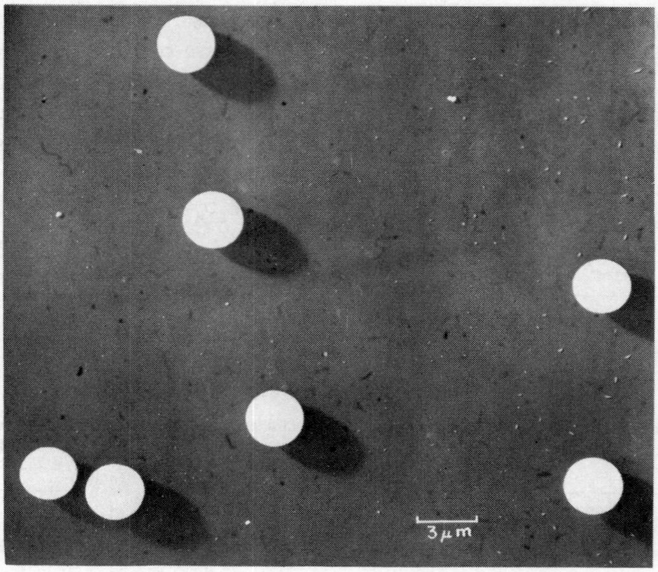

FIGURE 7. Uniform spherical aerosol particles of ZrO_2 produced with the Fulwyler droplet generator from solutions of zirconium oxalate and degraded to the oxide with a heating column at 1100 °C.

produced by this general technique indicate that the densities of the particles tend to be about two-thirds of the intrinsic densities of the oxides. The 1150°C used to degrade the zirconium oxalate in this study is about one-half the melting point of ZrO_2 in degrees Kelvin. According to TAMMAN & SWORYKIN (1928), a solid which is heated to half the melting point on the absolute scale undergoes thermal agitation which

* The authors are indebted to Dr. Merle Atwood of Perkin Elmer Corporation, Norwalk, Conn., for these spectra which were generated with the Perkin Elmer Model 457IR Spectrometer.

causes reorganization of molecules and produces denser particles. If the ZrO_2 particles were heated to higher temperatures, it might be expected that the density would increase and approach the intrinsic density at 2700°C, the melting point.

Generation of monodisperse aerosols

Monodisperse aerosols can be produced by this method if uniform droplets of the solutions can be dispersed. The most popular device for dispensing uniform droplets has been the spinning disk aerosol generator first described by WALTON & PREWETT (1949). A new and promising approach to the dispersion of monodisperse droplets is the high frequency disturbance and subsequent disintegration of a thin liquid stream emitted from a small orifice (FULWYLER et al., 1969; and STROM, 1969).

Using a Fulwyler droplet generator uniform particles of insoluble zirconium oxide were produced by dispersing droplets of zirconium oxalate and passing these droplets through a heating column at 1150°C. An electron micrograph of such an aerosol is shown in Figure 7. Since the droplets produced with this device vary less than 1 % in volume, the resulting zirconium oxide aerosol tends to be of similar uniformity. It can be deduced from this uniformity of the particles in Figure 7 that the thermolysis technique produced particles which tend to have the same density even though the observed particle density was two-thirds of the intrinsic density of the oxide.

PRODUCTION OF AEROSOLS OF ALUMINOSILICATE SPHERES

General

Aerosols of aluminosilicate spheres can be produced in a heating column at 1150°C from droplets of clay suspensions (MCKNIGHT & NORGON, 1967). Using the natural ion exchange properties of clay, radionuclides can be ion-exchanged into the clay matrix and upon heat treatment become incorporated into the aluminosilicate particles. This procedure involves (a) preparation of the clay and radionuclide ion exchange, (b) aerosolization of the clay suspensions, and (c) heat fusion in the heating column to form the aluminosilicate spheres with the radionuclide incorporated. Montmorillonite clay obtained from Bayard, New Mexico, USA, was used in this study. The radionuclides ^{90}Sr-Y, ^{90}Y, ^{144}Ce-Pr, ^{137}Cs-Ba, ^{91}Y, ^{88}Y, and ^{140}La have been studied but other metals can be used.

Preparation of Clay

A relatively stable aqueous suspension of the montmorillonite clay is prepared by treating with 30% hydrogen peroxide solution to degrade organic impurities and break the individual clay particles into small pieces. It is then cleaned by running water dialysis with deionized water. The weight density of the various suspensions is determined by weighing the clay remaining after evaporation of a given volume of suspension. The projected area size distribution of the clay in suspension is approximately log-normal. The count median diameter of the clay micelles prepared in this way is about $0 \cdot 2 \ \mu$m with a geometric standard deviation of about $1 \cdot 8$. The density of the clay particles was found to be about $2 \cdot 2$ g/cm^3. The prepared clay is stored in deionized water at a concentration of about 10 mg/ml.

Ion Exchange

The ion exchange properties of the clay are used to replace some of the exchangeable clay ions with cations of the radionuclide of interest. The structure of montmorillonite clay is composed of alternating layers of silicate tetrahedra and aluminate octahedra. The ideal basic formula for montmorillonite clay is $Si_8Al_4O_{20}(OH)_4 \cdot nH_2O$. The framework of the clay acquires a net negative charge when ions such as Mg(II) and Fe(II) replace Al(III), or Al(III) replaces Si(IV) in the clay network. This negative charge is compensated by cations which move freely between the layers of the framework.

Ion-exchange reactions between insoluble ion exchangers suspended in solution and ions in the solvent are usually reversible reactions. The law of mass action appears to hold and, in time, ion-exchange equilibrium is attained. The concentration ratios of the two ion species, however, are not necessarily the same in both the exchanger and the solution phase. Factors which increase the affinity of the exchanger for a given cation include higher valence and smaller solvated volume. It seems evident that, in order to completely pack the clay exchanger with a given cation, an excess of the cation is needed in the supporting solution.

Sorption and exchange of an electrolytic solution by the clay take place. Sorption is perhaps more important in a two-dimensional layered clay, such as montmorillonite, than in three-dimensional lattice exchangers. According to HELFFERICH (1962), montmorillonites swell anisotropically and appear to have several different stable interlayer distances, depending upon the size and charge of the exchanged ions. For example, Cs, Ca, and Na packed montmorillonite clays have interlayer thicknesses of 10 Å, 20 Å and 40 Å, respectively. Sorption is usually reversible and the solution can be removed from the exchanger by washing with pure solvent.

The exchange capacity of Bayard, New Mexico, montmorillonite clay has been reported to be from $1 \cdot 17$ to $1 \cdot 36$ milliequivalents (mEq) per gram of clay at room temperature (AMPHLETT, 1958; ELIASON, 1966). ELIASON (1966) reported the formula $(Al_{3.14}Fe_{0.152}Mg_{0.60})(Si_8)O_{20}(OH)_4(Na_{0.18}Ca_{0.21})$ for this clay, in which the first parentheses represent octahedrally coordinated ions; the second, tetrahedrally coordinated ions; and the last, exchangeable cations. The calculated exchange capacity is about $1 \cdot 3$ mEq/g of clay. Radionuclide incorporation in montmorillonite clay takes place by the entry of the ion into the interlayer spaces and replacement of exchangeable cations. The particle size of the clay micelles in suspension has little effect upon the exchange capacity of montmorillonite.

From the thermodynamic data of AMPHLETT (1958), FRYSINGER & THOMAS (1960), HELFFERICH (1962), LEWIS & THOMAS (1963) and ELIASON (1966), one observes that the selectivity sequence of montmorillonite clay for various cations is

$$Li^+ < Na^+ < K^+ < Cs^+ < Mg^{++} < Ca^{++} < Sr^{++} < Y^{+++} < Ce^{+++}$$

The natural form of the clay probably contains calcium or magnesium in the exchangeable cation positions. To improve the exchange reaction, some clay was packed with sodium ion (Na-clay) to increase the selectivity of the clay for the chosen cation. The sodium packing was accomplished by adding a 5% NaCl solution to the clay suspension, decanting the supernatant from the flocculated clay, and repeating the process. The clay was then washed and the excess sodium ions removed by dialyzing the suspension.

Since it would be desirable to predict the specific activity of the clay for any isotope, it is necessary to know the percentage exchange as a function of the concentration of the exchanging cation. It is also desirable that the percent exchange be as high as possible; consequently, the concentration of all other cations must be kept as low as possible. To find the percentage exchange as a function of cation concentration, tracer-level experiments were done with $^{137}Cs^+$, $^{144}Ce^{+++}$, $^{85}Sr^{++}$, and $^{91}Y^{+++}$ as chloride salts. In addition to these tracer-level exchange studies, high-level exchange studies were done with $^{144}CeCl_3$, $^{91}YCl_3$, $^{90}SrCl_2$, $^{90}YCl_3$, and $^{137}CsCl$ in order to estimate the maximal attainable specific activity for the clay.

Factors that could be varied in the tracer-level exchange include stable ion concentration, pH, clay type, and time. Most of these factors were varied with only one or two ions and the results were judiciously applied to other cations. Both cesium and strontium exchanges were done with natural and Na-clay. All exchanges were done in neutral solution, if chemically possible, but satisfactory exchange was accomplished with yttrium in 1 N HCl solution. As much cation is exchanged into the clay in three hours as overnight (16–20 hr.).

The principal results of the tracer-level experiments are shown in Figure 8. The

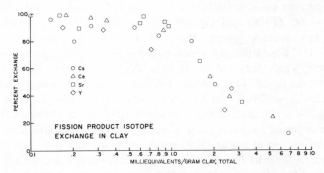

FIGURE 8. Percent exchanges as function of ion concentration with natural clay and pH 6 for cerium, Na-clay and pH 6 for strontium and cesium, and natural clay and pH 0 for yttrium.

percent exchange of the cations is shown as a function of the cation concentration. The conditions used during these exchanges were pH 6 and Na-clay for cesium and strontium, pH 6 and natural clay for cerium, and 1N HCl solution and natural clay for yttrium.

The data from some test experiments, including the initial concentrations of the solutions, the percent exchange, and the final specific activity of the clay are listed below. Optimum exchange is achieved if the initial cation concentration is about 2 mEq/g of clay.

Estimates of the specific activity of a nuclide in solution can be made from the percent exchange in the high-level exchanges. Contaminating cations in the radionuclides source material will reduce the effective specific activity and the amount of radioisotope that will exchange with the clay. For example, the 60 percent exchange of cerium reported below implies a concentration of about 1 mEq/g of clay or 0·05 mg

TABLE 1. TYPICAL CLAY EXCHANGE RESULTS

Isotope	Initial mCi/mg clay	Percent exchange	Final mCi/mg clay
137Cs-Ba	2·5	70	2
144Ce-Pr	9·8	60	6
91Y	16·0	40	6

of cerium per gram of clay and a specific activity of cerium or 120 mCi/mg. When the specific activity of the nuclide is known, an estimate of the specific activity of the clay for an initial concentration ratio can be made.

Aerosol Generation

After ion exchange the clay is filtered with a cellulose acetate membrane filter and washed with de-ionized water. It is then resuspended into deionized water off the filter by brief ultrasonic agitation. This final suspension is used for aerosolization. Using the Lovelace nebulizer and heating column at 1150°C, an aerosol of aluminosilicate spheres is produced from the clay suspension. Passage through the heating column is essential to firmly incorporate the nuclide in the particles, to create the desirable spherical shape and smooth surface for the particles and to make the particles less soluble. AMPHLETT (1958) and GINNELL & SIMON (1953) report that, when clay is heated to a temperature greater than 500°C, water is irreversibly lost from the lattice of the clay, the lattice collapses, and the exchanged cations become a part of the lattice itself, where they are firmly held. At temperatures above 1000°C the clay appears to become fused. This can be seen in comparing Figure 9, an electron micrograph of the clay aerosol before it is passed through the heating column with Figure 10, the fused clay. Note the undesirable particle shapes and densities of the unfused clay particles, as compared to the aerosol of dense smooth aluminosilicate spheres.

The size distribution of the aerosols produced from clay suspensions do not follow the concentration laws as for solutions since the micelles are relatively large. Also, the treatment of the clay including the type of cation used for the exchange affects the micelle size and state of aggregation of the micelles with a concomitant effect upon the aerosol size distribution from a given concentration of clay suspension. Sodium packed clay yields smaller aerosol particles. Some examples of the observed activity median aerodynamic diameter (AMAD as for equivalent unit-density spheres) and geometric standard deviation (σ_g) of aluminosilicate aerosols are given in Table II for differently treated clay.

The measurement of the densities of 10 aluminosilicate aerosol particles using the Millikan apparatus yielded an average value of $2·26 \pm 0·08$ (S.D.) g/cm^3.

The highest specific activity of radioactive aerosols which have been produced are given in Table III. These aerosols were made by diluting the 1·6 l/min flow of the Lovelace Nebulizer to 20 l/min after passing through the heating column.

SUMMARY

The use of a high-temperature heating column to make chemical and physical alterations in the character of aerosols is a useful technique for preparing a variety

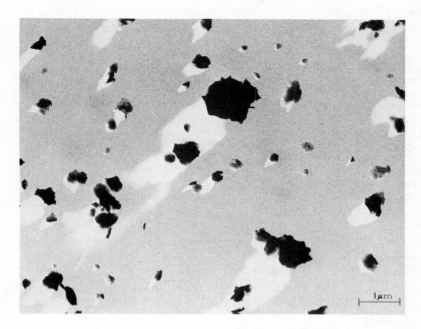

FIGURE 9. Electronmicrograph of a sample of clay particles (shadowed with chromium vapor) generated by nebulization of a clay suspension.

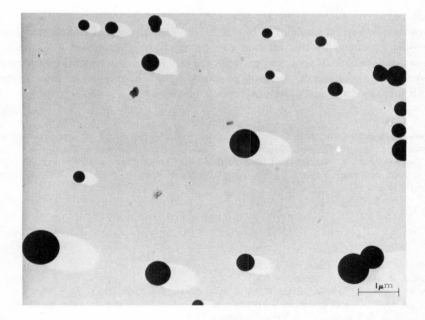

FIGURE 10. Electronmicrograph of a sample of fused aluminosilicate particles (shadowed with chromium vapor) generated by passing the clay aerosol shown in Figure 9 through a heating column at 1150 °C.

TABLE II. AERODYNAMIC SIZE DISTRIBUTION DATA FOR DIFFERENTLY TREATED CLAY

Clay type	Suspension concentration (mg/ml)	AMAD	(σ_g)
Natural clay with ^{144}Ce-Pr	1	1·1	2·1
Natural clay with ^{144}Ce-Pr	5	1·6	1·9
Natural clay with ^{144}Ce-Pr	10	1·7	1·8
Na-clay with ^{144}Ce-Pr	1	0·5	1·6
Na-clay with ^{144}Ce-Pr	5	1·1	1·5
Na-clay with ^{144}Ce-Pr	10	1·3	1·5
Na-clay with ^{90}Sr-Y	10	1·6	1·7
Na-clay with ^{90}Y	1	0·8	1·7
Na-clay with ^{137}Cs-Ba	4	1·4	1·6

TABLE III. HIGH LEVEL RADIOACTIVE AEROSOLS OF ALUMINOSILICATE SPHERES

Nuclide	Clay specific activity (Ci/g)	Suspension concentration (mg/ml)	Aerosol concentration (µCi/l)
^{137}Cs-Ba	0·4	10	5
^{90}Sr-Y	1·6	10	35
^{90}Y	$1·4 \times 10^3$	1	3000
^{91}Y	4·4	10	93
^{144}Ce-Pr	1·7	10	36

of aerosols of spherical particles of insoluble forms. The physical and chemical nature of aerosols produced by this method can be carefully investigated to provide well characterized aerosols of spherical particles for inhalation experiments and for studies of the properties of aerosols. Aerosols produced by this method which were described in depth include ZrO_2 and aluminosilicate from fused clay.

Acknowledgements — The authors are indebted to the many individuals who contributed to this work including, Drs. R. O. McClellan, Mary E. McKnight and Howard A. Boyd, and to Russell W. E. Norgon, Jerry E. Bennick and Richard L. Flores. The authors gratefully acknowledge the permission of Pergamon Press Ltd., for use of figures 1, 2, 4, 5, 6 and 7 which appeared in KANAPILLY *et al.*, 1970.

REFERENCES

AMPHLETT, C. B. (1958). *Endeavour* **17**, 149.
ELIASON, J. R. (1966). *Am. Miner.* **51**, 324.
FRYSINGER, G. R. & THOMAS, H. C. (1960). *J. phys. Chem., Ithaca* **64**, 224.
FULWYLER, M. J., GLASCOCK, R. B. & HIEBERT, R. B. (1969). *Rev. scient. Instrum.* **40**, 42–48.
GINNELL, W. S. & SIMON, G. P. (1953). *Nucleonics* **11**, 49.
HELFFERICH, F. (1962). *Ion exchange*. New York, McGraw Hill.
KANAPILLY, G. M., RAABE, O. G. & NEWTON, G. J. (1870). *Aerosol Sci.* **1**, 313.
LEWIS, R. J. & THOMAS, H. C. (1963). *J. phys. Chem., Ithaca* **67**, 1781.

McKNIGHT, M. E. & NORGON, R. W. E. (1967). *A study of the exchange characteristics of mont-morillonite clay for fission product cations for use in the generation of insoluble aerosols.* AEC Research and Development Report, LF–37. Albuquerque (N.M.), Lovelace Foundation for Medical Education and Research, U.S.A.

NEWTON, G. J., BENNICK, J. E. & POSNER, S. (1966). In: *Selected Summary of Studies on the Fission Product Inhalation Program from July 1965 through June 1966*, USAEC Research and Development Report LF–33, *Ed.* R. G. Thomas. Albuquerque (N.M.), Lovelace Foundation for Medical Education and Research, pp. 29–35.

NISSEN, D. A. (1967). *Thermal decomposition of plutonium (IV) oxalate hexahydrate*, AEC Research and Development Report SC–DC–67–1742, Albuquerque (N.M.), Sandia Laboratories.

PELTIER, S. & DUVAL, C. (1947). *Analytica chim. Acta* **1**, 346.

RAABE, O. G. (1970). In: *Inhalation carcinogenesis. Ed.* M. G. Hanna, Jr., P. Nettesheim & J. R. Gilbert. Oak Ridge (Tennessee), U.S. Atomic Energy Commission Division of Technical Information, pp. 123–172.

STROM, L. (1969). *Rev. scient. Instrum.* **40**, 778–782.

TAMMAN, G. & SWORYKIN, A. (1928). *Z. anorg. allg. Chem.* **176**, 46.

WALTON, W. H. & PREWETT, W. C. (1949). *Proc. phys. Soc. Lond.* **62**, 341–350.

WENDLANDT, W. W. (1958). *Analyt. Chem.* **30**, 58–61.

DISCUSSION

S. E. DEVIR: You did not emphasize that the method is for insoluble inorganics but not organic; the latter would not sustain even 300–400 degrees of heat in the tube. What is the difference, in principle, from Kerker's method for producing spherical NaCl aerosol? Do your particles keep their shape for a long time.

Dr. RAABE: Yes. We start with an organic material and convert it by heat degradation to an inorganic form.

Our method is very different from Kerker's in that there is no condensation process involved. The uniform particles are produced by first generating uniform droplets. The particles are very stable; the zirconium oxide particles in particular are extremely insoluble and had long residence times in the lungs of animals after inhalation.

H. N. MACFARLAND: Are any particular steps taken in returning the aerosols to ambient temperature?

Dr. RAABE: The aerosol is very easily brought to near ambient temperature by passing it through a 3 ft length of metal tube and then mixing it with cool diluting air.

K. R. MAY: You mention various devices for generating aerosols. When I visited your laboratory recently you showed me Babington's aerosol generator consisting of a glass bulb over which liquid is flowed while air is blown through a fine slit in the wall. His patent specification claims that this generates uniform particles which I find very hard to believe. Do you have a comment on that?

Dr. RAABE: The patent specification you refer to is couched in language of patent attorneys.

W. H. WALTON: What is the density of the particles? Is it uniform?

Dr. RAABE: The formation of dense spherical particles involves the preparation of a semi-suspension that must have micellular components; it must have small particles in suspension. If we work with pure solutions we obtain hollow spheres. This will be described in more detail in a paper which is to be published in the *Journal of Aerosol Science*. The density of particles that one gets upon heat degradation is not the intrinsic density of the material, except in cases where the temperature used exceeds the melting point of the material being formed. The density of particles which we have made is about two-thirds of the intrinsic density.

We get uniform densities, as is evident from the Figure showing uniform particles of zirconium oxide.

FLUID MECHANICS OF BRONCHIAL AIR-FLOW

M. F. SUDLOW, D. E. OLSON and R. C. SCHROTER

Physiological Flow Studies Unit, Imperial College, London, S.W.7, England

Abstract — Flow characteristics were studied in large scale models of typical junctions of the human bronchial tree and in casts of the trachea and first few generations of bronchi. Steady inspiratory flows were investigated at flow rates appropriate to man at rest, with blunt or parabolic velocity profiles entering the cast or model. In the models, secondary motions were observed at all flow rates and depending upon local geometry in the region of the junction, flow separation and reversed flow were observed. Velocity profiles were highly asymmetric downstream of the junction with peak velocities on the inner wall of the daughter tube. Similar velocity profiles were found in similar geometric situations in the casts. The results show that in the bronchial tree flow patterns are complex and it is unreasonable to assume parabolic flow simply on the basis of calculated Reynolds numbers.

THE bulk transport of air and particles from the mouth to the depths of the lung is by the bronchial tree—a network of branched tubes. While there has been much study of the overall characteristics of the system from the viewpoints of mechanics and particle deposition there has been little attention given to the characteristics of flow in individual airways.

In the first symposium on Inhaled Particles and Vapours, WEST (1961) described studies of fluid flow in a cast of the trachea and main bronchi. He demonstrated that turbulence could occur in the trachea and larger bronchi and that laminar flow appeared to be maintained in smaller airways. He could not examine the local flow details or measure velocity profiles. DEKKER (1961) with a cast of the trachea, larynx and main bronchi demonstrated that turbulence occurred in the trachea and main bronchi under some conditions. He claimed that turbulence was found at Reynolds numbers[*] less than 2000, the critical value for turbulence in long straight pipes.

Here we report the results of experiments on branched tube models of one or two junctions and also measurements of flow in casts of the upper airways of three human lungs. Some of the model experiments have been reported in detail elsewhere (SCHROTER & SUDLOW, 1969), as have some of the lung cast experiments (SEKIHARA & OLSON, 1968).

---

[*] Reynolds number (*Re*) is a non-dimensional index of the ratio of the inertial to viscous forces acting on a moving fluid. It thus enables us to scale the flow rate appropriately in the model studies (see later). For pipe flow it is defined as $\dfrac{ud}{\nu}$ where u is the mean velocity and ν the kinematic viscosity. In the model studies d is the tube diameter; in the lung cast where the cross-sectional area is not always circular, we used the hydraulic diameter, D_h. $(D_h = \dfrac{4 \times (\text{cross-sectional area})}{\text{perimeter}})$.

METHODS

Only steady air flows were investigated. Flows entering the system had either blunt velocity profiles or fully developed parabolic velocity profiles.

Models

Symmetrical, Y-shaped, large scale models of junctions were cast or machined in perspex using dimensions from recent anatomical studies (WEIBEL, 1963; HORSFIELD & CUMMING, 1967). They had a fixed branching angle (70°) appropriate for bronchi of 5th–15th generation. They were rigid and had smooth, dry walls. All the models studied had the same lengths, diameters and area ratios (details in Figure 2) but the local junctional geometry was altered in some as described later.

Cast

This was made from three normal human lungs obtained at post-mortem. They were degassed and then filled under water with silicone rubber (Silastic 521 Dow Corning). The relative density of the rubber was approximately 1·002 so that by filling the lung under water the effect of gravity on the geometry of the airways was negated. The rubber has practically no shrinkage on setting and could therefore give an accurate cast of the airways. The transmural pressure of the lungs was approximately 8 cm H_2O (end-expiratory pressure). After 7 days for setting the lung tissue was digested away in concentrated sodium hydroxide and after pruning up to sub-segmented bronchi the casts were used as moulds to produce hollow replicas of the major bronchi. This was made of a transparent polymer (Sylgard 184) which was cured by heating and then cut to remove the original Silastic cast. The hollow casts were carefully rejoined and sealed for velocity profile studies.

Flow Visualization

The flow patterns were observed in the models by visualizing the flow with fine tracers of "smoke" produced by a standard Wind Tunnel Smoke Generator (Taylor Instruments), using high grade kerosene oil. The smoke was either introduced via a fine hypodermic tube some distance upstream of the junction (in the case of expiration) or through a series of small holes from a manifold fitted along the outside edge of the daughter tube (inspiration). The secondary flow patterns were recorded by still photography using continuous frontal illumination at an incidence of 45° to the viewing path. Introduction of the smoke did not cause any disturbances to the flow patterns in the models.

Velocity Profile Measurements

In the models we measured point velocities with a hot wire probe introduced downstream with a micromanipulator and connected to a constant temperature anemometer. In the casts we used a Pitot tube device constructed from two fine hypodermic needles fixed together. The small pressures generated were recorded using an inclined alcohol micromanometer. The hot wire and pitot tube were calibrated in known velocity profiles at frequent intervals.

RESULTS

We used steady flows in the models and casts and will consider inspiration only. The results were similar for all Reynolds numbers studied. These were mainly in the nominal laminar regime (100–2000) but some, where indicated, were higher—up to 5000. The terminology used for the models is shown in Figure 1.

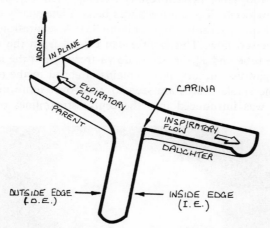

FIGURE 1. Section of model showing terminology used in text.

Flow Visualization Studies

These were only possible in the models. Secondary flows were observed at all flow rates and occurred regardless of the entering profile. On reaching the junction, the flow splits and is turned in curved paths. In consequence, secondary flows with a pair of vortices are established in each daughter tube, (Figure 3). This characteristic of fluid motion is similar to that seen in flow through a curved pipe. Within the transition region between parent and daughter tubes, the characteristics of the flow were very dependent upon the local geometry. Two factors appeared particularly impor-

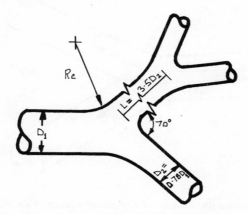

FIGURE 2. Dimensions of model junctions.

tant; the radius of curvature at the junction and the sharpness of the carina. Three models of a single bifurcation were constructed. In MODEL I the curvature of the junction was 1:1; in MODEL II it was 4:1 (ratio = radius of curvature at outer wall of junction:radius of curvature of parent tube—see Figure 2). MODEL III had a curvature at the junction of 4:1 and a "bluff" carina (see Figure 1). By introducing smoke through a series of holes in the outer side of the junction, flows were visualized for the first two models, for Re 100–4500. Typical results are illustrated. In MODEL I flow separation and reverse flow occur. The smoke traces behave irregularly and smoke can be seen to move upstream at several points (Figure 4a). A separation bubble is formed of sluggish and reversed flow. This bubble can extend from the outer wall, $\frac{1}{3}$ of a diameter across the tube and $1\frac{1}{4}$ diameters downstream from the level of the carina. In MODEL II no separation occurs, flow remains attached to the outer wall through the junction. All the smoke traces are seen to bend over uniformly (Figure 4b). In MODEL III smoke was introduced into the centre streamlines of the parent tube

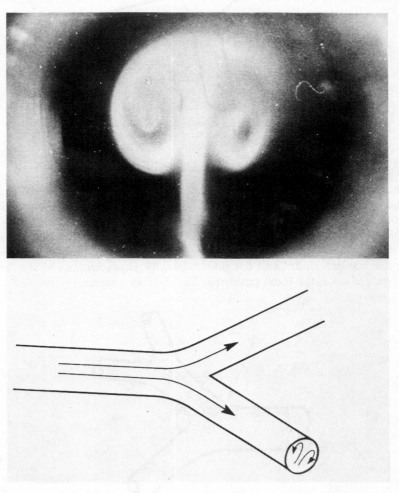

Figure 3. Secondary motions downstream of a single bifurcation. View from downstream of a daughter tube.

through a fine hypodermic tube. Results are illustrated and contrasted with flow at a sharp carina. In the later case (MODEL II) the central smoke labelled streamline is split at the sharp carina—smoke is dispersed to both daughters in the typical secondary motions already described (Figure 5a). With the bluff carina (MODEL III) a more complex pattern was observed. The smoke hits the bluff flow divider and some is turned back and outwards to start the secondary motions in the daughter tubes (Figure 5b).

Velocity Profiles

Typical velocity profiles and changes of the profiles with distance downstream of a single bifurcation are illustrated in Figure 6. In the plane of the bifurcation the bulk flow (integral of velocity profile) increases with the distance from the outer half of the

(a)

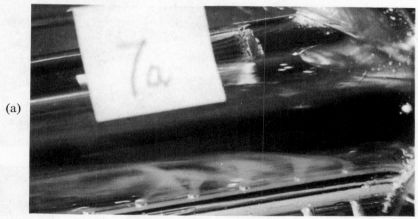

(b)

Figure 4. (a) Flow pattern just downstream of a single bifurcation in a daughter tube. Smoke introduced through fine holes on the outer side of the daughter tube. Smoke can be seen to move backward in the separation bubble. (b) As above but in Model II (see text) no separation in this case.

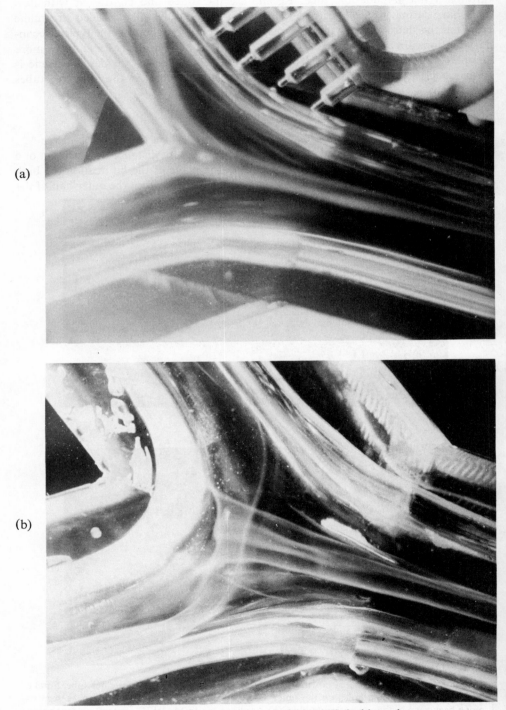

Figure 5. Behaviour of central streamlines, labelled with smoke:
(a) sharp carina of flow divider. (b) blunt carina.

tube and decreases with distances from the junction on the inner half of the tube. However the peak velocity near the inner wall remains approximately constant (twice the calculated mean flow velocity). In the plane normal to the junction the velocities are higher near the walls than in the core and again do not change with distance downstream. Very similar velocity profiles were found in the daughter tubes

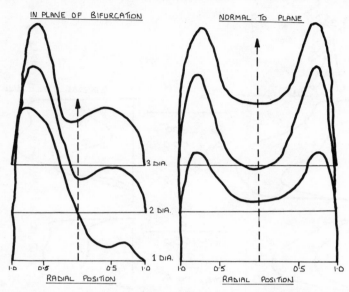

FIGURE 6. Changes in flow pattern downstream of a single bifurcation. $Re = 700$.

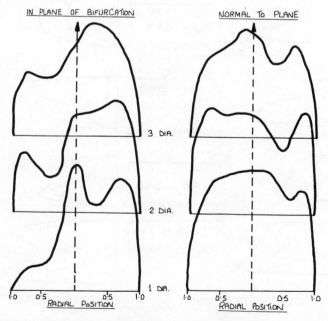

FIGURE 7. Changes in flow pattern downstream of a second bifurcation. Junction plane at right-angle to first junction plane. $Re = 450$.

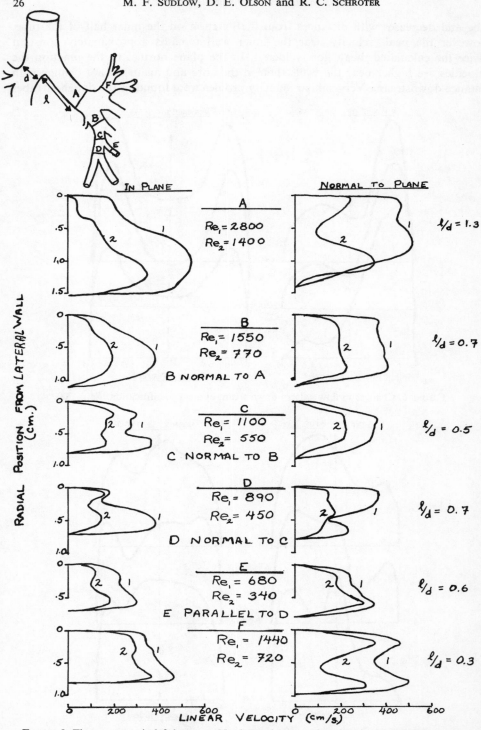

FIGURE 8. Flow patterns in left lung cast No. 3. Inspirations of 1000 ml/s and 500 ml/s at mouth. Flow in each branch is proportional to the lung volume distal to branch.

when blunt or parabolic velocity profiles were introduced in the parent tube. A second junction increases flow in a manner similar to the first but the effects are masked by the asymmetry of the entering flow. An example is shown in Figure 7 of flow profiles downstream of a second junction at right angles to the first. Typical velocity profiles from the lung casts are shown in Figure 8, together with the sites in the bronchial tree at which these typical measurements were made. The distance downstream from the flow dividers (carina) are also indicated. The velocity profiles for two different inspiratory rates (1000 cm/s and 500 cm/s) along with the corresponding Reynolds numbers in each tube are shown. It can be seen that some of the profiles measured are very similar to those seen in the model studies. Direct comparisons are difficult because of the asymmetrical branching, the changing curvature ratios and because the planes of successive bifurcations are not usually parallel or perpendicular to one another. The basic patterns can still be noted however, indicating that secondary motions, similar to those of the model studies, should be expected.

DISCUSSION

From the trachea to the alveoli both bronchial diameter and velocity fall. Hence the Re typical at any bronchus falls with distance from the trachea. For Weibel's symmetrical anatomy of the lung—assuming the airways have a circular cross-section, the variation of Re with bronchial size is shown in Table I for a flow rate appropriate for quiet breathing.

TABLE I. REYNOLDS NUMBERS AND LINEAR VELOCITIES (AFTER WEIBEL)
TRACHEAL FLOW RATE = 40 LITRES/MIN.

Generation	Number of branches	Average velocity (cm/s)	Reynolds number
0	1	256	3000
1	2	247	1980
2	4	236	1284
3	8	229	841
5	32	125	288
10	1024	32	27
15	32768	8	3·3
20	1048576	0·41	0·12

Three flow regimes may thus be described.

1. Nominal Turbulent Region

This includes the trachea and first few generations of bronchi. The lower limit of the region will be determined by the Re and by the rate of decay of turbulence (OWEN, 1969). Many of our measurements in the casts of the lungs were made in this region. We made measurements in this region where $Re > 2000$ and < 2000. They were similar in both cases. This is to be expected since the forces acting to cause asymmetric velocity profiles are present even in turbulent regimes and there is experimental evidence of skewed velocity profiles in turbulent flows in curved pipes, (HAWTHORNE, 1963).

2. *Nominal Laminar Region*

This region extends from region 1 to airways where $10 > Re > 1$ i.e. approximately generation 15 in the Weibel anatomy. Our model experiments were designed to investigate this region and we believe that flow patterns of the type we describe are found here.

3. *Nominal Stokes Region*

This comprises all airways where $Re < 1$. Bulk flow is of the Stokes type (with inertial forces negligible). The magnitude of the convective motion is of the same order as gas transport due to molecular diffusivity. This region will not be considered further here. The exact anatomical extent of all three regions will depend upon the overall volume flow rate and perhaps the pattern of breathing.

The flows described in the casts and models are applicable to the bronchial tree *in vivo* with certain reservations.

(i) We have assumed uniform entry conditions in the casts studied so far. In practice flow through the upper airways and larynx is complex and there seems to be a jet-like entry conditions into the upper trachea (Olson & Horsfield, 1969). The influence of such an entry profile on flow in the major bronchi is at present unknown but could modify the profiles described.

(ii) The exact anatomy of the airways at the nominal laminar region is at present unknown. Our own unpublished anatomical investigations suggest that the carina is sharp and that the ratio of the radius of curvature at the junction should be 4:1 or greater. There may of course be alterations in disease. The bronchial tree is asymmetric. Some asymmetry should not alter the qualitative prediction of flow from observation on symmetrical models but details could be affected. This can be seen by comparing the velocity profiles in the models with those in the casts. Even in the upper airways where asymmetry is most marked the velocity profiles in many situations are similar (note also that the walls of the casts were not smooth). Other factors which should be noted are the rigidity of our models and that they had dry walls. It seems unlikely on theoretical grounds that these will have little influence on flow characteristics (Schroter & Sudlow, 1969; Olson *et al.*, 1970).

(iii) All the reported studies were for steady flows. The flow of air in the lungs is unsteady (fundamental frequency app. $0\cdot25$ c/s). The frequency can increase on exercise or hyperventilation, and in addition cardiac pulsations (app. 1 c/s) are superimposed (West & Hugh Jones, 1961). There is yet no satisfactory analysis of oscillatory flow in complex geometries. Womersley (1965) showed theoretically that for established flow in straight tubes the imposition of pulsations can grossly disturb velocity profiles. He showed that quasi-steady flow could exist only if $\alpha < 1$,

$(\alpha = a\left(\dfrac{w}{\nu}\right)^{1/2}$ where a = tube radius, w = angular frequency and ν = kinematic viscosity).

In the nominal laminar region of the lung $\alpha < 1$ under most conditions, but $\alpha > 1$ in the turbulent region. α is an indication of the magnitude of the steady boundary layer to the oscillatory disturbances and it is probably more correct to regard "a" as the boundary layer thickness and not the tube radius (= tube radius for full developed pipe flow). The velocity profiles in our models indicate that the boundary layer is much thinner than the tube radius. If we calculate a new α on this basis, than α < 1 even in the turbulent region and a quasi-steady state exists. However, further analysis and experiment are required to validate this conclusion. As a practical point many experimental manoeuvres involve square wave breathing; under these circumstances, after an initial disturbance, a steady flow rate would be established.

(iv) Our studies are confined to inspiration. On expiration the variation in transmural pressure of airways may cause collapse and alteration in geometry of the airways, hence rigid model studies are of limited value. Further, if the carina is not perfectly rigid, disturbances in the flow may cause vibration and thus disturb flows downstream.

CONCLUSION

These studies demonstrate that flow patterns in the bronchial tree are complex and that it is unacceptable to assume established laminar parabolic flow. Junctions disturb flow in a reasonably predictable manner and the disturbances persist in the downstream airways. These disturbances are *not* turbulence since they are not random velocity fluctuations. The flow regime can best be described as laminar but distorted. Clearly such flow patterns are important in any consideration of gas or particle dispersion and deposition in the bronchial tree.

REFERENCES

DEKKER, E. (1961). Transition between laminar and turbulent flow in human trachea. *J. appl. Physiol.* **16**, 1060–1064.

HAWTHORNE, W. R. (1963). Flow in bent pipes. *Proc. Seminar in Aeronautical Sciences*, 1961. Bangalore (India), National Aeronautical Laboratory. pp. 305–333.

HORSFIELD, K. & CUMMING, G. (1967). Angles of branching and diameters of branches in the human bronchial tree. *Bull. math. Biophys.* **29**, 245–259.

OLSON, D. E., HORSFIELD, K., WAGNER, J., WAGNER, W. W. & FILLEY, G. F. (1969). Investigation of flow patterns in the upper airways during mouth breathing: twelfth Aspen Emphysema Conference. *Am. Rev. resp. Dis.* **101**, 456–457.

OLSON, D E., DART, G. A. & FILLEY, G. F. (1970). Pressure drop and fluid flow regime of air inspired into the human lung. *J. appl. Physiol.* **28**, 482–494.

OWEN, P. R. (1969). Turbulent flow and particle deposition in the trachea. Ciba Foundation Symposium, *Circulatory and Respiratory Mass Transport*, pp. 236–255.

SCHROTER, R. C. & SUDLOW, M. F. (1969). Flow patterns in models of the human bronchial airways. *Respiration Physiol.* **7**, 341–355.

SEKIHARA, T. & OLSON, D. E. (1968). Airflow regimes and geometrical factors in the human airway: eleventh Aspen Emphysema Conference, *Current Research in Chronic Respiratory Disease* (U.S. Public Hlth Service Publ. No. 1879), pp. 103–117.

WEIBEL, E. R. (1963). *Morphometry of the human lung*. Berlin, Springer Verlag.

WEST, J. B. (1961). Observations on gas flow in the human bronchial tree. In: *Inhaled particles and vapours*, Ed. C. N. Davies. Oxford, Pergamon Press, pp. 3–8.

WEST, J. B. (1966). Regional differences in blood flow and ventilation in; the lung. In: *Advances in respiratory physiology*, Ed. C. G. Caro. London, Arnold.

WEST, J. B. & HUGH-JONES, P. (1961). Pulsatile gas flow in bronchi caused by heart beat. *J. appl. Physiol.* **16**, 697–702.

WOMERSLEY, J. R. (1955). Oscillatory motion of a viscous liquid in a thin walled elastic tube. *Phil. Mag.*, Ser. 7, **46**, 199–221.

DISCUSSION

M. Newhouse: Have you tried using gases of different density to change the disturbance of laminar flow noted in your major airway model? This has clinical implications in patients with asthma in whom it has been suggested that a He–O$_2$ mixture be used to improve alveolar ventilation. Since a He–O$_2$ mixture might minimize mixing of inspired gas with alveolar gas it could even produce a deterioration in gas exchange! Would your data suggest that SF$_6$ might be a superior vehicle because it might improve gas mixing? Work by Bryan and his associates in Toronto has suggested this may be the case.

Dr. Sudlow: Even when breathing a mixture of sulphur hexachloride, the Reynolds number in the alveoli will be low — less than one. The sort of phenomenon we have described here would not be relevant in that region. Breathing sulphur hexachloride would, however, extend it further down the bronchial tree. Thus, by altering the mixing characteristics of the system, it could produce the effects Bryan and his colleagues have observed.

L. Friberg: Any large differences in the anatomical macrostructure might well have a constitutional background. The data presented by Sudlow suggest that such differences may be of importance for deposition and clearance. Rate differences between individuals have been found by Dr. Albert and will also be reported by Dr. Camner (p. 000). One approach to study the importance of constitutional factors would be to carry out deposition and clearance studies on pairs of monozygotic twins. We are planning such studies in Sweden on our twin registry. Epidemiological support for the importance of constitutional factors concerning bronchitis is found from the fact that a person with a genetic predisposition for bronchitis — even if he is a non-smoker — runs a higher risk of getting bronchitis than a smoker without such a genetic predisposition.

F. B. Meyer: Will the "laminar but disturbed flow" become a normal parabolic laminar flow again?

Dr. Sudlow: At the Reynolds numbers we are considering you still have a disturbed flow for at least 30 to 40 diameters from a bifurcation. Ultimately laminar parabolic flow would be re-established, but in the bronchial tree you have another bifurcation before this can happen.

As mentioned in the paper, there will be a region in the lungs where the linear velocities are much lower and where the Reynolds number is less than one. This is quite a long way down the lung and certainly does not include many of the conducting airways.

J. D. Brain: (i) Could you say more about the implications of your study for the spatial pattern of deposition of particles at airway branches. It seems obvious that the flow profiles you described will lead to higher particle deposition at the bifurcations as compared to the outer airway wall. Could you make additional comments? (ii) What is the effect of wall roughness on the flow profile in airways? Have you examined the effects of the cartilaginous rings and/or the mucus or flow profiles? (iii) Have you examined expiratory flow in your models?

Dr. Sudlow: We do not know what the effects of these disturbed flow patterns will be on particle deposition. It will be very interesting to find out, and we are planning these studies.

We did some measurements on expiration which I have not presented here. You have a disturbed flow with non-parabolic velocity profiles. Through a single bifurcation there are four pairs of secondary motions. I do not think the analysis is quite as valid as in inspiration — we know that during expiration airways can change in calibre a great deal, hence it is difficult to extrapolate from rigid models to the expiration of normal man.

From analogy with flow in long straight pipes, the wall roughness in the respiratory system should not affect the flow. Laminar parabolic flow would not be affected by wall roughness at these Reynolds numbers. The wall roughness may be most important in determining particle deposition.

E. D. Palmes: Since in your model the gas velocity at the wall is in all cases zero, would this imply that there is always a zone at the wall with zero aerosol concentration, even at the 23rd branching order of Weibel?

Dr. Sudlow: In all viscous flow theory it is assumed that velocity at a boundary is zero. Though I know little of particle mechanics I see no reason to suppose there is a zone at zero aerosol concentration at such a boundary.

A. Morgan: Dr. Jacobi of the Hahn Meidtner Institute in Berlin has studied deposition of spherical particles at bifurcations using tagged particles and autoradiographic methods. He shows enhanced deposition just downstream from bifurcations.

Dr. Sudlow: That is what you might expect from the theoretical knowledge we have at present.

Dr. C. N. DAVIES (*Chairman*): Two points occurred to me while the author was talking: The first is that laminar flow can or cannot be influenced by the inertia of the fluid. Deep down in the lungs in the fine distributing airways the Reynolds number is so small that the inertia of the fluid can be disregarded. In the region which the author was talking about (Reynolds numbers of about 100), where flow is well below Reynolds' classical limits for turbulence, the inertia terms play a part which becomes decreasingly important as the Reynolds number decreases.

The phenomena illustrated are due to the inertia terms in the differential equations. As regards the influence upon aerosol deposition, there are two factors. One is the movement of the aerosol particles due to aerodyamic effects arising from velocity gradients, or possibly cross airway movement, etc. The other factor, which is more important with compact-shaped particles, is the mixing of inhaled tidal air in each successive breath with the air remaining in the lung. We know from aerosol deposition experiments that particles inhaled in a given breath are partly — or mostly, if not too large — exhaled in the same breath. Some remain behind in the reserve of the lungs and can be recovered by deep exhalation. In the case of small particles, between $0 \cdot 1$ and 1 μm, a relatively small proportion get down into the residual air and deposit.

As regards deposition in the respiratory tract, the mixing of the tidal air and the reserve air is a very important factor for particles at about $0 \cdot 5$ μm diameter. This is where the velocity profile becomes important. When the Reynolds number is very small in the fine bronchioles, the inhalation and exhalation would, in principle, be exactly the reverse of one another. This would be the case for any kind of geometry. It implies that there is no mixing between the tidal air coming in and the air which is left over from previous expiration.

This is not true in the region of the lung that the author was talking about. When you get these complex velocity profiles with a double or a triple hump, due to the effect of multiple branching, the flow will not be reversible. The result will be a mixing and a transference of particles between the tidal air and the reserve air, and vice versa.

The author mentioned that he had carried out some experiments on reverse flow. When he is able to consider these in relation to the flow going in and possibly determine coefficients of mixing, he will be coming close indeed to aerosol considerations, of which he disclaims any knowledge at the moment.

THEORETICAL CONSIDERATIONS FOR PULMONARY DEPOSITION IN HIGH PRESSURE ENVIRONMENTS: A MODEL

ROBERT A. GUSSMAN*

Bolt Beranek and Newman Inc., Cambridge, Massachusetts

and

JOHN M. BEECKMANS

Faculty of Engineering Sciences, The University of Western Ontario, London, Ontario, Canada

Abstract — The placement of men in environments other than the ambient ones we are used to requires a reconsideration of deposition patterns within the lung. Such an environment is encountered in saturation diving experiments where exposures may last for many weeks at pressures up to 500 psia (pounds/inch², absolute).

An accepted model of pulmonary deposition has been restructured to permit the consideration of any desired pressure and atmospheric composition. In order to apply this model over a pressure range of 500 psia, it was necessary to calculate the aerosol parameters of sedimentation, diffusion, and the slip correction factor over the given pressure range for a breathing mixture of 160 mm partial pressure oxygen and the balance helium.

INTRODUCTION

OUR concern with pulmonary deposition was one phase of a continuing project† to investigate hazards that might arise from aerosols in a high pressure environment. Our experiments specifically pertain to the helium-oxygen atmosphere used in saturation diving vehicles. This paper includes theoretical evaluations of the physical properties of the atmosphere, variations in aerosol behavior caused by the pressure and composition of the atmosphere, a consideration of aerosol formation, how air cleaning mechanisms are affected, how the toxicological effects of aerosols might be altered, and appropriate first order experiments within the scope of the project.

Because of the nature of this atmosphere and the scarcity of relevant information in the available literature, a great deal of tabulated information had to be developed for successive project phases (GUSSMAN, 1969a). Before introducing our model,

* Presently with Billings and Gussman Inc., Boston, Mass.

† This work was sponsored by the Department of the Navy, Office of Naval Research, Washington, D.C. under contract numbers N00014–68–C–0271 and N00014–69–C–0228.

therefore, we discuss the physical properties of the atmosphere and the ways in which aerosol behavior is affected by these properties.

BOND (1964) states that the nitrogen component of the atmosphere is not suitable for long term exposures under high pressures and should, therefore, be replaced by helium. He also noted that, as the pressure is increased, the percentage of oxygen must be decreased, the requirement for life-support being a partial oxygen pressure of approximately 160 mm Hg. Although small percentages of nitrogen and other trace gases are used in the atmosphere, we have chosen to simplify our discussion by considering only a binary mixture of oxygen and helium. Thus, in calculating for depths to 1000 ft (approximately 500 psia or 34 atmospheres), our gas mixture is always considered as a partial oxygen pressure of 160 mm Hg plus a balance of helium. Figure 1 shows a working graph of the atmospheric composition for pressures ranging from 10 to 500 psia (pounds/in², absolute). Since the partial pressure of the oxygen is maintained at 160 mm Hg (3·095 psi), the percentage of oxygen content in the atmosphere decreases from 21% at 1 atmosphere to 0·62% at 34 atmospheres.

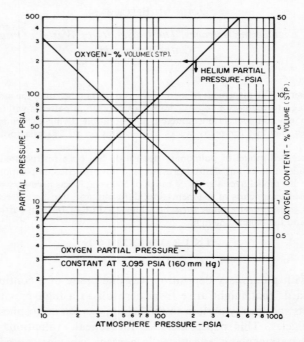

FIGURE 1. Oxygen-helium atmosphere, pressure *vs* composition. $P(O_2) = 160$ mm Hg; $T = 20°C$.

The density of the varying mixture increases with increasing pressure. The calculations assume the mixture to be an ideal gas. Errors arising from this assumption have been checked and are found to be less than 1% at 500 psia. The viscosities of the two gases are quite similar at atmospheric pressure and 20°C (He, 194 micropoise; O_2, 202 micropoise). Because of this similarity and because the viscosity of the mixture varies from 196·47 micropoise at 10 psia to 194·05 micropoise at 500 psia, all our calculations employed a fixed value of 195 micropoise. Values of the mean free path of the mixture, which are necessary in calculation of the aerosol slip correction, have been estimated according to equations given by LOEB (1961) for λ of one gas in the presence of a quantity of another.

When the size of aerosol particles in an atmosphere approaches the mean free path length of gas molecules, discontinuities in the medium become an important consideration and particle mobility is increased. The Cunningham correction or "slip correction factor", which accounts for such discontinuities, is then applied to the equations of motion for aerosol particles. In the case of pulmonary deposition, this correction must be applied to the equations for the sedimentation and the diffusion of submicron particles. However, the classical Cunningham correction proved inapplicable here, because of the composition of the environment. Therefore, we used the recent work of FUCHS & STECHKINA (1962) in determining the suitable factor. The resulting slip correction factor for the oxygen-helium environment versus absolute pressure and particle diameter was calculated and tabulated for this study by the relation given below (GUSSMAN, 1969a).

$$\left(1 + 1\cdot23\frac{\lambda}{d}\right)^{-1} + 3\cdot23\frac{\lambda}{d}, \tag{1}$$

where λ = mean free path of He-O_2 molecules at pressure of interest.
d = diameter of aerosol particle.

An explanation of the development of this data has been published elsewhere (GUSSMAN, 1969b), and since even a modest description of the logic and method for extrapolating the equations for sedimentation velocity and diffusion coefficient is far too lengthy to include in this discussion, the original report should be consulted (GUSSMAN, 1969a).

DEPOSITION MODEL

When aerosols are inhaled into the lung, they are deposited or not deposited according to many complex but predictable functions. The amount and location of deposition depends on aerosol properties (size, shape, density), flow dynamics (velocity, gas density), and physiological parameters (breathing rate, residence time, caliber of airway). The sites of deposition with regard to particle size vary, for a given aerosol, with breathing rate, i.e. with the activity or work rate of the breathing organism. Numerous deposition studies have been carried out over the years. The results of many of these studies have been somewhat codified by the Task Group on Lung Dynamics (ICRP, 1966).

In the simplest terms, the findings show that the larger particles deposit in the upper airways and the finest in the lower. Deposition is very high, being almost complete, for particles 10 μm and larger but decreases steadily with size to about 1 μm. For smaller sizes, deposition again increases to some unknown but high value approaching 70% or greater. This description of the variability of deposition with particle size is approximate for spherical particles ($\rho = 1$) and varies considerably with other aerosol properties.

All of our work has demonstrated that the composition and pressure of the atmosphere to be used for deep submergence systems will cause definite and measurable changes in the motions of the aerosol particles. In considering how deposition and the sites of deposition might be affected by this special atmosphere, we analyzed several existing methods for predicting pulmonary deposition.

The first of these, which was developed in 1935 by Findeisen (1935), considers pulmonary deposition as caused by three factors—sedimentation, impaction, and diffusion. Drawing upon the growing knowledge of the structure of the lung, Landahl (1950) published a revised and improved model. Landahl (1963) again revised this model, and his later work was reviewed by Hatch & Gross (1964). Beeckmans (1965a) also published a model that considers the same basic parameters and also takes into account the effects of air mixing and of residual undeposited aerosol from previous breaths. The simplified respiratory tract model used by Landahl, which distinguishes 12 separate regions in the respiratory tract, was subsequently expanded by Beeckmans (1965b) to 27 regions, in conformity with Weibel's (1963) respiratory tract model. The reader is referred to Beeckmans' first paper (Beeckmans, 1965a) for a description of the deposition equations used in the present report.

The question of how breathing mechanics are altered by pressure and composition was resolved by personal communication with Commander N. R. Anthonisen (1969), U.S. Naval Medical Center. Dr. Anthonisen, who has participated in studies of simulated dives to 825 ft, reports that flow rate cycle time and tidal volume are about the same in helium-oxygen as in air at ambient pressure. He expects that any possible change would be in the direction of increased tidal volume and decreased cycle time. His findings justify the use of existing breathing patterns in our model.

The breathing patterns for which calculations were made are

(1) Flow rate $= 300$ cm^3/s
    Cycle time $= 4$ s
    Tidal volume $= 450$ cm^3

(2) Flow rate $= 300$ cm^3/s
    Cycle time $= 8$ s
    Tidal volume $= 900$ cm^3

(3) Flow rate $= 300$ cm^3/s
    Cycle time $= 12$ s
    Tidal volume $= 1350$ cm^3

(4) Flow rate $= 1000$ cm/^{3}s
    Cycle time $= 4$s
    Tidal volume $= 1500$ cm^3

The aerosol deposition equations quoted below are basically those developed and used by Landahl (1950) and Beeckmans (1965a). However, they have been generalized to permit consideration of the pressure and composition of the He-O$_2$ environment.

The impaction equation that is used by both Landahl (1950) and Beeckmans (1965a), when put in general form, is

$$I = \frac{\rho d^2 V \sin \theta \, (s.c.)}{18\eta} \Big/ \left(R + \frac{\rho d^2 V \sin \theta \, (s.c.)}{18\eta} \right), \tag{2}$$

where $I =$ probability of inertial deposition
    $\rho =$ particle density
    $d =$ particle diameter
    $R =$ radius of airway
    $V =$ gas velocity
    $\eta =$ gas viscosity
    $\theta =$ branching angle of pulmonary airways
  $(s.c.) =$ slip correction factor

Equation (2) may be used as a general expression for any gas and aerosol system. The value of the slip correction $(s.c.)$ for our helium-oxygen atmosphere at the various pressures is obtained from our previously tabulated numbers (Gussman 1965a). If tabulated values of v—the sedimentation velocity—which include the slip correction, are to be used (GUSSMAN, 1965a), the equation may be stated as

$$I = vV \sin \theta/(gR + vV \sin \theta) \tag{3}$$

The equation used by LANDAHL (1950) and his predecessors for deposition due to sedimentation is stated in final form as

$$S = 1 - \exp\left(- gd^2\rho\tau \cos \psi'/18\eta R\right)(s.c.), \tag{4}$$

where S = probability of deposition due to sedimentation
τ = mean passage time of the particles
ψ' = angle of inclination of a tube with the horizontal

Cos ψ' iscommonly assigned a value of $2/\pi$ (LANDAHL, 1963; HATCH et al., 1964). This equation may be written more simply in terms of the sedimentation velocity and with cos ψ' equal to $2/\pi$ as

$$S = 1 - \exp\left(-\frac{2v}{\pi R}\right) \tag{5}$$

By using equation (5) one may directly substitute sedimentation velocity values that had been previously tabulated (GUSSMAN, 1969a), for the environment under considera-tion. These tabulations represent an improvement over simply calculated values inasmuch as they already contain the slip correction factor as well as corrected sedimentation equations for various ranges of Reynolds number. In fact, the simple Stokes sedimentation equation is used only up to a Reynolds number of $0 \cdot 05$. From $0 \cdot 05$ to 4 we have used Davies' equation (DAVIES, 1945), and from 4 to 400 we have used Klyachko's equation (FUCHS, 1964).

The equation used by BEECKMANS (1965a) for diffusion is

$$D_i = 1 - \exp[(- 7 \cdot 31kT\tau/6\pi R^2\eta d)(s.c.)] \tag{6}$$

where D_i = probability of deposition due to diffusion
k = Boltzmann's constant
T = absolute temperature

Equation (6) can be rewritten more simply in terms of the diffusion coefficient (D) and the slip correction:

$$D_i = 1 - \exp(- 7 \cdot 31D\tau/2R^2), \tag{7}$$

where D = diffusion coefficient with slip correction.

The slip-corrected diffusion coefficients for the atmosphere under investigation have previously been tabulated (GUSSMAN, 1965a), and are therefore suitable for direct substitution into this equation and into the model.

RESULTS

Calculations have been completed for the four previously stated breathing con-ditions. These conditions are typified by the parameters of flow rate, cycle time, and tidal volume. In discussing each condition, however, we reference only the tidal volume, as that is the number which is different in *each* of the four cases. A special report, (GUSSMAN *et al.*, 1969*b*), has been issued presenting all the tabulated and plotted results for the four breathing conditions at three particle densities; for purposes of clarity, we present here only the result for unit density particles. These data are depicted in Figures 2 to 5. For comparative purposes, we have also processed calculations for air at 14·7 psia and unit density particles, but we have plotted only the 10 and 500 psia extremes for the helium-oxygen environment as all other values lie within the envelope (with two very minor exceptions). We found that the computer program would not function in the 0·001 μm size range for the 450 and 900 cm³ tidal volume runs. To determine the

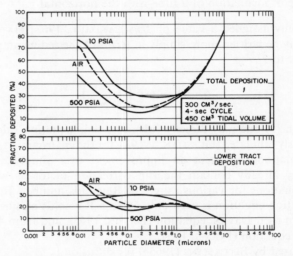

FIGURE 2. Total and lower respiratory tract deposition. He-O_2 $P(O_2) = 160$ mm Hg at various pressures.

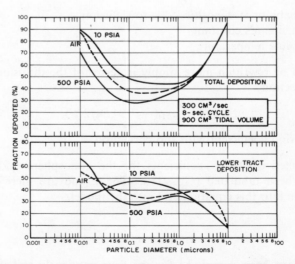

FIGURE 3. Total and lower respiratory tract deposition. He-O_2 $P(O_2) = 160$ mm Hg at various pressures.

cause of the program's inability to function would have been most difficult and time consuming, and we felt that the trends were clearly indicated by data obtained for the other two tidal volumes.

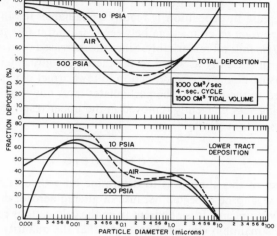

FIGURE 4. Total and lower respiratory tract deposition. He-O_2 $P(O_2)$ = 160 mm Hg at various pressures.

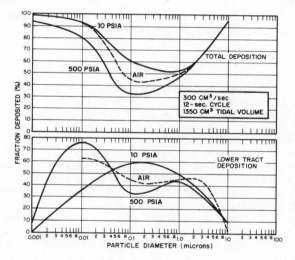

FIGURE 5. Total and lower respiratory tract deposition. He-O_2 $P(O_2)$ = 160 mm Hg at various pressures.

The most significant result apparent in this study is that the deposition curve for air almost always lies within the 10 to 500 psia envelope. Lower tract deposition in the helium-oxygen atmosphere decreases with increasing pressure and, at the highest pressures, is significantly less than in air. However, in the lower respiratory tract this situation reverses at particle diameters below approximately $0 \cdot 01$ μm, and deposition at the high pressures exceeds or equals that in air. While all the curves show the characteristic minimum deposition at approximately $0 \cdot 1$ μm diameter with the expected peaking at $0\cdot01$ μm, it was surprising to note that for the data available down to $0\cdot001$ μm (1500 and 1350 cm³ tidal volume) the lower tract deposition decreased remarkably—falling to almost zero at the lower pressures. We believe the explanation for this decrease in deposition is readily explainable. It will be noted that the curves for *total deposition* reach maxima between $0\cdot01$ and $0\cdot001$ μm even though the *lower tract deposition* falls off remarkably. Since the increased total and lower tract deposition below $0\cdot1$ μm is clearly ascribed to the increased diffusional mobility of particulates with decreasing diameter, the reduction in lower tract deposition below $0\cdot01$ μm can be attributed to the fact that the particulates have now become so highly mobile that they are being very efficiently removed in the upper respiratory tract and never reach the lower levels for collection.

CONCLUSIONS

The object of this study was to determine on a theoretical basis if increased personnel risk was to be expected because of altered aerosol deposition patterns in high pressure environments. It is apparent from the calculations presented here that deposition patterns maintain similar shapes and that the quantity deposited decreases with increasing pressure. One disturbing note, however, may be in the increased deposition in the upper respiratory tract for very small particles. While the mass is negligible, the surface area represented by this very tiny fraction is substantial. On the other hand, it is quite reasonable to assume that the same peaking for very small particles occurs in air and is not an item for great concern.

REFERENCES

ANTHONISEN, N. R. (1969). Personal communication.
BEECKMANS, J. M. (1965a). Can. J. Physiol. Pharmac. **43**, 157.
BEECKMANS, J. M. (1965b). Ann. occup. Hyg. **8**, 221–231.
BOND, C. E. (1964). Archs envir. Hlth **9**, 310.
DAVIES, C. N. (1945). Proc. phys. Soc. Lond. **57**, 259–270.
FINDEISEN, W. (1935). Pflügers Arch. ges. Physiol. **236**, 367–379.
FUCHS, N. A. (1964). The mechanics of aerosols. Rev. ed., Oxford, Pergamon Press.
FUCHS, N. A. & STECHKINA, I. B. (1962). Trans. Faraday Soc. **58**, 475.
GUSSMAN, R. A. (1969a). Rep. No. 1770, Cambridge (Mass.), Bolt Beranek & Newman.
GUSSMAN, R. A. (1969b). J. appl. Met. **8**, 999–1001.
GUSSMAN, R. A. & SACCO, A. M. (1969). Rep. No. 1884, Cambridge (Mass.), Bolt Beranek & Newman.
HATCH, T. F. & GROSS, P. (1964). Pulmonary deposition and retention of inhaled aerosols. New York, Academic Press.
INTERNATIONAL RADIOLOGICAL PROTECTION COMMISSION (1966). Hlth Phys. **12**, 173–207.
LANDAHL, H. D. (1950). Bull. math. Biophys. **12**, 43.
LANDAHL, H. D. (1963). Bull. math. Biophys. **25**, 29–39.
LOEB, L. B. (1961). The kinetic theory of gases. New York, Dover Publications.
WEIBEL, E. R. (1963). Morphometry of the human lung. New York, Academic Press.

DISCUSSION

D. C. F. MUIR: Surely the behaviour of an airborne particle in the lung depends only on its aerodynamic behaviour. If you calculate the stop distance of the particles under altered pressure it is possible to estimate the deposition pattern by considering the deposition of a particle of equivalent stop distance, under standard atmospheric conditions, from the original data of Beeckmans. Is it really necessary to recalculate the deposition pattern from the computer program?

Mr. GUSSMAN: Too many things change. We want to know what is going on at each pressure. Also some particles are below 1 μm in size and stop distance is not the only factor. It seems simpler to go through the whole calculation, particularly when done by computer, rather than try to adjust.

M. LIPPMANN: Is there any evidence that an inhalation hazard exists in an atmosphere such as Sealab? Have any air samples been collected in such places?

Mr. GUSSMAN: As far as I have been able to find out from the U.S. Navy, there has been no particulate sampling in any high pressure environment. I have been trying to arrange an experiment for the last few years and it looks as if I will be successful this year.

DISEASE

A NEW TECHNIQUE FOR STUDYING AIRWAY DEPOSITION, MORPHOLOGY AND MECHANISMS USING POWDERED TANTALUM*

J. A. NADEL and S. W. CLARKE

Cardiovascular Research Institute and Department of Medicine, University of California San Francisco, San Francisco, California, U.S.A.

ROENTGENOGRAPHIC outlining of airways is a valuable tool, but its usefulness has been limited by the toxicity, lack of radiopacity, and poor adherence of liquid contrast materials. We describe a new method for outlining the airways roentgenographically by insufflating finely powdered tantalum (mean mass diameter, 2·5 μm). Tantalum is superior because it is highly radiopaque, chemically inert, and adheres firmly to airway mucosa.

We have used this technique to study: (1) deposition of particles in the larynx with shallow panting, and at airway bifurcations with rapid deep breathing; (2) impairment of mucociliary clearance by mucosal trauma, tumors, or lung reimplantation; (3) the cough mechanism and its efficiency; (4) regulation of small airways (<1 mm diameter) *in vivo*, in conjunction with a fine focal spot X-ray tube; (5) anatomic abnormalities of airways in lung diseases.

* Full text of paper not received. Ed.

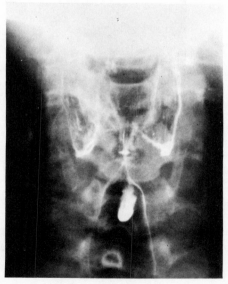

FIGURE 1. Normal larynx; glottis closed.

43

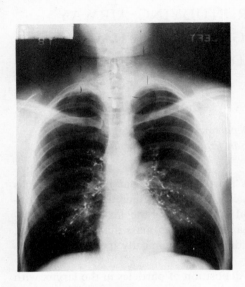

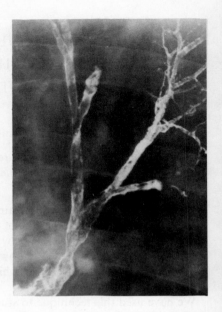

FIGURE 2. Rapid breathing —
bifurcations of airways.

FIGURE 3. Carcinoma of left upper lobe

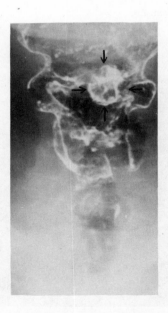

FIGURE 4. Laryngogram of carcinoma.

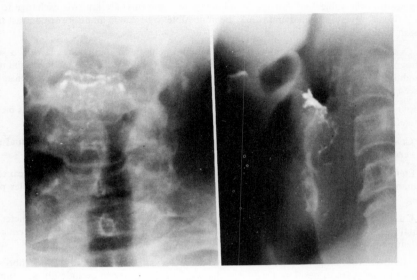

FIGURE 5. Follow-up laryngogram at 24 h showing clearance. A.P. and lateral.

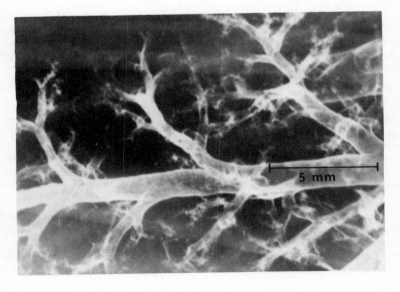

5 mm

FIGURE 6. Small airways of dog in vivo.

DISCUSSION

D. C. F. MUIR: From the clinical point of view, I think the old liquid methods may still have advantages. In a patient with a local area of bronchiectasis and otherwise normal lungs it is fairly easy to position the subject so that the liquid enters the abnormal section. Air exchange to such a region is usually severely limited and it may be impossible to persuade an airborne contrast medium to deposit in the required region.

Dr. CLARKE: To demonstrate a localized area of bronchiectasis one could perform a selective bronchogram with small volumes of tantalum, the particles of which adhere to the bronchial mucosa. Although liquid may run into an abnormal section of lung it may also run out again before X-rays have been taken; the volume required may also interfere with lung function.

M. LIPPMANN: I gather that the 2·5 μm size which you specify is the actual diameter as measured, and therefore the aerodynamic size would be quite different?

Dr. CLARKE: No. The aerodynamic size or mean mass diameter is 2·5 μm. The actual particle size is very much smaller than that.

M. LIPPMANN: There is one size which would go to a certain part of the lung because of its aerodynamic property. Have you used other sizes in order to characterize other smaller parts of the lung?

Dr. CLARKE: No. In most studies we have introduced the tantalum through a catheter in the bronchial tree. Because of this we have not really been able to measure deposition in different airways, dependent on particle size.

J. E. EPSOM: How long were patients kept under observation in order to exclude fibrosis? As silicosis can take years to develop it would perhaps be unwise as yet to exclude fibrous stimulating properties of tantalum.
Was early diagnosis a reference to observation by patient, e.g. amount of sputum, etc., or to observation of researcher?

Dr. CLARKE: On the slide shown, the patient had tantalum in the lung for a period of nine months with no significant reaction. In one patient there was one area of localized fibrous reaction to tantalum, but this was quite small and certainly not generalized. We have no evidence that it is likely to cause a long-term fibrous reaction; in general, tantalum is very inert.
Are you enquiring whether the patient had respiratory symptoms not clearly diagnosed by other techniques? We are putting forward the hypothesis that delayed clearance could be an interesting pointer in early diagnosis. Clearance may be impaired fairly early when surface squamous metaplasia occurs, for instance. This may be something one could pick up early, when perhaps symptoms of respiratory disease are minimal.

C. B. McKERROW: Have you evidence on any irritant properties of tantalum? For instance, are there any lung function changes after administration?

Dr. CLARKE: In a study where we did pulmonary function tests before and after tantalum bronchography there were no significant changes in pulmonary function, whereas with conventional iodine bronchograms there is a considerable change in pulmonary function.
W. T. ULMER: We have become very interested in this method and spent time on it, but our own results were not so good as yours. Is it possible to get the same good results under normal breathing conditions and without intubation? How thick must the lining be on the wall of the bronchi? Do you use a special X-ray technique?

Dr. CLARKE: I think the answer to the last part of your question is "no", at present. If one breathes shallowly then the majority of the particles deposit in the larynx and the trachea. If one wants to outline more peripheral parts of the bronchial tree one has to breathe at a faster rate, when air flow is more turbulent and the particles impinge on the mucosal surface providing fairly dense deposition at airway bifurcations. To get the best results bronchography using a small catheter is required.
We find that a layer only a few microns thick is satisfactory. It is essential to run the X-ray tube at about 120 kV peak, so that photons of the required energy to give adequate contrast are generated.

J. FERIN: Did you employ a single exposure or multiple exposures? What was the amount of dust inhaled? I wonder why so many particles were located extracellularly two days after exposure. This is quite different from TiO_2 (titanic oxide) particles as shown in my paper (p. 283).

Dr. CLARKE: We used two techniques, either single X-ray films or ciné-bronchograms. The amount of dust inhaled was on average about $0 \cdot 5$ ml.

I do not know why, in our diagram, more particles were not intracellular. We have not made a particular point of trying to get particles into the alveoli in man because of the slow clearance from that site.

THE EFFECT OF SHAPE ON PARTICLE PENETRATION AND RETENTION IN ANIMAL LUNGS

V. Timbrell and J. W. Skidmore

Medical Research Council, Pneumoconiosis Unit, Llandough Hospital, Penarth, Glamorgan, Wales

Abstract — Large particles of non-compact shape can be of sufficiently small aerodynamic size to permit penetration to the pulmonary air spaces. An inhalation experiment in animals has been performed to indicate how large dimensions may affect the deposition and retention of the particles in the lungs and whether the size-selecting gravimetric sampling instruments developed for use with particles of compact shape are suitable when the particles are of other shapes. Particles of large dimensions in one, two or three aspects were produced by fusing airborne glass fibres in various configurations. Results indicate that the horizontal elutriator is not complete as a selector of respirable fibrous dusts.

INTRODUCTION

THERE is general agreement that size-selecting gravimetric sampling instruments developed in recent years are satisfactory for collecting the respirable fraction of airborne dust when the particles are of compact shape, such as those of coal or silica. The reliability and excellent performance of these instruments prompts consideration of their suitability for collecting the respirable dust when the particles are of non-compact shape, such as flakes or fibres, or the possibility of modifying them for such applications. That their suitability cannot be taken for granted is indicated by the occurrence in lungs of fibres and flakes with dimensions in some aspects much larger than those of respirable coal or silica particles. The question arises how these large dimensions may affect the deposition and retention of the particles in the lungs and whether they are also factors in the sampling efficiency of the size selectors. Hollow lung casts (TIMBRELL *et al.*, 1970) have indicated some of the factors involved when non-compact particles are inhaled but the evidence is not complete since these models contain no clearance mechanism. Inhalation experiments in animals are therefore desirable.

We here describe such an experiment performed with an aerosol containing a high proportion of particles of sufficiently low aerodynamic size for them to be within the respirable range while possessing large dimensions in one, two or three aspects. Airborne glass fibres were treated in a furnace to produce an aerosol containing straight fibres, curved fibres and aggregates, together with spheres for purposes of comparison. Although the results are discussed in this paper in relation to the sampling of fibrous particles, the method has been designed to provide evidence on the behaviour of particles of other shapes; for example, an X-shaped particle consisting of two fibres fused together simulates a flake.

DESIGN OF THE EXPERIMENT

Fifteen male SPF rats were used. Four of these acted as a control group. The other eleven were exposed in the apparatus shown in Figure 1 to a dust concentration of

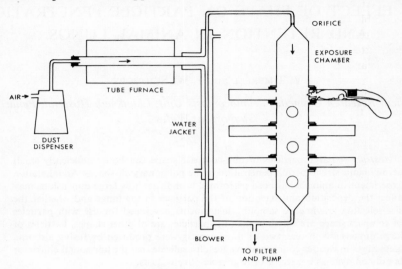

Figure 1. Diagram of apparatus.

180 mg/m³ for a period of 8 hours a day during 10 days. Continuous dust sampling was performed covering the whole exposure period for determination of the size distributions of the various types of particles. On the day following the last day of exposure six rats were killed and the dust extracted from their lungs for determination of the size distributions of the various types of particles. The results given in this paper refer to these six rats. The remaining five rats were killed 28 days later, but the results are not yet complete.

DETAILS OF THE EXPERIMENT

The dust dispenser used was a type designed earlier (Timbrell *et al.*, 1968) for generating dust clouds from the fibrous UICC standard reference samples of asbestos. The dispenser was packed with the fibrous dust produced by cutting with a microtome strands of glass (Johns Manville micro-fibre, sp. grav. 2·6, nominal diameter range 0·75–1·5 μm) embedded in wax (water-soluble Aquax), and washing in water. The dust contained fibres with a wide distribution of length up to about 100 μm. This method of preparation was more satisfactory than grinding, which produced too high a proportion of fine non-fibrous particles.

Air supplied to the dust dispenser carried the glass particles through an electrically-heated tube furnace maintained at a wall temperature of 1040°C. Because of temperature differences particles were softened to varying degree, and the airstream emerging contained spherical particles, straight fibres, curved fibres and aggregates of fibres firmly welded together. At the T-junction the airstream merged with air being recirculated by a blower in a loop formed of 2 cm diameter copper tubing and the exposure chamber. The orifice promoted uniform distribution of the dust in the air entering the exposure chamber. A pump extracted air from the system through a dust filter. Operation of the apparatus at a pressure slightly below atmospheric eliminated dust leaks. The water jacket maintained the air in the exposure chamber at a comfortable temperature for the animals.

The exposure chamber was a vertical aluminium cylinder, 15 cm in diameter and 90 cm long, fitted with conical ends and a total of 12 ports distributed around the circumference and along the length. Each rat was contained in a removable aluminium tube fitted with a soft rubber collar which sealed it in one of these ports. One end of the tube was closed by a perspex disc containing a hole through which the rat's nose protruded into the airstream: the rat was held in the tube by a rubber bung from which a segment had been removed to allow the tail to pass through. The tube was sealed by a plastic bag held in position by a rubber band. The bag served as a receptacle for faeces and urine and also as a sensitive indicator of reduced pressure in the exposure chamber.

The twelfth port accommodated the inlets of two dust samplers which collected the dust on membrane filters. One, the total-sampler, collected unelutriated dust. The other, the respirable-sampler, collected the dust which had passed through a horizontal elutriator removed from an MRE sampler.

Samples were also taken with an aerosol spectrometer for determinations of the size distributions of the spherical and fibrous particles as functions of aerodynamic diameter.

The dusts extracted from the lungs of the rats killed the first day after exposure were ashed at 380°C, washed with 0·5 N hydrochloric acid, pooled and a sample taken for size analysis. The same procedure was applied to the dusts collected by the two samplers. Each of the three samples thus produced was dispersed in ethanol in an ultrasonic bath for 30 min and the size distributions of the four types of particles were measured by optical microscopy. The spheres were sized according to diameter, the straight fibres according to length, and both the curved fibres and fibre aggregates according to the length and breadth of the smallest circumscribing rectangle.

DATA AND DISCUSSION

Penetration Curve of the Elutriator and Retention Curve of the Rat Lungs for Spherical Particles

Table I shows the size distributions of the glass spheres collected by the respirable-sampler and the total-sampler and those extracted from the rat lungs.

TABLE I. SIZE DISTRIBUTION OF THE GLASS SPHERES

Diameter: μm	Total-sampler	Respirable-sampler	Rat lungs
0·8–1·2	502	515	392
1·2–1·7	405	439	428
1·7–2·4	120	152	154
2·4–3·3	91	78	25
3·3–4·7	72	41	2
4·7–6·7	28	1	
6·7–9·4	4		

Figure 2 shows the penetration curve of the elutriator and the retention curve of the rat lungs, each calculated from the appropriate pair of size distributions. The penetration curve conforms closely to the theoretical curve. The retention curve is in good agreement with that obtained in a previous experiment (CARTWRIGHT & SKIDMORE, 1964), and resembles the penetration curve of an elutriator with 50% penetration for 2 μm diameter glass spheres.

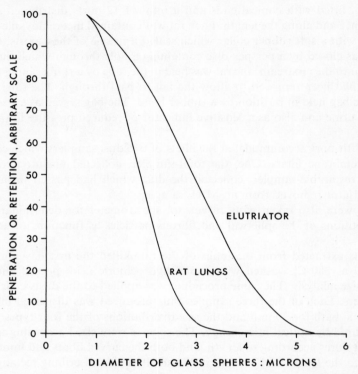

FIGURE 2. Penetration curve of the elutriator and retention curve of the rat lungs for glass spheres.

Aerodynamic-Diameter Distributions of the Spheres and Fibres

Figure 3 shows the size distributions of the spheres and fibres measured by means of the aerosol spectrometer. Comparison of the slopes of the curves shows that in terms of aerodynamic diameter the spheres and the fibres were similar in size distribution. This result is not inconsistent with the presence of long fibres in the dust cloud, since it has been previously shown that the aerodynamic diameter of a fibre is approximately proportional to fibre diameter and not very sensitive to fibre length (TIMBRELL, 1965).

Length Distributions of the Straight Fibres

Table II shows the length distributions of the straight fibres collected by the two dust samplers and those extracted from the rat lungs. Comparison of the data in columns 2 and 3 shows that the length distribution of the fibres collected by the respirable-sampler was similar to that of the fibres collected by the total-sampler. This result is consistent with the aerodynamic-diameter distribution of the fibres given in Figure 3, which shows that a high proportion of the fibres were, from the standpoint of aerodynamic size, within the respirable range. The result is also in agreement with that of an earlier experiment (TIMBRELL, 1971) which showed that for fibres of the length used in the present experiment, penetration through an MRE elutriator is governed by the aerodynamic size of the fibres and is virtually independent of their length. In contrast, comparison of the length distribution (column 4) of the straight fibres extracted from the rat lungs with that (column 3) of the fibres collected by the respirable-sampler, shows in the former a more rapid decrease in particle frequency with increasing fibre length.

TABLE II. SIZE DISTRIBUTION OF THE STRAIGHT GLASS FIBRES
(Relative number of fibres)

Length: μm	Total-sampler	Respirable-sampler	Rat lungs
5– 10	461	401	524
10– 15	171	116	36
15– 20	67	44	12
20– 25	24	21	5
25– 30	11	7	1·2
30– 40	11	5	0·6
40– 50	4	4	0·2
50– 60	3	3	
60– 70	1	1	
70–100	1	0·3	
100–130			

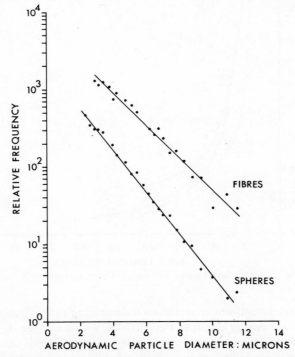

FIGURE 3. Size distributions of the glass spheres and fibres according to aerodynamic particle diameter.

Fibre length is therefore an important factor in the retention of fibres in the rat lungs, but the experiment does not indicate whether this is associated with the deposition or the clearance processes. Experiments (TIMBRELL, 1970) in hollow lung casts have demonstrated a major involvement of fibre length and shape in the deposition of fibres in the fine lung airways, but one would expect that these parameters also affect the clearance. The absence of a comparable influence of fibre length on the ability of fibres to penetrate the horizontal elutriator indicates that the device is not complete as a size-selecting system for use with particles of elongated shape.

Retention of Straight Fibres, Curved Fibres, Fibre Aggregates in the Rat Lungs

Table II shows the length distributions of the straight fibres collected by the two dust samplers and those extracted from the rat lungs. The retention curve of the rat lungs for straight fibres, calculated from the data in columns 3 and 4, is shown in Figure 4. Tables III and IV show the corresponding data for the curved fibres and the fibre aggregates respectively, and the retention curves of the rat lungs calculated for these types of particles are also shown in Figure 4.

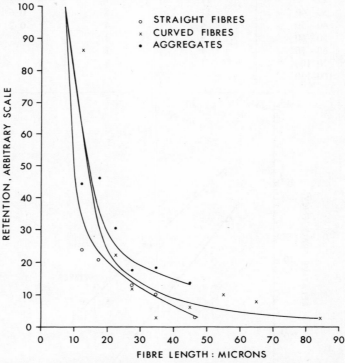

Figure 4. Retention curves of the rat lungs for straight fibres, curved fibres and fibre aggregates.

Each of the three retention curves shows a decreasing rate of retention of fibres in the rat lungs with increasing length of the particles, with a change in the slope of the curve at about 20 μm fibre length. A possible explanation for this change in the slope is that the clearance processes are less efficient for fibres longer than 20 μm.

As is evident from the scatter of the points, the retention curves are not sufficiently accurate to permit valid comparison of the retention of straight, curved and aggregated fibres This indicates that an experiment to facilitate such a comparison would require a higher proportion of long and more-curved fibres in the cloud. The data for the shapes of the curved fibres and fibre aggregates in the present cloud are given in Table V.

TABLE III. SIZE DISTRIBUTION OF THE CURVED GLASS FIBRES

Length: μm	Total-sampler	Respirable-sampler	Rat lungs
5– 10	419	515	465
10– 15	201	178	139
15– 20	55	124	27
20– 25	40	45	9
25– 30	20	30	3·2
30– 40	18	26	0·6
40– 50	8	11	0·6
50– 60	4	6	0·5
60– 70	1·7	5	0·4
70–100	0·7	3	0·1
100–130	0·7		

TABLE IV. SIZE DISTRIBUTION OF THE FIBRE AGGREGATES

Length: μm	Total-sampler	Respirable-sampler	Rat lungs
5– 10	227	405	430
10– 15	226	233	110
15– 20	155	127	63
20– 25	84	87	28
25– 30	82	53	10
30– 40	59	46	9
40– 50	13	20	3
50– 60	9	14	
60– 70	10	10	
70–100	1		
100–130	1		

TABLE V. FIBRE-SHAPE

Length of circumscribing rectangle: μm	Respirable-sampler		Rat lungs	
	Mean ratio length/breadth	Range of breadth: microns	Mean ratio length/breadth	Range of breadth: microns
4	1·7	1·4– 4	1·9	1·4– 4
6	2·3	1·4– 4	2·5	1·4– 4
8	2·8	1·4– 6	2·9	1·4– 6
11	2·7	2– 7	3·4	2–11
16	3·1	2–15	3·1	2–15
23	4·2	2–15	3·6	4–15
32	4·8	3–21	4·3	4–23
45	5·1	3–20	4·3	7–15
70	6·0	4–20	5·7	4–15

SUMMARY OF RESULTS

The results at present available are as follows:

(i) The experimental penetration curve of the horizontal elutriator for spherical particles is in good agreement with the theoretical curve.

(ii) The retention curve of the rat lungs for spherical glass particles resembles the penetration curve of a horizontal elutriator with 50% penetration of glass spheres of 2 μm diameter.

(iii) In the size range of interest, fibre length is a minor factor in the fibre penetration of the horizontal elutriator, but is a major factor in the retention of fibres in the rat lungs. This indicates that the horizontal elutriator is not complete as a size selecting system for use with particles of elongated shape.

(iv) There is a change of slope in the retention curve of the rat lungs at about 20 μm fibre length. A possible explanation is a lower efficiency of the clearance processes for longer fibres.

(v) There is no clear difference indicated between the rate of retention of straight fibres, curved fibres and fibre aggregates in the rat lungs. The influence of fibre length is so great that evidence on the effect of the fibre shape and secondary dimensions will require a dust cloud which contains higher proportions of long and more-curved fibres than used in the present experiment.

REFERENCES

CARTWRIGHT, J. & SKIDMORE, J. W. (1964). *Ann. occup. Hyg.* **7**, 151–167.

TIMBRELL, V. (1965). *Ann. N.Y. Acad. Sci.* **132**, 255–273.

TIMBRELL, V. (1970). In: *Pneumoconiosis*. Proc. int. Conf., Johannesburg, 1969. *Ed.* H. A. Shapiro. Cape Town, Oxford University Press. pp. 3–9.

TIMBRELL, V. (1971). Proc. third Rochester int. Conf. on Environmental Toxicity, Rochester, 18–20 June 1970. (In Press.)

TIMBRELL, V., BEVAN, N. E., DAVIES, A. S. & MUNDAY, D. E. (1970). *Nature* **225**, 97–98.

TIMBRELL, V., HYETT, A. W. & SKIDMORE, J. W. (1968). *Ann. occup. Hyg.* **11**, 273–281.

DISCUSSION

D. C. F. Muir: Since the length of the fibre is so important, do you think experiments carried out on rats, whose airways are small, are relevant to the human being?

Mr. Skidmore: Yes, some useful experiments may be made in this way. The reason for this is that while the difference in the overall size of the human lung and the rat is very marked, the difference in diameters of airways at the terminal and respiratory bronchiole level is not nearly of the same order — about 300 μm cf. 200 μm.

S. E. Devir: Have you considered the effect of electric charges on the asbestos fibers, in regard to effective fibre diameter, fiber orientation, etc.

Mr. Skidmore: We have not investigated any specific electric charge effect.

W. Stober: I have made some independent measurements on the aerodynamic diameter of asbestos fibres. In essence I agree with Mr. Skidmore's statement that there is not a strong dependence on the fibre length, but if your have a perfect fibre, as found frequently with amosites, you can detect a slight effect which is theoretically of the order of the sixth root of the length of the fibre.

The data seem to be consistent with theory if we assume that the asbestos fibres (if they are perfect) are orientated parallel to the stream lines in the airways. I have no very good explanation why this is so, and I wonder if somebody can help me.

Dr. Timbrell: The tendency of a straight fibre to assume an orientation parallel to the axis of an airway is readily explained. In the presence of the parabolic velocity profile in the viscous flow, the air velocity varies along the length of the fibre, being higher at the end nearest the axis than at the end nearest the wall. The torque which is thus applied to the fibre gradually turns it into alignment with the streamlines.

J. D. Brain: It should be remembered that we are not examining the deposition of fibres in the lung and comparing that with deposition in the size-selective samplers. The lung fibres have had clearance processes superimposed on the initial deposition. Since the animals were exposed for 10 days and an additional day elapsed prior to sacrifice, probably the majority of initially deposited fibres have been cleared from the lungs. Site of deposition and hence clearance varies with fibre length and shape. Thus the size distribution of fibres found in the lung is critically dependent on the time interval between exposure and sacrifice.

J. L. Balßer: In our observations at autopsy of asbestos workers, it is not uncommon to find random fibres 100 μm or almost 200 μm in length in the alveolar region. This illustrates the complexity of the deposition process.

A. G. Heppleston: Were the glass fibre aggregates welded so firmly before inhalation as to prevent their disaggregation by ultrasonics with the liberation if isolated fibres in material recovered from the lung?

Mr. Skidmore: The aggregated fibres that passed through our furnace were fused in position; ultrasonic dispersion did not break them apart.

M. Newhouse: Could the 100 μm asbestos fibres seen in autopsy specimens in alveolar regions have been carried there from larger airways during the cutting process?

J. L. Balßer: This was questioned. To my satisfaction I think we have fairly well eliminated the possibility of contamination. The sections were cut without fixation.

A. L. Reeves: Suppose subjects are exposed to identically created aerosols of chrysotile and amosite. In view of our data on the differences in sedimentation characteristics of these dusts, would you expect the amounts inhaled to be similar or different? If different, do you think that this might be the reason for the supposed difference in the pathogenicity of these compounds?

Dr. Timbrell: It depends on what part of the lung is being considered. In the upper respiratory tract, where deposition is mainly by sedimentation and depends on fibre diameter there should be little difference between the rate of deposition of chrysotile and amosite fibres. As regards penetration to the alveoli, the fact that amosite fibres are efficiently orientated parallel to the axes of the airways enables them to penetrate much farther than the curly chrysotile fibres which do not exhibit this feature and are readily deposited by interception in the respiratory bronchioles. As regards penetration to the pleura, crocidolite, because it is usually thinner and shorter, can be expected to reach this region more efficiently than amosite, whereas chrysotile will very rarely penetrate that far.

THE NOSE — A DEFENCE AGAINST THE ATMOSPHERIC ENVIRONMENT*

Donald F. Proctor and David L. Swift

*Department of Environmental Medicine,
Johns Hopkins School of Hygiene and Public Health,
The Johns Hopkins University, Baltimore, Maryland 21205, U.S.A.*

Abstract — The anatomical shape of the nasal air passages results in air flow characteristics which affect their function as filters for inhaled substances. Nasal mucociliary function, the flow of mucus from the paranasal sinuses and the location of the adenoid tissue all combine to complete the effectiveness of the nose in defence against the atmospheric environment.

THE nose has developed phylogenetically as an organ providing the olfactory sense and, at the same time, assuring protection of the remainder of the respiratory tract against drying or thermal injury from the inspired air. It is a fortunate by-product of this development that the nose acts as a filter providing protection against noxious environmental vapors, gases and particulates. In this paper we analyze the anatomical and physiological characteristics of the nose to show how they produce an effective defence organ and indicate what nasal disorders might reduce its effectiveness.

The nose is the natural entrance to the respiratory tract. Most mammals, other than man, are equipped with an epiglottis which makes nasal breathing possible even when the mouth is open, thus assuring the protection offered by olfaction. Human infants are compulsory nasal breathers and only after several months of life will they voluntarily breathe through the mouth except when crying. In spite of the fact that the nasal airway accounts for nearly half of the total resistance to respiratory air flow most of us prefer nasal breathing in most circumstances. Therefore, it is clear that the nose is the first target for noxious environmental air influences and it should be the first line of defence against them.

NASAL ANATOMY

In contrast to the trachea the nose offers a complex air passage. It is divided into two parts by the nasal septum, each part in turn spreading from a small entrance just beyond the nostrils into a narrow space along the septum leading to the equally narrow folds of the meati and communicating through small orifices with the adjoining paranasal sinus cavities (PROCTOR, 1964): Figure 1. The total surface area of nasal mucosa (both sides) probably approximates 160 to 180 cm², perhaps double that in

* Work supported by U.S.P.H.S. Grants HE 10342 and ES 00454.

the trachea. The length of the nasal passage from nostril to nasopharynx in the adult ranges from 8 to 11 cm.

From the functional point of view the key points about this passage are its small entrance, the narrowness of the long main passage, the large surface and cross-sectional area, and the fact that the main line of the nasal passage is at an angle to the entrance at the nostrils and the exit at the nasopharynx: Figure 2.

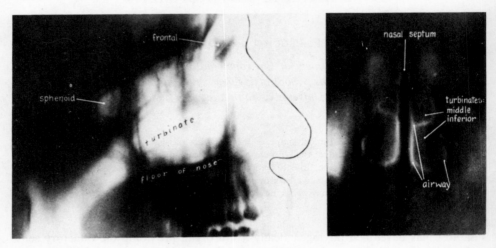

FIGURE 1. Radiographs to show the shape of the nasal airway. Note coronal view on right showing narrow and complex passage. With the permission of the American Physiological Society (PROCTOR, 1964).

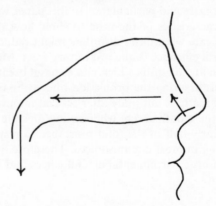

FIGURE 2. Direction of nasal air flow during inspiration. Note the entrance and exit directions at angles to the main passage.

The small entrance offers a cross section smaller than that in any other part of the respiratory tract (BRIDGER, 1970): Figure 3. The smallest cross section of the nasal passage lies about 2 cm posterior to the nostrils. Our estimates of its size are in good agreement with the measurements from radiographs by MASING (1970). In the average adult it is probably between 20 and 40 mm² on each side (0·4 to 0·8 cm² both sides). This should be compared with Weibel's estimates of total cross sections elsewhere in the respiratory tract, 2·54 cm² in the trachea, a narrow point at the third generation of bronchi of 2·0 cm² and 1,600 cm² at the twentieth generation of pulmonary airways (WEIBEL, 1963).

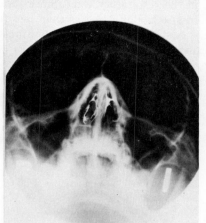

FIGURE 3. The entrance to the nasal airway is outlined with tantalum dust best shown in the right nostril (left of figure). With the permission of Dr. Patrick Bridger (BRIDGER, 1970).

The paranasal sinuses are air spaces in the bones of the face surrounding the nose on three sides, lined with respiratory epithelium. The maxillary antra and the ethmoids communicate with the nasal passages through small openings along the middle meati and above the posterior middle turbinate. Each frontal sinus communicates with the nose through a duct opening at the anterior end of the middle meatus and each sphenoid sinus opens just above the posterior tip of the middle turbinate: Figure 4. While these sinuses are probably useful in insulating the brain from injury through blows to the face and the nasal passages from extremes of environmental air temperature, their major service to nasal function may lie in their mucous secretions, a point to be discussed below.

Although the term respiratory mucous membrane connotes morphological homogeneity the actual structure of this important tissue varies widely throughout the respiratory tract. In the tracheobronchial tree there are differences in the relative frequency of goblet cells and mucous glands; and, at its peripheral termination, there is a transition from ciliated mucus secreting epithelium, through an area with reducing numbers of cilia and goblet cells, to the alveolar epithelium.

On the surface, nasal mucous membrane resembles that in the tracheobronchial tree; but, beneath the basement membrane, there is in the nose a rich vasculature and a venous plexus which makes possible the gross changes which regularly occur in response to a variety of stimuli from season to season and hour to hour. Even in the face of severe inflammatory response tracheobronchial mucosa rarely thickens as much as 1 mm, while that in the nose, in the face of ordinary climatic variations or emotional stress, may change its thickness by 2 to 3 mm. For this reason it has been compared to the erectile tissue of the genital organs. The mucosa lining the paranasal sinuses is an extremely delicate mucus secreting ciliated membrane and not nearly so vascular. What differences there may be in the character of mucous secretions from these different areas of mucosa is not known.

Nasal Air Flow

Nasal air flow, as a result of this anatomical configuration, differs in several respects from air flow elsewhere in the respiratory tract. Since the anterior entrance to the nasal passages offers a cross-sectional area less than one third the narrowest point beyond, the linear velocity of the air passing this point must be about three times as high as in any other portion of the respiratory tract. Just beyond this point of high

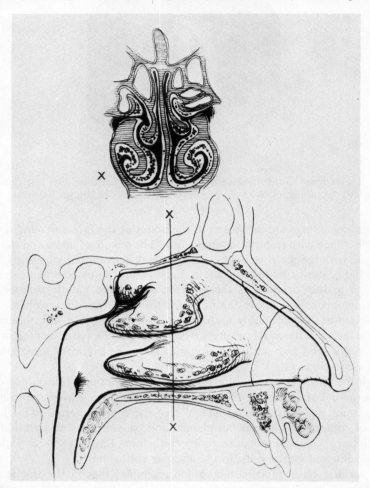

FIGURE 4. Crude diagram of the nose and nasopharynx as seen in sagittal section and a coronal section (above) (Compare Figure 1). Note the relations of paranasal sinuses and nasopharynx. With the permission of the Editors *Bacteriological Reviews* (PROCTOR, 1966).

velocity the air stream must bend and widen and some turbulence develops in the flow. The linear velocity through the long main nasal passage is sharply reduced. During inspiration, although all parts of the passage are probably involved in the movement, the main inspiratory flow seems to occur along the space between the middle meatus and the septum with a somewhat lesser stream along the floor of the nose. These factors will vary somewhat depending upon the degree of vascular congestion in the turbinates. Finally, at its posterior terminus in the nasopharynx, another bend must be negotiated by the air to move downward into the oropharynx after which there is a relatively straight line of flow downward to the bifurcation of the trachea (PROCTOR, 1966, 1969): Figure 2.

We have conducted studies in models constructed from casts obtained at autopsy. Although our measurements have not yet permitted study of the pulsatile to and fro air flow occurring in life, they do reflect some of the probable characteristics of that flow: Figures 5 and 6.

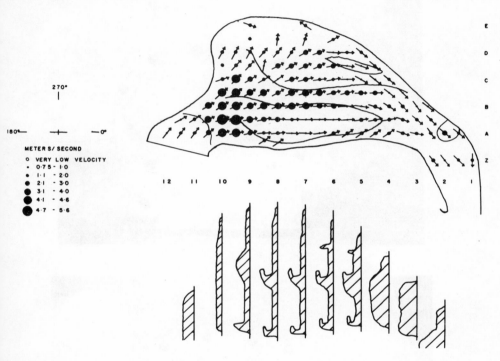

FIGURE 5. Chart of direction and linear velocity of air flow through a model of one side of the nasal passage. Sections below show the rough approximations of actual passage used in this model (compare Figures 1 and 4).

It seems certain that, during quiet breathing, the linear inspiratory velocity at the entrance reaches a minimum of 4·5 to 5 m/s, possibly as high as 10 to 12 m/s. This is to be compared with estimates of maximal flow during quiet breathing in the bronchial tree of 2 m/s. These figures are based upon inspiratory flow of 0·4 l/s. Among normal adults inspiratory peak flows during quiet breathing range between 0·2 and 0·6 l/s. During heavy exercise peak flows are likely to reach 2 l/s but the cut off point at which nasal breathing is abandoned for the lower resistance of the mouth is about 1·5 l/s.

Just beyond the nasal entrance a portion of the stream is sharply deflected downward along the floor of the nose, another smaller portion is deflected upward above the middle turbinate where small whirls and eddies seem to form, while the main stream is directed along the space between the middle meatus and the septum. At the same time those directional changes occur the linear velocity falls off sharply. The linear velocity through the main nasal passage will vary with changes in the nasal mucosa. Small eddies and whirls occur also along the middle meatus.

Finally, the now more slowly moving stream impacts against the posterior wall of the nasopharynx and bends downward. The cross section of the nasopharyngeal airway is about equal to that in the trachea (Proctor, 1964).

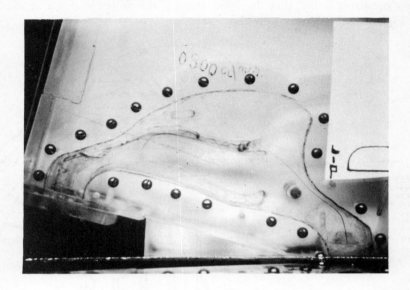

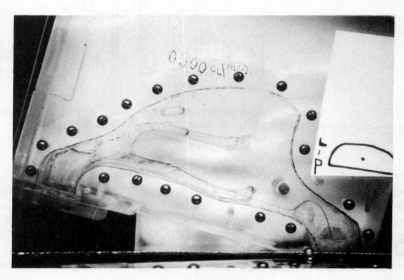

FIGURE 6. Photographs of fluid flow through nose model with Reynolds number kept equal to normal flow with air. Jet of dye added to stream at different parts of the nostril entrance. Above, one part of the stream bending and passing into the middle meatus where whirls are noted. Below, another part of stream bending sharply to pass along the floor of the nose.

Mucociliary Function

We have studied the nasal mucociliary stream in man through the external detection of the motion of radioactively tagged materials carried by it (QUINLAN *et al.*, 1969; PROCTOR & WAGNER, 1967, 1969). It moves everywhere toward the nasopharynx although by devious routes: Figures 7 and 8. It is important to realize that the mucociliary stream from the paranasal sinuses joins the nasal stream all along the middle meatus and above the posterior end of the middle turbinate, an arrangement admirably designed to bathe the very areas most likely to be contaminated by inspired materials.

At the nasopharynx the cilia disappear and the mucus arriving in this area is dispatched downward by swallowing during which the soft palate tends to wipe the posterior nasopharyngeal wall.

The Adenoids

The adenoids lie across the posterior wall of the nasopharynx. This tissue is characterized by multiple pits (crypts) surrounded by a rich network of blood vessels

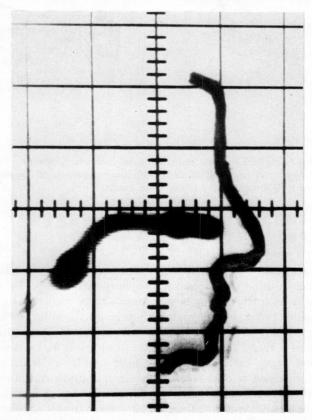

FIGURE 7. Photograph of the image from an Anger camera of the mucociliary transport of a single tagged particle through the human nose. Darker areas are those of slower rate of motion. With the permission of *American Review of Respiratory Disease* (QUINLAN *et al.*, 1969).

and lymphoid tissue. It seems probable that small samples of inspired foreign materials, including particles carrying microorganisms, are entrapped in these crypts through impaction at the nasopharyngeal bend in the air stream and through the mucociliary stream, a portion of which passes over and around the adenoids. The adenoids may thus be involved in the development of immune processes in relation to inhaled materials just as the tonsils are in relation to ingested materials.

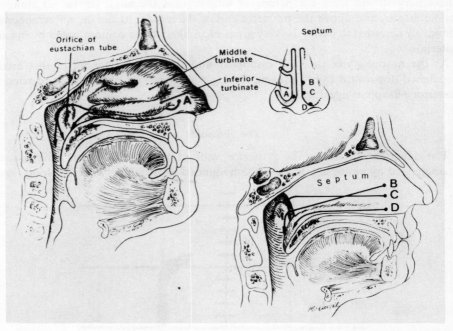

FIGURE 8. Chart showing various paths of human nasal mucociliary clearance depending upon point at which particle is originally placed. With the permission of *American Review of Respiratory Disease* (QUINLAN *et al.*, 1969). Note passages over nasopharynx which would include adenoid tissue.

The Oropharynx

Since we do not always breathe through the nose some consideration should be given to the effect of using the alternative oropharyngeal airway. Breathing through other airways such as tracheostomy is well known to be fraught with the hazard of pulmonary infection and atelectasis and will not be discussed further here.

Owing to the mobility of the lips, tongue, soft palate and lateral pharyngeal walls, the oropharyngeal airway, in contrast to the nose, is a highly variable passage: Figure 9. During heavy exercise, requiring high ventilatory rates, this passage is widened and straightened to offer a relatively direct and low resistance access of the air stream to the trachea. During quiet breathing, or during the quick breaths which regularly intersperse conversation, the oropharyngeal airway simulates the nose in many ways. There are relatively sharp bends at the entrance and exit, the air passage between the tongue and the palate is narrow, and relatively high linear velocities occur.

One might expect that the shape of the air passage at the larynx might result in turbulence in the glottic air stream. Studies in models indicate that during inspiration the air stream converges slightly along stream lines to pass between the vocal cords, and only at some distance down the trachea is there evidence of disturbance in the stream lines of flow. During higher flow rates such disturbance will develop higher in the trachea but not above the larynx.

DEPOSITION OF INHALED MATERIALS

Knowing only these facts we might deduce that there would be a very high deposition of inhaled particles at and just beyond the nasal entrance, and, during mouth breathing through a narrow oropharynx, in the mouth and over the posterior pharynx.

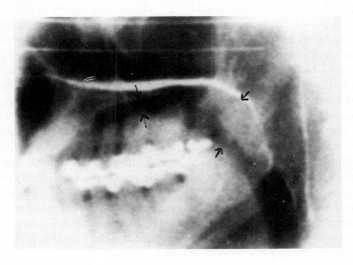

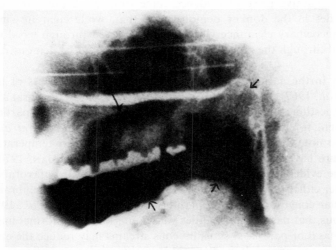

FIGURE 9. Frames from cineradiograph showing oropharyngeal airway during a breath between conversational phrases (above) and during deep breathing as during heavy exercises (below). Relative narrow air passage during former is indicated by arrows.

We might also deduce that the narrowness of the main nasal air stream, its low linear velocity and the large surface area over which it passes would assure not only the highly efficient modification of air temperature and water vapor pressure which has been recognized for a long time, but also the absorption of foreign gases and vapors into the nasal mucus.

The latter has been demonstrated for SO_2 which is almost totally removed in the nose when breathed in concentrations exceeding those found in air pollution peaks (SPEIZER & FRANK, 1966; FRANK, 1970). Under what circumstances of chronic exposure to this and similar vapors this efficiency of nasal absorption may break down is not known.

Early estimates of nasal filtration of particulates underestimated the efficiency of the nasal filter because the initial high linear velocity had not been recognized. More recent investigations of nasal breathing of aerosols has demonstrated a higher efficiency even for quite small particles (WOLFSDORF et al., 1969; HOUNAM et al., 1971), but an accurate statement of the rate of filtration for all sizes is not as yet possible. Those particles which negotiate the nasal passage are highly likely to travel relatively unimpeded to the alveoli owing to the relative width of the stream, the lack of sharp bends in the tracheobronchial airways, and the very low linear velocities in the lower airways where the total cross-sectional area is so greatly increased.

We may further deduce that, in consideration of air flow characteristics, nasal mucociliary activity, and the stream of mucus being continually added from the paranasal sinuses, the nose is remarkably well equipped to defend against noxious materials reaching its surfaces. The nasal mucous carpet continually sweeps away materials deposited upon its surfaces. If injury occurs it is likely to be focused mainly upon the very areas over which fresh paranasal sinus mucus is continually passing.

One evidence that the nose is more adequately equipped to defend against injurious materials than is the remainder of the respiratory tract is the high incidence of pulmonary infections in patients with tracheostomy.

Another suggestive piece of evidence came from work done at New York University. Studies in the donkey demonstrated that, while cigarette smoke impaired bronchial mucociliary clearance when it was delivered through nasal tubes, when it was breathed through the nose no such impairment could be demonstrated (FRANCES et al., 1969).

Variations in the nasal mucosa may influence the effectiveness of the nasal filter (HILDING et al., 1967). Exposure to very cold air will reduce the nasal airway through vascular congestion, thus increasing the likelihood of filtration of particulates, but, if severe enough, forcing the resort to mouth breathing (TAKAGI et al., 1969). It is interesting to note that most other variations in inspired air temperature and water vapor pressure have little effect upon the nasal airway (SALMAN, 1970). In contrast there is some evidence that emotional factors may have an unfavorable effect upon the nasal filter either through marked shrinking of the mucous membrane or, through severe vascular congestion, forcing mouth breathing (HOLMES et al., 1950).

It is obvious that nasal abnormalities which interfere with normal nasal air flow or the normal nasal or paranasal sinus mucous streams may reduce the efficiency of the nose as a defence organ. It is also obvious that under conditions requiring wide mouth breathing, such as heavy work loads, inspired air will simply bypass this defence mechanism.

The ability of the nose to defend undoubtedly varies from person to person and time to time. Evidence for the significance of this variability in pneumoconiosis was pointed out many years ago (LEHMANN, 1935).

Septal perforations which follow chronic industrial exposure to certain chemical fumes are well known. More recently there have been interesting studies (ACHESON, 1968) implicating the inhalation of dusts in the furniture industry in nasal cancer. As far as I can discover uranium miners have not been susceptible to nasal cancer while their chances of lung cancer seem to be increased.

It is to be hoped that studies of such problems will include an attempt to correlate variations in nasal shape and function with susceptibility to nasal disease as well as with evidence of relative protection against pulmonary damage.

SUMMARY

The normal nose is characterized by differences from the remainder of the respiratory tract which make it an important defence against inhaled materials. Among these differences are:

1. The nature of the nasal mucous membrane.
2. The addition of paranasal sinus mucus to the nasal mucous stream.
3. The character of air flow, both the higher linear velocity at the entrance and the low linear velocity in the main passage.

These factors should be considered in the protection of those exposed to undue quantities of airborne noxious materials.

REFERENCES

ACHESON, E. D. (1968). *Br. med. J.* **2**, 587–596.

BRIDGER, G. P. (1970). *Archs. Otolar.* (In Press.)

FRANCES, R., ALESANDRO, D., LIPPMAN, M., PROCTOR, D. F. & ALBERT, R. (1969). *Am. ind. Hyg. Ass. J.* **30**, 110.

FRANK, N. R. (1970). Personal communication. Seattle (Washington), University of Washington.

HILDING, A. C., FILIPI, A. N. & ELSTROM, J. H. (1967). *Archs envir. Hlth* **15**, 584–588.

HOLMES, T. H., GOODELL, H., WOLF, S. H. & WOLFF, H. G. (1950). *The nose.* Springfield, Thomas.

HOUNAM, R. F., BLACK, A. & WALSH, M. (1971). This Symposium, pp. 71–79.

LEHMANN, G. (1935). *J. ind. Hyg. Toxicol.* **17**, 37–40.

MASING, H. (1970). *Rhinology* **8**, 17–26.

PROCTOR, D. F. (1964). *Handbook of physiology — Respiration I.* Washington, American Physiological Society, pp. 309–345.

PROCTOR, D. F. (1966). *Bact. Rev.* **30**, 498–513.

PROCTOR, D. F. (1969). *Ann. Otol. Rhinol. Lar.* **78**, 518–532.

PROCTOR, D. F. & WAGNER, H. N. (1967). In: *Inhaled particles and vapours II*, Ed. C. N. Davies. Oxford, Pergamon Press, pp. 25–35.

PROCTOR, D. F., SWIFT, D. L., QUINLAN, M. F., SALMAN, S., TAKAGI, Y. & EVERING, S. (1969). *Archs envir. Hlth* **18**, 671–680.

QUINLAN, M. F., SALMAN, S. D., SWIFT, D. L., WAGNER, H. N. & PROCTOR, D. F. (1969). *Am. Rev. resp. Dis.* **99**, 13–23.

SALMAN, S. (1970). Personal communication. Beirut (Lebanon), American University.

SPEIZER, F. E. & FRANK, N. R. (1966). *Archs envir. Hlth* **12**, 725–728.

TAKAGI, Y., PROCTOR, D. F., SALMAN, S. & EVERING, S. (1969). *Ann. Otol. Rhinol. Lar.* **78**, 40–48.

WEIBEL, E. R. (1963). *Morphometry of the human lung*, N.Y., Academic Press.

WOLFSDORF, J., SWIFT, D. L. & AVERY, M. E. (1969). *Pediatrics, Springfield* **43**, 799–808.

DISCUSSION

M. Newhouse: What is the clearance rate in the nose and does a change of position, i.e. gravity, affect this? If it does not, does this suggest to you that cilia are capable of adjusting the frequency or force of their beat to load?

Prof. Proctor: The rates average about 8 mm per minute in the human nose, but there is a wide variation. We have not studied the effect of gravity directly, but have not uncovered any evidence to show that it would have an effect. Studies seem to show that there is no direct effect on the cilia.

E. D. Dyson: Is clearance of the maximum deposition area of nasal mucosa backwards (to pharynx, and swallowed) or is it forwards? What is the rate, or half-time, of clearance? Is there much particle deposition in the para-nasal sinuses?

Prof. Proctor: Some material is cleared backward to the pharynx but most is cleared by nose wiping or blowing. Some work done at N.Y. University shows that clearance is easily effected by the use of a piece of Kleenex on the tip of a finger. Whatever material gets deposited beyond the anterior unciliated area is bound to be very small in amount.

The clearance rate averaged about 8 mm per minute, and there is a distance of about 8 to 11 cm to travel. But there is a wide variation, part of which may be attributable to the amount of humidity in the air at the time of the study.

Regarding your third question, I think it highly unlikely. There is a continuous mucous flow from the sinus orifices into the nose. There is a very small exchange of air between the sinuses and the nose. Any particles that got into the sinuses would be cleared by the mucocilary stream unless disease prevented it.

J. E. Cotes: Squadron Leader Sharp at the Institute of Aviation Medicine has evidence that the point of changeover from nose to mouth breathing is related to the pressure difference across the nose.

There is evidence that particles depositing on the lower airways cause reflex narrowing of the nasal passages. Does this increase the effectiveness of the nose as a filter?

Prof. Proctor: I have not read the paper you refer to, but I will look it up. We have asked people to voluntarily breathe through their noses more and more rapidly until they reach a "breaking" point and open their mouths. We then introduce 7 per cent. CO_2, which reduces the resistance. Interestingly enough, although higher flows are reached with the CO_2 than with voluntary hyper-ventilation, the subjects change over to mouth breathing at lower transnasal pressures. Roughly speaking, most people can go to about 1 l/s through the nose without changing over to mouth breathing.

I remain somewhat sceptical about the importance of the broncho-nasal reflexes. I am sure that there is evidence that they exist, but I rather doubt whether they produce significant changes in the nasal or bronchial airways.

A. Morgan: The deposition pattern of particles in the human naso-pharyngeal region has been investigated using 7 μm technetium - 99m labelled polystyrene particles administered by the same technique as described by Hounam et al. (p. 71). Measurements with both fixed and scanning detectors showed that, at a flow rate of 20 l/min, 80 per cent of the deposited activity was located in the anterior (unciliated) region of the nasal passages. The site of maximum deposition was 2 to 2·5 cm back from the tip of the nose. In five out of six subjects there was no fast clearance phase, the mean half-time of removal (in the absence of nose blowing) being about 7 h. One subject, however, did show a rapid clearance phase in which half the deposited activity was removed with a half time of 10 min followed by a slower phase.

Prof. Proctor: I agree. If you use single particles, as we have done in the pictures shown, most seem to clear fairly rapidly, within a range of about 0·2 to 1 cm per minute, but if you put in a drop of the material in solution some remains in the nose, from 20 minutes to an hour later.

THE DEPOSITION OF AEROSOL PARTICLES IN THE NASOPHARYNGEAL REGION OF THE HUMAN RESPIRATORY TRACT

R. F. Hounam, A. Black and M. Walsh

Health Physics and Medical Division, A.E.R.E.,
Harwell, Didcot, Berks, England

Abstract — Experiments have been made to measure the deposition of radio-active, monodisperse polystyrene particles of size between 1 and 10 μm diameter aspirated through the nose and mouth at known flow-rates. The arrangements permitted the pressure difference across the nose and mouth to be determined as deposition occurred. When, for particles of the same size, deposition is plotted against flow-rate there is considerable scatter in the results. A much closer relation-ship is found with the pressure difference. The results show some divergence from the relationship proposed by the Task Group on Lung Dynamics and an alternative working relationship is suggested.

INTRODUCTION

In common with other industries, precautions against the inhalation of toxic dusts have to be taken to protect those engaged in operations involving radioactive materials and one of the objects of the Inhalation Section of the Health Physics and Medical Division at A.E.R.E. Harwell is to study the deposition and retention of inhaled particles in the human respiratory system. Its initial investigation has been a study of the deposition in the human nose of aerosol particles in the size range between 1 μm and 10 μm.

The earlier work of Landahl & Black (1947) and of Landahl & Tracewell (1949) demonstrated the dependence of deposition on the size and density of the particles and flow-rate through the nose. After consideration of the factors affecting the interdependence of these parameters Landahl (1950) obtained results by calcula-tion which were in broad agreement with his experimental findings. Following experi-ments on nasal deposition using monodisperse spherical aerosols of methylene blue, Pattle (1961) suggested a simple mathematical relationship between deposition, particle size and flow-rate through the nose which has been adopted by the Task Group on Lung Dynamics of the ICRP (1966) as a basis for their calculations of deposition in the nasopharyngeal compartment.

Our experiments followed the somewhat artificial procedure of earlier investigators in which aerosols were drawn through the nose and mouth of breath-holding subjects at various flow-rates. Under these conditions deposition should be limited to the nasal passages, epipharynx and mouth. The aerosols used consisted of bromine-82 labelled polystyrene particles which were spherical, nearly monodisperse and with a density of $1 \cdot 2$ g/cm³. The pressure difference across the nose and mouth was measured continuously during each experiment. As deposition was found to be affected by pressure difference, supplementary measurements were made at selected flow-rates on a number of individuals to establish a range of values for normal subjects.

METHOD

A diagram of the apparatus for the production and administration of the test aerosol is shown in Figure 1. Briefly, a cloud of radioactive, monodisperse particles of known size is generated almost instantaneously by pipetting a small volume of a suspension of particles in alcohol into the atomizer. The cloud is mixed with diluting

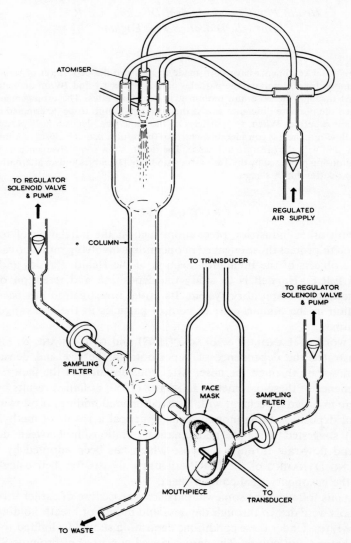

FIGURE 1. Diagram of inhalation apparatus.

air, so that the liquid evaporates and at the base of the column the aerosol consists of dry particles. At this point, part of the aerosol is drawn through a filter, part is drawn through the nose and mouth of a breath-holding subject and the undeposited particles are collected on a filter. Excess aerosol passes to waste. Measurement of the radio-activity on the two filters and the flow-rates through them, enables the deposition in the subject's nose, pharynx and mouth to be calculated. This technique reduces the breath-holding time to a minimum.

EXPERIMENTAL

BLACK & WALSH (1970) have described the preparation of monodisperse particles of polystyrene labelled with bromine-82. This is a $\beta\gamma$ emitter with a half-life of 36 hours. Leaching studies showed that the tracer did not dissolve out of the particles *in vivo*. For measurements of deposition a few nanocuries suffice for labelling the particles, and assuming those deposited are rapidly cleared from the nasopharyngeal region and swallowed, the critical organ is the lower large intestine. The maximum bromine-82 activity deposited in the nose in any experiment was 45 nCi and the resulting dose to the critical organ was 2·0 mrem (VENNART & MINSKI, 1962). The mean dose incurred in each experiment was 0·45 mrem and the total doses incurred by the three subjects used in these investigations were between 20 and 30 mrem.

The test aerosols were sampled on glass fibre or membrane filters and examined with a microscope. The aerodynamic diameter of the particles ranged from 1·78 μm to 7·96 μm and in no case did the geometric standard deviation of the particle size exceed 1·08. Aggregated particles were less than 5% of the total number.

Deposition measurements were made with the co-operation of three subjects at flow-rates of 5, 10, 20, 30 and 37 l/min. The pressure difference across the nose and mouth of the subject was recorded continuously during each experiment. Its value as deposition was taking place was determined by indexing the recording when the subject detected alcohol vapour in his nose. As a relationship was found between deposition and the pressure difference across the nose and mouth, the question arose whether the pressure difference, flow-rate characteristics of the three subjects fell within the normal range. To establish this, additional measurements were made with a sample of 24 subjects, including the three participating in the deposition experiments. A further series of measurements was also carried out on these same subjects to determine if the pressure difference across the nose under conditions of normal breathing differed from that across the nose and mouth during forced aspiration.

Fuller experimental details are to be published (HOUNAM et al., 1971).

RESULTS

Results of Measurements of Deposition

The results of measurements of deposition are summarized in Table I.

Results of Measurements of Nasal Resistance

Three sets of measurements of pressure difference at various flow-rates were carried out as follows:

TABLE I. RESULTS OF MEASUREMENTS OF THE DEPOSITION OF POLYSTYRENE PARTICLES IN THE NOSE AND MOUTH AND OF THE PRESSURE DIFFERENCE ACROSS THE NOSE AND MOUTH

Flow rate l/min	Particle diameter $(D_a) = 1\cdot78\ \mu m$						Particle diameter $(D_a) = 4\cdot23\ \mu m$						Particle diameter $(D_a) = 6\cdot41\ \mu m$						Particle diameter $(D_a) = 7\cdot96\ \mu m$					
	Subject A		Subject B		Subject C		Subject A		Subject B		Subject C		Subject A		Subject B		Subject C		Subject A		Subject B		Subject C	
	Dep.	Pnm mm W.G.	Dep.	Pnm mm W.G.	Dep.	Pnm mm W.G.	Dep.	Pnm mm W.G.	Dep.	Pnm mm W.G.	Dep.	Pnm mm W.G.	Dep.	Pnm mm W.G.	Dep.	Pnm mm W.G.	Dep.	Pnm mm W.G.	Dep.	Pnm mm W.G.	Dep.	Pnm mm W.G.	Dep.	Pnm mm W.G.
5	0·11	0·75	—	1·2	0	0·62	0·06	1·2	—	—	0	1·9	—	—	—	—	—	—	0·39	1·6	0·06	1·2	0	—
5	—	—	—	—	—	—	—	—	—	—	—	—	—	—	—	—	—	—	0·48	1·25	0	1·2	0	—
5	—	—	—	—	—	—	—	—	—	—	—	—	—	—	—	—	—	—	—	—	—	—	—	—
10	0·01	2·5	0	2·7	—	3·1	0·28	3·7	0·06	2·5	0·11	2·5	0·37	3·4	0·21	2·8	0·16	1·9	0·26	1·0	0·27	1·6	0·63	3·8
10	0	2·5	0	3·7	—	3·1	0·34	2·5	0·06	2·5	0·08	3·1	0·24	2·5	0·21	2·2	0·35	3·5	0·35	2·2	0·28	1·4	0·75	5·6
10	0	3·1	0	3·2	—	3·7	0·29	2·5	0·21	5·0	0·13	3·1	0·32	2·5	0·29	3·1	0·40	3·8	0·27	1·5	0·17	1·7	0·77	6·3
20	0·14	7·5	0·07	10·0	0·08	8·0	0·48	6·2	0·68	19·0	0·34	10·0	0·54	5·6	0·64	6·9	0·73	8·1	0·73	5·0	0·72	4·7	0·97	12·5
20	0·20	7·5	0·08	6·2	0·12	8·0	0·53	8·7	0·30	8·7	0·33	10·6	0·46	5·0	0·69	7·5	0·77	10·3	0·72	5·0	0·85	6·2	0·99	15
20	0·18	7·5	0·08	7·5	0·10	8·8	0·51	7·5	0·39	7·5	0·40	11·2	0·39	4·7	0·85	13·0	0·79	10·6	0·69	5·0	0·89	7·5	0·99	21
30	0·27	13	0·14	15·6	0·24	22·5	0·65	13·7	0·66	19	0·74	25	0·59	8·7	0·95	31	0·93	16	0·93	10	0·98	16	0·99	30
30	0·28	14	0·17	15·0	0·24	22·5	0·71	16·2	0·71	21	0·65	20	0·70	11·0	0·84	13·7	0·94	19	0·95	12·5	0·97	16	0·97	31
30	0·28	11	0·20	15·6	0·21	30·0	0·78	21·2	0·65	17·5	0·71	25	0·77	12·5	0·90	18·7	0·92	15	0·97	14	0·93	12·5	0·99	31
37	0·33*	19	0·18*	20	0·34*	50	0·88*	32	0·81*	28	0·87	44	0·84†	15	0·98†	39	0·99†	31	0·98†	26	0·96	14	—	—
37	0·31*	22	0·18*	23	0·37*	54	0·83*	26	0·76*	22	0·91	45	0·76†	13	0·91†	17·5	0·94†	19	0·98†	17·5	0·97	17·5	—	—
37	0·33*	20	0·18*	12·5	0·27*	49	0·90*	32	0·83*	29	0·78	27	0·79†	14	0·89†	16	0·97†	21	0·98†	26	0·98	19	—	—

* Rate of air-flow 36 l/min.

† Rate of air-flow 38 l/min.

(a) The pressure difference across the nose and mouth (P_{nm}) in mm water gauge (mm W.G.) was determined at specific flow-rates for subjects A, B and C during the course of measurements of deposition. These results are included in Table I.
(b) Similar measurements were made on a group of 24 subjects (including A, B and C) to ascertain the normal range of values of P_{nm} at selected flow-rates.
(c) Finally, the pressure difference across the nasal passages and nasopharynx (P_n) was measured for the same group of 24 subjects while breathing normally.

COTES (1965) reports that the difference in pressure between the alveoli and the mouth (P) may be related to the flow through the airways (F) by the following expression

$$P = RF^n \tag{1}$$

where R is the airway resistance and n is a constant. When P_{nm} or P_n in mm water gauge were plotted against flow-rate in l/min on log/log paper, the points could be fitted by a straight line which shows that a similar relationship holds for the nasopharyngeal region. A linear regression analysis for log P on log F was performed for each set of measurements to obtain values for n and R. The values of n so obtained are summarized in Table II. The airway resistance R corresponds to the pressure drop across the airways at a flow-rate of 1 l/min. As this is well outside the range of our measurements it was considered more useful to give values of P_{nm} or P_n corresponding to a flow-rate of 20 l/min. Values of P_{nm} given in Table II were derived directly from the logarithms of actual measurements at a flow-rate of 20 l/min. As there was no control over flow-rate during measurements of P_n, the values given in Table II were calculated from the regression lines for each set of results.

TABLE II. SUMMARY OF PRESSURE DROP/FLOW-RATE CHARACTERISTICS

Number of subjects	Pressure difference	P_{nm} or P_n at 20 l/min (mm water gauge)			n		
		Range	Mean	Median	Range	Mean	Median
3	P_{nm}	4·70–21·0	8·02	7·41	1·50–1·74	1·60	—
24	P_{nm}	2·20–56·0	9·60	8·71	0·52–2·56	1·47	1·52
24	P_n	2·13–45·6	8·94	8·13	0·48–3·06	1·52	1·58

DISCUSSION

In its model for the deposition of particles in the respiratory tract, the ICRP Task Group relates fractional deposition in the nasopharyngeal region (N) to the aerodynamic particle diameter in micrometers (D_a) and the flow-rate through the nose in l/min (F) by means of the following empirical expression

$$N = -0·62 + 0·475 \log D_a^2 F \tag{2}$$

This expression, derived from measurements of deposition made by PATTLE (1961), is shown in Figure 2, together with the results of our own experiments plotted on the same basis. It can be seen that there is a considerable scatter in values of deposition measured at particular values of $D_a^2 F$ and this applies even to results obtained with a single subject. It appears that the experimental results are best fitted by a sigmoid curve which only conforms with equation (2) at values of $D_a^2 F$ greater than 500.

In Figure 3 measurements of nasopharyngeal deposition made by other workers (Landahl, 1950; Landahl & Tracewell, 1949; Dennis & Sawyer, 1949) are correlated with the appropriate values of $D_a{}^2F$ and it can be seen that the theoretical deposition curve derived by Landahl (1950) corresponds most closely to our own results plotted in Figure 2.

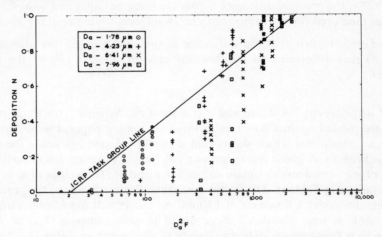

Figure 2. Relationship between deposition and $D_a{}^2F$.

The deposition in an impactor having 50% efficiency for the same value of $D_a{}^2F$ as the Lung Model nose is also depicted in Figure 3. The curve for the impactor is steeper than any of the nasal curves. Landahl derived his curve, which relates to a flow-rate of 18 l/min only, by simulating the nose to a succession of inertial collectors having different characteristics and by making allowances for sedimentation. When both impaction and sedimentation are considered, different curves will be obtained at different flow-rates when deposition is plotted against $D_a{}^2F$.

Initially it was considered that the scatter in our results might be due to inadequacies in the experimental technique, but elimination of all obvious sources of error

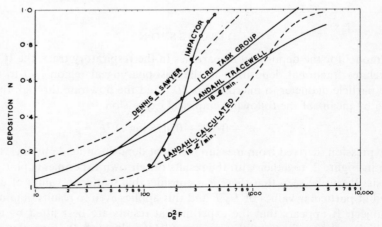

Figure 3. Comparison of deposition results of different experimenters.

did not produce results of greater consistency. Examination of Figure 2 shows that particles of different sizes appear to give different values for deposition at identical values of $D_a{}^2F$. The implication is that the experimental data cannot be correlated precisely in this way because particles of different sizes will produce different curves. For the reason stated at the end of the preceding paragraph perfect correlation with a simple parameter is not to be expected.

Examination of the results showed that in each set of three measurements on a single subject, using identical flow-rate and particle size, the highest deposition was usually associated with the highest value of P_{nm}. This suggested that deposition could be related to P_{nm} and in Figure 4 the correlation between these parameters is shown for each particle size. As pressure drop appears to be a more fundamental parameter

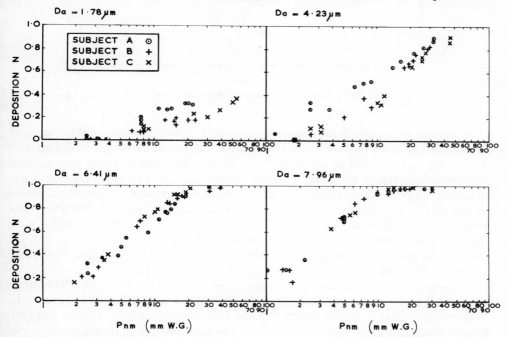

FIGURE 4. Relationships between deposition and P_{nm} for particles of four different diameters.

than flow-rate, the effect of plotting $D_a{}^2P_{nm}$ rather than $D_a{}^2F$ against deposition was investigated. As shown in Figure 5 a much improved correlation is obtained which holds for particles of all four sizes. This correlation can be represented by the following expression

$$N = -\,0\cdot975 + 0\cdot66 \log D_a{}^2P_{nm} \tag{3}$$

The scatter is greatest at low values of $D_a{}^2P_{nm}$. If the results for individual subjects are plotted separately slightly different curves are obtained, so that some of the scatter must be due to physiological or anatomical differences between subjects.

It is perhaps not surprising that a better correlation is obtained in terms of P_{nm} rather than F as the former is a complex function of interrelated variables all of which may influence deposition. These include the linear velocity of air flowing through the nose (rather than the total air flow), changes in the flow patterns with flow-rate and the degree of obstruction presented by the internal conformation of the nasal passages. Natural changes in the latter may result in local fluctuations in air velocity, even when the overall flow-rate remains constant.

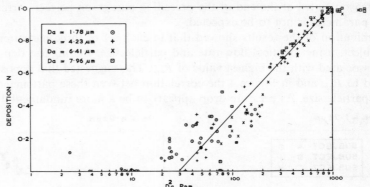

FIGURE 5. Relationship between deposition and $D_a{}^2 P_{nm}$.

A number of authors have reported values of P_{nm} obtained during the course of measurements of deposition. There is a considerable variation in observed values of P_{nm} at any flow-rate but as our own results lie between those of other workers they may be considered to represent "typical" values. As might be expected from their experimental procedure, which allowed an increase in pressure difference to occur, values of P_{nm} reported by Dennis & Sawyer are on the high side. However their results for deposition are also high and when plotted against $D_a{}^2 P_{nm}$ are in line with our own results. Pattle's values of P_{nm} are considerably lower than average and, on the basis of our own measurements, would lead to lower values for deposition than in fact he observed.

Although a better correlation is obtained when $D_a{}^2 P_{nm}$ rather than $D_a{}^2 F$ is plotted against deposition, there may be circumstances when a correlation with flow-rate is required. It is clear from our results that the $D_a{}^2 F$ correlation is inadequate and that greater mathematical weight should be given to the flow-rate as compared with the

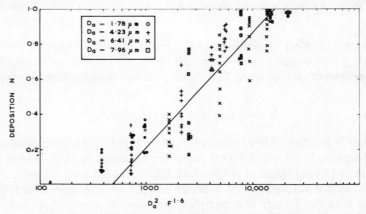

FIGURE 6. Relationship between deposition and $D_a{}^2 F^{1\cdot60}$

particle diameter. As shown in equation (1), pressure drop is equal to RF^n, where R and n are constants. For subjects A, B and C the mean value of n is $1 \cdot 60$. For these three subjects, therefore, a more satisfactory correlation should be obtained if $D_a^2 F^{1 \cdot 6}$ is substituted for $D_a^2 F$. Values of this expression are plotted against deposition in Figure 6 and comparison with Figure 2 shows that an improved correlation is obtained. The line in Figure 6 is represented by the following expression which is derived by substituting appropriate values of RF^n for P_{nm} in equation (3):

$$N = -1 \cdot 77 + 0 \cdot 66 \log D_a^2 F^{1/60} \tag{4}$$

As shown in Table II, the values of n for subjects A, B and C only cover a small part of the "normal" range. For each individual there will be a unique relationship between P_{nm} and F but this relationship may be quite different for the same subject on different occasions. For general application, therefore, it is suggested that equation (4) be modified to incorporate the median values of R and n based on the results obtained from 24 subjects. This leads to the following expression:

$$N = -1 \cdot 66 + 0 \cdot 66 \log D_a^2 F^{1 \cdot 52} \tag{5}$$

which should be used for relating deposition and flow-rate in the absence of more precise individual data.

Despite the change in the relationship between N, D_a and F suggested above, in the size range of interest the deposition of particles in the nose will still be due to impaction or sedimentation. It may therefore be presumed that for spherical particles of diameter D and density ρ the relation

$$D_a^2 = \rho D^2$$

will still apply.

The above results represent mean values. They have been derived on the assumption of a unique relationship between N and D_a and F. Such an assumption cannot be justified even for a standard nose of fixed conformation and in practice considerable spread about the mean line as indicated in Figure 6 can be expected.

Acknowledgements — We wish to express our appreciation to the volunteers who co-operated both in the deposition experiments and in the measurements of nasal resistance. Helpful advice on the conduct of the experiments was received from Dr. J. C. Evans and Dr. B. A. J. Lister and Mr. A. Morgan gave encouraging direction and constructive discussions.

REFERENCES

BLACK, A. & WALSH, M. (1970). *Ann. occup. Hyg.* **13**, 87–100.
COTES, J. E. (1965). *Lung function.* Oxford, Blackwell, p. 82.
DENNIS, W. L. & SAWYER, K. F. (1949). Porton Tech. Pap. 95.
HOUNAM, R. F., BLACK, A. & WALSH, M. (1971). *J. aerosol Sci.* **2**, 47–61.
LANDAHL, H. D. (1950). *Bull. math. Biophys.* **12**, 161–169.
LANDAHL, H. D. & BLACK, S. (1947). *J. ind. Hyg. Toxicol.* **29**, 269–277.
LANDAHL, H. D. & TRACEWELL, T. (1949). *J. ind. Hyg. Toxicol.* **31**, 55–59.
PATTLE, R. E. (1961). In: *Inhaled particles and vapours. Ed.* C. N. Davies. Oxford, Pergamon Press, pp. 302–311.
TASK GROUP ON LUNG DYNAMICS (1966). For Committee II of the International Commission on Radiological Protection. *Hlth Phys.* **12**, 173–207.
VENNART, J. & MINSKI, M. (1962). *Br. J. Radiol.* **35**, 372–387.

DISCUSSION

M. LIPPMANN: Your experiments were performed with the aerosol flowing at a constant rate during breath-holding. The nasal airway dimensions change during normal inspiration and expiration. Can you comment on the effect of the variable airway dimensions on particle deposition.

Mr. HOUNAM: The technique of drawing air in through the nose and out through the mouth is a convenient if somewhat artficial technique for studying the deposition of particles in this region of the respiratory tract. If the dimensional changes to which you refer are associated with the rate of inspiration then their effects would be taken into account in experiments covering a range of flow-rates.

G. W. DOLPHIN: Airway dimensions in the nose vary with air temperature. Did you take precautions to keep the air temperature constant or to measure the air temperature?

Mr. HOUNAM: No. The experiments were carried out at room temperature which is 65 to 70° F.

W. H. WALTON: To what do you attribute the form of the relationship between flow-rate and pressure drop, to a change in the geometry of the passages or to a change in the flow regime — i.e. a Reynolds' number effect?

Mr. HOUNAM: I suspect that the manner in which the pressure drop across the nose changes with flow-rate is attributable largely to changes that develop in the flow regime. Confirmatory evidence was obtained in experiments with a plastic model of the nasal passages which produced a similar relationship bstween the pressure drop and the rate of air flow to that found for real noses.

M. CORN: How was the density of $1 \cdot 2$ g/cm^3 for the particles obtained? Polystyrene is usually considered to have a density only slightly greater than $1 \cdot 0$.

Mr. HOUNAM: The polystyrene is mixed with bromostyrene and this increases its density. Although we did not make measurements on the particles themselves, a density of $1 \cdot 2$ g/cm^3 was found from measurements on the bulk material.

INHALED AEROSOL BOLUSES IN MAN

D. C. F. Muir, K. Sweetland and R. G. Love

Institute of Occupational Medicine, Edinburgh, Scotland

.

Abstract — The dispersion of a 200 ml. bolus of 0·5 μm diameter particles in the lungs has been studied in three normal subjects. No effect was observed when the expired flow rate was changed by a factor of three and little change was evident when the bolus was inhaled at different lung volumes. The dispersion of the aerosol appeared to be related only to the volume depth to which it had penetrated into the lung. It cannot be assumed that this is a continuous process. The results are consistent with a mixing mechanism which is not solely determined by convective mixing during the flow of air and no effect related to the mobility of the particles themselves could be demonstrated.

The use of aerosols to study airflow in the human lungs during steady state breathing was described by Altshuler et al. (1959) and a single breath method by Altshuler & Briscoe (1961). The single breath technique was used by Muir (1967; 1970) but was not found to be a very sensitive means of demonstrating abnormal airflow patterns in a group of patients with asthma and chronic bronchitis. Altshuler (1969) has pointed out that a bolus of aerosol admitted during the inhalation of a single breath of clean air enables the dispersion of aerosol in the lungs to be displayed in the greatest accessible detail. We have used this approach to investigate the effects of lung volume and the rate of airflow on the mixing of aerosols in the lungs of three normal subjects.

METHODS

Approximately uniform aerosols of di-2-ethyl hexyl sebacate (rel. density 0·917) were produced with a modified La Mer-Sinclair generator (Muir, 1965). The apparatus was adjusted to give a particle size of about 0·5 μm diameter as measured by the higher order Tyndall spectra (La Mer & Sinclair, 1943). The cloud was introduced into a bag-in-a-box (Donald & Christie, 1949) and the concentration of aerosol was measured close to the mouth with a Tyndallometer (Muir & Davies, 1967). An automatic valve allowed the subject to inhale aerosol or clean filtered air. The valve was controlled by a photo-electric cell attached to the spirometer and could be set to deliver a bolus of aerosol of any required volume into the inhaled airstream at any point. Exhaled air was directed into the box which was flushed with fresh aerosol before each experiment. The apparatus is shown in Figure 1.

Each subject breathed clean filtered air until the exhaled air was free of particles and then exhaled to residual volume. The automatic valve was actuated at this point and the bolus admitted during the next inspiration. The subject was instructed to inhale at a normal speed because the valve did not operate at a high enough speed to respond during a forced inspiration. This was not a problem during exhalation,

however, and measurements were made during slow and fast expiration. The volume
of the bolus was 200 ml and in each subject a series of experiments were carried out
in which the bolus was admitted into the inhaled air at a low, middle and high lung
volume. In each instance the bolus was followed by a further inspiration of 200 ml
to 3000 ml of clean air. The total volume of each inspiration was controlled by the
automatic valve which could be set to close at the desired point. Exhalation followed
with the minimum of delay.

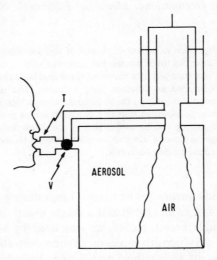

FIGURE 1. Inhalation apparatus showing the Tyndallometer (T) and automatic valve (V).

    Additional experiments included dummy runs in which an identical procedure was
followed but no aerosol was added to the inhaled air. This series served to establish
the true zero aerosol concentration during exhalation.
    The outputs of the Tyndallometer and of a potentiometer attached to the spiro-
meter were recorded during inspiration and expiration. An example of a record is
shown in Figure 2. The details of the subjects were as follows:

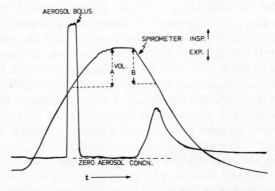

FIGURE 2. Example of a recording showing the spirometer trace and the aerosol concentration
signal. The aerosol bolus (200 ml) entered the airstream near the midpoint of a 1500 ml
inspiration. The dispersion of the bolus during exhalation is evident.

Subject	Age (yr)	Height (cm)	F.E.V._1 (l)	V.C. (l)	T.L.C. (l)	R.V. (l)
D.W.	35	182	4·13	5·2	6·7	1·5
D.C.M.	38	186	4·57	6·1	8·4	2·3
R.G.L.	25	180	4·82	6·6	8·4	1·8

All respiratory volumes are given at 37° C saturated (B.T.P.S.).

RESULTS

The mean rates of airflow and the lung volumes at which the boluses were admitted are shown in Table I. The increasing dispersion of the aerosol bolus as it was drawn

TABLE I. LUNG VOLUME (ABOVE R.V.) AT WHICH BOLUS ENTERED INSPIRED AIRSTREAM AND RATE OF AIRFLOW DURING INSPIRATION AND EXPIRATION

	Subject	Mean vol. (ml.) above R.V.	% V.C.	Mean rate of airflow (ml/s)		
				Insp.	Slow exp.	Fast exp.
Low lung volume	D.W.	350	6·7	1530	1284	2696
	D.C.M.	358	5·9	1435	1178	3095
	R.G.L.	318	4·8	1488	1458	2730
Mid lung volume	D.W.	1273	24·4	1640	1790	4140
	D.C.M.	1390	22·8	1148	1148	3450
	R.G.L.	1033	15·7	1486	1245	3400
High lung volume	D.W.	3815	73·5	1899	1677	5030
	D.C.M.	3540	58·0	1190	1155	3780
	R.G.L.	4980	75·5	1850	1640	3910

further into the lung is illustrated by the example shown in Figure 3. The peak concentration of the aerosol during exhalation together with the corresponding volume is shown for each experiment in Figures 4, 5 and 6. The depth to which each

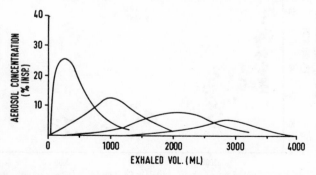

FIGURE 3. The effect of inhaling the bolus to different depths in the bronchial tree. The distribution of aerosol in exhaled air is shown when inhalation of the bolus was followed by further inspirations of 400, 1000, 2000 and 3000 ml of clean air.

bolus was drawn into the lung is indicated by the volume of air measured between the centre of the bolus and the point of maximum inspiration: Figure 2. Mean values for each group of experiments and the corresponding volumes at which the peak aerosol concentration appeared during exhalation are shown in Table II.

TABLE II. DEPTH TO WHICH THE BOLUS WAS DRAWN INTO THE LUNG (VOL. A) AND THE VOLUME AT WHICH THE PEAK AEROSOL CONCENTRATION APPEARED DURING EXHALATION (VOL. B). (MEAN VALUES FOR ALL SUBJECTS.)

	Rate of expiration	Vol. A (ml)	Vol. B (ml)	Difference (ml)	S.D. of differences
Low lung volume	Slow	301	235	66	28·6
	Slow	1042	898	144	67·8
	Slow	2109	1957	152	57·2
	Slow	3104	2870	234	99·1
	Fast	292	224	68	69·2
	Fast	1053	842	211	96·5
	Fast	2102	1956	146	65·4
	Fast	3034	2827	207	132·8
Mid lung volume	Slow	338	256	82	47·2
	Slow	1090	996	94	60·3
	Slow	2083	1934	149	141·0
	Slow	3178	2928	250	100·6
	Fast	337	308	29	39·9
	Fast	1077	937	140	133·7
	Fast	2071	1958	113	134·2
	Fast	3167	2947	220	204·4
High lung volume	Slow	299	289	10	61·1
	Slow	879	826	53	39·0
	Fast	289	289	0	59·4
	Fast	872	844	28	51·5

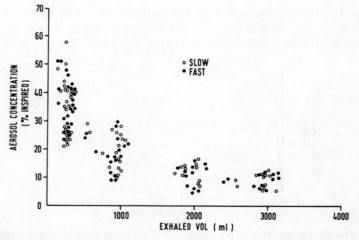

FIGURE 4. Peak aerosol concentrations and exhaled volumes at which they appeared following inspiration of the bolus to different depths. Effect of slow and fast exhalation.

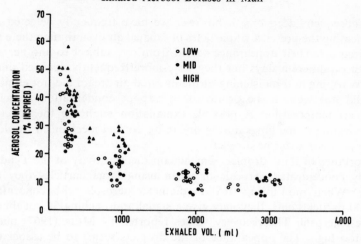

FIGURE 5. Peak aerosol concentrations and exhaled volumes at which they appeared following inspiration of the bolus to different depths. Effect of inhaling the bolus at low, mid and high lung volumes.

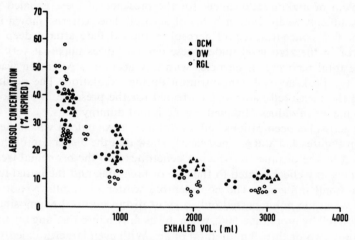

FIGURE 6. Peak aerosol concentrations and exhaled volumes at which they appeared after aspiration of the bolus to different depths. Individual variation.

DISCUSSION

The distribution of particles in exhaled air following a single inspiration of aerosol depends on the pattern of air mixing in the lung and also on the number of particles deposited on the surface of the respiratory tract. In previous work with a single inspiration of $0 \cdot 5$ μm diameter aerosols MUIR (1967) was unable to show any particle loss for inspirations of 500 ml followed by a maximum expiration. The recovery was about 95% for inspired volumes of 1600 ml. Corresponding values reported by ALTSHULER (1969) were 95% and 85%. The accuracy of the aerosol zero level is critical for the measurement of such small rates of particle loss. In the present experiments each subject first breathed clean air until the Tyndallometer reading was zero.

During a subsequent deep breath however we have frequently detected a positive reading indicating the presence of particles in exhaled air even though there were none in the inspired air. Their appearance varied from one subject to another and in the same subject on different days but they were more frequently detected during rapid breathing. Warming and moistening of the inspired airstream did not eliminate them and they did not seem to be produced by vapour condensation associated with changes in air temperature. A possible explanation might be the effect of moist surfaces separating in the lungs during breathing. Such a mechanism would certainly be likely to produce airborne droplets.

The importance of these droplets depends on the sensitivity of the Tyndallometer. With highly concentrated aerosols or when using large particles they are of no significance. When monitoring $0 \cdot 5$ μm diameter aerosols with concentrations of about 20 000 particles/cm³, they may give a signal approaching 5% of that obtained from the test aerosol. The recovery values reported by MUIR (1967) may thus be about 5% too high. The appearance of the droplets seems to be associated with a change in the breathing pattern and is unlikely to cause errors during steady state breathing measurements although we have not looked for them with increased sensitivities of the Tyndallometer.

The problem of making allowances for the presence of these exhaled particles is particularly difficult when using a bolus of aerosol. The patterns shown in Figure 3 illustrate the low concentrations of aerosol in the exhalate after a deep inhalation. A small error in the zero level under these circumstances makes it very difficult to estimate the total recovery of particles with any accuracy. Attention was therefore directed to the peak aerosol concentration during exhalation. The point is readily located and the measured value was corrected for the presence of spurious exhaled droplets by means of values obtained during initial dummy runs.

The peak aerosol concentrations and the volume of exhalate at which they appeared are shown in Figures 4, 5 and 6. They clearly show that the dispersion of the test bolus is determined by the distance to which it penetrates into the bronchial tree. We were unable to show any effect related to the rate of breathing and the initial lung volume had only a small influence. The considerable scatter of results is not difficult to understand when the bolus passed only a short distance into the lung since the peak concentration fell by more than 50% when it was drawn into the lung by an additional volume of only two or three hundred ml of air. With even larger inhaled volumes the results still showed a considerable scatter. Much of this is due to a difference between individuals (Figure 6). The experiments on each individual were completed on a single day, however, in order to ensure that the effects of lung volume and breathing rate were investigated with as little change in the aerosol cloud as possible. Confirmation that there are characteristic patterns for each individual must await further experimental work.

An alternative method of illustrating the information contained in Figures 4, 5 and 6 would be to relate the peak aerosol concentration to the linear distance down the bronchial tree to which the bolus had penetrated. This can be done by assuming plug flow on a symmetrically branching structure such as that described by WEIBEL (1963). The dispersion could also be related to the number of branching points that the bolus passes. These are attractive possibilities in that the dispersion could be analysed in terms of the known behaviour of fluids. The model has little meaning when the bolus is drawn into the fine lung structure however and our failure to detect any effect of a 2–3 fold change in airflow velocity suggests that the system is not very sensitive to the Reynolds number. Although this is exceedingly low in the small airways it is high enough in the larger airways for turbulent airflow to develop. Inertial effects at the branching points of small airways may also be sufficiently sensitive to the rate of airflow for some effect on the dispersion of the bolus to be demonstrated if the experiments were conducted at a wider range of airflows. Real difficulties unfortunately arise during very slow breathing as a result of particle deposition on the surface of the airways. Even in the results shown in this paper it is difficult to make precise allowances for this loss of particles. In Figures 4, 5 and 6 it is evident that the observed peak exhaled aerosol concentration continues to fall as the bolus is drawn deeper into the lung. Some of this fall is due to dispersion of the bolus and some to a fall in the total number of airborne particles. The fact that the concentration did not depend on the rate of breathing and thus on the time available for particles to sediment suggests that particle loss is not the dominant factor and that the peak aerosol concentration is a real measure of the dispersal of the bolus. It must be admitted, however, that an increase in the rate of airflow would reduce the loss of particles due to sedimentation but that any increased dispersion due to added turbulence would have the opposite effect on the peak aerosol concentration. It is just possible that the two effects might be balanced so that no change is observed in the peak concentration as the rate of airflow is changed. To decide this point it is essential to estimate the total amount of aerosol in the exhalate. This can probably be done by modifying the technique to make use of very much higher concentrations of aerosol than we have used (currently about 30 000 particles/cm³ of air) so that errors due to water droplets in the exhaled air are minimized.

Little effect was observed when the bolus was admitted at different lung volumes despite changes in the volume of the airways themselves and in regional distribution of inhaled air. The peak concentrations were slightly higher at the high lung volumes (Figure 5) but there was little difference between results obtained at middle and low lung volumes. The results suggest a diminution in the dispersion of the bolus at high lung volumes, but the total depth to which the bolus could be inhaled was of course limited by the vital capacity of the subject. MILIC-EMILI et al. (1966) have shown that inhaled air is distributed predominantly to the upper zones at very low lung volume. Although the volume of the bolus (200 ml) was larger than that reported in gas experiments, its entry into the airstream was complete at a volume below 10% of the V.C. in the low lung volume experiments and it was therefore distributed to a relatively small zone in the upper part of the lung. In association with the small volume of the upper airway in such a manoeuvre it must be presumed that the bolus passed further towards the alveoli than would be the case in a similar inspiration at a higher lung volume. The regional distribution is independent of the direction of airflow (SUTHERLAND et al., 1968) and, since this type of sequential ventilation is of the "first-in last-out" type it would not of itself contribute to the dispersion of units of air labelled with aerosol during breathing. This conclusion however is only true if the rate of airflow is the same in each direction. ROBERTSON et al. (1969) found that a slow inspiration (0·2–0·3 l/s) diverted more inhaled ^{133}Xenon to the upper zones at a low F.R.C. than a fast inspiration (3–5 l/s) at the same F.R.C. If there is a difference between the inspired/expired flow rates there must therefore be a difference in the pattern of filling and emptying of the lung. Such differences constitute sequential ventilation of the "first in – first out" type and the increased mixing of air in the

lung should be reflected in changes in the aerosol signal. We were unable to show
such differences but ROBERTSON *et al.* (1969) found that there was little change when
the rate of inhalation was increased from 3 to 5 l/s and really large effects could only
be shown when the rate of inspiration was as low as 0·2 to 0·3 l/s. It may be that
aerosol experiments conducted at these flow rates would demonstrate a change but
the inevitable loss of particles due to deposition must make the interpretation difficult.

The shape of the exhaled aerosol volume/concentration curve was not symmetrical
(Figure 3). The exhaled volume (Vol. B) at which the peak concentration appeared
was, on average, smaller than the corresponding volume between the centre of the
inhaled bolus and the point of maximum inhalation (Vol. A): Figure 2. The difference
between the two was related to the volume of A. This pattern is expected as a result
of the increasing dispersion of units of aerosol as they pass further into the lung. The
average differences between Vols. A and B were smaller in the high lung volume
experiments and this finding is consistent with the reduced dispersion of the bolus at
very high lung volumes already noted.

The use of a bolus of aerosol illustrates the dispersion of particles with great clarity
and is a well-established technique in standard pulmonary physiology. The method
does not however supply information which cannot be obtained from an inspiration
of aerosol alone. A synthesis of the two techniques is obtained (WALTON, W. H.,
personal communication, 1970) by considering two single inspirations of aerosol with
Vols. A and B where A–B is equal to 200 ml. If the concentration of aerosol at any
point in the exhaled curve of B is subtracted from the concentration at the same
volume of A then a curve C is obtained which is similar to that obtained after the
inhalation of a bolus of 200 ml. of aerosol (Figure 7).

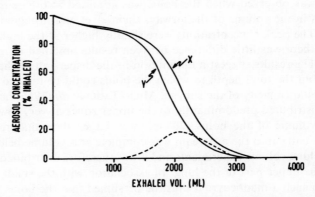

FIGURE 7. The distribution of aerosol in exhaled air following the inspiration of 2100 ml (X) and
1900 ml (Y) of aerosol. The dotted curve was obtained by subtracting Y from X.

Our results illustrate the increasing dispersion of units of aerosol labelled air as
they pass into the lung. It cannot be assumed on the evidence presented that this is a
continuous process. It is possible that much of the observed mixing really represents
the difference between airflow patterns at the end of inspiration and at the onset of
expiration. The fact that the dispersion was not related to the rate of airflow would
certainly support a mechanism related to a reversal of flow within an airway rather
than to a continuous process during flow. ALTSHULER (1969) has also considered the
effect of the movement of individual particles due to sedimentation and diffusion.

These are time dependent however and our results with an aerosol bolus and those of previous single breath studies (MUIR, 1967) show no effect related to the rate of breathing and thus to the time spent by the aerosol in the lungs. The observed dispersion thus appears to be little affected by the mobility of individual particles.

REFERENCES

ALTSHULER, B. (1969). *Circulatory and respiratory mass transport. Ed.* G. E. W. Wolstenholme & J. Knight. London, J. & A. Churchill, pp. 215–235.

ALTSHULER, B. & BRISCOE, W. A. (1961). In: *The intrapulmonary distribution of gases and aerosols,* Appendices III and IV. Report for U.S.P.H.S. Grant No. R.G-5587, N.Y.U. Institute of Industrial Medicine.

ALTSHULER, B., YARMUS, L., PALMES, E. D. & NELSON, N. (1959). *J. appl. Physiol.* **14**, 321–327.

DONALD, K. W. & CHRISTIE, R. V. (1949). *Clin. Sci.* **8**, 21–30.

LA MER, V. K. & SINCLAIR, D. (1943). O.S.R.D. 1668, Div. 10–501, 11–M6.

MILIC-EMILI, J., HENDERSON, J. A. M., DOLOVITCH, M. B., TROP, D. & KANEKO, K. (1966). *J. appl. Physiol.* **21**, 749–759.

MUIR, D. C. F. (1965). *Ann. occup. Hyg.* **8**, 233–238.

MUIR, D. C. F. (1967). *J. appl. Physiol.* **23**, 210–214.

MUIR, D. C. F. (1970). In: *Airway dynamics. Ed.* A. Bouhuys. Springfield, Thomas, pp. 319–325.

MUIR, D. C. F. & DAVIES, C. N. (1967). *Ann. occup. Hyg.* **10**, 161–174.

ROBERTSON, P. C., ANTHONISEN, N. R. & ROSS, D. (1969). *J. appl. Physiol.* **26**, 438–443.

SUTHERLAND, P. W., KATSURA, T. & MILIC-EMILI, J. (1968). *J. appl. Physiol.* **25**, 566–574.

WEIBEL, E. R. (1963). *Morphometry of the human lung.* New York, Academic Press.

DISCUSSION

S. E. DEVIR: You state that the particle size of the homogeneous aerosol of di–2–ethyl hexyl sebacate was about $0·5$ μm diameter, measured by the high-order Tyndall spectra (H.O.T.S.) method of La Mer-Sinclair. From my experience of measuring sizes of homogeneous aerosols in this range such as di–2–ethyl–hexyl phthalate (D.O.P.) or triphehyl phosphate (T.P.P.) aerosols, produced either by the original Sinclair–La Mer generator or the Rapaport–Weinstock (Devir) generator, this method is unreliable and you have to use other light scattering methods such as the Kerker's polarization method.

Dr. MUIR: The particle sizes measured by the H.O.T.S. method are approximate. We have found it sufficiently accurate for our purposes. The subject inhaled the same aerosol cloud each time and the absolute particle size is not of great importance.

P. B. MEYER: What is the meaning of the word "bolus"?

Dr. MUIR: It is a term widely used in physiology to describe a small volume of a gas (or aerosol) sandwiched between two larger volumes of another gas (in this case clean air) which enter the lung during inhalation.

M. SUDLOW: Have you looked at older subjects or smokers?

Dr. MUIR: No. We certainly plan to do this.

V. TIMBRELL: Was the Tyndallometer sensitive to particle size? If so, did it indicate any increase in the size of the particles due to the condensation of water vapour on them?

Dr. MUIR: The Tyndallometer is certainly sensitive to particle size. We investigated the possibility of water condensation by comparing results obtained when inhaling air at room temperature with those following the inhalation of air at body temperatures and fully saturated with moisture. There was no difference. This makes it most unlikely that the signal obtained during exhalation is caused by this means. We are driven to suggest that small particles are produced in the lung during the experiment.

S. W. CLARKE: What was the volume of air inspired before the bolus during the low lung volume experiments?

Dr. MUIR: About 340 ml.

R. F. HOUNAM: In what way would a gas bolus differ from an aerosol bolus?

Dr. MUIR: An insoluble gas would be distributed throughout the alveolar air in a normal subject. It would give a fairly uniform concentration or plateau during exhalation.

E. D. PALMES: You stated that you can get the same information from a bolus as using the difference between two single breaths. It appears to me that the bolus is a more reliable method and gives more information than does analysis of two breaths for determining fate of particles inhaled between, e.g. 1000–1200 ml of inspiration.

Dr. MUIR: The bolus is certainly more accurate. I was trying to show that they both measure the same thing and that there is no fundamental difference.

THE EFFECT OF BREATHING RATE ON THE DEPOSITION OF PARTICLES IN THE HUMAN RESPIRATORY SYSTEM

W. L. DENNIS

Chemical Defence Establishment, Porton, England

Abstract — The effect of increasing the breathing rate on the deposition of inhaled particles in the human respiratory system has been found to depend upon the method used to increase the rate. If the rate is increased artificially and the minute volume remains almost constant, the deposition decreases up to a respiration rate of about 15 to 20 per minute. If the subject is exercising the minute volume increases with respiration rate and so also does the percentage deposition. There are large individual variations in the depositions, probably due to different breathing patterns and mean values for a large number of subjects may conceal the effect of varying certain parameters.

INTRODUCTION

ACCORDING to HATCH & GROSS (1964) the first measurements of respiratory deposition in man with simultaneous recording of breathing frequency and minute volume were made by DRINKER *et al.* (1928). Their subjects inhaled dust-laden air from a cabinet in which the particulates were dispersed, and exhaled through an electrostatic precipitator into a spirometer. Samples were similarly taken with an electrostatic precipitator to determine the concentration-time curve of the inhaled dust. The materials used were zinc fume, preformed zinc oxide particles and calcium carbonate dust. They found an average deposition of 55% at 10 to 12 respirations per minute and that there was little difference between nose and mouth breathing. BROWN (1931) used essentially the same apparatus. His subjects were either at rest, operating a bicycle ergometer under various loads or breathing carbon dioxide enriched air. They wore a full facemask and breathed either through the nose or mouth at rest and through both while exercising and during heavy deep breathing induced by the carbon dioxide. He carried out a large number of experiments and concluded that the percentage deposition was inversely proportional to the minute volume and respiration rate below 20 per minute. The deposition was directly proportional to the particulate size and density.

VAN WIJK & PATTERSON (1940) gave an assessment of the effect of particle size on the deposition. They used three subjects in the naturally dusty atmosphere of a mine. The subject wore a mask fitted with two valves so that he inhaled from the outside air and then breathed out into a one foot cube box. A thermal precipitator was used to sample the inhaled dust at the breathing level of the subject and another sampled the air in the box. The mean respiration rate was 19 per minute. They obtained a curve showing the percentage deposition of siliceous dust particles against particle size and concluded that about 25% of particles of size 0·2 μm and about 80% of size 2 μm were removed during respiration and that between these sizes the percentage removal was nearly proportional to the square root of the size.

BROWN et al. (1950) employed an apparatus in which the essential device was a rotary valve connected through a central port to the facemask and electrically controlled from a Drinker respirator in which the subject was placed. Rotation of the valve successively opened eight ports round the periphery. One of these was connected to the dust dispenser and served as the air supply and the others through electrostatic precipitators to vinyl collecting bags so that the exhaled air could be partitioned into several fractions. The subject breathed through the nose at 15 respirations per minute. The concentration of carbon dioxide in the bags enabled the dead space (anatomical plus external) to be calculated and also the percentage of upper respiratory and lung air in each bag. From their experimental results they calculated the upper respiratory and alveolar deposition curves as a function of particle size. HATCH (1960) also derived values of the total deposition and the separate fractions deposited along the upper respiratory tract and in the pulmonary spaces for four different breathing frequencies from 6 to 20 per minute with equal ventilation rates. These showed that the percentage of dust deposited decreased over this increasing frequency range. DENNIS (1961) obtained similar results, the measurements being made on a single subject, who breathed in time with a metronome and consequently the minute volume only increased slightly with respiration rate. He found however that the deposition increased at rates above about 15 to 20 per minute.

According to MORROW (1960) it is probable that changes in the respiration rate and volume will produce changes in both the site and the amount of dust deposited and that although by creating better mixing and greater particle inertia, rapid breathing tends to increase the deposition, other factors such as shortened residence time may be more effective in reducing it.

He compares a number of experimental studies and concludes that the change in the site of deposition is comparable with that produced with different particle sizes. WILSON & LA MER (1948), using subjects breathing in time with a metronome, found that the deposition of particles was decreased when the respiratory rate was increased from 5·5 to 20 per minute, while LANDAHL (1950) concluded that there would be a similar result when the respiratory frequency was increased from 5 to 15 per minute and the minute volume remained constant.

MUIR & DAVIES (1967) measured the deposition of a monodisperse aerosol of 0·5 μm particles in the lungs during steady state breathing. They used three subjects only, breathing through a tube to the mouth, and measured the aerosol concentrations optically. They found that the deposition rose slightly with increasing tidal volume and fell with increasing frequency. Their deposition values were lower than any of those previously reported in the literature and they concluded that the fractional deposition of 0·5 μm particles was about 10% at all work loads and that the main factors which had lead to over-estimates in the past had been undetected instrumental losses of the aerosol and the use of non-uniform particles. More recently DRASCHE & REITER (1970) carried out deposition experiments in a limestone mine under working conditions. The inhaled dust was sampled with a breathing simulator synchronized with the respiration rate and minute volume of the subjects, who inhaled through the nose or mouth but exhaled only through the mouth into a filter box. The dusts were sampled with soluble plastic filters and the particles were sized and counted with a Coulter counter. From experiments on thirteen subjects under four different experimental conditions, they concluded that the percentage deposition was more dependent upon the respiratory frequency than on the type of inhalation.

From the above review it will be seen that although a few published papers have examined the effect of different breathing rates upon the deposition of particles in the respiratory tract, in most of the studies the subjects have been sedentary and their breathing rates artificially controlled at several frequencies by synchronizing them with metronomes or even with a mechanical device. If the subject is sedentary and doing no physical work then the tidal volume decreases with increasing respiration rate and the minute volume increases to a much lesser extent than when the subject is made to work. Some investigations have used rates as low as 5 per minute, a condition which rarely occurs naturally. From the practical point of view it is usually the deposition which would occur when doing physical work in a dusty atmosphere which is of interest. In the present work the deposition was measured in subjects working on an ergometer.

DESCRIPTION OF THE APPARATUS

The apparatus is shown in Figures 1 and 2. The test clouds consisted of aerosols having a mass median diameter of about 5 μm and a number median diameter of about 1 μm, generated with a conventional jet type spray from either melted stearic

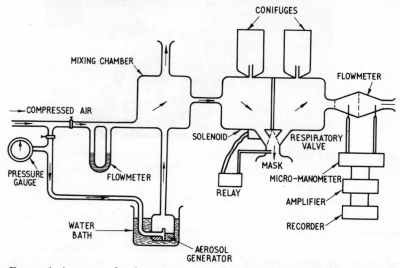

FIGURE 1. Apparatus for the measurement of respiratory retention of aerosols.

acid or a suspension of Calopake H, a precipitated calcium carbonate. The stearic acid particles were spherical in shape while the calcium carbonate particles were approximately spherical aggregates. The cloud passed to the bottom of a 20 litre aspirator bottle, acting as a reservoir and having two wide outlet tubes at the top, one being open to the atmosphere and the other connected through a length of convoluted tubing to a Perspex box. If necessary diluting air could be introduced into the bottle.

An essential requirement for this type of study is an automatic respiratory valve which will partition the inhaled and exhaled clouds. It must have a minimum dead space, a very low resistance to breathing, produce negligible loss of particles during transmission and be automatic in action so that the subject can breathe naturally at his own rate without restriction. Preliminary experiments showed that the use of the simple type of flap valve usually resulted in considerable loss of particles by impaction

FIGURE 2. Apparatus for the determination of the percentage deposition of particles in the human respiratory system.

either on the valve itself or on the walls of the surrounding tube. An automatic valve which was simple in construction had been previously designed (DENNIS, 1950) and for the present work it was still further simplified. The valve connected two adjacent Perspex chambers, each having a capacity of 5 litres, to a (modified) facepiece from a dust respirator. On inhalation the aerosol was drawn out of the top of the reservoir into one of these chambers and from there inhaled by the subject. The exhaled air passed to the other chamber. The dead space in the facepiece was reduced to a minimum by packing it with foam rubber, care being taken to ensure that there was no pressure which would constrict the nose or distort the normal shape of the mouth.

The automatic valve, shown in Figure 3, consisted primarily of two tubes each 1 in. internal diameter and inclined to each other at 30° to form a V-junction, the two arms of which were joined to the two chambers: Figure 2. With this arrangement the cloud could pass to and from the facepiece without loss of particles since there was sensibly no change in direction or obstruction in its path. The position of the Bakelite flap, which was mounted on a vertical spindle, was controlled by a solenoid. When the flap moved it swept out the whole of the space next to the mask and so reduced the effective dead space to a minimum. The solenoid and hence the flap was controlled by the small pressure changes which occurred in the facepiece during the breathing

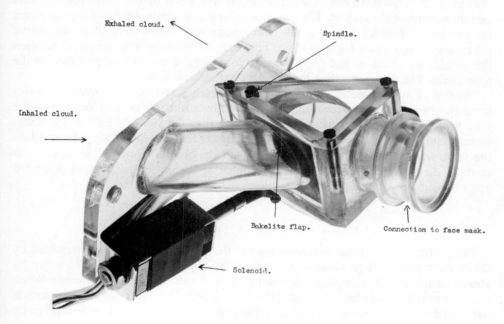

FIGURE 3. Automatic respiratory valve.

cycle. A narrow bore plastic tube transmitted these pressure changes to a small brass cell over one side of which was cemented a thin rubber diaphragm. Movement of the diaphragm made an electrical contact at its centre which in turn operated a relay connected to the solenoid. By adjustment of the contact it was possible to alter the positive or negative pressure at which the valve operated.

In the earlier work carried out with a similar apparatus the volumes of the two chambers containing the inhaled and exhaled air were originally 1 litre each and were subsequently increased to 2·5 litres when higher breathing rates were used. In the present work they had volumes of 5 litres each, which was considered adequate to meet criticism which had been made (DAVIES & MUIR, 1966; DENNIS, 1967) and to give true samples of both clouds. The chambers and valve were mounted as a unit above the handle-bars of an ergometer at such a height that the subject was comfortable when sitting on the ergometer and wearing the mask. The dial of a tachometer was fixed above one of the chambers so that the subject could check the rate at which he was pedalling.

The percentage of particles deposited in the respiratory system of the subjects was determined for each particle size from the ratio of their numbers in the two chambers. This was done most conveniently and accurately by the use of two conifuges (SAWYER & WALTON, 1950). With these instruments continuous samples could be taken over short periods and the counting of the particle deposits was much simpler than with any other sampling method. The two conifuges were mounted below the chambers and withdrew samples through holes in the bottom of each. They were mounted on a board hinged at the base so that they could be moved into a forward position to permit removal of the samples.

During all respiratory experiments a record was made of the breathing rate and minute volume of the subject. This was done using a conventional flowmeter in which the pressure difference across a fine wire gauze was measured with an electronic micro-manometer and a high speed pen recorder. A fibre-glass filter was fixed between the exhaled air chamber and the flowmeter to prevent deposition of particles on the wire gauze. The flowmeter thus recorded the exhaled air flow.

The flap of the automatic valve took approximately $\frac{1}{5}$ second to complete its movement and by watching the recording of the breathing rate it was possible at the same time to adjust the contact mentioned above so that the small "kick" in the trace, corresponding to the movement of the flap, was on the zero line. This indicated that the valve was operating at the correct point in the breathing cycle. This check was made at the commencement of each experiment as the precise adjustment depended upon the subject and his type of breathing.

CALIBRATION OF THE APPARATUS

The particle size-distance relationships for the two conifuges were determined by the method described previously (SAWYER & WALTON, 1950) and were found to be almost identical. The sampling rates were checked with a bubble flowmeter. When corrections were made for the small differences in the sampling rates and the particle size distributions on the sampling plates, the particle number concentrations given by the two conifuges for a series of clouds, each sampled simultaneously from the same chamber, were found to be in excellent agreement.

Accurate determination of the loss of particles during the passage of the cloud through the apparatus without the subject in position presented some difficulty. It was necessary that the cloud should pass through the apparatus intermittently and that the respiratory valve should operate in exactly the same way as during an actual respiratory experiment. The nearest approach to this condition was obtained by the use of a cylinder and piston with a capacity of 650 cm³ per stroke and a bore of 7·5 cm, operated manually in unison with the breathing rate of the operator. The experiments showed that the mean loss from the cloud in passing through the valve, entering the cylinder and back through the valve into the other chamber, was as shown in the following table.

TABLE I. LOSS OF PARTICLES IN THE RESPIRATORY VALVE AND CYLINDER WITH PISTON

Particle diameter (μm)	1	2	3	4	5	6
Maximum loss (%)	6	7	8	8	12	16

It was probable that the losses occurred chiefly in the piston chamber. However if it was assumed that they occurred equally in the two tubes of the valve and the cylinder, the correction to be made to the observed respiratory deposition values was small since the deposition was high above 3 μm.

EXPERIMENTAL PROCEDURE

A facemask of suitable size was fitted to the respiratory valve and a short trial run was made without the particulate cloud to test its fit and the comfort of the subject and if necessary to accustom him to the apparatus. When ready the spray was switched on and the subject breathed the cloud either through the nose or mouth only, according to instructions, in his own characteristic way. After a period of at least 1·5 min he removed his face from the mask and the valve opening was rapidly closed with a rubber bung to prevent diffusion of the cloud out of the chambers and then conifuge samples of the inhaled and exhaled clouds were taken for 1 or 2 min according to the concentration.

When the ergometer was being used, the subject was made to pedal for 5 min before and 2 min while inhaling the cloud. The same procedure as before was followed for sampling the aerosols. When the calcium carbonate was being used it was sometimes necessary to continue for a further 2 min and sample a second time on the same plates to obtain a deposit of sufficient density for accurate counting.

Counts of the particles on the sampling plates were made by the method described by SAWYER & WALTON (1950). Two curves were obtained showing the relative numbers of particles, size by size, in each sample and from these curves the percentage deposition could be directly determined, a small correction being made where necessary for the loss of particles in the valve.

In all experiments at least 15 litres were breathed through the apparatus before sampling was carried out. Calculation shows that if a volume equal to three times that of a chamber is passed through it, with perfect mixing, then the concentration of the cloud in the chamber will be equal to 98% of that of the original cloud.

From the records of the breathing rate the minute volume was obtained by planimetry of the area under the curves. The height, weight and age of each subject was recorded and his vital capacity was measured with a drum type flowmeter.

RESULTS AND DISCUSSION

Results of an earlier investigation using a similar apparatus have already been published (DENNIS, 1961). They showed the variation in the percentage deposition with particle size, both for nose and mouth breathing. These curves are reproduced in Figure 4 and it will be seen that the mean deposition is greater for nose breathing. The data for the nose breathing curves were obtained from 26 experiments on 22 adult male subjects varying in age from 17 to 56 years and having an average age of 35 years. These results agreed well with those of VAN WIJK & PATTERSON (1940). The measurement of deposition for mouth breathing was made using 11 subjects.

At the same time 12 experiments with nasal breathing and 6 experiments for mouth breathing were carried out using a single subject (W.L.D.) and it was found that for this particular subject the deposition was greater for mouth breathing: Figure 6. The deposition for nasal breathing was less than the mean for a large number of subjects. Subsidiary experiments indicated that this subject had a smaller than average resistance to air flow through the nose.

As mentioned above, the size of the chambers containing the exhaled and inhaled clouds were larger (5 litres) in the present study than in the previous one, but similar results were obtained in both cases. It had also been suggested (DAVIES & MUIR, 1966) that errors had occurred because sampling had been continuous throughout the breathing cycle, including the inhalation period, and that therefore the sample of exhaled air had contained an excess of small particles breathed out from the lower part of the lungs. This possible source of error was eliminated by stopping the subjects at random parts of the breathing cycle and sampling after they had removed their

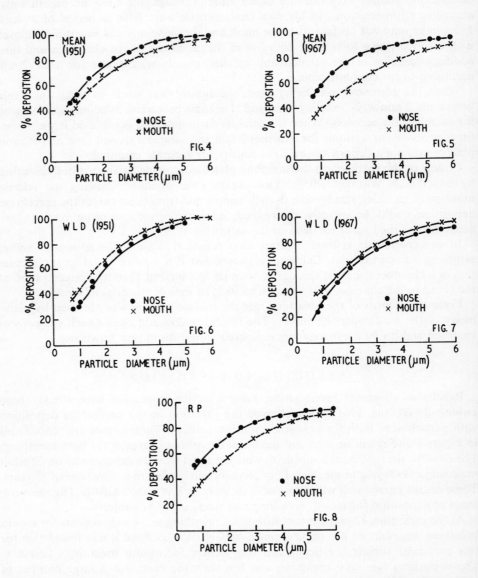

FIGURES 4–8. Variation in respiratory deposition of stearic acid particles with particle size. Subjects sedentary.

face from the mask. It will be observed that despite these modifications to the procedure the results of the two studies were similar: Figures 5 and 7.

In the first part of the present work only two subjects were used in an attempt to eliminate the large individual variation which was known to exist. Five experiments were carried out under each set of conditions of subject, work rate and nose or mouth breathing. Later measurements were made on a large number of subjects under sedentary and working conditions to obtain data for an average population.

One of the two subjects used for the special study (R.P.) gave retention curves similar to the average for a large number of subjects and the deposition for nasal breathing was higher than through the mouth, but with the other (W.L.D.) the reverse was the case: Figures 6 and 7). The effect of increasing the breathing rate of these two subjects under working conditions was generally to increase the deposition in both cases, except for R.P. where there was an indication of slightly lower deposition of the smaller sizes when nose breathing: Figures 9 and 10. In the case of W.L.D.

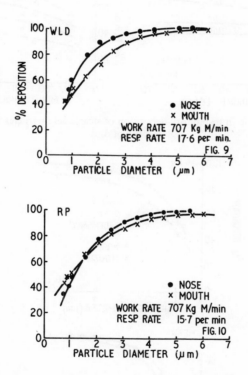

FIGURES 9 and 10. Variation in respiratory deposition of stearic acid particles with particle size. Subjects working.

there was a complete changeover and deposition became higher for nose breathing than through the mouth. These variations are difficult to explain but may be due to differences in the manner in which the subjects breathed, i.e. the extent to which the mouth was opened, the position of the tongue, etc. It was found that the best correlation for the results of all the experiments with five different work rates was obtained by plotting the percentage deposition against minute volume: Figures 11 to 14. For

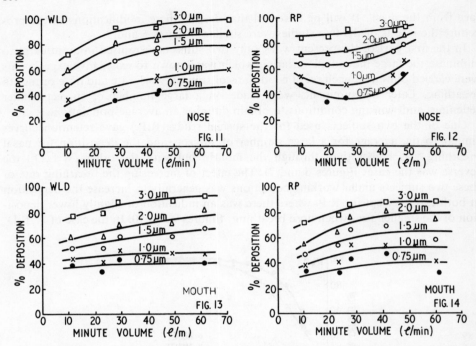

FIGURES 11–14. Variation in respiratory deposition of stearic acid particles with minute volume.
Subjects working.

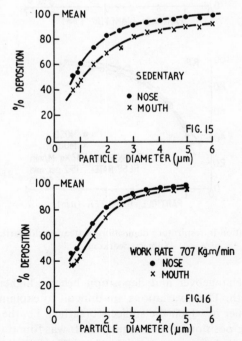

FIGURES 15 and 16. Variation in respiratory deposition of calcium carbonate particles with
particle size.

W.L.D. it will be observed that for both nose and mouth breathing the deposition increases with minute volume, the effect being greater for the larger particles. The results for R.P. were not quite so consistent. They appear to indicate a minimum deposition for nose breathing at a minute volume of about 25 litres. A similar effect was found for W.L.D. when breathing in time with a metronome (DENNIS, 1961). If the deposition for R.P. was plotted against respiration rate the minimum occurred at a rate of 15 per minute.

A series of experiments was also carried out in which a large number of subjects inhaled an aerosol of calcium carbonate particles. The density of these particles was determined from the size-distance calibration curve for the conifuge and was found to be almost identical with that of stearic acid. The results of these experiments are shown in Figures 15 and 16. Thirty subjects were used for the sedentary nose breathing experiments and 29 subjects for the mouth breathing. In addition, measurements were made of the deposition when the subjects were working, 15 men being used with nose breathing and a similar number with mouth breathing. It will be seen that the percentage deposition in sedentary subjects was similar to that with stearic acid particles, and that when the subjects were working at 707 kg.m/min there was little effect on the deposition except for the larger sizes. This is not in agreement with the previous findings using the two subjects only, probably due to large individual variations. In the subjects used in the sedentary experiments the respiration rate varied between 5·3 and 37·1 per minute with a mean of 19·9 when breathing through the nose. This rate increased to 22·1 when working, while the minute volume increased from 20·2 to 43·7 litres. In one of the two subjects, the respiration rate increased from 10·6 to 19·5 per minute and the minute volume from 9·9 to 43·8 litres.

Most of the previous workers investigating the effect of breathing rate on respiratory deposition have artificially varied the breathing rate of sedentary subjects, so that the minute volume remained almost constant. Under these conditions the deposition decreases with increasing respiration rate up to about 15 to 20 per minute (DENNIS, 1961). If the breathing rate is increased by the subject working then the minute volume shows a corresponding increase and so also does the deposition. In studying the effect of exercise on the percentage deposition of inhaled particles, the variation with minute volume rather than respiration rate should be determined. Individual variations in the breathing pattern are large and the mean values for large numbers of subjects may conceal the effects of certain parameters.

Acknowledgements — I wish to thank Miss M. M. P. MacCafferty who carried out most of the experimental work and computation of the results and Mr. R. Poynting who constructed part of the apparatus and was responsible for its calibration.

REFERENCES

BROWN, C. E. (1931). *J. ind. Hyg. Toxicol.* **13**, 285.
BROWN, J. H., COOK, K. M., NEY, F. G. & HATCH, T. F. (1950). *Am. J. publ. Hlth* **40**, 450.
DAVIES, C. N. & MUIR, D. C. F. (1966). *Nature, Lond.* **211**, 90–91.
DENNIS, W. L. (1950). *J. scient. Instrum.* **27**, 195–196.
DENNIS, W. L. (1961). In: *Inhaled particles and vapours.* Ed. C. N. Davies. Oxford, Pergamon Press, pp. 88–90.
DENNIS, W. L. (1967). *Nature, Lond.* **214**, 908.
DRASCHE, H. & REITER, R. (1970). Eighth Coulter Conference, Cardiff.

DRINKER, R., THOMPSON, R. M. & FINN, J. L. (1928). *J. ind. Hyg. Toxicol.* **10,** 17.
HATCH, T. F. (1960). In: *Proc. Pneumoconosis Conf., Johannesburg, 1959. Ed.* A. J. Orenstein. London, J. & A. Churchill, pp. 113–132.
HATCH, T. F. & GROSS, P. (1964). *Pulmonary deposition and retention of inhaled particles.* New York, Academic Press.
LANDAHL, H. D. (1950). *Bull. math. Biophys.* **12,** 43.
MORROW, P. E. (1960). *Hlth Phys.* **2,** 366.
MUIR, D. C. F. & DAVIES, C. N. (1967). *Ann. occup. Hyg.* **10,** 161–174.
SAWYER, K. F. & WALTON, W. H. (1950). *J. scient. Instrum.* **27,** 272.
VAN WIJK, A. & PATTERSON, H. S. (1940). *J. ind. Hyg. Toxicol.* **22,** 31.
WILSON, I. B. & LA MER, V. K. (1948). *J. ind. Hyg. Toxicol.* **30,** 265.

DISCUSSION

R. G. Love: In our studies we have found practically no difference in the percentage deposition when the subject was breathing naturally at the rate of 15 respirations per minute and when he was breathing in time with a metronome.

Mr. Dennis: I agree that at the normal breathing rate there is no difference in the percentage deposition under the two conditions. It is only at the higher breathing rates that the difference occurs, since if the subject is made to work in order to increase his respiration rate, the minute volume is greater than if he breathed in time with a metronome at the same rate.

R. G. Love: All of our experiments were carried out at 15 respirations per minute. It was the only rate at which we could compare values.

D. C. F. Muir: I do not think that untrained subjects breathing through a mouth piece or face mask breathe normally. I would also like to comment on your deposition values. For 1 μm diameter particles you obtain about 40% deposition while we obtain about half that level. I cannot see any obvious fault in either technique and I am unable to account for the difference.

Mr. Dennis: I also cannot see why our two sets of results should be inconsistent. I believe that we have obtained reliable results and I cannot see why there should be any error.

R. E. Albert: There are not the same subjects in the two cases.

Mr. Dennis: Yes, we have found that there are large individual variations between different persons. Perhaps it is for this reason that we have not found much difference between the curves of Figures 15 and 16 for which experiments I used 14 subjects. They were Army and Air Force personnel who were briefly told what we wanted them to do and then asked to breathe naturally through the face mask on the apparatus while either sedentary or pedalling on the ergometer. They had no experience of this type of investigation. When we used volunteers from the laboratories we obtained rather more consistant results since they tended to breathe more regularly than those from outside.

J. Dodgson: Are the particle diameters given in your figures microscope projected diameters or equivalent falling sizes.

Mr. Dennis: They are microscope projected diameters. The aerosols used consisted either of spherical stearic acid particles or approximately spherical aggregates of precipitated calcium carbonate. In both cases the apparent density of the materials was approximately unity, so that the aerodynamic diameters and the microscope projected diameters were almost the same.

THE REGIONAL DEPOSITION OF INHALED
AEROSOLS IN MAN*

MORTON LIPPMANN, ROY E. ALBERT and HAROLD T. PETERSON, JR.†

*Institute of Environmental Medicine, New York University Medical Center,
550 First Avenue, New York, N.Y. 10016, U.S.A.*

Abstract — Direct measurements of regional aerosol deposition in man have been made using insoluble monodisperse test aerosols, tagged with gamma-emitting isotopes, and an array of external scintillation detectors. On the basis of the retention measurements made immediately after the test aerosol inhalation, the inhaled aerosol can be subdivided into a number of component fractions, i.e., the head deposit, tracheal deposit, whole lung deposit, and exhaled aerosol. Part of the whole lung deposit is rapidly cleared via mucociliary transport within 24 hours, while the balance is cleared at a very much slower rate. The part which clears rapidly has been equated with tracheobronchial (T-B) deposition and the residual deposit with alveolar deposition.

Over 200 tests on 65 subjects, including 14 non-smoking normals, 29 current cigarette smokers, 6 bronchitic patients, and 1 asthmatic, have been performed. It has been concluded that for aerosols with aerodynamic diameters >2 μm, deposition in the head and larger airways is due primarily to the impaction mechanism. For smaller particles in normals, gravitational sedimentation on the smaller sized airways of the mucus escalator becomes a major component of the T-B deposit. The T-B deposition for a given particle size varies greatly from subject to subject, but each individual has a characteristic size *vs* deposition relation.

T-B deposition of 1–5 μm diameter particles was very much higher in the asthmatic and bronchitic patients than in the non-smoking normals, and most of the increase was in airways beyond the trachea. As a group, the current cigarette smokers had higher tracheal and overall T-B depositions than the non-smoking normals, although the differences were smaller than for the bronchitic patients and the data for the group overlapped part of the broad normal range.

INTRODUCTION

IN a previous publication (LIPPMANN & ALBERT, 1969) a technique for the direct functional measurement of the regional deposition of inhaled aerosols in man was described and the results of 93 mouth breathing studies on 34 subjects were discussed. For monodisperse spherical insoluble test aerosols of ferric oxide with unit density diameters from 2·1 to 12·5 μm, it was demonstrated that lung clearance during the

* This investigation was supported by grant EC 00231 from the Environmental Control Administration, Environmental Health Service, Public Health Service, Department of Health, Education, and Welfare and by the AMA Education and Research Foundation. It is part of a center program supported by grant ES 00260 from the National Institute of Environmental Health Sciences.

† On assignment from the Bureau of Radiological Health, Environmental Health Service, U.S. Department of Health, Education and Welfare.

first 24 hours after the test inhalation was clearance from the bronchial tree to the stomach, and that the amount of such clearance provided a functional measure of the amount of tracheo-bronchial deposition. Furthermore, it was concluded that: (1) there were very large differences in the efficiency of the tracheo-bronchial tree as a particle collector among the normal healthy adult human males tested; (2) in mouth breathing with an open mouth the efficiency of the head as a particle collector approaches, but is generally lower than, the efficiency of the tracheo-bronchial tree; and (3) deposition of particles in the tracheo-bronchial tree for mouth breathing results largely from impaction, at least for particles larger than 4 μm unit density.

The number of mouth breathing inhalation tests has now been increased to over 200 and the subject population to 65. These include 14 normals who have never smoked cigarettes, 29 current cigarette smokers, six elderly bronchitic patients, and one young non-smoker with a history of asthma.

The bronchitics and the asthmatic had much more tracheo-bronchial deposition than the non-smoking normals. Some of the bronchitics also had abnormally high tracheal deposition. Both tracheal and overall tracheo-bronchial deposition were also higher among some cigarette smokers although most cigarette smokers exhibited regional deposition values within the rather broad limits established by the non-smoking normals.

In each inhalation test, the pattern of bronchial clearance was also measured by means of serial retention measurements throughout the following day exposure. These measurements provide a basis for describing the kinetics of bronchial clearance in man; they are discussed in another paper to this Symposium (ALBERT et al., 1971).

METHODS

The techniques developed to study regional aerosol deposition in man have been fully described previously (LIPPMANN & ALBERT, 1967, 1969; ALBERT et al., 1969a) and therefore will be only briefly discussed here.

The subject inhales a monodisperse ferric oxide aerosol ($\sigma_g \cong 1 \cdot 10$), tagged with a non-leaching radioisotope, through a mouthpiece or nosemask. The breathing frequency is 14 per min, the tidal volume between 700 and 1200 cm^3, and the inhalation period is usually 1 min. In most cases, two 1 min inhalations have been performed sequentially. The aerosols are produced with a spinning disc generator with multiple liquid feed lines. Each liquid feed line to the disc contains a different isotopic tag, and can also differ in ferric oxide content, which will change the aerosol size. The inhaled activity is normally 100 nCi of Au–198 in the first aerosol, and 0·5 to 1 μCi of Tc–99m in the second. The exhaled air is separated from the inhaled by a timer-controlled, solenoid-actuated 2·5 cm diameter, 3-way ball valve. The exhaled particles are collected in a respirator filter canister.

After the end of aerosol inhalation, the subject walks to the nearby Whole Body Counter, and is positioned for retention measurements. The first measurement begins within 1 min after the end of the test aerosol inhalation. Simultaneous measurements are made employing a four-detector whole lung ring, a tracheal detector, and a stomach detector. The counting sensitivity of the lung ring array is uniform for particles in the lung field anywhere from 2·5 cm below the larynx to the alveoli, except for the lowest 2·5 to 5 cm of lung. It is necessary to sacrifice the measurement of the aerosol in this region in order to avoid measuring swallowed activity in the adjacent stomach as lung activity. The tracheal detector has a vertical slit collimator, restricting its primary viewing area to the trachea and the proximal ends of the major bronchi.

Each detector sees activity in its primary viewing area at high sensitivity, and activity elsewhere at a lower but not insignificant sensitivity. The contribution of each region to each detector has been determined from phantom measurements and simultaneous equations are solved to determine the activity within each region.

The initial measurement is made with the subject positioned so that the lung ring detector axis is at the estimated location of the tracheal bifurcation. The seat height is adjustable for variable subject size. The initial measurement yields estimates of the overall chest deposition, initial tracheal deposition and (from the stomach detector count) the amount of head deposit inadvertently swallowed before the retention measurement. Immediately after this first retention measurement, which usually lasts 1 min, the subject shifts to a lower seat position for a second 1 min reading. The ring detectors now measure the activity within the head. After this measurement, particles in the mouth are recovered by gargling and rinsing.

The initial whole lung measurement made with the lung ring includes both tracheo-bronchial and alveolar deposit. A comparable measurement made 24 hours later, after bronchial clearance has been completed, indicates the alveolar component of the initial deposition.

The lung deposition data to be discussed are based on these two measurements for each test, i.e. the 1 min and 24 h chest retention measurements. In most cases, many other retention measurements were made during the first day, and these permit an analysis of the kinetics of bronchial clearance. These intermediate measurement data are discussed in another paper (ALBERT et al., 1971).

SUBJECTS

All of the subjects tested were volunteers who gave their informed consent. Those identified as non-smokers, cigarette smokers, and cigar and ex-smokers were all "healthy" individuals without known disease as determined by questionnaire. The bronchitics were either hospital or clinic patients referred for these tests by their attending physician. The characteristics of the subjects are further described in Tables I and II.

TABLE I. VITAL STATISTICS OF INHALATION SUBJECT GROUP. (FIGURES 1–4).

Group	No. of subjects		Age —Years			Height — Inches			Weight — Pounds		
	Male	Female	Av.	Median	Range	Av.	Median	Range	Av.	Median	Range
Non-smokers	14	0	27·6	27·5	18–42	70·8	71	62–74	181·1	177·5	145–248
Cigarette smokers	25	4	33·9	31	24–67	69·8	70	62–79	165·5	158	109–250
Cigar, pipe and ex-smokers	6	1	42·1	42	24–73	69·4	70	62–74	174·4	185	126–200
Bronchitic patients	6	0	68·0	68·5	62–71	67·7	66·8	64–73	143·8	142·5	120–180
Asthmatic	0	1	27	—	—	63	—	—	115	—	—

Table II. Vital Statistics for Individual Inhalation Subjects in Figures 5 and 6

Smoking classification	Subject no.	Sex	Age, years	Height, inches	Weight, pounds	Smoking history		
						Cigarettes per day	No. of years	Filter
Non-smoking normals	1	M	21	68·5	170	0	0	—
	5	M	21	74	175	0	0	—
	8	M	34	70	175	0	0	—
	18	M	30	70	248	0	0	—
	65	M	22	71	182	0	0	—
Cigarette smokers	2	M	25	69	167	30	8	Yes
	3	M	53	75	250	40	20	Yes
	12	M	36	79	220	20	15	No
	13	M	48	70·5	155	30	20	Yes

RESULTS

The regional deposition data are presented in a series of summary graphs. Figure 1 shows the overall head deposition in mouth breathing experiments as a function of the parameter $\rho d^2 Q_a$, where ρ is the density in g/cm^3, d is the particle diameter in μm, and Q_a is the average inspiratory flowrate in l/min. This dimensional parameter incorporates the experimental variables affecting impaction deposition, and permits the data collected in tests with variable average inspiratory flowrates to be normalized. The upper scale shows the unit density diameter normalized to 30 l/min, which was close to the average inspiratory flow for these tests. Panel A shows the results obtained with non-smoking normals and cigar, pipe and ex-smokers. Panel B shows results obtained with cigarette smokers and subjects with lung disease. Figure 2 shows a comparable plot for tracheal deposition.

The trachea in this context is not the anatomical trachea, but the area viewed by the tracheal detector. It extends from about one inch below the larynx to the base of the trachea, and includes the tracheal bifurcation and short segments of the major bronchi. Figure 3 shows the data for deposition within the entire tracheo-bronchial tree, i.e., from about one inch below the larynx to the most distal ciliated area of the lung. Figure 4 presents a summary of the alveolar deposition data. Figure 5 shows tracheo-bronchial deposition data for selected individual subjects, and Figure 6 shows alveolar deposition in the same subjects.

DISCUSSION

Head Deposition

The non-smoker data points in Figure 1A, while exhibiting a fair amount of scatter, nevertheless appear to form an S-shaped curve of the type exhibited on such coordinates by an impaction type of particle collector. This is entirely appropriate since impaction is the predominant mechanism for removal of particles passing through the head. Eye-fit limit lines were drawn above and below the non-smoker data points on the ascending portion of Figure 1A. These limit lines were reproduced

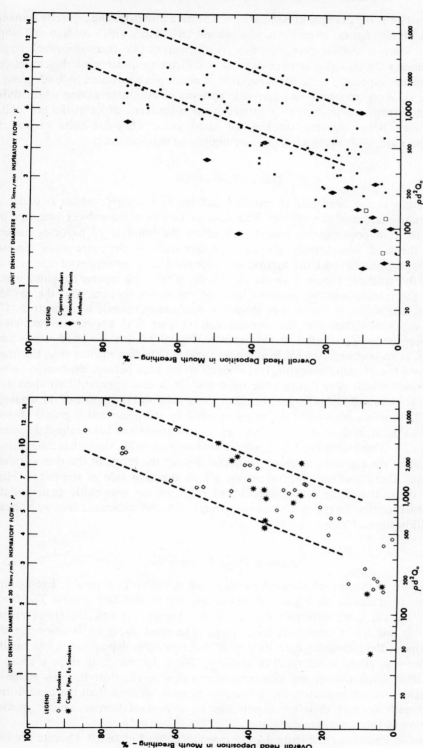

FIGURE 1. Particle deposition in the head during mouthpiece inhalation. Panel A at left shows data for non-cigarette smoking normals. Panel B at right shows data for cigarette smokers and subjects with lung disease.

on Figure 1B for the purpose of comparison. The data points for the cigarette smokers in Figure 1B also appear to conform to a general "S" shape, with a median and slope similar to the non-smoker data. However, it is apparent that there is a much larger scatter among the cigarette smoker data. It is difficult to understand the causes for this difference, especially since the same style of mouthpiece was used by both groups. Cigarette smokers may have characteristic patterns of mouth breathing which differ significantly from mouth breathing patterns in non-smokers. Most of the bronchitic patients were heavy cigarette smokers for many years. They are quite variable in head deposition, with many showing very high head depositions.

Tracheal Deposition

Deposition in the head during mouth breathing is a variable which is under at least partial control of the subject. The manner in which the subject bites on the mouthpiece and positions his tongue will affect the removal of particles passing through the head. Accordingly, the data for deposition in the more distal regions, that is, in regions beyond the larynx, are expressed as percentages of the aerosol entering the trachea. Figure 2 shows deposition within the tracheal region, which includes the trachea and the proximal ends of the major bronchi. For the particle sizes used, deposition in the trachea should be due almost entirely to impaction. The percent deposition data for the non-smokers (Figure 2A) appears to exhibit a dependence on $\rho d^2 Q_a$ similar to that seen in Figure 1A for the head deposition. However, as an impactor, the tracheal region appears to be less efficient than the head. Since it is a less efficient impactor, it is difficult to get high percent deposition values with aerosols which pass through the head first. It is also apparent that there is a large range of variability among non-smoking normals, and that most of the cigarette smoker data points fall within the range covered by the non-smoker points. Eye-fit limit lines similar to those of Figure 1A were drawn above and below the data points on Figure 2A. These same limit lines, reproduced on Figure 2B, show that a significant percentage of the cigarette smokers' points lie outside the range of the non-smokers' points, and that these outlying points are all on the high side of the range. High tracheal deposition is also characteristic of some of the bronchitic patient data. Tracheal deposition in the non-smoking subject with the asthmatic history appears to be within normal limits.

Tracheo-Bronchial Deposition

Deposition in the entire tracheo-bronchial tree is shown in Figure 3. Eye-fit limit lines have been drawn on Figure 3A above and below the data points. The lower limit line has the same slope as the limit lines in Figures 1A and 2A. However, the upper limit line has a somewhat lower slope. The most likely explanation for this lower slope is the increasing contribution of sedimentation deposition in the smaller ciliated airways at the smaller values of $\rho d^2 Q_a$. Since the change in slope is small, it appears that impaction is the dominant deposition mechanism for this range of $\rho d^2 Q_a$ values. As an impactor, the T-B region is more efficient than the head during mouth breathing, and therefore constitutes an important barrier against particle penetration to the non-ciliated regions.

The eye-fit limit lines of Figure 3A are reproduced on Figure 3B. Despite the very

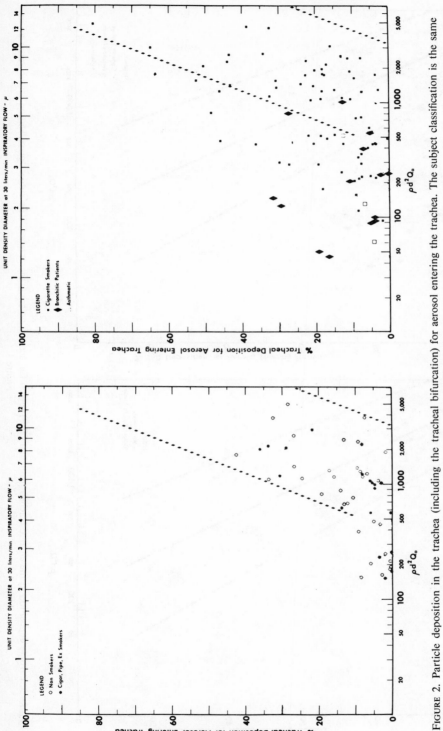

FIGURE 2. Particle deposition in the trachea (including the tracheal bifurcation) for aerosol entering the trachea. The subject classification is the same as in Figure 1.

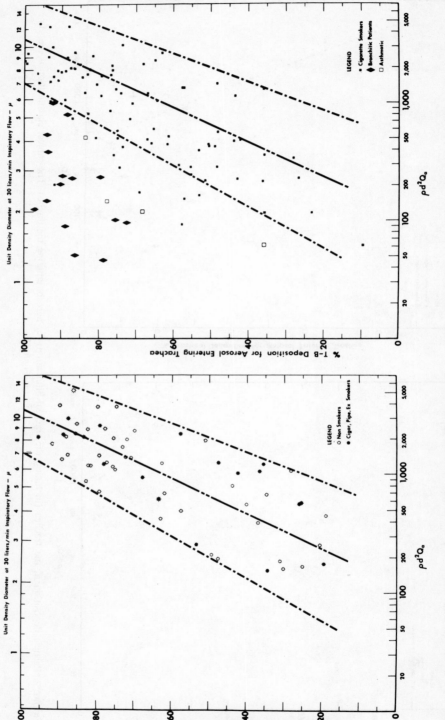

FIGURE 3. Particle deposition in the ciliated tracheo-bronchial (T-B) region for aerosol entering the trachea. The subject classification is the same as in Figure 1.

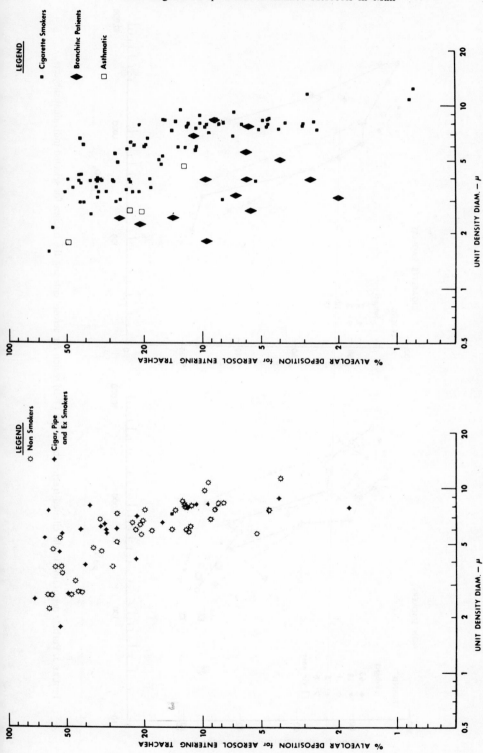

FIGURE 4. Particle deposition in the non-ciliated (alveolar) region for aerosol entering the trachea. The subject classification is the same as in Figure 1.

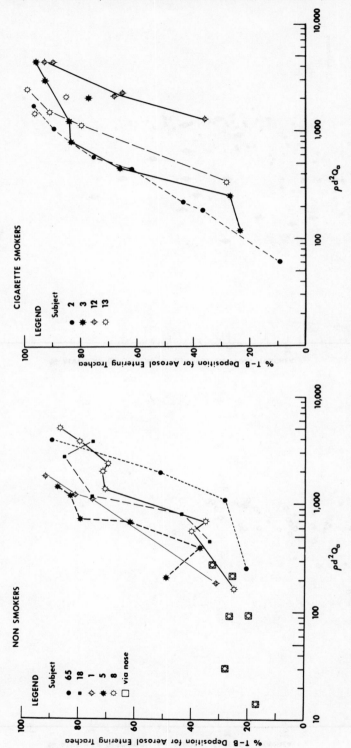

FIGURE 5. Particle deposition in the ciliated tracheo-bronchial (T-B) region for aerosol entering the trachea for selected individual subjects.

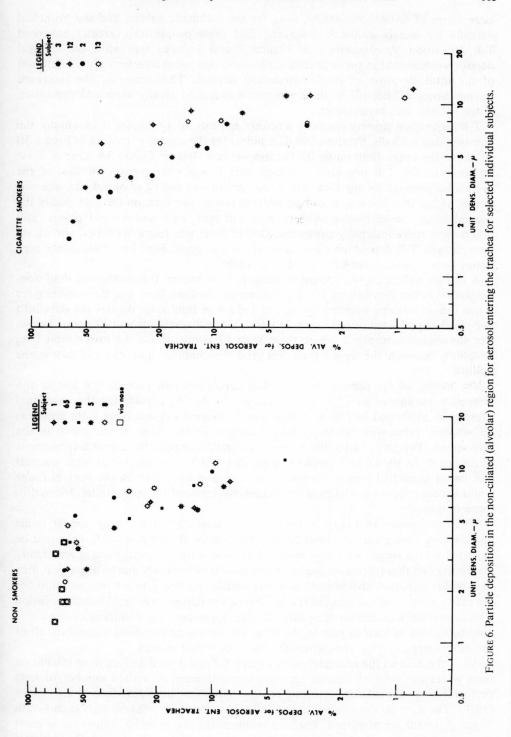

FIGURE 6. Particle deposition in the non-ciliated (alveolar) region for aerosol entering the trachea for selected individual subjects.

large range of normal variability, data for the asthmatic subject and the bronchial patients are clearly different, indicating that these people have greatly enhanced T-B deposition. A comparison of Figures 2 and 3 shows that while the tracheal deposit was elevated in the bronchitics, this elevation accounted for only a small part of the total elevation of tracheo-bronchial deposit. Thus, most of the increased tracheo-bronchial deposit in these patients was due to greatly enhanced deposition in the bronchi and bronchioles.

T-B deposition among cigarette smokers appears to be higher than among the non-smoking normals. Twelve of 90 data points for the cigarette smokers in Figure 3B lie above the upper limit curve for the non-smoker data of Figure 3A. One of these points indicated T-B deposition so high that it was characteristic of that of the bronchitic patients. Of the three other tests performed on the same subject, one was clearly higher than the normal range, while the other two were on the high side of the normal range. Several other subjects also had both high and normal points. Still others were more internally consistent. One of them was tested six times, and all six tests showed T-B deposition close to or above the upper limit line. Four other high points were from two subjects tested twice each.

A further indication that cigarette smokers have higher T-B deposition than non-smokers is in the distribution of the points within the limit lines. For the non-smokers a line drawn midway between the upper and lower limit lines divides the data into two nearly equal sized groups, with 21 points above the midline and 19 points below. For the cigarette smokers, where there were 12 points above the upper limit line, 56 points between the upper limit line and the midline, and only 22 below the midline.

The nature of the relation between T-B deposition and particle size and/or the impaction parameter $\rho d^2 Q_a$ can be examined further by considering the individual subjects as illustrated in Figure 5. For each individual subject, there is an apparent "S"-shaped curve with relatively little variation in the slope of the curve in the mid-region. The great variability between subjects is apparently one of displacement of the curve. As shown by LIPPMANN & ALBERT (1969), variations in average tracheal and major bronchial airway diameters from subject to subject in the normal range could account for a variability in impaction efficiency of the magnitude observed in these studies.

While the curves in Figure 5 appear to have an "S" shape, they appear to be approaching asymptotes at about 20 and 90% rather than 0 and 100% as would be expected with a simple impactor model. The elevated lower asymptote is apparently due to the fact that tracheo-bronchial deposition is not entirely due to impaction. For the smaller particles, sedimentation in the smaller ciliated airways may account for the major portion of the reduced tracheo-bronchial deposit, and unlike sedimentation would increase with diminishing flow. At the upper end, the rounding of the curve may be related at least in part to the effect of the respiratory dead space. Not all of the air penetrates to the sites where the particles would impact.

All of the data on the summary plots Figure 1, 2 and 3 were derived from inhalation tests where the subjects inhaled through a mouthpiece. A limited number of tests performed with the inhalation through a nose mask have been described by LIPPMANN (1970). The data on the tracheo-bronchial deposition in six of these tests is shown in Figure 5 for subject number 8. The four points at the higher $\rho d^2 Q_a$ values are in good general agreement with the single mouth inhalation point in that range. On the basis of these limited data it appears that tracheo-bronchial deposition may remain fairly constant at about 20% in the 1 to 2 μm range.

All of the individual curves in Figure 4 show a rather steep slope in the mid-range. Lines have been drawn connecting the data points. In several of these, e.g. subjects 1 and 13 in Figure 5, the mid-range slope may be somewhat greater than that drawn. Additional tests on these subjects with tracheo-bronchial depositions of the order of 50% would be necessary to confirm this suggestion.

Alveolar Deposition

Figures 4A and 4B show deposition in the nonciliated alveolar region as a function of unit density particle diameter. For both smokers and nonsmokers, alveolar deposition falls off rapidly with increasing size for particles larger than 5 μm unit density. Since all of the bronchitics and some of the cigarette smokers had elevated tracheobronchial deposition, it is not surprising that there are lower alveolar deposition values for these populations than for nonsmoking normals. The manner in which the alveolar deposition varies with size is difficult to discern from the summary plots, as it was for tracheobronchial deposits. Thus, Figure 6 shows the variation of alveolar deposition with size for individual subjects. It can be seen that there are consistent differences among the subjects, with each one providing a fairly smooth curve.

Based on the work of ALTSHULER et al. (1967) and BROWN et al. (1950), there should be a size for maximum deposition in the alveolar region in the 1 to 3 μm range as total deposition decreases with decreasing size because of an increasing fractional exhalation of the inhaled particles. The data from mouth breathing tests shown in Figure 6 do not extend to small enough sizes to demonstrate such a maximum. In Figure 6, as well as in Figure 5, the data for subject number 8 have been extended by including six additional points derived from a series of inhalations through the nose. In the size range 2 to 5 μm, where there are both nose and mouth points, the data are in fair agreement, and the three nose breathing points below 2 μm show a long plateau rather than a maximum. Additional data with small particles are needed to clarify this point.

Regional Deposition in Bronchitics

Increased tracheobronchial deposition among bronchitics has also been reported recently by LOURENCO et al. (1969) and by THOMSON & SHORT (1969).

Lourenco used a gold-198 tagged ferric oxide test aerosol produced by a spinning disc generator of the LIPPMANN & ALBERT (1967) design, and made serial measurements of chest retention and distribution with a gamma camera. With 3 μm (unit density) particles, he found that bronchitics having a higher than normal airway resistance also had abnormally large early (two to four hour) bronchial clearance. While total (24 hour) bronchial clearance, i.e., tracheobronchial deposition, was not measured in all cases, the data reported by Lourenco on early bronchial clearance in bronchitics and normals are consistent with the data reported in this paper.

THOMSON & SHORT (1969) studied the mucociliary clearance of 5 μm diameter polystyrene particles produced with a spinning top of the MAY (1949) design and tagged with chromium-51 or technetium-99 m. Sixteen subjects inhaled 110 ml of aerosol in a single breath followed by three seconds of breath holding. Serial measurements of chest retention were made within a shadow-shield by a NaI (T1) scintillation detector with its collimator in contact with the chest. Five bronchitics and one asthmatic averaged 72% 24-hour clearance (range 57–81%), while three non-smoking normals averaged 58% 24-hour clearance (range 56–60), and two cigarette smoking normals had 40 and 69% 24-hour clearance.

It is difficult to make a valid comparison of the Thomson & Short data with the results reported in this paper. With a 110 ml breath and three seconds of breath holding, particle deposition should be largely confined to large airways and be due to sedimentation. This was partially confirmed in two subjects, where gamma camera measurements were made at 1·25 hours after inhalation. In both a normal and an asthmatic the retained particles were in airways below the trachea, with a more distal distribution in the normal. The deposition pattern for such a breathing protocol would differ radically from the deposition of similar particles during 1 liter breaths at 30 l/min, for which the deposition is primarily by impaction.

Significance of Increased Bronchial Deposition

All of the bronchitic patients tested were current or former heavy cigarette smokers. This is consistent with the association between cigarette smoking and chronic bronchitis cited in *Smoking and Health*, the report of the Advisory Committee to the Surgeon General of the Public Health Service (1964). The very high T-B depositions observed among the bronchitic patients, and the less high but still elevated T-B deposition among the "normal" cigarette smokers tested may be indicative of the natural progression of the disease syndrome called chronic bronchitis.

Bronchoconstriction in man can be caused by exposure to cigarette smoke as shown by Loomis (1956), Nadel & Comroe (1961), and Guyatt et al. (1970), or by exposure to inert dusts as shown by Dautrebande et al. (1948), and Dubois & Dautrebande (1958). The mechanisms involved have been discussed by Nadel et al. (1965), Nadel (1968) and Dubois (1969). Bronchoconstriction, by reducing the cross section for flow in the conductive airways, results in increased air velocities and turbulence. Increased velocity can result in greatly increased deposition by impaction at the airway bifurcations, while increased turbulence can account for an increase in deposition by eddy diffusion. Since surface area increases with depth in the lung, a proximal shift in the deposition pattern results in a much greater surface concentration of deposited particles.

When the surface concentration of irritant bearing particles is sufficiently high, it could produce either or both of two undesirable effects. It could cause still further bronchoconstriction, and/or it could disrupt the normal mucociliary cleansing mechanism, increasing the contact time between the irritant and the bronchial epithelium. Retardation of mucociliary clearance function by whole fresh cigarette smoke has been demonstrated in donkeys by Albert et al. (1969b). Abnormal and delayed mucociliary clearance patterns in human cigarette smokers have been described by Albert et al. (1969a) and by Albert et al. (1971). Such clearance abnormalities could be caused either by alterations in ciliary beat or in the properties of the mucous sheath. An increase in thickness of the mucus could affect deposition as well as clearance, by reducing the effective cross section for airflow.

SUMMARY AND CONCLUSIONS

The effect of particle size on aerosol deposition in the head, trachea, tracheo-bronchial tree and alveoli was studied in mouth breathing experiments on a group of 65 human subjects, including 14 normals who have never smoked cigarettes, 9 current cigarette smokers, 1 non-smoking asthmatic, and 6 bronchitic patients. The regional depositions were determined from external measurements of the gamma rays emitted by the deposited particles of ferric oxide which were tagged with gamma emitting isotopes. The measurements made immediately after the inhalation of the monodisperse test aerosol indicated the head, tracheal and whole lung depositions. Measurements made one day later indicated the fraction of the whole lung activity deposited in the alveoli.

The non-smoking subjects have been considered to be representative of the normal population with respect to regional deposition. The inhalation tests on these subjects demonstrated that for inhaled aerosols with aerodynamic diameters larger than 2 μm:

(1) Head deposition during mouth breathing takes place by impaction and does not vary greatly from subject to subject.
(2) Deposition in the trachea (including the tracheal bifurcation) is also due to impaction. As an impactor, the trachea is less efficient than the head, and there is a much greater variation in deposition efficiency among the individual subjects.
(3) Deposition in the entire tracheo-bronchial region is primarily due to impaction, but sedimentation produces a significant increment for aerodynamic sizes of the order of 2 μm and smaller. The T-B deposition for a given particle size varies greatly from subject to subject, which is most likely due to variations in airway diameters. Each individual subject had a characteristic size *vs.* deposition relation.
(4) Alveolar deposition decreased rapidly with increasing aerodynamic size above 5 μm. Between 2 and 5 μm there was much less variation with size.

The effects of smoking history and pre-existing lung disease on regional particle deposition was investigated by comparing deposition data from subjects who smoke or had lung disease with the comparable data for the non-smoking normals. The tracheo-bronchial deposition of 1 to 5 μm diameter particles was much higher in the asthmatic and the bronchitics than in non-smoking normals. It was so much higher that there was no overlap in the data even though both groups had a large variability. Some of the bronchitics had abnormally high tracheal deposition, but even in these cases, most of the increase in tracheo-bronchial deposition was in airways beyond the trachea.

As a group, the current cigarette smokers had higher tracheal and tracheo-bronchial depositions than the non-smoking normals. However, in this comparison, the differences were smaller than for the subjects with diagnosed lung disease, and since both groups had a large variability, there was considerable overlap in the data. Some of the cigarette smokers had tracheal and/or tracheo-bronchial depositions which were clearly abnormal. For others, tracheal and T-B depositions were within the normal range, but were dominantly within the upper limits of the normal range.

Cigarette smoke is known to produce bronchoconstriction, which would tend to produce a proximal shift in the deposition pattern of inhaled aerosols. The higher tracheal and T-B depositions observed for cigarette smokers in this study thus provides confirmation for this hypothesis.

A limited number of inhalation tests performed on cigar, pipe and ex-smokers did not yield any deposition data significantly different from that of non-smoking normals.

REFERENCES

ALBERT, R. E., LIPPMANN, M. & PETERSON, H. T., JR. (1971). This symposium, pp. 165–180.
ALBERT, R. E., LIPPMANN, M. & BRISCOE, W. (1969a). *Archs envir. Hlth* **18**, 738–755.
ALBERT, R. E., SPIEGELMAN, J. R., SHATSKY, S. & LIPPMANN, M. (1969b). *Archs envir. Hlth* **18**, 30–41.
ALTSHULER, B., PALMES, E. D. & NELSON, N. (1967). In: *Inhaled particles and vapours II*. Ed. C. N. Davies. Oxford, Pergamon Press, pp. 323–337.
BROWN, J. H., COOK, K. M., NEY, F. G. & HATCH, T. (1950). *Am. J. publ. Hlth* **40**, 450–458.
DAUTREBANDE, L., ALFORD, W. C., HIGHMAN, B., DOWNING, R. & WEAVER, F. L. (1948). *J. appl. Physiol.* **1**, 339–349.
DUBOIS, A. B. & DAUTREBANDE, L. (1958). *J. clin. Invest.* **37**, 1746–1755.
DUBOIS, A. B. (1969). *Envir. Res.* **2**, 397–403.
GUYATT, A. R., BERRY, G., ALPERS, J. H., BRAMLEY, A. C. & FLETCHER, C. M. (1970). *Am. Rev. resp. Dis.* **101**, 44–54.
LIPPMANN, M. & ALBERT, R. E. (1967). *Am. ind. Hyg. Ass. J.* **28**, 501–506.
LIPPMANN, M. & ALBERT, R. E. (1969). *Am. ind. Hyg. Ass. J.* **30**, 257–275.
LIPPMANN, M. (1970). *Ann. Otol. Rhinol. Lar.* **79**, 519–528.
LOOMIS, T. A. (1956). *Proc. Soc. exp. Biol. Med.* **92**, 337–340.
LOURENCO, R. V., ANDERSON, T. O. & LEVINE, H. (1969). Proceedings of the 61st Annual Meeting of the American Society for Clinical Investigation, Atlantic City, N.J., May 5, 1969. Abstract in *J. clin. Invest.* **48**, 53a.
MAY, K. R. (1949). *J. appl. Phys.* **20**, 932–938.
NADEL, J. A. (1968). *Archs envir. Hlth* **16**, 171–174.
NADEL, J. A. & COMROE, J. H. (1961). *J. appl. Physiol.* **16**, 713–716.
NADEL, J. A., SALEN, H., TAMPLIN, B. & TOKIWA, Y. (1965). *Archs envir. Hlth* **10**, 175–178.
THOMSON, M. L. & SHORT, M. D. (1969). *J. appl. Physiol.* **26**, 535–539.

DISCUSSION

S. E. DEVIR: You mention that subjects who were volunteers gave their informed consent. I have been told the story that some volunteers in other work suffered afterwards from breathing too-big an amount of radio-active sodium. Have you made any calculations of the risk that volunteers are taking, even with their consent, in making these experiments?

Dr. LIPPMANN: The maximum amount of radio-activity inhaled in each test was $0 \cdot 35$ μCi of Au–198 or 2 μCi of Tc–99 m. Volunteers generally get a standard chest X-ray examination before the test inhalation. In most cases they get more radiation dose from the X-rays than from the inhalation of the tagged particles. We have chosen our test technique because of its very low radiation dosage. If we used a gamma camera for retention measurements we would require at least two orders of magnitude more isotope. We feel that the radiation dosage received in our test inhalations is insignificant.

J. D. BRAIN: How was the percentage deposition in the three compartments measured? Why does the sum of the deposition percentages of a given particle size for all three compartments often add up to more than 100%? How do you measure the concentration of aerosol entering the trachea?

Dr. LIPPMANN: The total deposition is the sum of the head and chest burdens measured immediately after inhalation, and the exhaled aerosol collected in a filter canister. The head depositions were plotted as a % of this total. The % tracheal, tracheobronchial and alveolar depositions were based on the aerosol passing beyond the head and entering the trachea. This aerosol was assumed to be equal to the sum of the initial chest burden and the exhaled aerosol. This assumes that a negligible fraction of the aerosol leaving the trachea is lost in the mouth during exhalation. The tracheal deposition was based on the initial reading of the tracheal detector, corrected for the contribution from the activity in the surrounding lung. The tracheobronchial region, which includes the trachea, is part of the initial whole lung burden which was cleared within 24 hours. The alveolar deposition was the residual lung burden at 24 hours, corrected for radioactive decay. Sums of the percentage, in the head, tracheobronchial and alveolar regions can be greater than 100% because they represent percentages of different sums as discussed above. We do not actually measure the concentration of aerosol entering the trachea, but calculate it as discussed above.

G. W. DOLPHIN: Have you any data on the deposition of 1 μm diameter particles? We have a value of 40% from Dennis (p. 91) and a value of 20% measured by Muir (p. 81). There seems to be some doubt about the amounts deposited at this particle size.

Dr. LIPPMANN: The curves in the paper contain essentially all the data we have so far. They include very few tests at around 1 μm. We intend to do more tests in that range in the future. These will serve two purposes; to get data on regional deposition, and to get additional information on the kinetics of bronchial clearance from the smaller airways. With particles <3 μm you get less information on bronchial clearance because there is less bronchial deposition. It would be possible to increase the number of tests for regional deposition if we were to forgo measurements of clearance. It takes a full day of measurements to make one clearance test. If we were interested in deposition only, we would need only the initial measurement and one on the next day. On this basis we could do many tests each day.

M. NEWHOUSE: How long after inhaling aerosol were studies performed? Since the œsophagus passes behind the trachea, left mainstem bronchus and left lung, could not radioactivity swallowed both immediately after eating and drinking, or following clearance from the trachea during the 5 min. counting period, introduce error into the deposition measurements in spite of your obvious precautions?

Dr. LIPPMANN: The subjects are generally seated and the measurements begun within one minute. Some elderly subjects take slightly longer. There is not too much of a problem unless the subject swallows the head deposit before the initial chest measurement. After the first retention measurement the subject washes out the mouth deposit and eats some pastry which pushes material in the throat and œsophagus into the stomach. If the head deposit were allowed to dribble slowly down the œsophagus, this would create problems. We know what happens because the stomach detector is making a measurement at the same time as the lung detector, and provides a basis for correcting the raw lung count.

L. FRIBERG: What exact evidence do you have that there has been no significant alveolar clearance during the first 24 hours? The alveolar clearance rate might be bigger during the first hours than shown from your curves after 24 hours. If such early alveolar clearance is not insignificant then there might be an error in your bronchial deposition values. Why do you take the 24-hour value, and not the retention at some other time?

Dr. Lippmann: We do not have experimental evidence that there is no alveolar clearance in the first 24 hours. Our evidence indicates that essentially all of the first day's lung clearance passes through the trachea and stomach. It is certainly possible that some of the particles taking this clearance pathway originated in the alveoli and were somehow transported on to the ciliary escalator. However, if there is such a transport mechanism, it should work for all particle sizes. We have shown that 24 hour alveolar retention increases rapidly with decreasing size below 10 μ, reaching 80% at 3 μ for an average non-smoking normal. Certainly, much of the remaining 20% which is cleared via mucociliary transport within 24 hours, was deposited in the smaller ciliated airways by sedimentation. It follows that the proportion of the alveolar deposit which clears via the trachea within 24 hours is much less than 20%.

After 24 hours, the clearance rate is very slow. For most, but not all subjects, bronchial clearance is completed by 10 hours. However, for these subjects the differences between the 10 and 24 hour values are small and the use of the 24 hour value introduces little error.

EFFECT OF CHRONIC OBSTRUCTIVE PULMONARY DISEASE ON RATE OF DEPOSITION OF AEROSOLS IN THE LUNG DURING BREATH HOLDING*

E. D. PALMES, ROBERTA M. GOLDRING, CHIU-SEN WANG†
and BERNARD ALTSHULER

*Departments of Environmental Medicine and Medicine,
New York University Medical Center and The Chest Service,
Bellevue Hospital, New York, New York, U.S.A.*

Abstract — Previous work at this laboratory has demonstrated a change in deposition rate of aerosols in the human respiratory tract during breath holding in normal subjects at different degrees of lung inflation. In each subject it was found that the rate was lower when the lung volume at the time of breath holding was greater. This was attributed to the increased average size of the pulmonary spaces which necessitated longer time, on the average, for an aerosol particle to attain a wall. Because of destruction of alveolar walls in some patients with chronic obstructive pulmonary disease (COPD) and the resultant enlargement of air spaces, it was deemed advisable to extend the studies to patients with COPD. Groups of hospital patients were examined along with normal subjects. Differences, as well as similarities, between patients and normal subjects and their physiological implications are discussed.

INTRODUCTION

THE work to be presented represents an extension of the studies reported at the Second Symposium in this series (PALMES *et al.*, 1967). These studies dealt with the persistence (remaining airborne) of aerosol in the human respiratory tract during breath holding. The procedures, although modified somewhat, are quite similar to those used in earlier studies. It was shown that during breath holding aerosol disappeared exponentially with time of breath holding for about 0–30 s over the range of particle sizes of approximately $0·1$ to $1·0$ μm diameter. The particles were triphenyl phosphate, a non-hygroscopic, non-irritant material used at this laboratory for a number of years (ALTSHULER *et al.*, 1957; PALMES *et al.*, 1967). It was reported by PALMES *et al.* (1966) that the rate of loss of aerosol during breath holding was influenced by the degree of lung inflation at which the breath was held. These observations have been extended on normal subjects, but the results have not been

* This investigation was supported under Grant No. EC 00227, Environmental Control Administration, Consumer Protection and Environmental Health Service, and is part of a center program supported by the National Institute of Environmental Health Sciences Grant No. ES 00260.
† Present Address: Department of Chemical Engineering and Metallurgy, Syracuse University, Syracuse, New York 13210.

previously published. It appeared to be feasible to use the approach for the measurement of the dimensions of the lung air spaces accessible to aerosol in the hope that the observations might furnish a diagnostic criterion for characterizing chronic obstructive pulmonary disease (COPD). This presentation will include the data on effect of lung volume on persistence and preliminary results on normal subjects and patients with COPD.

RATIONALE

The basis for the approach used in these studies is that the rate of deposition of monodisperse aerosol particles during breath holding should vary inversely with the size of the air spaces in which the particles are contained during breath holding. It is presumed that an inhaled particle has a certain probability, designated p_{IN}, of reaching a particular locus within the air space of the respiratory tract during inhalation without hitting a wall. Similarly, an airborne particle in the respiratory tract at the beginning of exhalation has a probability, designated p_{EX}, of being exhaled without being deposited. If the breath is held, there is the third probability, p_H, that the particle will survive for the breath holding time without being deposited. If these three probabilities are independent of each other, then the product $p_{IN} \times p_H \times p_{EX}$ is the probability of that particle being exhaled on the particular breath, *i.e.* its persistence, P. It has been demonstrated experimentally both at our laboratory (Altshuler, 1969) and by Muir (1970) that after exhalation of twice the inhaled volume there is virtually a zero aerosol concentration in the exhaled air. In all of the studies to be reported, the maneuver requires an exhalation of a volume twice the inhaled volume.

The persistence was shown by Palmes et al. (1967) to be an exponential function of time of breath holding. Aerosol in the lungs during breath holding under defined conditions thus has half life, $t_{1/2}$, characteristic of the aerosol and the subject. The theory for the relationship of half life and size of spaces is not satisfactory as pointed out previously by Palmes et al. (1967) so that the term is used here to show an empirical relationship which is convenient for purposes of comparison.

EXPERIMENTAL

The apparatus and procedures were essentially the same as those used in previous studies; the final apparatus is described in detail elsewhere (Palmes & Wang, 1970). Essentially it is a "bag in a box" device with a system of valves which permits fixing the lung volume (LV) at which the breath is held at a value any desired volume less than the total lung capacity (TLC). If the breath is held at different volumes while maintaining constant inhaled and exhaled volume, then the average size of the lung spaces would be greater at larger volumes and it would be expected that the half life would be greater at the larger volumes. This was investigated as follows:

Effect of Lung Volume on $t_{1/2}$

Three normal subjects were examined for aerosol persistence when the breath was held at 3 to 5 volumes between TLC and residual volume (RV). Because of the volumes used, one litre inhaled and two litres exhaled, the lowest volume was required to be at least two litres greater than RV. The results for the three subjects are shown in Table I which gives for each run the particle diameter, the lung volume at which the breath was held, persistence of inhaled aerosol at zero time, *i.e.* without breath holding, and the measured half life. The lung volumes were measured by subtracting the volume calculated from the spirometer tracing for the particular breath and TLC (the breathing maneuver included inhalation to TLC) previously measured for the subject by helium dilution.

TABLE I. EFFECT OF LUNG VOLUME ON PERSISTENCE

Subject	Run	Particle Diameter (μm)	LV (l)	Aerosol Persistence at 0 Seconds	$t_{1/2}$ (s)
Alt.	7	0·56–0·60	4·6	0·83	16·9
			5·0	0·84	19·4
			5·4	0·87	21·7
			5·8	0·87	24·3
Mar.	27	0·53–0·58	3·4	0·81	9·1
			3·8	0·82	11·6
			4·2	0·83	13·2
			4·6	0·84	15·8
			5·0	0·84	17·0
Mar.	31	0·51–0·53	3·7	0·86	12·3
			4·3	0·86	15·2
			4·9	0·85	19·2
Pal.	28	0·50–0·55	4·8	0·73	13·7
			5·2	0·77	14·4
			5·6	0·80	16·0
			6·0	0·82	16·7
			6·4	0·84	21·0
Pal.	30	0·49–0·50	5·1	0·75	15·2
			5·7	0·78	17·0
			6·3	0·82	20·0

It is seen that the lung volume at which the breath is held has a much greater influence on the half life than on the persistence at 0 seconds. In other words, the handling of aerosol during the dynamic phase of the breathing maneuvre is relatively insensitive to the changes in volume when compared to the static phase during breath holding. In fact, the effect on half life is much greater than would be expected from the usual geometric considerations. This is shown in Figure 1 in which $t_{1/2}$ is plotted against lung volume at which the breath was held. First, it is seen that for all three subjects $t_{1/2}$ increases approximately linearly with LV. If the half life varies as an average linear dimension of the air spaces in which the aerosol is contained then the spaces would appear to be changing their internal dimensions in proportion to about the first power of the volume. This would not be true of either spherical nor elongated cylindrical spaces where the diameter would change as the 1/3 or 1/2 power of the volume. One could visualize the lung as inflating primarily by increasing the size of the alveolar ducts. This would be equivalent to separating two alveolated surfaces (increasing the duct size) rather than filling the alveoli while retaining a fixed duct size. Individual units would then approach the configuration of small bellows and would change their effective linear separations as volume was changed. In such a system RV would be the volume at which there is no separation. It is seen that $t_{1/2}$ extrapolated to zero is quite close to the measured residual volumes of subjects Alt. and Pal. The RV was not measured for subject Mar. but it was less than $1\cdot4$ litres.

It is recognized, of course, that the conducting airways play a role in establishing the half life. Using the model of WEIBEL (1963) the respiratory tract going from the

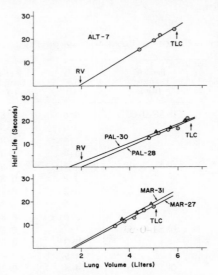

FIGURE 1. Effect of lung volume on aerosol persistence.

trachea to the 16th branching order decreases in size from approximately 18 mm to $0\cdot6$ mm, thereafter, going to the 23rd branching order, the size of the spaces decreases only to $0\cdot4$ mm. The total volume, mouth to 16th branching order, is approximately 200 ml. An inhaled volume of 1000 ml was chosen, therefore, to insure that most (about 80%) of the inhaled volume would be in the lung parenchema. In other words, an attempt was made to overwhelm the contribution of the conducting airways.

Preliminary Results on Normal Subjects and COPD Patients

Because of the rather long time and considerable number of breaths involved in the above studies, it was desirable to use only one volume and as few times of breath holding as possible to establish the slope of the persistence *vs*. time curve for a series of normal subjects as well as patients with COPD. These results are presented below.

It was the initial intent to use only a one litre inhalation and two litre exhalation and to measure breath holding at 0 and 15 seconds. It turned out that this was a somewhat difficult maneuvre for a number of patients both in terms of exhaled volume and time of breath holding. For this reason it was necessary to work with smaller volumes and at shorter times with some of the patients, and some could not be measured by the procedures described here. Obviously, it was necessary to work as close to TLC as possible. The results on two groups of patients and on normals are shown in Table II. The spirometric and nitrogen washout data are included for all where available. Inhaled aerosol volumes are given and the exhaled volume was twice

TABLE II. SPIROMETRY, NITROGEN WASHOUT AND AEROSOL HANDLING

Name	VC		FEV$_1$		RV		TLC		N$_2$ Washout			P at 0 sec.	t$_{1/2}$	Aer. Inh.
									End-tidal % N$_2$		Alv. % N$_2$			
	ml	% Pred.	ml	% VC	ml	% Pred.	ml	% Pred.	3 min	7 min	7 min	%	s	ml
Normal Subjects														
Alt.	4010	102	3790	94	1940	117	5950	106	1·5	0·4	0·6	93	23·2	1000
Pal.	4560	117	3740	82	2000	121	6560	118	2·1	0·9	—	86	23·5	1000
Wan.	3760	95	3210	85	1280	98	5040	96	—	—	—	92	22·3	1000
Blo.	4000	93	3430	85	1900	104	5900	97	—	—	—	89	25·2	1000
Bronchitis with Emphysema														
Gar.	1200	33	420	34	4310	260	5572	116	—	—	—	65	17·2	500
Sie.	2100	67	1310	62	4107	300	6207	138	—	—	—	75	18·2	750
Roc.	2960	86	2210	74	1914	129	4871	97	—	—	—	91	28·1	950
Rod.	2620	63	730	28	3627	235	6131	120	24·0	9·5*	6·0	76	26·4	900
Rap.	1770	53	650	37	4370	290	6138	126	8·5	4·0	10·7	89	53·4	500
Gib.	2650	72	1480	56	4510	290	7160	138	—	—	—	74	52·2	800
Coo.	1330	53	490	36	3345	320	4675	128	—	—	—	70	38·0	500
Sol.	2420	60	970	40	2084	206	4500	102	6·0	2·6	9·8	81	20·4	550
McG.	1980	51	1130	54	3507	210	5550	101	—	—	—	75	21·5	550
Emphysema without Bronchitis														
Viv.	3500	127	2400	55	3900	263	7400	150	4·9	1·4	—	85	23·2	1000
Sch.	4000	99	2000	50	2500	185	6500	122	—	—	—	85	23·4	1000
McF.	3450	95	1260	37	3800	242	7250	138	11·5	4·0	4·0	83	23·6	1000
Lyn.	3990	104	2320	58	3170	184	7160	129	—	—	—	80	50·4	1000
Dun.	3010	90	1550	51	3003	200	5820	124	3·0	0·9	1·4	76	43·1	1000

* Four minutes.

that inhaled in all cases. The series presented was studied in order to obtain preliminary results to determine if all, or any, of the patients behaved in a markedly
different manner than did the normals. The diagnoses on all of the patients were
based on routine spirometry, N_2 washout, x-ray and clinical appraisal. The patients
were classified on the basis of these observations as having predominantly airway
disease, e.g. chronic bronchitis with associated varying degrees of emphysema, or
predominantly parenchemal disease, e.g. emphysema without associated bronchitis
according to accepted criteria (Briscoe & Nash, 1965; Davis & McClement, 1968).

It is seen from Table II that the normal subjects inhaling one litre of triphenyl
phosphate aerosol of $0 \cdot 5$ to $0 \cdot 6$ μm diameter showed half lives of $22 \cdot 3$ to $25 \cdot 3$ s;
both of those tested had normal N_2 washout. None of the patients characterized as
primarily bronchitic were able to perform the one litre/two litre maneuvre and all
were necessarily run at smaller volumes. Two of these patients, Gar. and Sie., showed
short half lives in spite of their small inhaled volumes. Three, Rap., Gib. and Coo.,
showed long half lives, but in Rap. and Coo. the small (500 ml) volume inhaled makes
interpretation difficult because of the probable contribution of the airways. The other
bronchitic patient, Gib., almost certainly has an abnormally increased half life. The
persistence at 0 time was generally lower for this group than for the normals. All of
the N_2 washouts on this group were abnormal.

Of the five classified as emphysematous but not bronchitic, all were able to accomplish the one litre/two litre maneuvre. The most interesting results were those on
patients Lyn. and Dun. who showed half lives almost twice as great as the normals.
The persistence at 0 time for this group was also lower than normal. Two of the three
on whom N_2 washout was measured, including Dun., had normal values despite the
large RV and TLC.

DISCUSSION

The results on normal and COPD patients are considered to demonstrate real
promise for this proposed diagnostic procedure. It is apparent that persistence would
be influenced by the size of the lung spaces in which the aerosol resides during breath
holding. In emphysema, where there is destruction of lung tissue including actual
loss of alveolar walls, the distance to the wall would be increased and could provide
a mechanism for increasing the half life of particles in these spaces. The loci of the
enlarged spaces might have a marked influence, however, on persistence since the
spaces accessible to the aerosol could be quite different from those accessible to gas
molecules. In this connection it should be pointed out that the coefficient of diffusion
of $0 \cdot 5$ μm particles is of the order of 10^{-6} that of oxygen molecules. Thus the aerosol
has access almost exclusively to spaces where it can be brought by convection. For
example, it is possible that an emphysematous patient might have large unventilated
air spaces but might ventilate only essentially normal lung tissue by convection; in
this case the half life of the aerosol would be expected to be normal. If on the other
hand there is enlargement of the spaces more accessible to the inhaled tidal air, then
the half life would be expected to be prolonged. Thus, it is hoped that this technique
might provide additional information on distribution of ventilation in the emphysematous lung. Persistence of aerosol at 0 time was reduced for all of the patients with
COPD as compared to the normal subjects; there was no marked difference between
the primarily bronchitic or primarily emphysematous patients.

REFERENCES

ALTSHULER, B. (1969). Behaviour of airborne particles in the respiratory tract. In: *Circulatory and respiratory mass transport*. Ed. G. E. W. Wolstenholme & J. Knight. London, J. & A. Churchill. pp. 215–235.

ALTSHULER, B., YARMUS, L., PALMES, E. D. & NELSON, N. (1957). Aerosol deposition in the human respiratory tract. I. Experimental procedures and total deposition. *A.M.A. Archs. ind. Hlth.* **15**, 293–303.

BRISCOE, W. A. & NASH, E. S. (1965). The slow space in chronic obstructive pulmonary disease. *Ann. N.Y. Acad. Sci.* **121**, 706–722.

DAVIS, A. L. & MCCLEMENT, J. H. (1968). The course and prognosis of chronic obstructive pulmonary disease. Proc. Eleventh Aspen Emphysema Conf. pp. 219–234.

MUIR, D. C. F. (1970). The effect of airways obstruction on the single breath aerosol curve. In: *Airway dynamics*. Ed. A. Bouhuys. Springfield, Thomas. pp. 319–325.

PALMES, E. D., ALTSHULER, B. & NELSON, N. (1967). Deposition of aerosols in the human respiratory tract during breath holding. In: *Inhaled particles and vapours* II. Ed. C. N. Davies. Oxford, Pergamon Press. pp. 339–349.

PALMES, E. D., MARRERO, H. M. & ALTSHULER, B. (1966). Deposition of aerosols in the human respiratory tract as influenced by degree of lung inflation. *Physiologist, Wash.* **9**, 261 (Abstract).

PALMES, E. D. & WANG, C. S. (1970). An aerosol inhalation apparatus for human single breath deposition studies. Submitted to *Am. ind. Hyg. Ass. J.*

WEIBEL, E. R. (1963). *Morphometry of the human lung*. New York, Academic Press, p. 139.

DISCUSSION

D. C. F. Muir: This is a fascinating approach to the diagnosis of emphysema. Would you agree that you have a very long-term experiment since the final answer, at present, is only obtained at post mortem examination?

Prof. Palmes: I agree.

J. E. Cotes: A possible factor reducing the apparent difference in half-time between the normal subjects and the patients with lung disease is that the patients, on account of obstruction to the lung airways, exhale at a lower rate. This effect has been assessed quantitatively by my colleagues Messrs. K. Houston and M. J. Saunders. They found for 12 normal young adults who inhaled approximately 2·0 l of 0·7 μm particles from FRC under standard conditions, that the deposition increased linearly with the duration of exhalation; the mean increase with time was 0·8 %/s. This is, on average, half the rate observed by Dr. Palmes and by ourselves for similar subjects in whom the deposition was increased by breath-holding; for our subjects the average increase during breath-holding was 1·66 %/s (half-time 18·2 s). These results suggest that a correction can be made for the effect on the half-time in the patients of a slow expiration. I wonder if Dr. Palmes has considered this possibility and if so if use of the correction would increase the number of patients in whom the half-time for breath-holding was increased?

Prof. Palmes: We attempted in all our studies to keep the manoeuvre the same for all breaths for a given subject, and we only used data from breaths in which the subject exhaled twice the inhaled volume in a reasonably short time. Because of this we were not able to get satisfactory data on a number of patients. If it were possible, as you suggest, to derive a correction for aerosol loss during prolonged exhalations, it would make the breath-holding procedure described applicable to many more patients with COPD. I might add that we have given this some thought and are inclined to agree that it should be feasible to make such a correction.

AEROSOL DEPOSITION IN THE LUNGS OF COALWORKERS

R. G. Love, D. C. F. Muir and K. F. Sweetland

Institute of Occupational Medicine, Edinburgh, Scotland

Abstract — Measurements of the deposition of 1 μm diameter aerosols in the lungs of two groups of coalworkers with and without simple pneumoconiosis have been carried out during steady state breathing using a modified La Mer-Sinclair generator.

It was shown that there was little or no difference in the amount of aerosol deposited at a given tidal volume for the two groups. However, there was a wide range of values within each group.

It is concluded that pneumoconiosis is unlikely to be caused by a high rate of dust deposition *per se* and that the deposition rate does not increase once X-ray changes of simple pneumoconiosis have developed.

INTRODUCTION

ALTHOUGH it has been recognized for many years that coalworkers' pneumoconiosis is caused by the accumulation of airborne dust in the lungs, very little is known of the relative importance of the factors which determine the development of the disease by an individual miner. The most important factor is the concentration of inhaled dust (JACOBSEN *et al.*, 1971). Other considerations include:

1. Physiological factors affecting the amount of dust deposited in the alveoli.
   (a) Minute ventilation (HADDEN *et al.*, 1967).
   (b) Tidal volume and frequency of breathing.
   (c) Percentage of inhaled dust deposited in the lung.
   (d) Regional pattern of lung deposition.
2. Rate of removal of dust from the alveoli.
3. Individual reaction to alveolar dust.

Individual variation in the percentage deposition of inhaled dust was first noted in three normal subjects by ALTSHULER *et al.* (1957). At a constant tidal volume and breathing frequency they showed that there was a consistently higher rate of particle deposition in the lungs in some subjects compared to others. We have investigated this problem in coalworkers in order to determine whether there is any evidence that miners with simple pneumoconiosis have a higher rate of dust deposition in their lungs when compared with those whose chest x-rays are normal despite apparently similar dust exposure. This is clearly a matter of considerable practical importance in dealing with a disease which must be eliminated by prevention rather than by cure and where acceptable dust standards are aimed at safeguarding the health of all underground workers. In this study we have used an experimental aerosol to investigate possible individual differences in rates of deposition.

METHODS

The experimental aerosol consisted of approximately uniform spheres (1·0 μm in diameter) of di-2-ethyl hexyl sebacate (rel. density = 0·918 g/cm³) produced in a modified La Mer-Sinclair generator (Muir, 1965). The subject inhaled the aerosol through a mouthpiece attached to a Tyndallometer (Muir & Davies, 1967) which continuously monitored the concentration of aerosol in the inspired and expired air by means of a photomultiplier measuring light scattered at a right angle. The expired air flow was recorded by a Fleisch (1925) pneumotachograph and a differential pressure transducer (Mercury Type M3). The outputs from this and the photo-multiplier were recorded on punched tape at approximately 0·1 s intervals by means of an electronic sample and hold device and a digital voltmeter. Continuous chart records of the aerosol concentration and expired airflow were also made. The apparatus is illustrated in Figure 1.

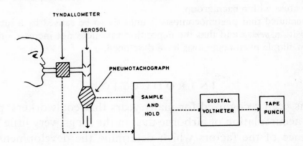

FIGURE 1. Diagram of apparatus.

The particle size was measured by observing the higher order Tyndall spectra (La Mer & Sinclair, 1943). All the airstreams were maintained at body temperature (37° C) and were fully saturated with water vapour. This avoided the necessity for inhaled/exhaled volumetric correction factors.

SUBJECTS

The experimental subjects were 58 coalworkers selected from the South Scottish coalfields. All men still at work in the industry who were known to have been certified as having category 2 simple pneumoconiosis (I.L.O. scale) and who lived within a reasonable distance of the laboratory were invited to take part in the trial. This group consisted of 18 men. A second group of 40 men from the same pits, matched for age and occupational history but with normal chest x-rays, were selected to act as controls.

The individual X-rays were mixed and examined by an experienced reader (Dr. S. Rae) who confirmed the original readings. The 18 men with category 2 pneumoconiosis represented about half the total number of men with this degree of pneumoconiosis from a total population of 7260 miners. This figure is in keeping with the well-known low prevalence of the disease in Scotland (HICKS *et al.*, 1961). The details of the subjects are shown in Table I.

TABLE I. MEANS STANDARD DEVIATIONS AND RANGES OF ANTHROPOMETRIC DATA, LUNG FUNCTIONS AND OCCUPATIONAL HISTORY FOR TWO GROUPS OF COALWORKERS

	No. of subjects	Age (yr)	Height (cm)	Weight (kg)
X-ray Category 2	18	58·5 ± 6·2 (50–64)	170 ± 1 (155–179)	76 ± 14·6 (57–95)
X-ray Category 0	40	58·4 ± 5·0 (48–64)	168 ± 1 (156–186)	73 ± 8·2 (45–92)

	F.E.V.$_{1·0}$ (l)	F.V.C. (l)	No. of years underground	No. of years at the face
X-ray Category 2	2·45 ± 0·71 (0·92–3·55)	3·66 ± 0·78 (2·32–5·02)	42·7 ± 6·3 (28–51)	34·3 ± 13·3 (20–51)
X-ray Category 0	2·71 ± 0·53 (1·73–4·00)	3·94 ± 0·73 (2·77–5·72)	40·4 ± 9·5 (11–51)	34·6 ± 15·2 (4–50)

EXPERIMENTAL PROCEDURE

The subject sat on a bicycle ergometer and was asked to breathe in time to a metronome at 15 breaths per minute at rest and while pedalling against workloads ranging between 100 and 700 kg.m/min. Each subject pedalled the bicycle until in the steady state (3 minutes), the first two minutes while breathing clean, filtered air and the third minute breathing aerosol. During the succeeding twenty breaths the inspired and expired aerosol concentrations and expired air flow were recorded.

Some subjects had difficulty in maintaining the higher workloads and others the rate of breathing, in which case they completed the highest workload which they could maintain at 15 breaths per minute.

CALCULATION OF RESULTS

The amount of aerosol expired was calculated in arbitrary units by integrating (Simpson's Rule) with an I.C.L. 1904 computer the instantaneous readings of airflow and aerosol concentration. The amount of aerosol inspired was derived in the same units from the product of the inspired aerosol concentration and the integral of the expired flow. The assumption that the volume of air inhaled is the same as that exhaled is not strictly true if the respiratory exchange ratio is less than unity. During exercise it approaches unity but at rest it may be as low as 0·8; in this case the amount of aerosol expired would be over-estimated by a maximum of 0·5% which is small enough to be neglected.

There may also be a change in the mean lung volume between one breath and the next, so that the exhaled volume is not equal to the inhaled volume during a single respiratory cycle. The mean lung volume must remain constant on average during steady state exercise, however, and there is unlikely to be any significant error when the results are averaged over 20 breaths. The deposition of aerosol in the lungs was calculated by subtraction and expressed as a percentage of the inhaled amount.

A correction was made to account for the dead space of the apparatus, since the first part of the inspired breath did not contain aerosol at the full inspired concentration. The concentration of the first part of the inspired aerosol was considered to be equal to the end tidal concentration and, although it is probably slightly greater than this, no significant error is likely to arise from this assumption. The dead space of the mouthpiece assembly was measured by pouring water into it through the mouthpiece after sealing the inlet and outlet valves and was found to be 50 cm³.

RESULTS

An example of a recording of inspired and expired aerosol concentration and expired air flow is shown in Figure 2. Average percentage deposition was calculated for each subject at four workloads and the results plotted graphically against tidal volume (Figure 3). In the majority of cases deposition increased or showed little

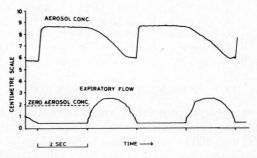

FIGURE 2. Example of recording of steady state breathing of aerosol.

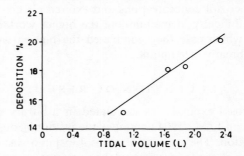

FIGURE 3. Effect of tidal volume on deposition at 15 breaths/minute.

change with tidal volume, while a few subjects showed a slightly decreased deposition as tidal volume increased. The slopes of deposition against tidal volume were calculated using the method of least squares and linear regression equations were thus obtained for each subject.

The fractional deposition at a standardized tidal volume of 1·6 1 (B.T.P.S.) was calculated for each subject and the frequency distribution plotted for the two groups of pneumoconiotic and control subjects (Figure 4). At this tidal volume the mean deposition is 20·9% for the control group and 21·3% for the pneumoconiotic group. The average deposition at tidal volumes of 1·0 and 2·2 1 was 19·8% and 22·1%

for the normal group and 19·4% and 23·1% for the pneumoconiotics, the latter being a slightly greater but insignificant rate of increase of deposition with volume. Therefore at tidal volumes within the normal working range there is no more than a difference of 1% fractional deposition between the two groups.

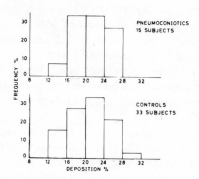

FIGURE 4. Histograms of percentage deposition at tidal volume of 1·6 litres for pneumoconiotic and control subjects.

DISCUSSION

Individual variation in the fractional deposition of aerosols, ranging in diameter from 0·14 to 3·2 μm, in the lungs of man was first noted by ALTSHULER et al. (1957). It is possible that such a variation could be a factor contributing towards the development and progression of lung diseases caused by inhalation and retention of respirable particulate matter. Coalworkers' pneumoconiosis is an obvious case where men are exposed continuously over a long period of time to airborne dust.

An aerosol consisting of 1 μm diameter particles was chosen, because such particles are well within the range for maximum penetration to the alveolar regions. 1–2 μm diameter is also the optimum size for particles in the development of fibrosis in diseases such as silicosis. From a practical point of view such particles are close to the maximum size that can be measured by observing the higher order Tyndall spectra.

It can be seen immediately that there is little difference in the range of deposition of 1 μm diameter aerosols in the lungs of coalworkers with or without simple pneumoconiosis. The frequency distributions are very similar for both groups with no apparent bias in favour of higher deposition in the pneumoconiotic group.

It cannot be assumed from the data presented that there are no differences in deposition between the groups when using particles of other sizes. The studies of ALTSHULER et al. (1957; 1967) indicate that such differences are unlikely since in a particular group of subjects those with high deposition for one size invariably exhibit high deposition at other sizes also. Different breathing rates could also influence the relative deposition rates but it is likely that results similar to those presented here would be found.

The mean F.E.V.$_1$ was 2·45 ± 0·71 l for the pneumoconiotic group and 2·71 ± 0·53 l for the normals. This difference, although not significant for the small size of the sample, is in keeping with the change recognized in large surveys by previous workers

(Gilson *et al.*, 1955; Rogan *et al.*, 1961; Ashford *et al.*, 1968). It is clear that the small change in ventilatory capacity associated with simple pneumoconiosis of the pinhead or micronodular type is insufficient to cause any noticeable alteration in the fraction of aerosol deposited in the respiratory system.

More severe airway obstruction has been shown to have considerable effects on the behaviour of inhaled aerosols (Muir, 1970). For a group of normal subjects (F.E.V.$_1$ = 111% of predicted) and a group of asthmatic and bronchitic patients (F.E.V.$_1$ = 27% of predicted) the amount of $0\cdot5$ μm diameter aerosol recoverable in a single breath was found to be about 80% and 50% respectively for an inhaled volume of $1\cdot2$ l (B.T.P.S.). Studies of aerosol breathing in the steady state have not yet been presented for a group with such severe ventilatory impairment but it is likely that there would be a pronounced difference in deposition rates between this and a normal group of subjects.

Brown *et al.* (1950), Altshuler *et al.* (1957), Dautrebande & Walkenhorst (1961), Dennis (1961) and Beeckmans (1964) have reported deposition rates ranging from 26% to 53% for 1 μm diameter aerosols. The wide range of results illustrates the technical difficulty of carrying out their inhalation experiments. Our results are lower than those values obtained by other authors but are clearly consistent and are based on over 240 experiments with 58 subjects. In each experiment twenty breaths were examined. The comparative values obtained between the two groups are certainly reliable. The ratio between the highest and lowest values in the two groups is about twofold but confirmation that this is a consistent finding must await further experiments on selected individuals.

The results show that there is no difference in the amount of 1 μm diameter particles which deposit in the lungs of coalworkers with or without simple pneumoconiosis. Jacobsen *et al.* (1971) have found that the progression of pneumoconiosis depends upon the concentration of inhaled dust and on the X-ray category of pneumoconiosis. Those men who have developed X-ray changes are more likely to progress than those whose X-rays are normal. Our results suggest that the development of pneumoconiosis is unlikely to be related to an initially high rate of dust deposition *per se* and that the presence of dust in the lungs does not increase the deposition rate.

Acknowledgements — The calculation of the results for this investigation involved the analysis of a large amount of data and we would like to express our sincere thanks to Mr. R. C. Steele for patiently writing the computer programme and for organizing the subsequent analysis. Our thanks are also due to the miners who co-operated during the course of the investigation.

REFERENCES

Altshuler, B., Palmes, E. D. & Nelson, N. (1967). In: *Inhaled Particles and vapours* II. *Ed.* C. N. Davies. Oxford, Pergamon Press, pp. 323–337.
Altshuler, B., Yarmus, L., Palmes, E. D. & Nelson, N. (1957). *A.M.A. Archs ind. Hyg.* **15**, 293–303.
Ashford, J. R., Brown, S., Morgan, D. C. & Rae, S. (1968). *Am. Rev. resp. Dis.* **97**, 810–826.
Beeckmans, J. M. (1965). *Can. J. Physiol. Pharmac.* **43**, 157–172.
Brown, J. H., Cook, K. M., Ney, F. G. & Hatch, T. (1950). *Am. J. publ. Hlth*, **40**, 450–458.
Dautrebande, L. & Walkenhorst, W. (1961). In: *Inhaled particles and vapours*. *Ed.* C. N. Davies. Oxford, Pergamon Press, pp. 110–121.
Dennis, W. L. (1961). Discussion of Paper by C. N. Davies. In: *Inhaled particles and vapours*. *Ed.* C. N. Davies. Oxford, Pergamon Press, pp. 88–91.

Fleisch, A. (1925). *Pflügers Arch. ges. Physiol.*, **209**, 713–722.

Gilson, J. C. & Hugh-Jones, P. (1955). *Spec. Rep. Ser. med. Res. Coun.*, (290).

Hadden, G. G., Jones, C. O. & Morgan, D. C. (1967). In: *Inhaled particles and vapours* II. *Ed.* C. N. Davies. Oxford, Pergamon Press, pp. 37–48.

Hicks, D., Fay, J. W. J., Ashford, J. R. & Rae, S. (1961). *The relation between pneumoconiosis and environmental conditions*, London, National Coal Board.

Jacobsen, M., Rae, S., Walton, W. H. & Rogan, J. M. (1971). This Symposium, pp. 903–917.

La Mer, V. K. & Sinclair, D. (1943). O.S.R.D. 1668, Div. 10–501, 11–M6.

Muir, D. C. F. (1965). *Ann. occup. Hyg.* **8**, 233–238.

Muir, D. C. F. (1970). In: *Airway dynamics. Ed.* A. Bouhuys. Springfield, Thomas, pp. 319–325.

Muir, D. C. F. & Davies, C. N. (1967). *Ann. occup. Hyg.* **10**, 161–174.

Rogan, J. M., Ashford, J. R., Chapman, P. J., Duffield, D. P. & Fay, J. W. J. (1961). *Br. med. J.* **1**, 1337–1342.

DISCUSSION

W. T. Ulmer: Perhaps you will find differences between non-coalworkers and coalworkers and also for other lung function studies, for example, PA_{0_2} and a measurement of mixing. There are practically no differences between coal miners with or without X-ray signs of pneumoconiosis, but there are clear differences between dust-exposed and non-dust-exposed workers.

Mr. Love: We do not have any results on non-coalworkers at present. We have, as I have shown, matched the two populations for age and occupational history, so that the main difference between the groups was the degree of pneumoconiosis. However, that is an interesting point which we would hope to investigate and clarify.

J. E. Cotes: One factor contributing to deposition of particles is the possible co-existence of lung disease. Would the speaker care to comment on his selection of subjects from this point of view?

Mr. Love: The presence of lung disease other than simple pneumoconiosis was not a factor influencing the selection of subjects. However, we have looked at the lung function for each subject and it would appear, although the results are not presented here, that there is a higher percentage of aerosol deposition in those with abnormal lung function.

M. Lippmann: Your data were for 1 μm particles and you showed that there was no significant difference in deposition between the two groups. Have you given any thought to using large particles where there might be a difference in deposition?

Mr. Love: Naturally we would like to extend the studies to include larger particle sizes, but we do not have any results at the moment, so that I cannot enlarge on this.

A. G. Heppleston: Although the dust deposition rate may not increase with the development of simple pneumoconiosis, my histological studies in rats with pneumoconiosis suggest that particles subsequently inhaled may penetrate more readily to the periphery of the lung acinus, where they may remain to exert a deleterious effect.

Dr. Muir: We were measuring total deposition only. I do not think that it is possible to estimate alveolar deposition solely from the exhaled aerosol concentration curve.

I would also like to pay tribute to Dr. J. T. Arlidge, a Staffordshire physician, who wrote in 1892: "Persons pre-disposed to respiratory diseases and phthisis ought not to engage in dusty occupations". We are trying to follow his advice and pick out those individuals, perhaps with an alveolar disease such as emphysema, who are more likely to develop coalworkers' pneumoconiosis.

J. C. Gilson: Did you find any difference between Category 0 and Category 2 among subjects who were also without bronchitis, since this may be an important factor.

Mr. Love: I did not mention the influence of bronchitis specifically in the paper. We are still analysing some of the results, so that I cannot give a definite answer to that, although at a preliminary inspection it would appear that most of the bronchitic subjects exhibited a higher than average deposition for particles of 1 μm diameter. We do intend to look at a group of non-coal workers with bronchitis of varying severity for this reason with regard to variations in deposition rates at different particle sizes.

J. D. Brain: I am not sure that the present study answers the question of whether individual differences in aerosol deposition might determine the development of pneumoconiosis by a miner. Ideally, this question could best be answered by examining aerosol deposition in the pre-employment period in persons not yet exposed to coal dust and not yet having lung disease. Then these persons (divided into those having high aerosol depositions and those having low aerosol depositions) could be followed during their exposure to coal dust to see whether the incidence of lung disease differed.

In the present study it is possible, although admittedly improbable, that the persons with category 2 pneumoconiosis initially had abnormally higher aerosol depositions prior to the development of their disease. Then the pathological lesions associated with the pneumoconiosis may have lowered aerosol deposition back toward normal values. Palmes (this symposium) has suggested that emphysema can decrease aerosol deposition because of increased alveolar dimensions. Thus the presence of the disease itself may have altered the original deposition characteristics of the lungs.

Mr. Love: Obviously we would have liked to have followed a group of coalworkers from pre-employment over a period of several years underground. But as pneumoconiosis takes a long time to develop this is not a practical proposition. However, the fact that we have demonstrated that there is no difference in deposition between pneumoconiotics and non-pneumoconiotics on the one hand and that there does appear to be a difference between those with and without abnormal lung function on the other hand (not here presented) partially answers that, I think. I would take you up on the point that emphysema decreases aerosol deposition. Palmes' results would seem to show that although the particles may persist longer during breathholding the deposition (persistence at 0 time) is greater than normal in these same subjects rather that reduced, similar to the bronchitics.

SECTION II
PULMONARY CLEARANCE

CLEARANCE FUNCTION OF THE RESPIRATORY CILIATED EPITHELIUM IN NORMAL AND BRONCHITIC RATS

J. IRAVANI

Aus der Medizinischen Abteilung des Silikose-Forschungsinstitut der Bergbau-Berufsgenossenschaft Bochum, W. Germany
(Chefarzt: Professor Dr. W. T. Ulmer)

INTRODUCTION AND METHODS

MOST investigations on ciliary activity and mucus transportation have been carried out utilizing nasal epithelium, trachea or isolated portions of bronchi (ANTWEILER, 1956; BALLENGER, 1949; DALHAMN, 1956; HILDING, 1965; KILBURN, 1968; RYLANDER, 1966). Because of the difficulties in achieving *in vitro* conditions with an intact tracheo-bronchial tree, the most important questions concerning distal mucociliary activity had not been solved. We have developed an *in vitro* method of studying the muco-ciliary clearance function in the entire intact tracheobronchial tree of the rat (IRAVANI, 1967), and would like to present some of the pertinent observations made in the past few years. In brief, our method consists of rapidly isolating inflated lungs from anesthetized animals and then continuing the dissection under ice-cold saline. All intrathoracic structures are removed leaving the heart lobe in communication with the trachea for further examination. The specimen, mounted in a jacketed bath and bathed in Krebs solution (KREBS & HENSELEIT, 1932), can be studied under strict control of environmental conditions. Mucociliary activity can be observed through the intact tracheobronchial wall by means of incident light microscopy. In ideally prepared specimens mucociliary function could be studied for up to five hours. Two groups of animals were used: one consisted of normal animals, the others had bronchitis.

RESULTS

Normal Rats

In normal rats ciliary activity was observed in all portions of the airway except in the distal 50–100 μm of the terminal bronchioles. Although the general direction of the effective stroke of the ciliary beat was observed to be cranially, it was noticed that individual groups of cells had a distinct organization. These individual groups of ciliated cells, because of a peculiar multicellular coordination, were named meta-chronal fields (IRAVANI, 1969). The metachronal fields were very irregular in shape and varied extremely in size, from a few cells to several hundreds. In most instances, ciliary beat was organized metachronously in the cranial direction and synchronously

143

at right angles to this axis. All metachronal fields, even though they were almost contiguous, were differently organized in respect of ciliary frequency, amplitude and direction of beat, which may diverge as much as 180° from the direction of beat in other metachronal fields. The frequency of ciliary beat was location dependent, increasing progressively with the distance from the terminal bronchioles upwards. At a bath temperature of 35° C the ciliary frequency measured stroboscopically was 360–420 beats/min in the terminal bronchioles whereas in the midtrachea it was measured at 1200–1300 beats/min. This represents an approximately three-fold increase of the frequency in the trachea as compared to the terminal bronchioles. Contrary to general assumptions based on the work of LUCAS & DOUGLAS (1934), we have not ever observed a continuous mucus blanket in any portion of the bronchial tree in normal healthy rats. Mucus was transported in the form of individual homogeneous flakes varying in size from about 4 μm to 70 μm, or as aggregations of several of these flakes which we have termed plaques (IRAVANI & VAN AS, 1970). In larger airways these plaques tend to coalesce and are transported in streams over the ascending metachronal fields. These streams are most clearly defined in the trachea. However the individual small flakes reflect the mode of transport from one metachronal field to another more accurately. It could be observed that these flakes followed the metachronal direction from one contiguous field to another, clearly describing a zigzag path cranially. Mucus transport as result of the ciliary activity does not only vary in velocity at different levels of the airway, but also varies in closely adjacent areas at the same level. Another important factor determining the velocity of transportation is the size of mucus component being transported. Although for practical purposes the majority of transport is in the form of plaques, we have decided for the sake of analysis and comparison of mucus transport velocities, to measure only the velocity of flakes of 14–20 μm in diameter. Thus, using this parameter of measurement, the velocity of transport increased progressively cranially, and was found to be about 20–40 times greater in the trachea than in terminal bronchioles: Figure 1.

Rats with Bronchitis

On examining the secretion in the trachea of bronchitic rats, it was found to be mucopurulent in all cases. Macroscopically, patchy opacities and thickening were

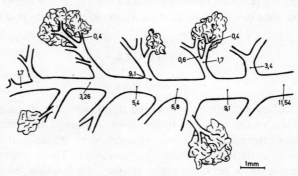

FIGURE 1. Reproduction of the main bronchus, side bronchi and a few peripheral airways in the heart lobe of the rat. Figures represent the average velocities of mucus transport in mm/min at various levels of the system. (Temperature: 37°C.)

observed on the trachea and major bronchi. Histological examination of these areas revealed the typical features of bronchitis and peribronchitis. The epithelium under-lying these patches could be studied after this thick adherent peribronchial tissue had been dissected off. In general, abnormalities of mucociliary activity were confined to these areas of bronchitis and peribronchitis, the rest of the intervening mucosa showing normal patterns with an overall accelerated function.

Two main abnormalities of mucus transport were observed: firstly, there were numerous areas of stasis of mucus; and secondly, where mucus movement was present in these patches, the flakes were seen to move in a rotary fashion without being transported from that spot: Figure 2. Occasionally this resulted in whirlpool forma-tion. Usually no ciliary activity was noticed in the areas of mucus stasis, but it could be activated under certain circumstances. In the areas where abnormal mucus transport occurred, a coordinated reversal of the direction of the effective stroke of the ciliary beat was observed in numerous adjacent metachronal fields. In addition to this ciliary reversal, abnormalities of multicellular coordination and ciliary beat form were frequently present.

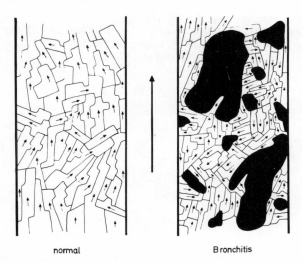

normal   Bronchitis

FIGURE 2. Schematic representation of metachronal fields in the ciliated epithelium of normal rats (left) and rats with bronchitis (right). The small arrows represent the direction of mucus transportation over a single metachronal field. The outlines illustrate the variability in size and shape of the metachronal fields. In the normal situation it can be seen that the general direction of transport is cranially (the arrow in the center of the figure represents the direction of the cranial flow). On the right the shaded areas represent the inactive zones. As well as this the coordinated ciliary reversal is well demonstrated.

SUMMARY AND CONCLUSIONS

From our observations three main conclusions may be drawn:

1. In spontaneously occurring bronchitis in rats the pathology is generally localized in patchy areas and the intervening ciliated epithelium may exhibit normal function, but is more frequently hyperactive.
2. Specific abnormalities of the ciliary mechanism appear to be associated with

bronchitis. These consist of inactive ciliated cells and of alterations in some characteristic features of ciliary movement.

3. In considering the pathogenesis of bronchitis, we would like to postulate that the primary event is the occurrence of an abnormality in the ciliary mechanism. A variety of specific or non-specific stimuli may impair ciliary function and allow the penetration of viral or bacterial agents which give rise to the classical inflammatory processes.

REFERENCES

ANTWEILER, H. (1956). *Beitr. Silikoseforsch.* **2**, 509–535.

BALLENGER, J. J. (1949). *Ann. Otol. Rhinol. Lar.* **58**, 351–369.

DALHAMN, T. (1956). *Acta physiol. scand.* **36**, Suppl. 123, 1–161.

HILDING, A. C. (1965). *Medna thorac.* **22**, 329–345.

IRAVANI, J. (1967). *Pflügers Arch. ges. Physiol.* **297**, 221–237.

IRAVANI, J. (1969). *Pflügers Arch. ges. Physiol.* **305**, 199–209.

IRAVANI, J. & VAN AS, A. (1970). (In preparation.) Mucus transportation in normal and bronchitic rats.

KILBURN, K. H. (1968). *Am. Rev. resp. Dis.* **98**, 449–463.

KREBS, A. & HENSELEIT, K. (1932). *Hoppe-Seyler's Z. physiol. Chem.* **210**, 33–66.

LUCAS, A. M. & DOUGLAS, L. C. (1934). *Archs Otolar.* **20**, 518–541.

RYLANDER, R. (1966). *Am. Rev. resp. Dis.* **93** (Suppl.), 67–85.

DISCUSSION

C. R. RYLANDER: This is a beautiful paper which provides much needed information on the effects of exposure. I would however like to question your conclusion that the primary event in the chain of abnormality leading to chronic bronchitis is an effect on the beating of cilia. Our own studies on cigarette smoke, SO_2, dust particles, ozone and other agents show that the effect on the cilia is not found until the exposure level reaches excessive heights. An alternation of the mucus flow does however occur even at fairly low levels, first as an acceleration and later as a decrease. As you have studied only late effects and indeed wash away the mucus layer, it would not be possible to draw any conclusions as to which abnormality occurred first.

Dr. IRAVANI: In some experiments on bronchitic rats I rinsed the epithelial surface with Krebs-solution by means of a micropipette and washed the mucus away. The abnormalities of the ciliary mechanism persisted, although there was no mucus then present. I therefore think the impairment of the ciliary function is the primary event and not the consequence of the altered mucus composition.

Furthermore, I made some observations in rats with acute bronchial catarrh in which the clinical signs showed that the acute bronchitis had existed for only a few days. Although there were no gross anatomical changes of the bronchial wall the ciliary mechanism of numerous ciliated cells was altered.

H. W. SCHLIPKOTER: Did you induce bronchitis in the rats experimentally and which method did you use? If you used animals which had developed bronchitis spontaneously, I should like to ask how you differentiated between animals with and without bronchitis before examination of the mucociliary activity. Was the diagnosis of bronchitis based on clinical examination of the rats or did you base it exclusively on subsequent histological changes in the bronchial tubes.

Dr. IRAVANI: We diagnosed bronchitis clinically. Approximately 50% of originally SPF-rats showed under our normal stall conditions clinical signs of airway catarrh with sniffing, sneezing and pulmonary crepitations. If these animals were studied within a few days, the ciliary mechanism of many of the ciliated cells, which were very widely dispersed throughout the tracheo-bronchial tree, was altered. However, no gross histological changes in the bronchial wall were observed. If the rats which had had acute bronchial catarrh were examined after some months, the alterations of the ciliary mechanisms were confined to areas with histopathological signs of chronic bronchitis. The slides I showed were prepared from the airways of chronic bronchitis rats.

J. C. MARTIN: Have you noted any correlation between the modified ciliary dynamics you have just described and the histological changes in the ciliated epithelium?

Dr. IRAVANI: We have not studied the areas with altered ciliary mechanism electromicrographically.

H. ANTWEILER: You described the disturbance of the ciliary action of the bronchial epithelium as the primary change occurring during the development of bronchitis in the rat. According to the results of my own tests with rats, the primary damage consists of a change in the mucus of the bronchi. The disturbance of the ciliary action, particularly the co-ordination of movement, is only of a secondary nature.

Dr. IRAVANI: We found that the abnormalities in ciliary function persisted after the mucus had been washed away. In other experiments we applied solutions of methylcellulose of varying viscosities upon the ciliated bronchial epithelium. With high viscosities the amplitude of the ciliary beat diminished. We never observed any alterations in the direction of the ciliary beat. Neither to my knowledge has "ciliary reversal" ever been produced in the tracheobronchial ciliated epithelium experimentally. As a result, I am inclined to believe that the alteration of the ciliary function is not the consequence of abnormal mucus, rather it might be the direct result of the foreign agents which give rise to bronchitis.

M. NAVRATIL: In my opinion you have described a condition of acute bronchitis rather than a chronic one. In humans however the chronic process is the more important. Is it possible to draw any conclusions about it on the basis of your experiments?

Dr. IRAVANI: Pathologists I consulted told me that histological changes practically identical to those I showed in my slides are present in the chronic bronchitis of man. Most of the animals we examined were chronic bronchitic rats.

S. E. DEVIR: You mentioned homogeneous flakes, but I would question whether they are homogeneous flakes when you have a size range of from 4 to 70 μm.

Have you observed any aggregation between the flakes? Could it not be that in bronchitis the abnormality consists of a change in the rate of aggregation between these flakes?

Dr. IRAVANI: From the physical point of view the flakes are homogeneous.

In bronchitic rats we see a well-marked tendency towards aggregation of flakes and plaques in some portions of the airway. This might be the consequence of hypersecretion.

A. G. HEPPLESTON: In human chronic bronchitis, hyperplasia of mucus-secreting cells is an early feature. Did you find similar evidence in the bronchitic standard rats?

Rat bronchitis is often associated with lymphoid hyperplasia and bronchial narrowing. Do you consider that these changes affected ciliary transport?

Dr. IRAVANI: In our histological examinations, many areas with abnormal ciliary mechanism showed hyperplasia of the goblet cells.

I don't think narrowing of the airways is of major importance in the development of alterations in the ciliary mechanism. Narrowing of the bronchial lumen by means of external pressure or following the application of acetylcholine causes no abnormalities in ciliary function.

CLEARANCE RATES DETERMINANTS: PARAMETERS INFLUENCING CLEARANCE RATES OF PARTICLES IN THE UPPER RESPIRATORY TRACT

ALBERT A. SPRITZER, JOSEPH A. WATSON and JUDITH A. AULD

*Department of Radiation Health, Graduate School of Public Health,
University of Pittsburgh, Pittsburgh, Pennsylvania, U.S.A.*

Abstract — A new method for obtaining the effective linear particle transport velocity of the mucociliary escalator of the trachea of the rat is described. Clearance rates of particles from the trachea into the oropharynx are determined by the effective linear particle transport velocity of the mucociliary escalator of the trachea and the linear density distribution of particles along the trachea. This latter distribution is shown to be uniform during the slower phases of pulmonary clearance. The linear particle transport velocity is obtained by dividing the particle clearance rate by the density distribution parameter. The mean linear particle transport velocity obtained by this method with 20 rats exposed to lead chromate particles by inhalation is $2 \cdot 01 \pm 0 \cdot 26$ mm per minute.

Homeostatic mechanisms which maintain the clearance rates of particles from the upper respiratory tract are discussed in terms of the above concepts.

INTRODUCTION

THE mucociliary escalator of the tracheobronchial tree is the final common pathway of particulates which are carried from the deeper pulmonary system to the oropharynx of mammals. The rates at which particles are carried along the mucociliary escalator have been determined by direct visualization of excised tracheobronchial segments, observations in the trachea through tracheostomy orifices or by roentgenologic evaluation of the velocity of opaque media in the trachea (HATCH & GROSS, 1964; TASK GROUP ON LUNG DYNAMICS, 1966). Particle velocities in the trachea have ranged from zero to 36 mm/min in mammals and from 2 to 16 mm/min in the rat (RIVERA, 1962; BATTIGELLI *et al.*, 1966).

The velocity of particles is important in determining the clearance rate from the tracheal orifice into the oropharynx. The more fundamental factors which determine the number of particles which enter the oropharynx per unit time from the trachea (clearance rate) are the effective particle transport velocity of the mucociliary escalator and the numerical distribution of particles along the trachea, which we refer to as the mean linear density distribution parameter. This concept may be summarized as

$$R = V \cdot D$$

where:

R is the clearance rate of particles leaving the trachea (no./min),

149

V is the effective linear particle transport velocity of the mucociliary escalator along
the trachea (mm/min), and

D is the linear density distribution of particles along the trachea (no./mm).

Clearance rates, R, from the rat lung can be experimentally measured (SPRITZER &
WATSON, 1964; WATSON et al., 1966). If a meaningful density distribution, D, can be
established, then V can be determined.

The experiments reported below were undertaken to demonstrate that D can be
determined. Subsequently by using experimentally determined values of D and R,
the effective linear transport velocity was derived and shown to be independent of the
clearance rate R.

MATERIALS AND METHODS

Particle Preparation

The procedure for preparing lead chromate particles labeled with radio-chromium
(Cr^{51}) has been described previously (WATSON et al., 1969). The size of the particles
used in these experiments was distributed log-normally with a geometric mean
diameter of $0 \cdot 4$ μm and a geometric standard derivation of $1 \cdot 94$. The particle
suspensions were subjected continuously to ultrasonic treatment prior to use to
minimize agglomeration.

Inhalation Exposure System

A description of the inhalation exposure system and the method of aerosol generation has appeared (WATSON et al., 1969). The rats were exposed to the aerosol for a
2 h period in groups of 8 rats each. Clearance rate measurements were initiated at
designated times (see below) following the termination of the inhalation exposure.

Clearance Rate Determination

The esophageal collection method used for clearance rate measurements has been
described previously (SPRITZER & WATSON, 1964). Adult male rats (Wistar strain)
weighing between 400 and 450 g were used. A polyethylene tube was inserted into the
esophagus to a level approximately 1 cm below the esophageal orifice. The caudad
end of the tube was passed through the stomach wall, the abdominal wall, and
through the cap of a polyethylene collection bottle. The cap was sutured to the
animal's flank to hold a collection bottle in place during the experiment. All swallowed
material entered the collection bottle which was changed at designated intervals. The
surgical procedure was performed on rats fasted for 48 h and anesthetized with
pentobarbital (Nembutal). Exposure of the rats to the radioactively labeled particles
was initiated 24 h following surgery.

At designated times following inhalation exposure, the esophageal collection tubes
in the animals were flushed with 10 cm³ of normal saline solution by introducing a
blunted, 18-gauge needle into the esophagus through the mouth. Three consecutive
sputum collections were then made at 5 min intervals by flushing the system in a
similar manner. The radioactive content of the three 5 min sputum collections were

averaged to obtain an estimate of the clearance rate, i.e., the number of particles cleared from the trachea per 5 min interval. This result was then expressed as the number of particles cleared from the trachea per minute (R).

Linear Density Distribution of Particles

Immediately following the above collections for clearance rate determinations, the rats were killed using a guillotine. The entire trachea was quickly removed and divided into $3 \cdot 4$ mm segments along the longitudinal axis from the tracheal orifice to the corina.

Preliminary studies to characterize the distribution of particles along the trachea at various times after exposure demonstrated that the particle distribution was approximately uniform if the trachea were divided into segments greater than 2 mm in length. A tracheal segment length of $3 \cdot 4$ mm was adopted in these experiments. This length enhanced the apparent uniformity of particle distribution and diminished the random error associated with cutting the trachea into smaller segments. For the rats used, the tracheas yielded 5 to 7 segments of $3 \cdot 4$ mm length, with approximately 80% of the animals having 6 tracheal segments. Only the latter animals were used.

The number of particles per segment was measured by radioactive analysis and averaged for the entire trachea. This result was then expressed as the mean number of particles per mm of trachea (D).

RESULTS

Determination of the Linear Density Distribution Parameter

The numerical distribution of particles along the tracheal surface is generated in two ways. Initially, particles are deposited on the tracheobronchial surfaces in a manner governed by processes such as gravitational settling, diffusion, inertial settling, etc. (HATCH & GROSS, 1964; TASK GROUP ON LUNG DYNAMICS, 1966). These particles are quickly swept to the oropharynx during the first "rapid" phase of clearance, which in the rat extends over the first 2 or 3 h following exposure (SPRITZER et al., 1967). Subsequently, the linear density distribution of particles along the trachea is determined by the rate of transfer of particles from deeper portions of the bronchial tree and lungs to the mucociliary escalator and also by the transport velocity of the mucociliary escalator of the trachea.

The trachea of a 450 g rat averages approximately 20 mm in length from the carina to the tracheal orifice. Based on direct particle velocity determinations in rats (HATCH & GROSS, 1964; TASK GROUP ON LUNG DYNAMICS, 1966), it is highly probable that particles traverse the rat trachea in less than 20 min. During the second "slower" phases of clearance, it is reasonable to assume that both the mucociliary escalator transport velocity and rate of particle clearance from the deeper bronchial tract and lung would show minimal variations over a 20 min period. If these assumptions are valid the particle distribution along the rat trachea would approximate uniformity following the first or "rapid" phase of clearance.

To test the hypothesis that the distribution of particles along the trachea was uniform during the "slower" phases of clearance, 32 rats were exposed to $PbCr^{51}O_4$ particles by inhalation. At varying times ranging from 2 h to 10 h following the termination of the exposures, the animals were killed and the tracheas removed and cut into 3·4 mm sections. The tracheas of 25 rats yielded 6 segments per trachea. Table I gives the number of particles in each intact trachea and in each of the 6 tracheal segments, together with the calculated number of particles per mm of trachea (D).

TABLE I. DISTRIBUTION OF LEAD CHROMATE PARTICLES ALONG THE RAT TRACHEA FOLLOWING INHALATION EXPOSURE

Time after exposure (h)	Rat No.	Number of particles per trachea* (10^2)	Number of particles per 3·4 mm segment of trachea (10^2) Segment number						Mean number per 3·4 mm segment (10^2)	D (10^2/mm)
			1	2	3	4	5	6		
10	1	99·2	12·4	6·2	43·4	18·6	6·2	12·4	16·55	4·84
	2	68·2	6·2	24·8	12·4	6·2	6·2	12·4	11·35	3·34
	3	80·6	24·8	12·4	18·6	6·2	6·2	12·4	13·43	3·95
	4	117·8	12·4	37·2	18·6	12·4	18·6	18·6	19·63	5·77
	5	93·0	18·6	18·6	18·6	12·4	6·2	18·6	15·50	4·56
	6	111·6	12·4	18·6	12·4	12·4	31·0	24·8	18·60	5·47
	7	105·4	12·4	18·6	18·6	18·6	18·6	18·6	17·57	5·17
6	8	899·0	142·6	148·8	223·2	173·6	111·6	99·2	149·8	44·06
	9	390·6	43·3	55·8	49·6	74·4	105·4	60·2	65·10	19·15
	10	558·0	55·8	80·6	105·4	105·4	80·6	130·2	93·00	27·35
	11	105·4	18·6	12·4	31·0	31·0	0	12·4	17·57	5·17
	12	440·2	49·6	37·2	43·4	18·6	62·0	229·4	73·37	21·58
	13	204·6	31·0	12·4	55·8	18·6	43·4	43·4	34·10	10·03
	14	62·0	18·6	18·6	0	12·4	6·2	6·2	10·33	3·04
4	15	148·8	12·4	18·6	12·4	37·2	6·2	62·0	24·80	7·29
	16	1959·2	254·2	198·4	458·8	365·8	365·8	316·2	326·5	96·04
	17	241·8	124·0	12·4	18·6	12·4	31·0	43·3	40·30	11·85
	18	762·6	167·4	179·8	192·2	37·2	105·4	80·6	127·1	37·38
	19	694·4	68·2	74·4	62·0	155·0	62·0	272·8	115·7	34·04
	20	167·4	6·2	12·4	12·4	80·6	31·0	24·8	27·90	8·21
2	21	8363·8	843·2	1556·2	1370·2	1103·6	657·2	2833·4	1394·00	410·0
	22	3410·0	545·6	638·6	694·4	508·4	483·6	539·4	568·3	167·1
	23	5747·4	669·6	669·6	1574·8	1116·0	756·4	961·0	957·9	281·7
	24	4563·2	737·8	868·0	700·6	694·4	787·4	775·0	760·5	223·7
	25	3354·2	719·2	607·6	539·4	465·0	527·0	496·0	559·0	164·4

* Conversion factor: 62 particles per c/m of Cr^{51}. (Radioactivity was measured by counting the 0·332 MeV photons of Cr^{51} with a single channel gamma ray spectrometer; WATSON et al., 1969.)

The D values decreased with time following exposure, reflecting the decreasing particle clearance from the lungs.

Assuming uniform distribution of particles along the trachea, each 3·4 mm tracheal segment should contain an average of $\frac{1}{6}$ (0·167) of the number of particles found in the trachea. The data in Table I were expressed as the fractional particle distribution in each tracheal segment (Table II). The grand combined mean of the 150 tracheal segments was 0·166 ± 0·01 S.E. A chi square test of the fractional distribution in the 6 segments indicated no apparent deviation from uniform particle distribution

$(P = 0\cdot995)$. A test of the standard error of the difference between means indicated no significant difference $(P = 0\cdot01)$ of the fractional distribution of particles in the various tracheal segments. Based on the above data and analyses we conclude that a linear density distribution parameter of particles along the trachea can be determined and represented by a single average number of particles per unit length of trachea.

TABLE II. FRACTIONAL DEPOSITION OF LEAD CHROMATE PARTICLES PER 3·4 MM SEGMENT OF RAT TRACHEA

Time after exposure (h)	Rat No.	Tracheal segment					
		1	2	3	4	5	6
	1	0·125	0·063	0·438	0·188	0·063	0·125
	2	0·091	0·364	0·182	0·091	0·091	0·182
	3	0·308	0·154	0·231	0·077	0·077	0·154
10	4	0·105	0·316	0·158	0·105	0·158	0·158
	5	0·200	0·200	0·200	0·133	0·067	0·200
	6	0·111	0·167	0·111	0·111	0·278	0·222
	7	0·118	0·176	0·176	0·176	0·176	0·176
	8	0·159	0·166	0·248	0·193	0·124	0·110
	9	0·111	0·143	0·127	0·190	0·270	0·159
	10	0·100	0·144	0·189	0·189	0·144	0·233
6	11	0·176	0·118	0·294	0·294	0·000	0·118
	12	0·113	0·085	0·099	0·042	0·141	0·521
	13	0·152	0·061	0·273	0·091	0·212	0·212
	14	0·300	0·300	0·000	0·200	0·100	0·100
	15	0·083	0·125	0·083	0·250	0·042	0·417
	16	0·130	0·101	0·234	0·187	0·187	0·161
4	17	0·513	0·051	0·077	0·051	0·128	0·179
	18	0·220	0·236	0·252	0·049	0·138	0·106
	19	0·098	0·107	0·089	0·223	0·089	0·393
	20	0·037	0·074	0·074	0·481	0·185	0·148
	21	0·101	0·186	0·164	0·132	0·079	0·339
	22	0·160	0·187	0·204	0·149	0·142	0·158
2	23	0·117	0·117	0·174	0·194	0·132	0·167
	24	0·162	0·190	0·154	0·152	0·173	0·170
	25	0·214	0·181	0·161	0·139	0·157	0·148
Mean		0·160	0·160	0·180	0·163	0·134	0·200
Standard error		0·02	0·02	0·02	0·03	0·01	0·02

Grand combined mean $= 0\cdot166 \pm 0\cdot01$

Determination of the Effective Linear Particle Transport Velocity of the Mucociliary Escalator of the Trachea

Clearance rates were determined for three consecutive 5 min periods for each of the 25 rats of the previous experiment immediately prior to sacrifice. These measurements were averaged and the clearance rates (R) determined.

The clearance rates of rats in the 2 h post-exposure group (number 21 through

25 in Table I) were not used because contamination of the nares, mouth and oro-pharynx with particles from the inhalation exposure interferred with the clearance measurements.

Table III gives the experimental data on rats 1 through 20. The mean clearance rates for the 4, 6 and 10 h post-exposure groups are 3927 ± 906, 2804 ± 736 and 862 ± 106 particles/min, respectively. The decreasing clearance rates reflect the diminishing amount of material removed from the lungs and tracheobronchial tree with time following exposure.

Table III also gives the linear density distribution parameter (D) for each rat from Table I. The mean values for the 4, 6 and 10 h post-exposure groups are 3246 ± 515, 1863 ± 502 and 473 ± 30 particles/mm, respectively. Again the decreasing values reflect the diminution in the absolute amount of material removed from the pulmonary system with time following exposure.

In Table III, the transport velocity, V, of the cleared particles for each rat is given. This was obtained by dividing the clearance rate by the density distribution, i.e., $V = R/D$. The mean velocities for the 4, 6 and 10 h post-exposure groups are $2 \cdot 31 \pm 0 \cdot 64$ mm/min, $1 \cdot 87 \pm 0 \cdot 40$ mm/min and $1 \cdot 88 \pm 0 \cdot 25$ mm/min, respectively. No significant difference among these means was found by applying the test of the standard error of the difference between means ($P = 0 \cdot 01$). The grand mean effective linear particle transport velocity of the mucociliary escalator of the trachea for the 20 rats is $2 \cdot 01 \pm 0 \cdot 26$ mm/min. These values are consistent with values determined by other methods in the literature.

TABLE III. CLEARANCE RATE MEASUREMENT AND DETERMINATION OF THE MUCOCILIARY ESCALATOR VELOCITY OF THE TRACHEA

Time after expo-sure (h)	Rat No.	Clearance rate (10^2 particles/5 min)			Mean rate (10^2/5 min)	R (10^2/min)	Mean R (10^2/min)	D (10^2/mm)	Mean D (10^2/mm)	V (mm/min)	Mean V (mm/min)
		1	2	3							
	1	24·8	24·8	18·6	22·7	4·55		4·84		0·94	
	2	68·2	31·0	31·0	43·4	8·68		3·34		2·60	
	3	43·4	43·4	31·0	39·3	7·85	8·62	3·95	4·73	1·99	1·88
10	4	18·6	31·0	37·2	28·9	5·79	±1·06	5·77	±0·30	1·00	±0·25
	5	49·6	37·2	74·4	53·7	10·75		4·56		2·36	
	6	43·4	31·0	62·0	45·5	9·09		5·47		1·66	
	7	43·4	55·8	105·4	68·2	13·64		5·17		2·64	
	8	285·2	204·6	421·6	303·8	60·76		44·06		1·38	
	9	142·6	415·4	105·4	221·1	44·23		19·15		2·31	
	10	173·6	173·6	204·6	183·9	36·78	28·04	27·35	18·63	1·34	1·87
6	11	37·2	31·0	18·6	28·9	5·79	±7·36	5·17	±5·02	1·12	±0·40
	12	37·2	31·0	37·2	35·1	7·03		21·58		0·33	
	13	223·0	124·0	118·0	155·0	31·0		10·03		3·09	
	14	68·2	49·6	43·4	53·7	10·75		3·04		3·54	
	15	105·4	86·6	43·4	78·5	15·71		7·29		2·16	
	16	217·0	173·6	111·6	167·4	33·48		96·04		0·35	
4	17	105·4	310·0	210·8	208·7	41·75	39·27	11·85	32·46	3·52	2·31
	18	142·6	37·2	136·4	105·4	21·08	±9·06	37·38	±5·15	0·56	±0·64
	19	514·6	458·8	291·4	421·6	84·32		34·04		2·48	
	20	198·4	241·8	148·8	196·3	39·27		8·21		4·78	

DISCUSSION

A new method is presented which permits the determination of the effective linear particle transport velocity of the mucociliary escalator in the trachea of rats. The experimental work confirms the formulation given previously of the relationships between clearance rates, density distributions and transport velocities of particles in the upper respiratory tract.

These experiments indicate that variation of clearance rates of particles may not reflect a simultaneous variation of particle transport velocities. In the three groups of rats studied 4, 6 and 10 h following inhalation exposure, the effective linear particle transport velocity remained unchanged in spite of the decreasing clearance rates of the particles. This is shown to result from a decreasing linear density distribution of particles along the trachea as time elapses.

The demonstrated interrelationships in which the clearance rates of particles in the upper respiratory tract is determined by the product of the density distribution of particles (no./mm) and the effective linear particle transport velocity (mm/min) suggest that partial inhibition of the mucociliary escalator would result in only a transient drop in particle clearance rates, because if the mechanism(s) in the deep lung which transfer material to the escalator remains intact, the decreased particle transport velocity would be compensated for by an automatic increase in the density distribution of particles along the tract. This would re-establish normal clearance rates. If mucus flow up the respiratory tract persists to some degree with even complete ciliostasis only transient depression of particulate clearance would be expected. The studies of BATTISTA & KENSLER (1970) suggest that during periods of partial or complete ciliostasis induced by cigarette smoke in fowl, mucous production is increased and the mucous becomes more viscid. These changes would increase the transport capacity of the mucous blanket. Perhaps this is why no clinically significant effects of ciliostasis on particle clearance have been found.

Acknowledgements — This investigation was supported in whole by Public Health Service research grant ES U100421 from the National Center for Urban and Industrial Health.

REFERENCES

BATTIGELLI, M. C., HENGSTENBERG, F., MANNELLA, R. J. & THOMAS, A. P. (1966). *Archs envir. Hlth* **12**, 460–466.
BATTISTA, S. P. & KENSLER, C. J. (1970). *Archs envir. Hlth* **20**, 326–338.
HATCH, T. F. & GROSS, P. (1964). *Pulmonary deposition and retention of inhaled aerosols.* New York, Academic Press.
RIVERA, J. A. (1962). *Cilia, ciliated epithelium and ciliary activity.* Oxford, Pergamon Press.
SPRITZER, A. A. & WATSON, J. A. (1964). *Hlth Phys.* **10**, 1093–1097.
SPRITZER, A. A., WATSON, J. A. & AULD, J. A. (1967). *Archs envir. Hlth* **15**, 39–47.
TASK GROUP ON LUNG DYNAMICS (1966). *Hlth Phys.* **12**, 173–207.
WATSON, J. A., SPRITZER, A. A., AULD, J. A. & BRADLEY, F. J. (1966). *Archs envir. Hlth* **13**, 586–592.
WATSON, J. A., SPRITZER, A. A., AULD, J. A. & GUETTHOFF, M. A. (1969). *Archs envir. Hlth* **19**, 51–58.

DISCUSSION: *See page* 181.

INTRA-INDIVIDUAL STUDIES OF TRACHEOBRONCHIAL CLEARANCE IN MAN USING FLUOROCARBON RESIN PARTICLES TAGGED WITH ^{18}F AND ^{99m}Tc

P. CAMNER and K. PHILIPSON

National Institute of Public Health and Institute of Hygien,
Karolinska Institutet, Stockholm, Sweden

Abstract — Human tracheobronchial clearance was studied with a test aerosol of 6–7 μm particles of fluorinated ethylene propylene (Teflon 120, Dupont) tagged with ^{18}F and ^{99m}Tc. The intra-individual differences in clearance were found to be small compared to the inter-individual differences. The lung clearance pattern was to a great extent dependent on inhalation of the test aerosol and to a certain extent on particle size within the range of $4 \cdot 9$–$7 \cdot 8$ μm. Lung clearance was studied in a small group of smokers during "normal" smoking, during acute exposure to tobacco and about a week after they had stopped smoking. Finally a study was made of four persons suffering from diseases of the lung.

INTRODUCTION

THE mucociliary transport mechanism is to be regarded as an important defence mechanism against inhaled particulate materials. From the point of view of hygiene it is of great interest to study how this is affected by various air pollutants, including tobacco smoke. An important question here is whether air pollution can produce pathological conditions in the lungs by damaging the transport mechanism. Conversely it is of interest from the clinical point of view to ascertain the condition of the mucociliary transport in different lung diseases as well as the effect on it of drugs and other forms of treatment.

Mucociliary transport can in principle be studied by arranging for subjects to inhale particles tagged with a radionuclide and then measuring radioactivity externally. Such investigations have been performed here on animals (HOLMA, 1967) and recently, on human subjects (CAMNER *et al.*, to be published, *b*), and by others (ALBERT *et al.*, 1969; BOOKER *et al.*, 1967; LUCHSINGER *et al.*, 1968; MORROW *et al.*, 1967). One difficulty with this method is that the clearance pattern obtained is dependent on deposition as well as the elimination mechanism.

It is a reasonable assumption that deposition of the test aerosol varies less in repeated exposures of the same individual than between different individuals. Consequently the effect of various factors on mucociliary transport ought to be studied intra-individually. It has also been shown in studies of both animals (HOLMA, 1969) and human beings (ALBERT *et al.*, 1969) that intra-individual differences are smaller than inter-individual differences during the first hours of lung clearance.

With repeated determinations of tracheobronchial clearance in the same individual

157

it is desirable to use a radionuclide with a half-life that is long enough for the process to be followed (one or more hours), but permits still repeated exposures to be made as frequently as possible without the radioactivity from one exposure interfering with the measurements from the next. Both ^{18}F (positron emitter, half-life 110 min) and ^{99m}Tc (γ-emitter, half-life $6 \cdot 0$ h) should be suitable radionuclides in this respect.

MATERIALS AND METHODS

The test aerosol was produced with particles of fluorinated ethylene propylene, FEP, in the form of an aqueous dispersion of $0 \cdot 1$–$0 \cdot 2$ μm particles (Teflon 120 Dupont). Part of this dispersion was added to an alcohol water solution (33 %) and run onto a spinning disk. The particles, 6–7 μm in diameter, were then collected on a filter and heated for 5 min at 240° C to make them stable in water. The particles were tagged with ^{18}F by irradiation with protons in a cyclotron, whereupon the reaction p + ^{19}F → ^{18}F + p + n occurred. A more detailed description of the production of the particles and their tagging with ^{18}F is given by CAMNER et al., (to be published, a). The particles were tagged with ^{99m}Tc by adding the radionuclide to the FEP suspension in the alcohol water solution prior to the spinning disk process.

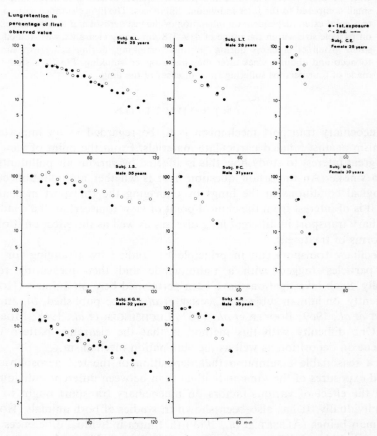

FIGURE 1. Lung clearance patterns of eight subjects. Each subject was exposed twice. Radionuclide ^{18}F.

There was very little leakage of ^{18}F from the particles suspended in water, but there was considerable leakage – about 10% – of ^{99m}Tc during the first $\frac{1}{2}$ h. However this leakage fell considerably in time, amounting to no more than about 1% in 24 h after about 1 h leaching. Accordingly the particles tagged with ^{99m}Tc were leached for 2 h before use.

The particles were then suspended in a 0·2% water solution of a wetting agent, trimethylnonylether of polyethylene glycol (Tergitol TMN, Union Carbide Chemical Co.) and sprayed up with an air brush in a 10 or 25 l glass tower, from which the subjects performed about twenty maximal inhalations (beginning from maximal exhalations) for about 3 min. Expiration took place outside the tower. Airflow during inhalation was determined by measuring the velocity of the air flowing into tower during inhalation by means of a thermo-anemometer (Wallac, GGA 23 S) connected to a recorder.

Inhaled radioactivity was measured with two opposed 3 in. × 2 in. NaI crystals fitted with focussing collimators which profile-scanned at a speed of 3·48 m/h over the thorax of the supine subject. The radioactivity was registered on a recorder and the total activity in the lungs was determined by planimetric evaluation.

RESULTS

Eight subjects, all non-smokers and without any known lung diseases, were each exposed twice within the space of a few days (most of them in one day). The inhalation

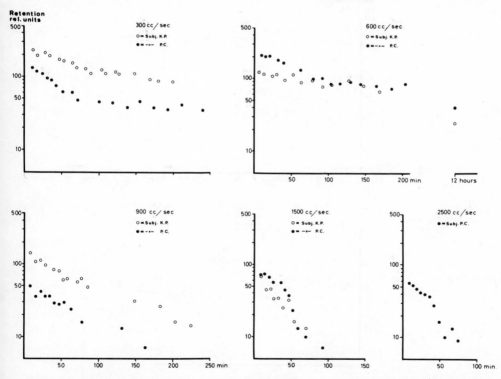

FIGURE 2. Lung clearance patterns of two subjects. The test aerosol was inhaled at different rates. Radionuclide ^{99m}Tc.

rate was about 1 l/s apart from subject B L, whose inhalation rate was 2 l/s. Figure 1 shows that, while the subjects' clearance patterns agree well intra-individually, there are considerable inter-individual differences. Figure 1 also shows that the logarithm of radioactivity in the lungs is an approximately linear function of time. A regression line was therefore determined for each clearance pattern using the least squares method. Variance analysis showed that the difference in slope within the individuals was significantly smaller than the difference between them, $0 \cdot 01 > p > 0 \cdot 001$. The study is described more in detail by CAMNER *et al.* (to be published, *b*).

Figure 2 shows the clearance patterns of two persons, PC and KP, using different inhalation rates of the test aerosol. The exposures were made within 3 days. The Figure shows that the clearance is very much dependent on airflow during inhalation of the test aerosol. As one might expect, increased airflow gives faster clearance, except that 600 cm³/s apparently gives a slower clearance than 300 cm³/s. The subjects supervised the airflow themselves by keeping the recorder reading at the level corresponding to the desired inhalation velocity.

The effect of particle diameter on the clearance process was also studied in the two above-mentioned persons within a narrow range of size ($4 \cdot 9$, $6 \cdot 7$ and $7 \cdot 8$ μm) with an inhalation rate of $1 \cdot 2$ l/s, see Figure 3. This study was made within two days. It is evident from Figure 3 and Table I, which show the biological half-lives of the particles (the half-lives are based on the measurements from the first 60 min only) that clearance increases with particle diameter even within this narrow range.

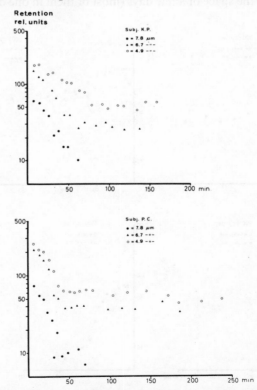

FIGURE 3. Lung clearance patterns of two subjects. Different particle sizes were used. Inhalation rate of the aerosol $1 \cdot 2$ l/s. Radionuclide 99mTc.

TABLE I. THE BIOLOGICAL HALF-LIVES FOR PARTICLES OF DIFFERENT SIZES.
INHALATION RATE 1·2 l/s

Subject	Particle diameter (μm)	Biological half-life (min.)
PC	4·9	23
	6·7	18
	7·8	16
KP	4·9	52
	6·7	21
	7·8	19

The lung clearance of six male smokers aged between 24 and 41 was studied. All of them had a smoke anamnaesia of many years' standing and consumed between 15 and 20 cigarettes a day. Apart from the occasional slight cough in the mornings, none of them had experienced any irritation in the respiratory tract as a result of smoking. On the first day the subject was exposed to the test aerosol without any restrictions on his smoking except for ½ h prior to exposure. On the second day the subject was again exposed to the test aerosol, but this time he chain smoked immediately afterwards, inhaling as deeply as possible. Two persons, however, started

TABLE II. CIGARETTE SMOKING IN CONNECTION WITH LUNG CLEARANCE MEASUREMENTS (SECOND DAY)

Subject	Number of cigarettes ½ h before aerosol exposure	Number of cigarettes during the clearance measurements	Duration of measurements (min)
HE	0	9	75
K-E B	4	2	30
GK	0	5	70
JW	4	3	50
PK	0	4	35
HS	0	4	40

TABLE III. THE BIOLOGICAL HALF-LIFE OF THE PARTICLES IN LUNG CLEARANCE MEASUREMENTS, (1) AT "NORMAL" SMOKING, (2) AT HEAVY ACUTE EXPOSURE TO TOBACCO SMOKE AND (3) APPROXIMATELY ONE WEEK AFTER ABSTAINING FROM CIGARETTES. INHALATION RATE 1·2 l/s

Subject	Biological half-life (min)		
	(1)	(2)	(3)
HE	26	81	108
K-E B	11	12	26
GK	48	24	44
IW	19	24	84
PK	29	11	—
HS	30	23	—
Average*	25·9	35·2	65·2

* Average calculated for the first four persons only.

chain smoking about 30 min before exposure. Table II shows tobacco consumption in connection with the second day's clearance measurements. The cigarettes used in the experiment had a standard nicotine content of 1·9 mg/cig. and a tar content of 31 mg/cig.

On the third day the subject stopped smoking. Between the seventh and fourteenth days the subject was exposed once more (two of the subjects dropped out at this point). Table III shows the half-lives in the clearance process at the three measuring points. There is no clear tendency to reduced clearance in connection with acute exposure to tobacco smoke, indeed, two persons show a striking increase. But the most remarkable feature in Table III is the consistently slow clearance about a week after the subjects stopped smoking.

A study has recently begun of the lung clearance in patients suffering from diseases of the lung. So far, however, only four patients have been exposed to the test aerosol. Table IV gives schematic data concerning the patients together with the half-life of their lung clearance curves, which is obviously well within the limits obtained for both smokers and non-smokers.

TABLE IV. PERSONAL DATA AND BIOLOGICAL HALF-LIFE

Subject	Age (yr.)	Sex	Diagnosis	Biological half-life (min)
GW	59	Male	Bronchit. chron.	12
I-B B	36	Female	St. post. op. bronchestasia	18
LL	53	Male	Bronchit. chron.	61
GS	52	Male	Emfysema pulm.	28

DISCUSSION

The results show that the inhalation rate of the test aerosol has a marked effect on the clearance, as does particle diameter to a certain extent although only a narrow range of sizes has been studied. But it is also evident that reproduceable clearance patterns can be obtained by standardizing these parameters, i.e. it has been possible to standardize deposition. Consequently it should be possible in intra-individual studies to determine changes in mucociliary transport from changes in the lung clearance pattern.

In experiments on animals, both HOLMA (1969), and ALBERT et al. (1969) have found slower clearance in connection with acute exposure to tobacco smoke. Exposure to tobacco smoke was probably greater in their experiments than in the present study, though the subjects tried to smoke as heavily and as long as possible. All of them evinced some form of general effect such as cold sweat, tiredness, dizziness or nausea. Three of the subjects, GK, PK and HS showed faster clearance in connection with acute exposure to tobacco smoke, which is also described in some cases by ALBERT et al. (1969). It is a reasonable working hypothesis that tobacco smoke first stimulates mucociliary transport only to inhibit it if the dose increases beyond a certain limit.

The most striking result from the studies of the smoking group is the slow clearance about a week after the subjects had stopped smoking. However, this involved only four persons. Even if the result were representative for persons who stop smoking, it is not necessarily indicative of reduced mucociliary transport. As a result of the subjects giving up smoking, the cross sections of the airways may have changed and given different deposition of the test aerosol.

REFERENCES

ALBERT, R. E., LIPPMAN, M. & BRISCOE, W. (1969). The characteristics of bronchial clearance in humans and the effects of cigarette smoking. *Archs envir. Hlth* **18,** 738–755.

ALBERT, R. E., SPIEGELMAN, I. R., SHATSKY, S. & LIPPMAN, M. (1969). The effect of acute exposure to cigarette smoke on bronchial clearance in the miniature donkey. *Archs envir. Hlth* **18,** 30–41.

BOOKER, D. V., CHAMBERLAIN, A. C., RUNDO, I., MUIR, D. C. F. & THOMSON, M. L. (1967). Elimination of 5 μ particles from the human lung. *Nature, Lond.* **215,** 30–33.

CAMNER, P., PHILIPSON, K. & SVEDBERG, J. Production of 7 μ monodisperse fluorocarbon resin particles tagged with [18]F. (To be published in *J. appl. Radiat. Isotopes*) (*a*).

CAMNER, P., PHILIPSON, K., FRIBERG, L., HOLMA, B., LARSSON, B. & SVEDBERG, J. Human tracheo-bronchial clearance studied with fluorocarbon resin particles tagged with [18]F. (To be published in *Archs envir. Hlth*) (*b*).

HOLMA, B. (1967). Lung clearance of mono- and di-disperse aerosols determined by profile scanning and whole-body counting: a study on normal and SO_2 exposed rabbits. *Acta med. scand.* **182,** Suppl. 437.

HOLMA, B. (1969). The acute effect of cigarette smoke on the initial course of lung clearance in rabbits. *Archs envir. Hlth* **18,** 171–173.

LUCHSINGER, P. C., LAGARDE, B. & KILFEATHER, J. E. (1968). Particle clearance from the human tracheo-bronchial tree. *Am. Rev. resp. Dis.* **97,** 1046–1050.

MORROW, P. E., GIBB, F. R. & GAZIOGLU, K. M. (1967). A study of particulate clearance from the human lungs. *Am. Rev. resp. Dis.* **96,** 1209–1221.

DISCUSSION: *See page* 181.

THE EFFECTS OF CIGARETTE SMOKING ON THE KINETICS OF BRONCHIAL CLEARANCE IN HUMANS AND DONKEYS*

R. E. ALBERT, M. LIPPMANN and H. T. PETERSON, JR.†

Institute of Environmental Medicine, New York University Medical Center, 550 First Avenue, New York, N.Y. 10016, U.S.A.

Abstract — Studies in this laboratory to characterize the patterns of normal bronchial clearance and the effects of cigarette smoking in humans and donkeys are summarized. Normal clearance in the donkey is exponential, while most humans show a two-phase pattern of clearance. The inter-subject variability of clearance is considerably greater in humans than donkeys.

In donkeys, acute, high-level exposures to cigarette smoke produces a dose-dependent slowing of clearance which is greater in the trachea than the lower bronchi. Recovery is generally rapid but persistent impairment can occur.

Several kinds of abnormal clearance patterns are present in some of the human cigarette smokers including: (1) a prolonged delay in the onset of clearance due to slowing of upper bronchial clearance; (2) tracheobronchial stasis, with or without refluxing, but commonly associated with spasmodic clearance.

The average clearance time for smokers was increased only at the 90–100% level of bronchial deposition but the difference between smokers and non-smokers was relatively small; significantly increased clearance times were found in bronchitics.

The paradoxial finding of abnormal clearance patterns without substantial differences in bronchial clearance times between smokers and non-smokers is explained by: (1) the wide inter-subject variability in clearance rates regardless of smoking habits, (2) differences in individual susceptibility to the effects of smoking and (3) the predominance of smoking effects in the trachea and upper bronchi where clearance impairment has relatively little effect on total clearance times. The pathogenesis of chronic bronchitis in cigarette smokers is discussed from the standpoint of increasingly severe damage to the clearance mechanism.

INTRODUCTION

INHALED radioactive particles were first used in humans by WILSON & LAMER (1948) for the measurement of pulmonary deposition. ALBERT & ARNETT (1955) adapted the method for the study of bronchial clearance. Since then, the method has been used with conventional scintillation detectors by ourselves and by TOIGO *et al.* (1963),

* This investigation was supported by grant EC 00231 from the Environmental Control Administration, Environmental Health Service, Public Health Service, Department of Health, Education and Welfare and by the AMA Education and Research Foundation. It is part of a center program supported by grant ES 00260 from the National Institute of Environmental Health Sciences.

† On assignment from the Bureau of Radiological Health, Environmental Health Service, U.S. Department of Health, Education and Welfare.

MORROW *et al.* (1967), LUCHSINGER *et al.* (1968), THOMSON & SHORT (1969) and CAMNER & PHILIPSON (1971). More recently, the technique has been modified by using gamma cameras as the detection device by KLIMEK *et al.* (1969), NEWHOUSE *et al.* (1970) and ISAWA *et al.* (1970).

Five years ago, at the second BOHS Symposium, we reported our first bronchial deposition and clearance results on 11 human subjects using monodisperse radio-active ferric oxide particles (ALBERT *et al.*, 1967a). Since then, we have extended our series to approximately 70 subjects, and have also carried out parallel studies on the effects of whole cigarette smoke and its components, and sulfur dioxide on bronchial clearance in donkey. The results of the human studies with respect to the characteristics of pulmonary deposition have been reported separately at this Symposium (LIPPMANN *et al.*, 1971). The purpose of this paper is to summarize and interrelate the normal kinetics of clearance in the human and the donkey with particular emphasis on the changes produced by cigarette smoking.

METHODS

The techniques used to generate the monodisperse test aerosols and to make the particle retention measurements have been previously described (ALBERT *et al.*, 1967a; 1969a). The insoluble test aerosols inhaled by the human and donkey test subjects are composed of monodisperse ferric oxide spheres (rel. density = 2·5) containing non-leaching tags (^{198}Au or ^{99m}Tc), and were produced by a spinning disc generator (ALBERT *et al.*, 1967a; LIPPMANN & ALBERT, 1967). Serial chest measurements in man began within a few minutes after a 1 min inhalation of a single aerosol or consecutive 1 min inhalation exposures to two aerosols differing in particle size and/or radio-isotopic tag. Frequent measurements were made during the 10 h period after inhalation and again during the following morning. Each subject was seated within a low background steel chamber in a reclining chair which supported four cylindrically collimated scintillation detectors (5 in. diameter) in a radial array around the chest to obtain the total radioactive burden of the lung. The detection efficiency for the deposited radionuclide was fairly independent of its regional distribution (LIPPMANN & ALBERT, 1969). The field of view excluded the lower 10–20% of the lungs in order to minimize the measurement of radioactivity in the stomach.

A separate tracheal detector was used with a field of view extending from about 1 in. below the larynx to just below the tracheal carina. The bifurcations of the major bronchi and more distal airways were seen with very low counting efficiencies.

Donkeys inhaled the aerosol in a 3–5 min period through the nose using a feed-bag type of mask (ALBERT *et al.*, 1968). The donkeys were confined in a metal crib on wheels between a pair of scintillation detectors recessed within lead brick shields. The detectors were collimated to a 3 × 8 in. vertical field. Sequential measurements were made for 5 to 10 h at three positions on the donkey. One field corresponded to the lower lung, the second to the upper lung at about the bifurcation of the trachea, and the third to the trachea in the mid-neck region. Reproducible counting geometries were attained without rigid restraint or sedation using a photocell actuated relay controlling live time on the counter. Procedures have been described for giving the donkeys acute exposures to SO_2 (SPIEGELMAN *et al.*, 1968) and whole fresh cigarette smoke (ALBERT *et al.*, 1969b; FRANCES *et al.*, 1970; ALBERT *et al.*, 1970).

NORMAL KINETICS OF BRONCHIAL CLEARANCE

Donkeys: More than one hundred studies have been done on six donkeys. Each of these animals has had consistent deposition and clearance characteristics. The clearance rates of the four male donkeys were very similar but the two females were three times faster.

The general characteristics of clearance were similar for all donkeys. Figure 1 presents an example of the normal characteristics of clearance from the lower and upper lung fields (positions 9 and 7, respectively) as well as the neck (position 5). Clearance from the lower lung began promptly and proceeded rapidly at first and then at a diminishing rate. Particle movement through the bronchial tree produced a wave of activity which passed successively through the middle and upper lung and then through the neck.

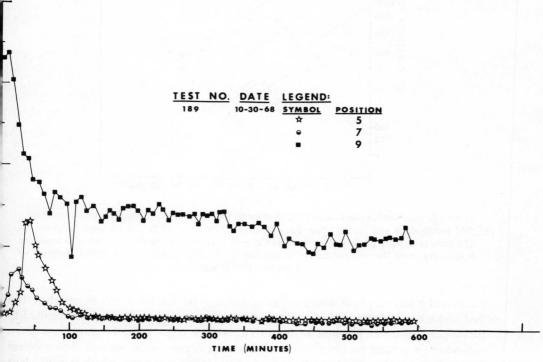

FIGURE 1. Normal donkey clearance of 1·8 μm particles from lower lung (position 9), upper lung (position 7) and trachea in the neck (position 5). There is continuous depletion in the lower lung with waves of activity appearing first in the upper lung and then the trachea.

The exponential character of bronchial clearance is demonstrated in Figure 2. The radioactivity measurements, after subtraction of the residual activity present at the end of clearance, are shown for the combined lower and mid-lung fields (positions 8 and 9), the upper lung field (position 7) and the trachea in the neck (position 4). The wave of activity passing through the upper lung field and the trachea (after subtracting the exponential clearance component) had the same final slope as that in the lower lung.

Human: Clearance in individual human subjects was relatively consistent but the patterns were more complex and the inter-subject variability was greater than in donkeys. The previous finding of a two-phase clearance pattern in many subjects remains valid (ALBERT & ARNETT, 1955; ALBERT *et al.*, 1967a, 1969a); this pattern consists of a short first phase of rapid clearance, which is completed within a few

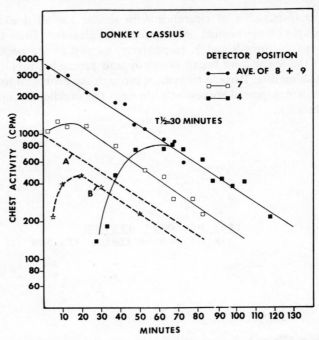

FIGURE 2. Exponential clearance in the donkey as shown by the combined mid and lower lung field (positions 8 and 9), the upper lung (position 7) and the trachea in the neck (position 4). The activity curve in position 7 is shown as Curve B after subtracting the exponential component (Curve A) from the activity curve in position 7. (Reproduced from the *AMA Archives of Environmental Health.*)

hours and a second phase which varies in duration from a few hours to one day. The first and second phases undoubtedly represent the clearance of particles deposited in the upper and lower portions of the bronchial tree respectively because, in a given individual, a greater proportion of the clearance occurs in the second slower phase for smaller particles. The overall amount of bronchial clearance, which is dependent upon the total deposition efficiency, varies considerably from subject to subject (LIPPMANN *et al.*, 1971). The shape of the whole lung clearance curve is determined by the relative magnitude of deposition in the upper and lower bronchi and the onset and duration of the two phases. The two phases are defined by the waves of radioactivity passing through the trachea.

Figure 3 shows two-phase clearance in Subject 1, a 25-year old healthy non-smoking male; the simultaneously measured whole lung and tracheal activity curves are shown for 1·6 and 3·7 μm particles. The initial whole lung activity curves are normalized to 100%; the tracheal activities are calculated as described elsewhere (ALBERT *et al.*, 1969a) and are also normalized. There are 2 tracheal waves for each particle size with peaks at 0·5 and 2·5 h. There is a relative reduction in the amount of first phase clearance with the smaller aerosol. Figure 4 shows a less distinct form of two-phase clearance in Subject 57, a 24-year old healthy non-smoking male. With the larger particle size, there is overlapping and blurring of the two clearance phases; only the second phase of clearance occurs with the smaller particle size.

The diversity in clearance patterns among healthy non-smoking male subjects aged 20–30 years is illustrated by the three whole lung clearance curves shown in Figure 5. The curve for Subject 1 was also shown in Figure 3. In all three cases the total bronchial deposition was about the same at 70–85%. Subjects 1 and 6 had two-phase clearance,

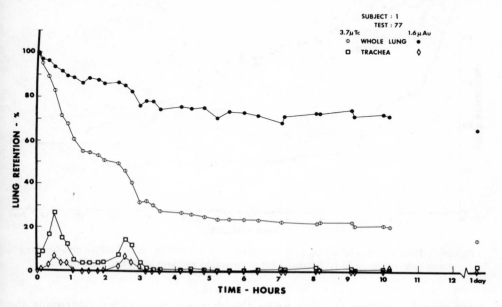

FIGURE 3. Whole-lung and tracheal clearance curves for a 25-year old healthy non-smoking male. Two distinct clearance phases are exhibited in the whole lung retention curves which correspond to the activity waves seen by the tracheal detector.

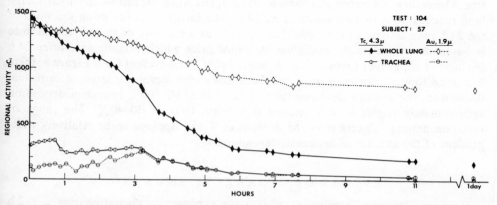

FIGURE 4. Whole-lung and tracheal clearance curves for a 24-year old healthy non-smoking male showing two relatively indistinct clearance phases for the 4·3 μm particles and only the second phase for the 1·9 μm particles.

but with marked differences both in the relative amounts cleared in each phase and the duration of the second phase. Subjects 6 and 39 had delays in the onset of clearance of about 1 h.

The weighted average clearance time for the various levels of bronchial deposition are plotted in Figure 6 for the 18 non-smoking subjects. This category includes three pipe and cigar and two ex-smokers. The weighted average clearance time was

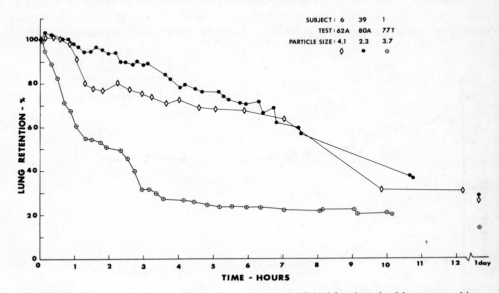

FIGURE 5. Diversity in whole lung clearance patterns exhibited by three healthy non-smoking males (age range of 20 to 30 years) for comparable amounts of bronchial clearance.

determined by dividing the area under the clearance curve (after subtracting the residual activity) by the total amount of bronchial clearance. This value represents the average residence time in the lung of particles which are cleared via the bronchial tree. Mucociliary clearance was considered complete when the loss of activity from the lung reached 90% of that achieved by 24 h. The justification for using the ratio of the 24 h lung activity to the initial lung activity as a measure of bronchial clearance is based on the relatively negligible clearance rates which predominate after 24 h (ALBERT et al., 1969a; LIPPMANN & ALBERT, 1969). As is evident from Figure 6, there is a trend toward shorter average clearance times with increasing levels of bronchial deposition; the average clearance time of 125 min at 90–100% bronchial deposition approximately triples at a bronchial deposition level of 30–40%. The range of variation among subjects is in the domain of 3 and appears to be relatively independent of the amount of bronchial deposition.

EFFECTS OF CIGARETTE SMOKING

Donkey: Clearance impairment after acute exposure to cigarettes over a 1–2 h period is dose-dependent ranging from minor effects with 18 cigarettes to severe impairment with 36 cigarettes (ALBERT et al., 1969b). Figure 7 shows the acute effects

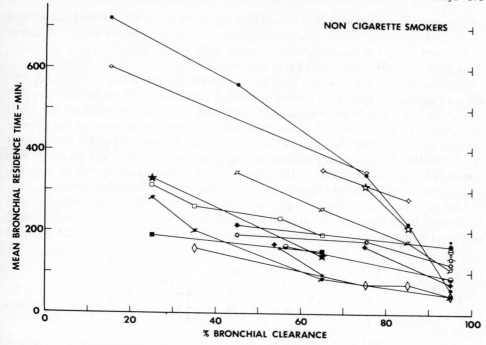

FIGURE 6. Mean bronchial residence (or clearance) times for 18 healthy non-cigarette smoking human subjects. Dependence of clearance or residence time on level of bronchial deposition is evident.

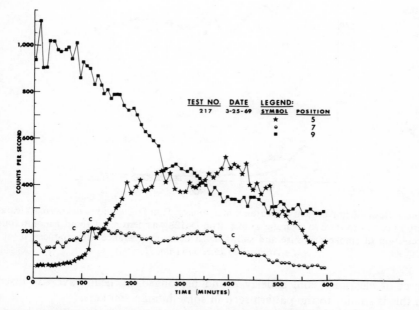

FIGURE 7. Abnormal clearance in a donkey produced by cigarette smoking as evidenced by slowing of lower lung clearance (position 9), upper lung clearance (position 7), and marked prolongation of tracheal wave (position 5).

on one donkey of 24 cigarettes. There is slowing of the lower lung clearance with loss of its exponential character and prolongation of the activity waves in the upper thorax and neck. Of the five donkeys tested with acute cigarette smoke exposure, three showed a 40% increase in bronchial deposition.

Since the radioactive counting efficiency was reproducible in the same donkey, the effect of cigarette smoking on the transit time of particles across the measured region of the trachea could be determined and compared to the effects on lower bronchial clearance. The mean tracheal transit time was estimated as the ratio of the average tracheal activity during clearance to the average rate of lower lung clearance (ALBERT *et al.*, 1969*b*). At very heavy exposures, the impairment of tracheal transport was several times greater than that in the deeper lung, *i.e.*, there appeared to be a diminishing effect of cigarette smoke with respect to depth in the bronchial tree.

Recovery from the effects of single exposures was very rapid and clearance returned to normal in a few days in five of six donkeys. The remaining donkey showed persistent impairment of clearance for several months (Figure 8) with a 2 h delay in

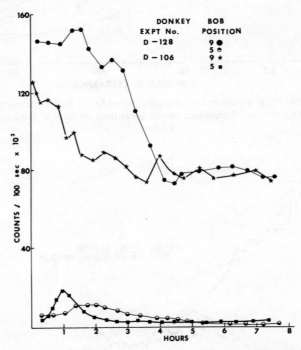

FIGURE 8. Residual impairment of clearance in a donkey. Run D–106 shows the normal clearance pattern prior to exposure to cigarette smoke. Run D–128 was performed about 1 month following cessation of smoke exposure and shows a 2 h delay in clearance. (Reproduced from the *AMA Archives of Environmental Health.*)

the onset of clearance, and a delayed and prolonged tracheal wave. As discussed below, this is similar to the pattern seen in some human smokers.

Three donkeys smoked 30 cigarettes two to three times per week for six to eight months. All three donkeys showed a build-up of clearance impairment over a period of several months, with a greater severity of effect in the trachea than in the lower bronchi. There was a reversal of the impairment in the latter part of the exposure period, suggesting the development of tolerance to cigarette smoke (ALBERT et al., 1970).

With acute exposures to cigarette smoke, two of the five donkeys developed a two-phase clearance pattern as shown in Figure 9 which was similar to that in humans (Figure 3).

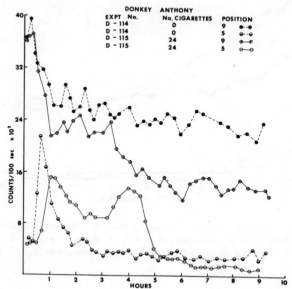

FIGURE 9. Development of a two-phase clearance pattern in a donkey after an acute exposure to cigarette smoke. The clearance curves from the lower lung (position 9) and trachea are shown for two successive studies, D–114 without cigarette smoking, and D–115 after 24 cigarettes. Note that the additional clearance (i.e. bronchial deposition) following cigarette smoking occurs in the second clearance phase from 3·5–6·0 h. (Reproduced from the *AMA Archives of Environmental Health.*)

Human: Abnormal clearance patterns were observed in a number of cigarette smokers. The genesis of abnormal clearance is illustrated by the changes which took place over a 3-year period in Subject 2. Figure 10 shows the whole lung and tracheal clearance for two studies, 49T and 134T. The first, 49T, was done on March 15, 1967, when the subject was 26 years old and had been smoking for 8 years at a level of 1–2 packs of filter cigarettes/day. At the time of study 49T, Subject 2 had a very pronounced form of two-phase clearance which was almost identical to that of the non-smoking Subject 1 (Figure 3).

Study 134T was done 3 years later. In the interval, the subject's smoking habits were essentially unchanged. The overall bronchial deposition efficiency remained constant over the three-year period since the same particle size and inspiratory flows produced the same amount of bronchial clearance. However, the two clearance phases became merged, which together with a 90 min delay in the onset of clearance, and a delayed initial tracheal wave, indicated a slowing of upper bronchial clearance. The weighted average bronchial clearance time increased from 61 min to 221 min over the 3-year period. The mean tracheal transit time increased from 23 min to

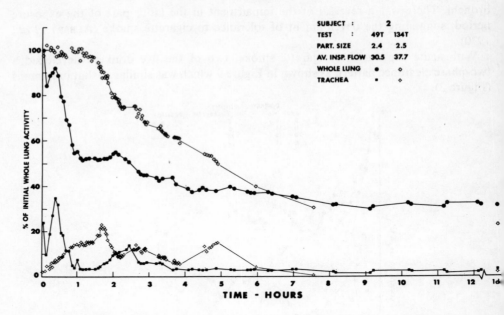

FIGURE 10. Chronic effects of cigarette smoking on particle clearance in a 29-year old human. Run 134T was performed three years after Run 49T. A delay in whole-lung clearance and a corresponding delayed and prolonged tracheal activity wave are evident in the later run.

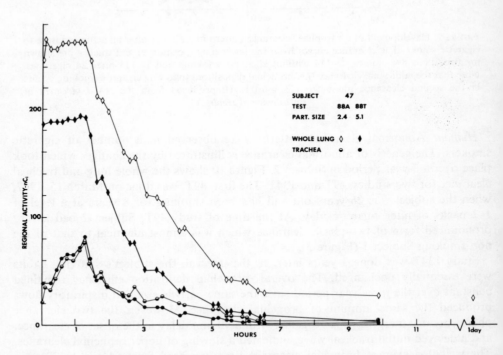

FIGURE 11. Abnormal clearance in a 32-year old cigarette smoker with a 1·4 h delay in the onset of clearance and the peak of tracheal activity.

52 min. The type of abnormal clearance pattern consisting of a pronounced delay in onset of clearance followed by a steady progression to completion may be pathognomic for cigarette smoking since it was seen in the one donkey that had residual clearance impairment (Figure 8) as well as three other human cigarette smokers, but not in any of the non-smoking humans or donkeys. Another example of this pattern is shown in Figure 11 for a 32-year old healthy male who smoked one pack of non-filtered cigarettes daily for 10 years. Several other abnormalities of clearance have been observed in smokers consisting of spasmodic clearance, tracheobronchial stasis, and refluxing of particles (Figure 12) (ALBERT *et al.*, 1969a) for abnormal clearance.

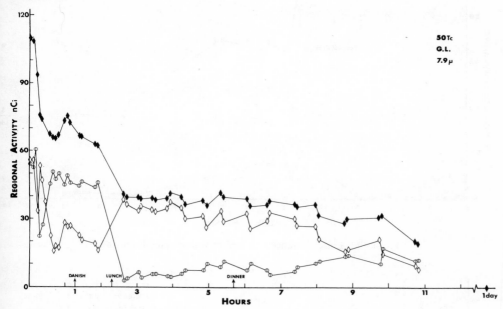

FIGURE 12. Tracheal stasis and refluxing in a 36-year old smoker. Symbols: Whole-lung = ◆. Tracheal activity = ○. Whole-lung less trachea = ◇. There is a period of tracheal stasis between 1 and 2 h with a sustained high level of tracheal activity in the absence of whole lung clearance. Between 2·0 and 2·5 h there is emptying of trachea with about half of the activity leaving the lung and the remainder sliding backward with a deeper level of the bronchial tree. (Reproduced from the *AMA Archives of Environmental Health*.)

The most pronounced delays in the onset of clearance were seen in bronchitics, an example of which is shown in Figure 13. There was no clearance for the first 5 h after inhalation of 1·5 μm particles and very slow clearance of the tracheal deposit of 3·4 μm particles. Activity appeared in the trachea immediately after the two-hour period of postural drainage and bronchodilator therapy and just before the onset of clearance. It is characteristic of bronchitics to have a very high level of bronchial deposition for small particles (LIPPMANN *et al.*, 1971).

Another study on Subject 2, which was done several months earlier than 134T shown in Figure 10, examined the effects of a 12 h period of abstinence from cigarette smoking followed by an intensive smoking exposure (Figure 14). Clearance during the 2 h period before the onset of smoking was even slower than that obtained in study 134T (Figure 10) and was unaccompanied by a tracheal activity wave. The smoking of 10 cigarettes in the brief period of about 1 h made the subject feel nauseated and resulted in a bout of productive coughing which removed almost all of the remaining bronchial deposit from the lung, *i.e.*, the time to complete bronchial clearance was foreshortened by 4–6 h. The second inhalation of particles of the same

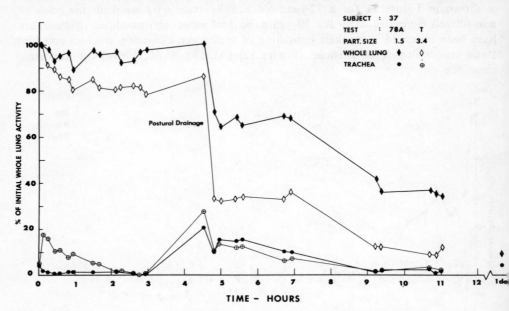

FIGURE 13. Lung clearance in a subject with chronic bronchitis.

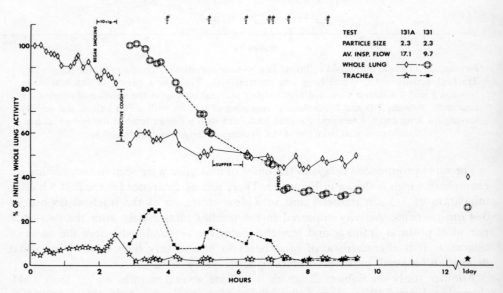

FIGURE 14. Effect of acute cigarette smoking on clearance. Run 131A was begun prior to smoking. Exposure to aerosol in 131T followed a chain-smoking episode, and showed more rapid clearance. The effect of coughing is also illustrated.

size (2·3 μm) showed an increased level of bronchial deposition because there was a greater amount of clearance in spite of a lower respiratory flow rate. The clearance of the second aerosol was substantially faster than that which occurred either after the first particle inhalation in the same study or in the later study 134T (Figure 10).

The weighted average bronchial clearance times for individual smokers is shown for various levels of bronchial deposition in Figure 15. A wide range of inter-subject variability is seen in smokers, as was the case for non-smokers (Figure 6). The only

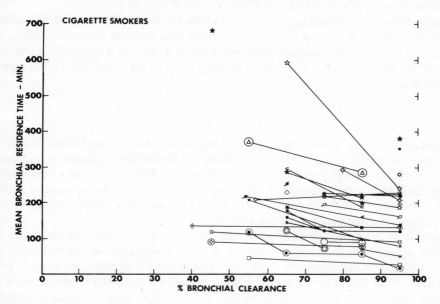

FIGURE 15. Mean bronchial residence (or clearance) times for 19 cigarette-smoking subjects.

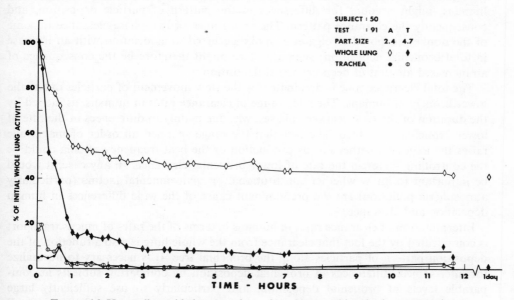

FIGURE 16. Unusually rapid clearance shown by a 30-year old male cigarette smoker.

difference in the clearance times of smokers and non-smokers occurred at the bronchial deposition level of 90–100% where the upper limit of clearance times for non-smokers was 175 min, while 10 of the 19 smoking subjects exceeded this limit. However, the average for the smokers as a group was 170 min (standard error = 18) which was not very much greater than the average of 126 min (standard error = 14) for the non-smokers. The six bronchitics thus far studied had significantly slower clearances at 90–100% bronchial deposition than non-smokers, with an average clearance time of 238 min (standard error = 33; $P \sim 0.01$).

Many of the smokers had fast clearance. In fact, the fastest clearance of any subject so far measured was that of a 30-year old male who smoked filtered cigarettes for 11 years (Figure 16). His average clearance time of 45 min at a bronchial deposition level of 50–60% was almost an order of magnitude lower than that of the slowest non-smoker.

DISCUSSION

Donkey clearance studies have been a useful adjunct to the human studies in providing information on the reproducibility of bronchial clearance in individual animals, the inter-subject variability (particularly sex differences), the predominance of tracheal and upper bronchial clearance impairment following acute cigarette smoke exposure and the rapid recovery from the clearance impairment even after tri-weekly exposures over a 6-month period.

There is no ready explanation as to why donkeys have exponential clearance and humans generally have two-phase clearance. The arrangement of the bronchial tree within the lung is quite different in the two species. In the donkey, the main bronchi emerge close to the upper end of the lung; within the lung the larger bronchi are straight tubes which run relatively parallel to the spine; their immediate branches emerge in a "fir tree" pattern. This branching pattern, which is different from that in humans, might account for differences in the pattern of particle deposition, and consequently the clearance pattern. The appearance of two-phase clearance in some of the donkeys exposed to cigarette smoke occurred in association with an increase in total bronchial deposition; such a pattern might therefore be the consequence of an increased amount of deep bronchial deposition.

The total clearance time is dominated by the slow movement of particles out of the lower bronchi in humans. The wide range of clearance rates in humans, as judged by the duration of the two clearance phases, was due mainly to differences in the rate of lower bronchial clearance. The fact that the range spanned an order of magnitude raises the issue of whether mucus production or the beat frequency of cilia could be the controlling factor in the rate of lower bronchial clearance. In any case, it would be important to know whether constitutional or environmental factors (particularly atmospheric pollution) are the predominant cause of the wide differences in human deposition and clearance.

Interpretation of clearance rates in humans in terms of the rates of mucus transport is complicated by the fact that clearance from the whole lung is also a function of the deposition pattern of particles along the bronchial tree. It is necessary to normalize for inter-subject differences in bronchial deposition by comparing subjects at comparable levels of bronchial deposition, and particularly to use sufficiently large particles in order to assess upper bronchial clearance rates and sufficiently small particles to evaluate lower bronchial clearance. Contrary to the results of PAVIA *et al.* (1970) and LUCHSINGER *et al.* (1968) who found no clearance differences between smokers and non-smokers, we have continued to find as reported earlier (ALBERT *et al.*, 1969a) in agreement with SANCHIS *et al.* (1971) that some smokers do have prolonged upper bronchial clearance, but this effect is seen only at bronchial deposition levels of 90–100%. The group averages are not very different because some of the smokers have rapid clearance, as also shown by CAMNER & PHILIPSON (1971). Although we have relatively few data at low levels of bronchial deposition, there is some suggestion of abnormally fast lower bronchial clearance in some smokers. The most striking changes associated with cigarette smoking in humans are in the patterns of clearance as illustrated in Figures 10–14, which reflect a slowing or stasis of upper bronchial clearance, spasmodic clearance, and tracheobronchial refluxing of mucus.

The above observations support a tentative pathogenesis for chronic bronchitis in cigarette smokers from the standpoint of mucociliary function. Although there is considerable inter-subject variation both in susceptibility and the rate of progression of clearance abnormalities in cigarette smokers, there are roughly three stages of increasing severity and irreversibility of mucociliary injury.

Stage 1. The early effects of smoking are rapidly reversible so that the observed abnormalities depend on the intensity of recent smoking experience; these early effects interact in various ways, some of which are antagonistic, and include: (1) increased mucus production, which tends to accelerate lower bronchial clearance; (2) bronchial constriction which tends to increase total bronchial deposition and shifts particle deposition to the more proximal parts of the bronchial tree, causing an apparent acceleration of overall lung clearance; (3) a ciliastatic effect which is greater in the trachea and larger bronchi than in the lower bronchi, thus tending to slow upper bronchial clearance more than lower bronchial clearance. Thus, in the early stages of cigarette smoking, i.e., the first one or two decades, one would expect to see (depending on the balance of the above factors) some individuals with fast lower bronchial clearance and some with slow upper bronchial clearance.

Stage 2. In moderately advanced cigarette smoking injury, equivalent to mild chronic bronchitis, excess mucus production combined with upper airway damage to the ciliated mucosa results in stasis and refluxing of mucus in the large airways and coughing. At this stage, cigarette smoking has an expectorant action which facilitates clearance; this effect might represent a dependence on the irritant action of cigarette smoking for adequate mucus flow.

Stage 3. With the severe chronic bronchitis associated with exertional dyspnea, the changes described for Stage 2 are increased in severity, and extend into the smaller airways, producing obstruction of air flow.

REFERENCES

ALBERT, R. E. & ARNETT, L. C. (1955). *A.M.A. Archs ind. Hlth* **12**, 99–106.
ALBERT, R. E., LIPPMANN, M. & BRISCOE, W. (1969a). *Archs envir. Hlth* **18**, 738–755.
ALBERT, R. E., LIPPMANN, M., SPIEGELMAN, J., STREHLOW, C., BRISCOE, W., WOLFSON, P. & NELSON, N. (1967a). In: *Inhaled particles and vapours II.* Ed. C. N. Davies. Oxford, Pergamon Press. pp. 361–378.
ALBERT, R. E., LIPPMANN, M., SPIEGELMAN, J., LIUZZI, A. & NELSON, N. (1967b). *Archs envir. Hlth* **14**, 10–15.
ALBERT, R. E., SPIEGELMAN, J., LIPPMANN, M. & BENNETT, R. (1968). *Archs envir. Hlth* **17**, 50–58.

ALBERT, R. E., SPIEGELMAN, J., SHATSKY, S. & LIPPMANN, M. (1969b). *Archs envir. Hlth* **18**, 30–41.
ALBERT, R. E. *et al.* (1970). *Archs envir. Hlth.* In Press.
CAMNER, P. & PHILIPSON, K. (1971). This Symposium. pp. 157–163.
FRANCES, R., ALESSANDRO, D., LIPPMANN, M., PROCTOR, D. E. & ALBERT, R. E. (1970). *Archs envir. Hlth* **21**, 25–31.
ISAWA, T., WASSERMAN, K. & TAPLIN, G. V. (1970). *Am. Rev. resp. Dis.* **102**, 161–172.
KLIMEK, M. F., KLICH, C. J., LEVINE, H. & LOURENCO, R. V. (1969). *J. nucl. Med.* **10**, 460.
LIPPMANN, M. & ALBERT, R. E. (1967). *Am. ind. Hyg. Ass. J.* **28**, 501–506.
LIPPMANN, M. & ALBERT, R. E. (1969). *Am. ind. Hyg. Ass. J.* **30**, 257–275.
LIPPMANN, M., ALBERT, R. E. & PETERSON, H. T. (1971). This Symposium. pp. 105–120.
LUCHSINGER, P. C., LAGARDE, B. & KILFEATHER, J. E. (1968). *Am. Rev. resp. Dis.* **97**, 1046–1050.
MORROW, P. E., GIBB, F. R. & GAZIOGLU, K. (1967). In: *Inhaled particles and vapours II.* Ed. C. N. Davies. Oxford, Pergamon Press. pp. 351–359.
NEWHOUSE, M. T., WRIGHT, F. J., DOLOVICH, M. & HOPKINS, O. L. (1970). In: *Airway dynamics.* Ed. A. Bouhuys. Springfield, Thomas. pp. 313–317.
PAVIA, D., SHORT, M. D. & THOMSON, M. L. (1970). *Nature, Lond.* **226**, 1228–1231.
SANCHIS, J., DOLOVICH, M., CHALMERS, R. & NEWHOUSE, M. T. (1971). This Symposium, pp. 183–188.
SPIEGELMAN, J. R., HANSON, G. D., LAZARUS, A., BENNETT, R. J., LIPPMANN, M. & ALBERT, R. E. (1968). *Archs envir. Hlth* **17**, 321–326.
THOMSON, M. L. & SHORT, M. D. (1969). *J. appl. Physiol.* **26**, 535–539.
TOIGO, A., IMARISIO, J. J., MURMALL, H. & LEPPER, M. N. (1963). *Am. Rev. resp. Dis.* **87**, 487–492.
WILSON, I. B. & LAMER, V. K. (1948). *J. ind. Hyg. Toxicol.* **30**, 265–270.

DISCUSSION OF PAPERS PRESENTED BY DR. SPRITZER (p. 149), DR. CAMNER (p. 157), AND DR. ALBERT (p. 165)

W. KLOSTERKOTTER: Do you think a reduction in bronchial clearance has any effect on the development of pneumoconiosis?

Dr. ALBERT: I would doubt it.

J. M. ROGAN: Could you please expand your reply to Prof. Klosterkotter's question on the relationship between dust deposition in bronchitis and pneumoconiosis. Presumably in the bronchitic, dust is deposited higher up the respiratory tracts; on the other hand clearance is reduced.

Dr. ALBERT: My reply to Dr. Klosterkotter's question concerned only the relationship of abnormal clearance to pneumoconiosis. In cases of pneumoconiosis it would not appear to be important whether the removal of particles deposited on the bronchial mucosa was somewhat slower since the disease is caused by particles deposited in the alveoli. The high bronchial deposition efficiency for particles in the bronchitic would tend to protect the alveoli.

M. NEWHOUSE: There still seems to be great confusion about the effects of smoking in man — could this have been due to differences in the experimental conditions — what in your smokers was the time relationship between smoking and the study — was it consistent and standardized? In your smoker you gave the second isotope and studied clearance, *after* the subject had started chain smoking. This would grossly alter distribution and would itself lead to a speeding of clearance.

Dr. ALBERT: From our donkey studies, it is clear that impairment of bronchial clearance by acute high level exposure to cigarette smoke is a rapidly reversible effect. One would expect that human smokers depending on their long-term and recent smoking patterns would show an admixture of rapidly and slowly reversible changes. The subject referred to by Dr. Newhouse showed a consistent slowing of clearance which developed over a three-year period without change in smoking pattern. We were astonished to find that abstinence from smoking since the previous evening produced even slower clearance in the morning; this was followed by acceleration of clearance and increased bronchial deposition immediately after a short period of intensive smoking. This observation raises the possibility that in some stage of a smoker's history there may develop a dependence on cigarette smoking for maintenance of adequate clearance.

D. C. F. MUIR: Do the results confirm something familiar to patients with long-standing chronic bronchitis — namely that the first morning cigarette is the only thing that helps them to clear their chests of mucus?

Dr. ALBERT: Yes. Clinically, this is a well-recognized effect.

Dr. SPRITZER: Does Dr. Albert think it possible to compare clearance rates in the kind of experiment where the rate is determined before stress, a stress is then given and the clearance rate measured again? I do not think you can.

I also want to make the point that deposition has to be analogous in each subject before you can compare clearance rates.

Dr. ALBERT: Experimental results have validity only within the limits of the experimental circumstances. The matter of altered clearance in an individual who has been a heavy smoker when abstaining or increasing his smoking is a particular circumstance.

On your other point, clearance rates were compared in our subjects only at comparable total levels of bronchial deposition.

J. C. GILSON: Have you any information about the amount of sputum produced by these smokers and the type of clearance curve. It is well recognized that there is a considerable variation in this respect between people who smoke a lot and have only a small increase of sputum — and other people who have a lot. Those with no increased sputum have apparently practically normal clearance curves. It is also well known that a collection of sputum first thing in the morning relates quite well with the total volume produced during the day.

Dr. ALBERT: Most of these smokers that we have studied have not had an appreciable cough. My impression is that those smokers with the type of clearance abnormality consisting of a long initial delay in clearance followed by a steady clearance to completion had very little sputum production. On the other hand, smokers with mucus refluxing did have a productive cough.

W. J. SMITHER: There are those who believe that a man with bronchitis is less likely to develop asbestosis. There are others, I am among them, who cannot accept this. I would like to add my own plea to that of Dr. Rogan for closer study of this matter. It would be unfortunate if this idea that bronchitis protects a man from asbestosis should enter the folk lore of pneumoconiosis as the idea that a cigarette "clears the bronchial tubes" has entered the folk lore of smoking.

O. G. RAABE: My question concerns the sizes of the particles used by Dr. Spritzer. You report a geometric mean diameter of $0 \cdot 4$ μm. Is this based upon optical measurement? If so does this mean that the activity median aerodynamic diameter of these particles must be equal to or greater than $0 \cdot 4$ μm?

Dr. SPRITZER: Yes, that is true. They were irregularly shaped particles. We specifically did not want uniformity because we wanted to test whether exposure to particles which were not uniform would give a meaningful density distribution parameter.

REGIONAL DISTRIBUTION AND LUNG CLEARANCE
MECHANISMS IN SMOKERS AND NON-SMOKERS*

J. Sanchis, M. Dolovich, R. Chalmers and M. T. Newhouse

Respiratory Unit, St. Joseph's Hospital and McMaster Medical School, Hamilton, Canada

Abstract — The distribution and clearance of an inhaled heterodisperse aerosol of I131 tagged human serum albumin solution was compared quantitatively in a group of smokers undergoing a repeated smoking exposure, as well as a control group of non-smokers. Data were obtained by means of a scintillation camera-multichannel analyzer-magnetic tape computer system for three crescentic areas of right lung providing data from an inner perihilar zone (mainly large ciliated airways), an intermediate, and a peripheral zone (mainly small ciliated and non-ciliated airways and alveoli). Our data indicate that in smokers there is a considerable slowing of the normally fast first clearance phase in large airways and at the same time a relative speeding of the second clearance phase, resulting in a relative accumulation of activity at the hilus, i.e. "log-jam" effect. In addition, considerably less inhaled aerosol was deposited distal to the ciliated airway in smokers than non-smokers, as evidenced by an abnormal peripheral clearance curve, as well as the retention in non-smokers of approximately twice as much activity in the lung at the end of 24 hours, strongly suggesting the presence of small airway obstruction in otherwise healthy smokers.

The effect of tobacco smoke on mucociliary function has been the subject of many reports. These have shown inhibition in some (Albert *et al.*, 1969; Ballenger, 1960; Krahl & Bulmash, 1969), no effect whatever in others (Blair, 1966; Thompson & Short, 1969) and, in rare instances, even stimulation of clearance (Albert *et al.*, 1969).

In none of the previous human studies was it clear whether the subjects were merely chronic smokers undergoing investigation of mucociliary clearance or whether during the procedure, they were actually being repeatedly exposed to cigarette smoke. We therefore set out to study regional mucociliary clearance in smokers given a relatively standardized smoking exposure and compared them to a similar group of healthy non-smokers.

METHOD

We studied two groups of healthy adult volunteers, mainly females, the study group consisting of nine subjects who had smoked over 15 cigarettes a day for more than five years, who, according to the British Medical Research Council Bronchitis Questionnaire, had only minimal or no evidence of bronchitis (Med. Res. Council,

* Supported by Can. TB and RD Assn., Muskoka Hospital Foundation, Ont. Thoracic Soc. and M.R.C.

1960). The control group consisted mainly of young females who had never smoked and did not smoke during the present study. Biometric data were similar in both groups.

The experimental design was identical for both except for the fact that the smokers inhaled a cigarette of their favourite brand every 20 to 30 minutes throughout the day, starting immediately after inhalation of labelled aerosol, while the control group did not smoke. Smokers abstained from smoking for at least one hour prior to aerosol inhalation because it has been shown that smoking may produce a considerable acute alteration of flow resistance and distribution of ventilation (Nadel & Comroe, 1961; James, 1970). Prior to inhaling the radioactive aerosol, subjects were given 15 drops of Lugol's iodine to block thyroid uptake of I131. Furthermore, subjects were trained in a slow breathing pattern to, as far as possible, reproduce relaxed resting tidal ventilation. They were carefully positioned in front of the scintillation camera as described previously (Newhouse et al., 1970), so that the camera could "look at" the whole of the right lung. Marks were then made on the upper anterior thorax and lighted arrows from flashlights fastened to the opposite wall focused on them. This allowed precise repositioning throughout the study and made it unnecessary for subjects to remain completely still except during fairly brief periods of data collection. Prior to inhalation of I131 labelled human serum albumin aerosol (RISA), subjects re-breathed Xe 135 for three to five minutes until equilibration had been achieved and the distribution of radioactivity in the lung was then recorded photographically and stored simultaneously in a multichannel analyzer. This manoeuvre allowed us to delineate the edge of the lung accurately and provided a reference point for the analysis of aerosol distribution and clearance. After all the Xe 135 had been washed out of the lung, subjects inhaled RISA aerosol from an ultrasonic nebulizer which provided a droplet aerosol of mass median diameter 3 μm (range 1 μm to 10 μm) determined by means of a Cascade Impactor and confirmed by electron microscopy. RISA was inhaled at tidal volumes between six and seven hundred cm^3 and a frequency of 12 to 14 per minute from a non-rebreathing circuit for a period of ten minutes. This provided approximately 50 000 counts from the right lung of our subjects in a period of five minutes at the beginning of the procedure.

Within two minutes of inhaling aerosol, subjects were seated in front of the scintillation camera and data were collected and stored as previously described (Newhouse et al., 1968). For the purpose of the present study, data were collected from about 30 areas of lung 2·5 cm square grouped into three crescentic zones arranged concentrically about the lung hilus. The outer and intermediate zones were each 2·5 cm wide, while the inner lung zone varied between 5 and 7·5 cm, depending on the size of the individual lung. Following the initial data collection, which provided information about the distribution of the inhaled lung burden of RISA, repeat measurements were undertaken every 15 minutes for two hours, every 30 minutes for the next two hours, and then hourly for approximately eight hours, with repeat determinations on two or three occasions the following day.

In order to obtain clearance curves, the per cent retention of activity in the lung was followed as a function of time, starting with 100% at time 0 for each of the areas described. These were selected arbitrarily, so as to provide regions from which data could be obtained representing activity from mainly ciliated, major airways (inner perihilar zone), largely non-ciliated airway (peripheral zone) and an intermediate area which reflects both of these regions.

To compare data in smokers and non-smokers, individual clearance curves were obtained from each of the three lung zones in each subject, were smoothed graphically and then averaged for the ten smokers and nine non-smokers, as seen in Figures 1A and B. To obtain clearance half times, the technique of "stripping off" exponentials was used and the result plotted in Figure 2.

All subjects were free of any previous or present history of known pulmonary disease and had completely normal pulmonary function studies, as seen in Table 1:

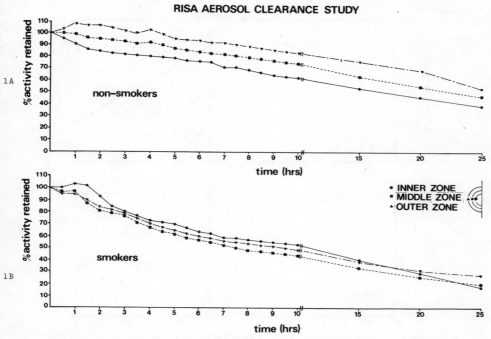

FIGURES 1A and B. RISA aerosol clearance — comparison of non-smokers and smokers.

TABLE I. PULMONARY FUNCTION. MEAN VALUES

	Smokers	Non-Smokers
Age, yrs	33	31
V.C.	3·94	3·7
I.C.	2·68	2·33
E.R.V.	1·22	1·33
F.R.C.	2·65	2·82
R.V.	1·42	1·48
T.L.C.	5·33	5·15
M.E. %	58	56
Max. M.E.F.R. l/s	4·08	4·58
F.E.V. (1·0). l/s	3·38	3·35
$D_L CO.$ (ss).Rest	15·9	16·8
$D_L CO.$ Fractional	0·46	0·47
V_T ml	705	565

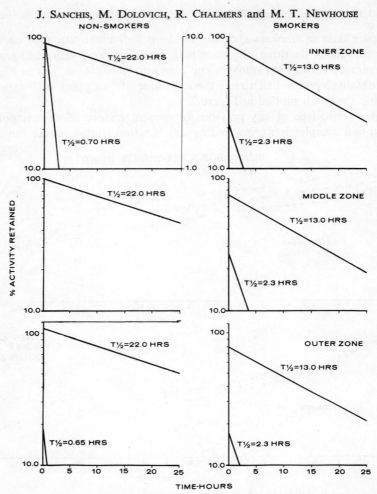

FIGURE 2. Stripped exponentials from curves in 1A and B.

RESULTS

Comparison of Figures 1A and B shows that the shape of the clearance curves in non-smokers and smokers was quite different, as were the clearance half times shown in Figure 2. In the perihilar zone in non-smokers, there is an immediate fairly rapid decrease in activity or fast first phase of clearance, with a $T_{1/2}$ of $0 \cdot 70$ hours, followed by a second much slower phase with a $T_{1/2}$ of 22 hours. By contrast, the same zone in the smoking group shows very little change in activity for the first two hours, after which activity decreases with a $T_{1/2}$ of $2 \cdot 3$ hours, followed by a second clearance phase of $T_{1/2}$ 13 hours.

In the intermediate zone, the $T_{1/2}$ for non-smokers was 22 hours, while that for smokers was 13 hours. However, there were no striking differences in the shapes of the two curves.

The peripheral zone again showed considerable differences between non-smokers and smokers, the former showing an initial small increase in activity for about $1 \cdot 5$ hours with a $T_{1/2}$ of $0 \cdot 65$ hours, following which there is a slow phase of clearance with a $T_{1/2}$ of 22 hours. In smokers, on the other hand, this clearance pattern is absent and the peripheral zone is identical to the intermediate zone, with clearance half times of 2·3 and 13 hours respectively.

It is also of interest that at the end of 24 hours, when removal of activity by the mucociliary escalator is generally thought to be complete, about twice as much of the initially deposited activity was present in non-smokers than smokers.

DISCUSSION

A number of inter-related factors determine both the deposition and removal of an inhaled droplet or particulate aerosol from the lung. Deposition of an aerosol such as the one used in this study will depend mainly upon impaction of larger aerosol droplets proximally, and sedimentation of smaller droplets (less than 5 μm) more peripherally. Among other things, the uniformity of deposition and penetration of droplets to the periphery of the lung will depend upon such things as flow rates and patency of peripheral airways. The clearance of the inhaled lung burden will in turn depend upon deposition, as well as the quantity and quality of mucous production and ciliary function.

Our data support previous evidence in animals and man that cigarette smoking inhibits mucociliary transport, but does not suggest that a fairly heavy smoking exposure such as that seen in normal man, causes complete paralysis of ciliary movement, as suggested by BALLENGER (1960). Furthermore, the relative accumulation of activity in the perihilar area which persists during the initial clearance period in smokers, together with slowing of the first clearance phase and acceleration of the second clearance phase, suggests a differential effect of inhaled cigarette smoke on the airway. FALK et al. (1959), in animal studies, showed that the greatest ciliary depressant effects were noted in those parts of the respiratory tract exposed to the largest concentration of particulate matter in smoke, while when such particles were completely eliminated by filtration, little or no effect on ciliary function could be observed. It seems reasonable to suggest, therefore, that in our smoking subjects, whose proximal airways were exposed to the highest concentration of smoke and particulate material, inhibition of clearance should occur, while in the more peripheral airway, the more dilute smoke might have very little effect on the respiratory mucosa and could even act as a ciliary stimulant. As a result, inflow of mucous into the perihilar airways could be expected to exceed removal, resulting in a "log-jam" effect, as seen in our studies.

In spite of the slower first phase clearance in smokers, they paradoxically cleared the inhaled RISA from their lungs more quickly than normal. This was obviously due to the fact that a much smaller percentage of the inhaled aerosol was delivered to that part of the airway distal to the terminal bronchiole (i.e. non-ciliated airway) and this strongly suggests the presence of small airway obstruction in otherwise apparently healthy young smokers. Much of this effect on the small airway might be acute rather than chronic and further studies are being done to clarify this.

Acknowledgements — We wish to acknowledge the considerable help provided by our volunteers, the Department of Physics and Chemistry at McMaster University, Mr. Monti Smith for his technical assistance, and the Department of Nuclear Medicine at St. Joseph's Hospital.

We would also like to express our thanks to Dr. Paul Morrow and Dr. Thomas Mercer of the

188   J. SANCHIS, M. DOLOVICH, R. CHALMERS and M. T. NEWHOUSE

Radiation Biology Institute, University of Rochester Medical School, for their great help in droplet size measurement, as well as their critical encouragement of our studies.

REFERENCES

ALBERT, R. E., LIPPMAN, M. & BRISCOE, W. (1969). *Archs envir. Hlth* **18**, 738–755.
BALLENGER, J. J. (1960). *New Engl. J. Med.* **263**, 832–835.
BLAIR, W. J. (1966). *Pacif. NW. Lab. A. Rep.* 1965 BNWL 280, 66–70.
DALHAMN, T. (1956). *Acta physiol. scand.* **36**, Suppl. 123.
FALK, H. L., TREMER, H. M. & KOTIN, P. (1959). *J. natn. Cancer Inst.* **23**, 999–1012.
JAMES, R. H. (1970). *Am. Rev. resp. Dis.* **101**, 105–107.
KRAHL, V. E., BULMASH, M. H. (1969). *Am. Rev. resp. Dis.* **99**, 711–718.
MEDICAL RESEARCH COUNCIL (1960). *Br. med. J.* **2**, 1665.
NADEL, J. A. & COMROE, J. H. Jr. (1961). *J. appl. Physiol.* **16**, 713–716.
NEWHOUSE, M. T., WRIGHT, F. J., DOLOVICH, M. & HOPKINS, O. L. (1970). *Airway dynamics. Ed:* A. Bouhuys. Springfield, Thomas. pp. 313–317.
NEWHOUSE, M. T., WRIGHT, F. J., INGHAM, G. K., ARCHER, N. P., HUGHES, L. B. & HOPKINS, O. L. (1968). *Respir. Physiol.* **4**, 141–153.
THOMSON, M. L. & SHORT, M. D. (1969). *J. appl. Physiol.* **26**, 535–539.

DISCUSSION

M. LIPPMAN: The particles were organic and may be subject to clearance by methods other than mucociliary. Do you have any evidence of this?

Dr. NEWHOUSE: Yes, we made blood studies and the curves were totally different from the lung curves. Only about 4 per cent of the lung activity appeared in the blood in 24 hours, and we did not feel that this could seriously alter our results.

Furthermore, in some studies the subject's hand was placed on the camera adjacent to the chest wall. Using the hand as an analogue of the chest wall, which has much the same structure, we were not able to detect activity from the hand throughout the study.

S. E. DEVIR: Did you actually determine the size distribution of the aerosol droplets; does not the size of the droplets change (by evaporation) before inhalation? The size distribution of your aerosol is not comparable to that produced by cigarettes. Do you know what the electrical charge was on the aerosol?

Dr. NEWHOUSE: No. The point of the study was to see whether smoking produced some change in the clearance, not to compare our aerosols with cigarette smoke. The particulate material in cigarette smoke is deposited for the most part approximately in the area where the hold-up of activity in our studies was demonstrated. Our aerosol particles had a small electric charge of about one unit; this was measured by Dr. Mercer and his associates at Rochester.

J. E. COTES: The findings do not differentiate between the long term and the short term effects of smoking. Do you have data for subjects who abstained from smoking for a longer period than one hour before exposure and also for smokers who did not smoke during the period of clearance?

Dr. NEWHOUSE: Most of our smokers abstained for considerably longer than the minimum period of one hour prior to the start of the study; most did not smoke at all on the morning of the study. The clearance in smokers who have not smoked for a day is not as abnormal as that demonstrated in our paper. These studies are in process and I cannot give the final results yet.

D. C. F. MUIR: Is it possible that a larger fraction of the inhaled cloud is deposited in the lungs of smokers and that the alveolar burden is greater despite the more rapid clearance?

Dr. NEWHOUSE: The absolute counts show that this is not so. There are fewer counts in the periphery of the lung in smokers at the beginning of a study than in non-smokers.

R. E. ALBERT: I am impressed with the extraordinary uniformity with respect to the deposition and rates of clearance in the individual groups. I envy you because I have had experience of a wide range of deposition and clearance characteristics.

How do you distinguish between altered bronchial deposition and impaired clearance? We have observed healthy, non-smoking individuals who have a wave of activity passing through the trachea which simulates the wave of activity seen on your curve for smokers. We regard this as being related to the initial deposition pattern rather than to an effect of clearance. You have shown that the two groups differ in deposition pattern, how can you be sure that the clearance process is slow in the smokers? Perhaps you could have obtained a similar pattern by using larger particles with the non-smokers.

Dr. NEWHOUSE: We cannot be sure that the wave or plateau in the activity-time curve represents delayed clearance. We are looking at a situation where particles are entering a region as well as being cleared from it. We can only observe the net change, and this only represents the absolute clearance from a region after the peripheral region has been cleared so that no further activity enters the region being studied.

The rapid-component of the clearance in normal subjects had a half time of about 42 minutes. In smokers the half time was considerably longer, 2·3 hours. We assume that clearance at this rate was effective from the start of the experiment. This would seem to be a reasonable assumption since the subjects began smoking immediately after inhaling the aerosol and continued to smoke a cigarette every 20 minutes throughout the period of the study.

A. M. COETZEE: Would the speaker please comment on the inference that smokers exposed to a dusty environment would inhale less dust into their alveoli than non-smokers.

Dr. NEWHOUSE: Your conclusion is correct, a miner who smokes all day will probably deposit relatively less dust peripherally. However, I do not think one should conclude that it would be useful for a miner to smoke, since it has been shown that a combination of the effects of smoking and inhaling dust is even worse for the lung than either one alone.

K. ROBOCK: The results are in good agreement with the measurements of Professor Klosterkotter

(*Silikoseberichte Nordrhein Westfalen* 7, 1969) who found that rats, in long term experiments (six months or so), have a better lung clearance when they have inhaled tobacco smoke after inhalation of quartz dust.

Dr. NEWHOUSE: That is interesting, but has little bearing on our study.

P. C. PRATT: I should like to mention that my examinations of smokers' lungs at autopsy by quantitative methods reveal that smokers do indeed accumulate more pigment than non-smokers in the same environment. This will be reported in detail (see p. 661).

M. NAVRATIL: Does lung clearance of smokers and non-smokers show a relationship with the pulmonary mixing curves of nitrogen or helium?

Dr. NEWHOUSE: Most of our subjects were smokers of less than ten years' duration. We did pulmonary function studies including helium mixing curves, and we found no abnormality whatsoever. I suspect that the helium mixing test is not sensitive enough to detect these changes.

The normal subjects, for the most part, were nuns who lived in an air-conditioned building most of their lives. They were not smokers, and they were not exposed to industrial fumes.

N. KAVOUSSI: My recent experiments have shown no difference between the smoker and non-smoker as regards pathogenic dusts producing pneumoconiosis. But in my recent work on the incidence of pneumoconiosis in the silos of Teheran, I found less pulmonary disease in the smoker than in the non-smoker.

Dr. NEWHOUSE: I still do not think that it is a good idea to smoke.

J. C. GILSON: Epidemiological evidence in the U.K. indicates that pneumoconiosis in coalminers is not related to smoking. In foundry workers the findings are different, the more the smoking the more the amount of pneumoconiosis. Foundry workers may smoke while being exposed to dust, but this is not so of course in coalmining where smoking is prohibited.

M. GRUNSPAN: What is to be understood by "small airway obstruction", an anatomical change or a bronchial spasm? This can be examined by use of a bronchodilatory aerosol. Our own observations on the guineapig show that smoking causes broncho-spasm. This can be prevented by the use of an isopropolyladrenalin but not with antihistamine. The question is what is the cause in tobacco smoking, the substances that stem from the burning of paper or from the burning of tobacco?

Dr. NEWHOUSE: We are doing studies now to determine whether the change is chronic or reversible. I do not know the answer to your second question but perhaps one might be able to establish this by delivering the cigarette smoke through an inert holder.

K. F. KERREBIJN: What is the influence of cough on the clearance rate of your smokers?

Dr. NEWHOUSE: None of our smokers coughed during the study. They were young people who had not been smokers for an extremely long period of time, and they did not have chronic bronchitis. This was established by use of the MRC questionnaire prior to the study. We are studying cough now in other subjects.

M. L. THOMSON: We have found that clearing the throat (without coughing) can remove appreciable quantities of radioactively tagged aerosol from the lungs.

Dr. NEWHOUSE: Our smokers did not in any way suggest that they were clearing mucus out of their lungs other than by ciliary mechanisms.

D. C. F. MUIR: Were the non-smokers a selected group who had not taken up the habit because they had unusual airways and reacted more violently than usual on first attempting to smoke?

Dr. NEWHOUSE: I have mentioned that most of the non-smokers were nuns. They certainly took up the habit but it was not the smoking habit.

M. CORN: Caution is urged in extrapolating these results to field situations involving occupational exposure to dust, with or without smoking. The interaction between cigarette smoke and dust is complex, whether on a simultaneous exposure or sequential exposure basis. As an illustration, in a recent medical screening of cotton textile workers, every worker with diagnosed byssinosis based on pulmonary function tests, was a smoker. This contrasts with the controversial findings with coalminers and smokers.

J. FERIN: One cannot compare this experiment with the situation of miners. For example, the subjects inhaled the test aerosol only once, whereas miners inhale dust particles multiple times. Commenting on the remark of Dr. Robock, I found in rats that cigarette smoke decreases the clearance of SiO_2 particles (single exposures of smoke and particles). It seems that much depends on the circumstances of the experiment.

A. A. SPRITZER: If particulate deposition in the smoking population differs from deposition in the controls, you cannot legitimately compare variation of clearance rates. To do this you must assume that you are dealing with analogous pulmonary compartments in both groups. If the stress does alter clearance rate kinetics, there is no assurance that the measurements are dealing with comparable compartments.

A. MORGAN: What were the amounts of radioactivity administered in those experiments, were any measurements of urinary clearance made? Did you check the thyroid for iodine?

Dr. NEWHOUSE: The total dose of radioactivity, including re-breathing, was between 200 and 300 μCi; the I 131 comprised about two-thirds of that. There was no radioactive iodine in the thyroid as we blocked this with Lugol's iodine prior to the study.

Y. IRAVANI: You measured the total clearance function. In rats and hamsters which had been exposed to cigarette smoke, we observed multiple areas with altered ciliary function mainly in the trachea and upper portions of the airway. The abnormalities were very similar to those we found in bronchitis. Because of the compensatory improvement of the mumociliary activity in the intervening mucosa, the total clearance of mucus only showed a significant diminution if the areas with abnormal ciliary mechanism were present in great number. The overall clearance of inhaled tagged materials is therefore inefficient in studies of the effects of pollutants as long as the response is confined to a relatively small portion of the ciliated epithelium.

You have compared nuns with smokers, rather than normal non-smokers. I have found that SPF rats, compared with normal ones, showed much less clearance in their airways.

Dr. NEWHOUSE: I am not sufficiently sure of the circumstances of your experiment to relate it to our data.

We were trying to find people who were least likely to have any impediment of their clearance mechanisms. To compare the general population with smokers would be doing a slightly different experiment.

L. LE BOUFFANT: Your study deals with short periods and the results concern essentially bronchial clearance but not alveolar clearance. This latter (as we have demonstrated) can perhaps be reduced by the inhalation of dusts or tobacco smoke without this appearing during the first hours of measurement. Studies of long duration utilizing an appropriately labelled radioactive marker can show the eventual alteration in alveolar clearance.

RETENTION KINETICS OF INHALED FUSED ALUMINOSILICATE PARTICLES*

ROBERT G. THOMAS

Fission Product Inhalation Program,
Lovelace Foundation for Medical Education and Research,
Albuquerque, New Mexico 87108, USA

Abstract — Inhalation of aluminosilicate particles fused with radionuclide tracers resulted in different retention patterns among mice, rats and dogs. The differential retention has been ascribed to the difference in particle size distribution reaching the deep lung, and dissolution has been treated as the only means of loss to the blood. From a model previously presented and described herein, the controlling half-lives of retention in the lung are 50 days for mice, 200 days for rats and 400 days for dogs. Based on these variant half-lives and a solubility of 10^{-7} gm/cm² per day for aluminosilicates, median diameters for the particles deposited in the lung were calculated as 0·22, 0·88 and 1·76 μm, respectively, for the mouse, rat and dog.

INTRODUCTION

THE effects of various radiation characteristics upon tissues of the respiratory tract are of concern to those responsible for evaluating the inhalation hazards associated with the nuclear industry. Both quality of the incident particles and the rate at which their energy is delivered are important variables worthy of study. One experimental approach to the problem is to use a common aerosol vehicle to deposit radioactive sources in animals, by inhalation. In this laboratory, the radionuclide of interest has been encapsulated, by heat fusion, into an aluminosilicate (montmorillonite clay). By maintaining the particle-size distribution characteristics, reasonably consistent initial deposition patterns can be attained in the respiratory tract, thus restricting the ensuing biological effects to a comparison of the physical characteristics of the encapsulated radionuclide.

A by-product of such studies, and the subject of this paper, is the ability to describe certain biological parameters of the aluminosilicate particles by following the behavior of the encapsulated radioactive tracer. An interspecies comparison of the behavior of these particles is described in the form of a rather universal model. The solubilization characteristics in the lung fluid of mice, rats and dogs are described in terms of the particle size distributions that must be present in the three species. As might be expected, the mouse appears to deposit a much smaller particle distribution; however, since the surface-to-mass ratio is large compared to that of the dog, the solubilization would be much greater.

* This work performed under USAEC Contract AT(29–2)–1013 between the United Statee Atomic Energy Commission and Lovelace Foundation for Medical Education and Research.

METHODS

Aerosol production techniques were similar for all biological studies to be reported. The two radionuclides used, ^{144}Ce and ^{137}Cs, were first exchanged with the raw ground aluminosilicate particles by mixing at room temperature. The raw clay had previously been "packed" with sodium to replace the more tenaciously bound di-valent cations that normally occupy exchange sites within the lattice. The ^{144}Ce and ^{137}Cs thus exchanged readily with the sodium, giving a suspension of labeled clay particles. The suspension was subsequently nebulized during animal inhalation exposure, and the droplets passed through a heating column at $1100°$ C. The resulting spherical particles, now fused aluminosilicate containing radionuclide, were then directed toward the animal's nose and a fraction subsequently deposited in the respiratory tract. The aerosols were log-normally distributed, and generally had activity median aerodynamic diameters (AMAD) of approximately $1·5$ to $2·0$ μm, with a geometric standard deviation (σ_g) less than $2·0$. The preparation of these aerosols has been detailed elsewhere (McKnight & Norgon, 1967; Raabe, 1971).

The dogs used in the inhalation studies were obtained from the Lovelace Beagle colony. Single exposures of approximately 10 min duration were given in an exposure apparatus designed for one dog per run (Boecker et al., 1969). Radioactivity localization within the dogs after exposure was determined by profile scanning or gross whole-body counting, with tissue distribution data being obtained through serial sacrifice. The data used in the ensuing discussion were taken from experiments by others and have been detailed previously (Boecker et al., 1969). The rat exposures to ^{137}Cs fused into the aluminosilicate particles have also been described previously (Thomas, 1969). Albino rats of the Holtzman strain were similarly subjected to the aerosol for approximately 10 min. Following exposure, they were whole-body counted at regular intervals; periodic deaths or sacrifices enabled the accumulation of tissue

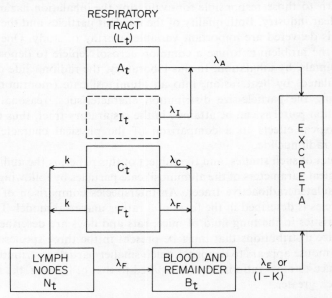

Figure 1. Compartmental model showing the likely pathways for radionuclides having entered the respiratory tract in fused, aluminosilicate particles.

distribution data. As opposed to the dogs and rats, mice were not exposed nose-only, but in more of a head-only configuration. They were held in position in test tubes which had the bottom removed. The open end was inserted into an exposure chamber into which the aerosol was introduced. After inhalation, the mice were whole-body counted and serially sacrificed to yield tissue distribution data with time post-exposure. The data on mice to be discussed are from studies by MORGAN et al. (1970).

It is re-emphasized that, for the discussion to follow, the experimental data on mice and dogs are from studies by other investigators. This paper is designed to describe the overall behavior of aluminosilicate particles in body fluids, not to detail the individual studies except where necessary to emphasize a point.

RESULTS AND DISCUSSION

A model recently described by the author appears to be sufficiently universal to fit retention data from a number of inhaled, relatively insoluble materials (THOMAS, 1970). The model (Figure 1) describes an interspecies comparison of major lung retention using first order (exponential) kinetics. The lung is divided into two compartments, one (noted as F) with an arbitrary very long retention half-life of 10 000 days and the other (noted as C) with a half-life of retention which is species dependent. For the mouse, retention appears to be 50 days; for the rat, 200 days; and for the dog, 400 days. An additional intermediate lung compartment (I) must be added for rodent data ($t_{1/2} = 15$ days) to make the theory fit the data. Although it is not certain what this component really represents, it appears to be necessary to fit the whole-body retention data from studies with mice and rats, and represents about 20% of the initial body burden. To complete this metabolic scheme for inhaled materials, a fraction, k, is assumed removed from each lung compartment (C and F) for translocation to the tracheo-bronchial lymph nodes. The rest of the body, referred to as remainder, builds up solely from the lung and lymph node compartments. Loss from the latter also assumes a half-life of 10000 days. Excretion has been handled in two ways in this model, either by exponential loss of what enters the blood (remainder) or by stating that a constant fraction, K, of what enters the blood is retained for an extremely long time. Thus, for the dog, the model gives the following simple scheme.

Respiratory tract burden, $L_t = A_0 e^{-\lambda_A t} + C_0 e^{-(\lambda_C + k)t} + F_0 e^{-(\lambda_F + k)t}$

Rate of build up in lymph nodes, $\dfrac{dN_t}{dt} = kC_t + kF_t - \lambda_F N_t$,

where C_t and F_t are the amounts present in these lung compartments at any time, t, and N_t is the quantity in lymph nodes at any time.

Rate of buildup in remainder of the body, $\dfrac{dB_t}{dt} = \lambda_C C_t + \lambda_F F_t + \lambda_F N_t - \lambda_E B_t$,

where λ_E is the rate of excretion for those materials entering the blood which have a finite residence time in the remainder sample (internal organs), and B_t is the amount there at any time.

For those materials having the fraction K which remains indefinitely after entering the blood,

$$\left(\frac{dB_t}{dt}\right)\left(\frac{1}{K}\right) = \lambda_C C_t + \lambda_F F_t + \lambda_F N_t.$$

Use of these equations from the model has been successful in describing the biological behavior of fused aluminosilicate particles, as will be discussed below.

Whole-body counting data from studies with mice, rats and dogs are shown in Figure 2, as percent of the initial count. The inhaled aluminosilicate particles were

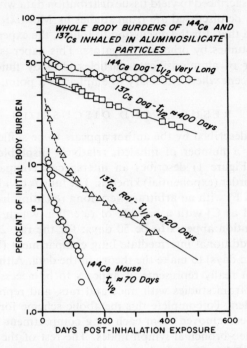

FIGURE 2. Whole-body retention patterns for [144]Ce and ^{137}Cs inhaled in aluminosilicate particles by mice, rats and dogs. Half-lives indicated were derived by eye-fitting the long-term data points.

labeled either with [144]Ce or ^{137}Cs, as indicated. It should first be noted that the long-term component of retention (biological) is smaller for mice (≈ 70 days), and rats (≈ 220 days) than for dogs. The second feature of Figure 2 is the profound difference between the two dog studies with ^{137}Cs leaving the body with a half-life of 400 days, and [144]Ce leaving very slowly. Let us consider these two points in light of the known metabolic behavior of these two radionuclides, along with the use of the above-mentioned model equation.

Cesium is very soluble in body fluids and demonstrates reported retention half-lives of 20–40 days (BOECKER, 1969; RICHMOND, 1958; NORRIS, 1964). Cerium, conversely, has a very long retention time in liver and bone and inhalation studies with the soluble chloride indicate that retention in these organs should not be described exponentially, but rather by a scheme such as the aforementioned K constant (BOECKER et al., 1969). A fraction of the cerium entering the blood from lung is retained tenaciously by the composite internal organs (remainder sample). Thus in one of the two dog cases illustrated, the 400-day half-life of retention in compartment C is used along with an exponential mode of excretion. A value of 25 days for the half-life of ^{137}Cs generates theoretical curves for the three major body compartments, as shown in Figure 3A. The fits could be made closer for lymph nodes and the internal organs by altering certain constants, but the principle involved is the important thing. It should be noted that the remainder sample quickly begins to level off and both it and the lymph nodes comprise a small fraction of the body burden. Thus, the whole-body curve for ^{137}Cs in Figure 2 shows a loss with the retention characteristic of lung compartment C, namely $t_{1/2} = 400$ days. The ^{144}Ce data in Figure 3B, however, show a different scheme, as described above. The remainder sample becomes more and more controlling of the whole-body burden, leading to the long retention time shown. Here the

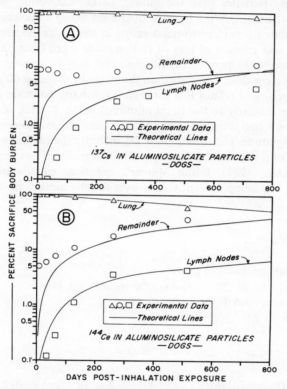

FIGURE 3. Comparison of theoretical estimates and actual data following inhalation of labeled aluminosilicate particles by the Beagle dog. Top graph (A) is for ^{137}Cs and bottom graph (B) is for ^{144}Ce.

constant K was valued at 0·5 but perhaps should be larger. This means that at least 50% of the ^{144}Ce entering the blood from lung is held tenaciously in internal organs such as liver and bone. Similar schemes have been used for the smaller species, rats and mice, but are not illustrated here. The lymph node samples from these smaller animals are difficult to quantitate also, but it can be done when extreme care is taken. To match the rat data shown, a $t_{1/2}$ for ^{137}Cs of approximately 10 days is used (RICHMOND, 1958; STARA & THOMAS, 1963), and for ^{144}Ce in mice the same constant K is used as for the dog.

The range in retention times for the controlling lung compartment, C, between laboratory subjects, is intriguing. If one ascribes to Mercer's premise that all material which leaves the deep lung (compartment C and F) does so solely by dissolution, then obviously solubility of aluminosilicate particles in the mouse is greater than in the rat, which is greater than in the dog (MERCER, 1967). It would thus appear, providing all aerosols inhaled were the same, that the surface to mass ratio of those particles reaching the lung was differing between species. This appears logical when one considers the anatomy of the respiratory tract for the three species. It is easy to speculate that larger particles in a distribution would find it more difficult to reach the lower tract in the case of the mouse. One would expect the dog, conversely, to deposit much larger particles than the mouse, perhaps covering particle diameters over the entire distribution. With the size of the rat being somewhere between, one might easily speculate on surface-to-mass ratios in the order described. Considering dissolution as the sole process of loss of radionuclide from lung, the Mercer model can be used to describe the particle distribution that may be present in the deep lung of these species. Mercer describes a median diameter in the lung (D_m) in terms of an effective half-life ($t_{1/2}$) and relates this through a solubility constant k. For materials expected to behave similarly to the fused aluminosilicate, a value of 10^{-7} g/cm^2 per day is probably not a bad estimate for k. Mercer cites several references giving values on this order of magnitude. His equation for D_m includes the surface and volume shape factors α_s and α_v for a sphere; the density ρ for this material has been determined to be $2 \cdot 3$ g/cm^3 (RAABE, 1969). Using Mercer's notation, calculations of a median diameter based on the compartment C half-lives for the mouse, rat and dog give the following results.

$$D_m = \frac{t_{1/2}\alpha_s k}{0 \cdot 6 \alpha_v \rho}$$

where $\rho = 2 \cdot 3$ g/cm^3

$t_{1/2} = 50, 200, 400$ days for mouse, rat, dog

$\alpha_s/\alpha_v = 6 \cdot 0$ for a sphere

$k = 10^{-7}$ g/cm^2 per day

For Mouse

$$D_m = \frac{50}{0 \cdot 6} (6 \cdot 0) \left(\frac{10^{-7}}{2 \cdot 3}\right) = 2 \cdot 2 \times 10^{-5} \text{ cm} = 0 \cdot 22 \ \mu\text{m}$$

For Rat

$$D_m = 0 \cdot 88 \ \mu\text{m}$$

For Dog

$$D_m = 1 \cdot 76 \ \mu\text{m}$$

There is something unrealistically large about the value for the dog, in that the aerodynamic median diameter of the inhaled particles was barely in this range. Very little change in k, however, would reduce this proportionately. For instance, a value of 5×10^{-8} g/cm^2 per day would reduce these values by one-half, a value more realistic with the size distribution breathed.

REFERENCES

BOECKER, B. B. (1969). *Proc. Soc. exp. Biol. Med.* **130,** 966–971.

BOECKER, B. B. *et al.* (1969). USAEC Res. Dev. Rep. LF–41, pp. 19–35, 105–110, 8–14. Albuquerque, Lovelace Foundation for Medical Education and Research.

MCKNIGHT, M. E. & NORGON, R. W. E. (1967). USAEC Res. Dev. Rep. LF–37. Albuquerque, Lovelace Foundation for Medical Education and Research.

MERCER, T. T. (1967). *Hlth Phys.* **13,** 1211–1221.

MORGAN, B. N., THOMAS, R. G. & MCCLELLAN, R. O. (1970). *Am. ind. Hyg. Ass. J.* **31,** 479–484.

NORRIS, W. P. *et al.* (1964). USAEC Res. Dev. Rep. ANL–6971.

RAABE, O. G. (1969). USAEC Res. Dev. Rep. LF–41, pp. 70–74. Albuquerque, Lovelace Foundation for Medical Education and Research.

RAABE, O. G. (1971). This Symposium, pp. 3–17.

RICHMOND, C. R. (1958). USAEC Res. Dev. Rep. LA–2207.

STARA, J. F. & THOMAS, R. G. (1963). USAEC Res. Dev. Rep. LF–4. Albuquerque, Lovelace Foundation for Medical Education and Research.

THOMAS, R. G. (1969). USAEC Res. Dev. Rep. LF–41, pp. 94–100. Albuquerque, Lovelace Foundation for Medical Education and Research.

THOMAS, R. G. (1970). Third Int. Conf. on Toxicology, Rochester (New York). (Proceedings to be published.)

Acknowledgements — The author acknowledges Drs. R. O. McClellan and O. G. Raabe for their contributions to many of the ideas incorporated into this paper, and Mr. F. C. Rupprecht for his editorial assistance.

DISCUSSION

P. GROSS: I have exposed rats and mice in the same inhalation chambers for the same length of time; the rats developed silicosis but the mice killed at the same time had normal lungs. No silicotic nodules could be demonstrated in the mouse lungs and no silica could be found in the incinerated lung sections. Dr. Thomas' work offers a nice explanation for this finding.

A. A. SPRITZER: Some years ago when working with Cember to induce squamous cell carcinoma in rat lungs with ^{144}Ce we prepared a series of cerium particles of varying *in vitro* solubilities.

We found that lung retention varied with *in vitro* solubility and that completely soluble CeCl$_3$ had the longest lung retention time. For lung retention the ^{144}Ce and lanthanide elements must be considered as protein binders and the cationic component of the Ce particle will have a major influence on retention.

Dr. THOMAS: I think the retention time that we are talking about, of the released cation, is going to be relatively short compared to the retention time of the fused clay particle. We might not be able to see this because of the overwhelming amount of the material associated with the aerosol vehicle. I think what you say is true.

M. NEWHOUSE: Could some of the differences between mice, rats and dogs be related to the inter-relationship between airway calibre and flow rates — the relatively higher flow rates in the smaller animals perhaps determining a somewhat more proxial deposition (although of course still distal to the terminal bronchiole), and hence faster clearance in mice? This might also partly explain the absence of silicosis in mice referred to by the previous questionner.

Dr. THOMAS: There is one problem with that. The higher flow rates would bring about a greater deposition by the process of impaction.

We are talking about a difference in long-term retention, presumably by those particles which would be deposited mostly by sedimentation or diffusion.

INHALATION STUDY ON METABOLISM OF INSOLUBLE URANIUM COMPOUNDS

G. P. GALIBIN and YU. D. PARFENOV

Institute of Biophysics, Ministry of Health, Moscow, USSR

Abstract — When rats are subjected to single inhalation (10 mg/m³ and 30 mg/m³) of insoluble uranium compounds—ammonium diuranat ($(NH_4)_2U_2O_7$), uranium tetrafluoride (UF_4) and uranium octoxide (U_3O_8), 14–25% of the total inhaled amount is retained in the animal body.

The principal organ for deposition of these uranium compounds is skeleton. Biological half-life of uranium for the skeleton is 310–375 days. Lungs, kidneys and liver are other organs of retention. The deposition level of ammonium diuranat and UF_4 in the liver is 3–5 times as high as that of U_3O_8.

The mobilization of uranium from the lungs is described by the sum of 4 exponentials. Effective half-life of uranium for the liver and kidneys is not more than 30 days. A similar pattern of uranium metabolism is obtained for chronic inhalation of these compounds.

Estimation of uranium content in the body is based on concentration in the urine.

THE kinetics of insoluble uranium compounds in the body (respiratory intake) are of great practical value for estimation of possible hazards and determination of maximum permissible levels. Data on long-term retention and distribution of uranium in the body after inhalation intake are of particular interest.

The present investigation is concerned principally with the distribution, retention and clearance in the rat of inhaled insoluble compounds of uranium — ammonium diuranat ($(NH_4)_2U_2O_7$), uranium tetrafluorid (UF_4) and uranium octoxide (U_3O_8).

METHODS

Albino rats with a mean weight of 200 g were exposed in 100 l inhalation chamber with small boxes for animals. Duration of inhalation exposure was 4 h for ammonium diuranat and 1 h for UF_4 and U_3O_8. Uranium aerosol was supplied from an electromagnetic generator by compressed air. Particle size varied from $0 \cdot 5$ to $5 \cdot 0$ μm. (Table I.)

Average aerosol concentrations in terms of uranium content were 10 mg/m³ for ammonium diuranant, 30 mg/m³ for U_3O_8 and 29 mg/m³ for UF_4.

Solubility of the used uranium compounds was analysed in distilled water, physiological solution, blood serum and hydrochloric acid ($0 \cdot 3\%$). (Table II.)

Rats were sacrificed at various time intervals after inhalation: 10–15 min, 1 h, 3 h, 1 day, 2, 4, 8, 16, 32, 64, 128, 256, 512 and 768 days; 3–5 rats at each time. Main

Table I. Particle aerosol sizes of inhaled uranium compounds
(per cent of the total particle number)

Particle size (μm)	0·1–0·5	0·6–1·0	1·1–2·0	2·1–3·0	3·1–5·0	5·1–10·0
Compounds	(per cent of the total number of counted particles)					
$(NH_4)_2U_2O_7$	8·0	19·0	31·0	30·0	11·0	1·0
U_3O_8	18·0	28·0	35·0	13·5	5·0	0·5
UF_4	8·0	12·0	24·0	36·0	19·0	1·0

Table II. Solubility of Uranium compound (mg/100 ml)

Solvent	Uranium compound		
	UF_4	$(NH_4)_2U_2O_7$	U_3O_8
	at 20 °C		
Distilled water	3·0	0·30	0·06
Physiological solution	2·4	0·25	0·03
Blood serum	3·4	0·30	0·04
Hydrochloric acid 0·3%	180·0	300·0	0·60
	at 40 °C		
Distilled water	6·0	0·5	0·08
Physiological solution	4·2	0·3	0·04
Blood serum	7·0	0·8	0·04
Hydrochloric acid 0·3%	220·0	350·0	0·08

tissues for analysis were liver, kidneys, lungs, spleen, muscles and skeleton. Tissue uranium concentration was determined by a luminescent method on electrophoto-meter "ЛИОФ–57". Sensitivity of the method was 1×10^{-9} g per g of wet tissue.

Uranium content in the organs was expressed in per cent of inhaled dose. Assuming a lung ventilation rate for rats of 7 l/h, the inhaled dose of uranium was 280 μg for ammonium diuranat, 203 μg for UF_4 and 213 μg for U_3O_8.

Uranium concentration in the organs was expressed as a differential accumulation coefficient (DAC), equal to the ratio of isotope concentration in 1 gm of tissue to administered isotope dose per 1 gm the animal body weight.

Accumulation of uranium in various organs of rats at chronic daily inhalation was investigated with ammonium diuranat for 128 days. Daily inhalation lasted 4 h, the aerosol concentration being 6 mg/m³.

RESULTS

Deposition coefficient. We determined deposition coefficient — the fraction of the uranium retained in the body from the total inhaled amount of uranium, for the 10–15 min after inhalation group. Inhalation results in the retention of approximately $14·2 \pm 2·5\%$ of uranium from the inhaled dose for ammonium diuranat, $23·2 \pm 4·8\%$ for UF_4 and $25·0 \pm 6·5\%$ for U_3O_8. After single inhalation exposure to different aerosol concentrations, relative retention and deposition of uranium (in per cent) are not dependent on aerosol concentration.

Lung. The deposition of the inhaled material in the lung itself is of particular importance. Maximum retention of uranium in the lung was observed 10–15 min after inhalation exposure: ammonium diuranat, $10 \cdot 0 \pm 1 \cdot 7\%$ of the total inhaled dose of uranium; UF_4, $19 \cdot 0 \pm 4 \cdot 2\%$; and U_3O_8, $23 \cdot 0 \pm 6 \cdot 1\%$ (Table III). It makes up $70 \cdot 4\%$, $81 \cdot 9\%$ and $81 \cdot 2\%$ respectively in per cent of retained uranium in the whole body up to this moment.

TABLE III. MAXIMUM RETENTION OF URANIUM IN THE WHOLE ORGAN IN PER CENT OF THE INHALED
AMOUNT AND MAXIMUM URANIUM CONCENTRATION IN DAC
(Rats sacrificed 10–15 mins after inhalation)

Compound	Lung		Skeleton		Liver		Kidneys		Spleen	
	%	DAC	%	DAC	%	DAC	%	DAC	%	DAC
$(NH_4)_2U_2O_7$	10·0	9·4	3·9	0·98	0·7	0·22	1·2	1·64	0·3	
UF_4	19·0	32	3·5	0·84	1·1	0·30	1·4	1·90	0·2	0·5
U_3O_8	23·6	39	1·8	0·43	0·2	0·06	0·7	0·8	0·05	

The mobilization of uranium deposited in the lung is described for each chemical compound by the sum of 4 exponentials (Figure 1):

for $(NH_4)_2U_2O_7$—
$50\% \cdot \exp[(-0 \cdot 693t_h)/3] + 20\% \cdot \exp[(-0 \cdot 693t_d)/3] + 24\% \cdot \exp[(-0 \cdot 693t_d)/25] + 6\% \cdot \exp[(-0 \cdot 693t_d)/240]$

for UF_4 —
$58\% \cdot \exp[(-0 \cdot 693t_h)/2] + 23 \cdot 4\% \cdot \exp[(-0 \cdot 693t_d)/2] + 16\% \exp[(-0 \cdot 693t_d)/35] + 2 \cdot 6\% \cdot \exp[(-0 \cdot 693t_d)/250]$

for U_3O_8 —
$48\% \cdot \exp[(-0 \cdot 693t_h)/3] + 28\% \cdot \exp[(-0 \cdot 693t_d)/3] + 18\% \cdot \exp[(-0 \cdot 693t_d)/20] + 6\% \cdot \exp[(-0 \cdot 693t_d)/500]$

$(t_h = $ time in hours, $t_d = $ time in days$)$

As is seen from the equations, lung clearance of uranium does not have any essential, statistically significant differences either for $(NH_4)_2U_2O_7$, or for UF_4 and U_3O_8 as 48–58% of uranium retained in the lung is eliminated with half-life $t_{1/2} = 2$–3 h; 20–28% — with $t_{1/2} = 2$–3 d; 16–24% — with $t_{1/2} = 20$–35 d and finally slower eliminated lung fraction of uranium accounts for $2 \cdot 6$ –6% with $t_{1/2} = 240$–500 days.

It should be noted that one year after single inhalation exposure, the lung content of U_3O_8 is 5 times more than that of ammonium diuranat and UF_4, as a result of slower clearance.

Absorption into the blood

Experimental data on kinetics of uranium in the body enable us to estimate absorption of uranium into the blood. This value is equal to the uranium content in the whole body minus the content in the lung and gastrointestinal tract. Ten-fifteen minutes after administration, uranium absorption into the blood is $2 \cdot 8\%$ of inhaled dose of uranium ammonium diuranat ($19 \cdot 1\%$ of the uranium retained in the whole body), $2 \cdot 6\%$ for UF_4 ($11 \cdot 2\%$ of the uranium retained in the whole body) and $1 \cdot 7\%$ for U_3O_8 ($6 \cdot 8\%$ of the uranium retained in the whole body). Maximum absorption into the blood is observed at 2–4 days after uranium administration. Absorption of uranium into the blood up to this time is $5 \cdot 3\%$ of the inhaled dose of uranium for ammonium diuranat $(37 \cdot 3\%$ of retained uranium), $5 \cdot 4\%$ for UF_4 $(23 \cdot 3\%)$ and $3 \cdot 1\%$ for U_3O_8 $(12 \cdot 4\%)$.

Blood. Uranium is rapidly eliminated from the blood with effective half-life 1 day. Less than $0 \cdot 01\%$ of the inhaled uranium amount remains in the blood at the 8th day after administration. It seems likely that uranium content in the whole body after single inhalation exposure cannot be determined by the concentration of uranium in the blood.

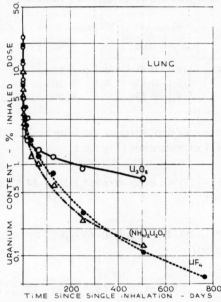

FIGURE 1. Uranium content of lung as percentage of inhaled dose.

Skeleton. Maximum uranium content in the skeleton for three investigated compounds is accumulated on the 4th day after administration. This value amounts to $3 \cdot 9 \pm 0 \cdot 3\%$ of the inhaled dose for ammonium diuranat, $3 \cdot 5 \pm 0 \cdot 4\%$ for UF_4 and $1 \cdot 8 \pm 0 \cdot 4\%$ for U_3O_8.

Figure 2 shows slow clearance of uranium deposited in the skeleton. Nearly half of the retained uranium is eliminated with $t_{1/2} = 50$ days. The remaining amount — for ammonium diuranat $64 \cdot 1\%$ of the deposited fraction is eliminated with $t_{1/2} = 310$ days; for $UF_4 - 60\%$ with $t_{1/2} = 320$ days and for $U_3O_8 - 72\%$ with $t_{1/2} = 375$ days.

Up to 512 days after administration, the skeleton content expressed as percentage of the body burden amounts to about $83 \cdot 3\%$ for ammonium diuranat, $87 \cdot 5\%$ for UF_4 and 41% for U_3O_8. During the whole period of observation, the skeleton content of U_3O_8 is 2 times lower than that of ammonium diuranat and UF_4. Four days after inhalation exposure of ammonium diuranat and UF_4, the uranium content in the skeleton exceeds that in the lung while after exposure of U_3O_8 the uranium content the skeleton and in the lung remain at the same level.

Other organs. Maximum accumulation of uranium in the liver is observed 3 h–1 day after inhalation exposure, for ammonium diuranat, $0 \cdot 7 \pm 0 \cdot 1 \%$; for UF_3, $1 \cdot 1$ $\pm 0 \cdot 2 \%$; and for U_3O_8, $0 \cdot 2 \pm 0 \cdot 05 \%$ of inhaled dose of uranium. Deposition level of UF_4 in liver is $1 \cdot 5$ times more than that of ammonium diuranat and $5 \cdot 5$ times more than that of U_3O_8.

Maximum uranium retention in the kidneys is observed 1 day after inhalation exposure and is — for ammonium diuranat, $1 \cdot 2 \pm 0 \cdot 3 \%$; for UF_4, $1 \cdot 4 \pm 0 \cdot 3 \%$; and for U_3O_8, $0 \cdot 7 \pm 0 \cdot 2 \%$ of the inhaled dose of uranium.

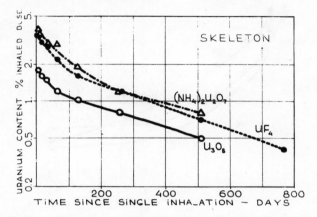

FIGURE 2. Uranium content of skeleton as percentage of inhaled dose.

Maximum uranium retention in the spleen was also observed in 1 day after exposure and is — for ammonium diuranat, $0 \cdot 3 \%$; for UF_4, $0 \cdot 2 \%$; and for U_3O_8, $0 \cdot 05 \%$ of inhaled dose of uranium.

Effective half-life of uranium in the liver, kidneys and spleen for all three compounds is nearly similar and is not more than 20–50 days (Figures 3 and 4).

Urinary excretion. An attempt was made to estimate uranium body burden on the basis of uranium excretion with urine. Figure 5 shows the ratio of uranium content in the body of rats and daily uranium excretion as a function of time since single

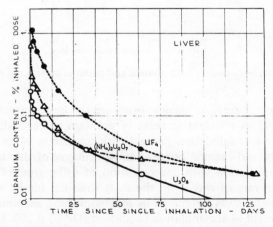

FIGURE 3. Uranium content of liver as percentage of inhaled dose.

inhalation exposure of ammonium diuranat. If one knows this ratio it is possible by multiplying it by the value of daily uranium excretion with urine to determine uranium content in the body at a given moment. As is seen from Figure 5, this ratio increases from 4 to 400 during 60 days after inhalation exposure of ammonium diuranat by rats. This is explained by the fact that the uranium fraction with a long half-life remains in the body at late periods after inhalation exposure.

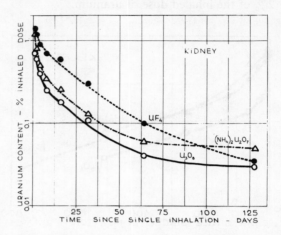

FIGURE 4. Uranium content of kidneys as percentage of inhaled dose.

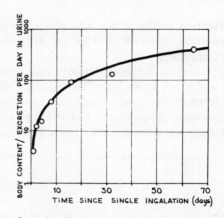

FIGURE 5. The ratio of uranium body content and uranium excretion per day in urine.

Chronic inhalation exposure. At chronic exposure the largest amount of uranium is deposited in the lung. A constant increase of uranium content was observed in the lung towards the end of inhalation process with maximum value 570 μg. Figure 6 gives the body, lung and skeletal burdens as percentages of the daily inhaled dose. Assuming aerosol inhalation with concentration of $6 \cdot 0$ mg/m³ of uranium for 4 h and lung ventilation rate of rats 7 l/h, the daily uranium intake will be 168 μg or, per 1 g of body weight, $0 \cdot 84$ μg/gm. Thus maximum lung accumulation multiple is $3 \cdot 4$ (Figure 6); differential accumulation coefficient (DAC) is 200. It should be noted that uranium concentration in the lung at the end of inhalation is 10 times more than that in the kidneys, 20 times more than in the skeleton, and 80 times more than in the liver at the same time.

It was of interest to consider dynamics of uranium content decrease in the organs of rats observed after the cessation of daily inhalation exposure. It was followed for about 400 days after cessation exposure. Lung clearance of uranium is analogous to that observed after single inhalation exposure. Deposited uranium is eliminated from skeleton with effective half-life about 30 days. Effective half-life of uranium in kidneys and liver as well as in the case of single exposure is not more than 25–30 days.

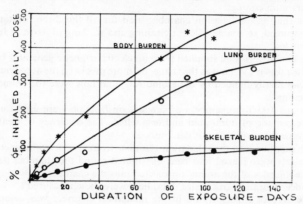

FIGURE 6. Body burden, lung burden and skeletal burden of uranium as percentage of inhaled daily dose of uranium.

SUMMARY

Comparing metabolism of three investigated compounds of uranium, $(NH_4)_2U_2O_7$, UF_4 and U_3O_8, it is obvious that after inhalation administration of U_3O_8 which is the least soluble of these compounds uranium in largest amount is retained in the lung and is more slowly eliminated from there. Owing to this, after inhalation administration of U_3O_8, deposition level of uranium in kidneys, liver and especially in skeleton is lower than after administration of $(NH_4)_2U_2O_7$ and UF_4.

Uranium absorption into the blood after administration of U_3O_8 is also $1 \cdot 5$–2 times lower than after administration of other investigated compounds. The main organs of uranium deposition after inhalation of these three compounds are lung and skeleton. Effective half-lives for slowly eliminating fractions of uranium deposited in these organs are 240–500 days for lung and 310–375 days for skeleton.

The data were also evaluated in terms of tissue concentration. In general, the time course is the same as that seen on an organ basis. Organ weights were relatively unchanged throughout the experiment.

The elimination kinetics in any organs are in general better described by exponentials than by a power function.

208 G. P. GALIBIN and YU. D. PARFENOV

DISCUSSION

R. MASSE (France): In the experiments on solubility which were described, what were the concentration of bicarbonate and the pH of the serum?

Dr. GALIBIN: We did not determine these.

E. D. DYSON: In the clearance of insoluble uranium from the respiratory tract, does the short half-period (2 to 3 hours) clearance represent clearance from the upper respiratory tract?

Dr. GALIBIN: We think that the short half-period (2–3 hours) clearance represents clearance from the upper respiratory tract except trachea. Trachea was not the component of the lung tissue taken for the analysis of uranium content.

S. E. DEVIR: Was the same inhalation chamber used for all the three substances? From what materials was it constructed, to enable efficient cleaning and washing of its walls from the deposited uranium aerosol particles?

You state that the U-aerosols were supplied from an electromagnetic generator by compressed air. What kind of generator was it? What was the shape, or, more precisely, the aerodynamic shape-factor, of the aerosol particles finally inhaled by the albino rats, and how were the animals exposed to the aerosol during inhalation?

Dr. GALIBIN: Various 100-litre chambers of similar construction were used for 3 uranium compounds; the walls were made of duralumin and enamelled. The efficiency of cleaning and washing deposited material from the walls was not determined.

The aerosols were supplied into the inhalation chamber from an electro-magnetic pulverizator by compressed air. The rats were placed into pens distributed round the chamber perimeter in such a manner that only the muzzles of the animals projected into the chamber.

O. G. RAABE: Concerning the particle size data, how were these measured?

Dr. GALIBIN: The aerosol concentration in the inhalation chamber was determined during the whole period of exposure. For this purpose the air with aerosol was sampled on filters made of Petryanov tissue by an aspirator. After determination of aerosol weight on the filter, the latter was made transparent with the help of acetone vapour and the aerosol particle size was determined by microscope. The dispersion of aerosol particles of the three uranium compounds is indicated in Table I. The size of about 80% of the particles was $0 \cdot 5$–$3 \cdot 0$ μm.

THE EFFECTS OF INCREASED PARTICLES ON THE NUMBER OF ALVEOLAR MACROPHAGES*

JOSEPH D. BRAIN†‡

Department of Physiology, Harvard University School of Public Health, Boston, Massachusetts, U.S.A.

Abstract — We have developed a method which attempts to quantify alveolar macrophages in the lungs and have examined the effects of intratracheally-injected particles on the numbers of alveolar macrophages. Various procedural factors affect the numbers of alveolar macrophages harvested by lung washing. The effects of such variables as gas-freeing the lungs, post-mortem delay times, wash volume, temperature, composition of washing fluid, time course of washing cycle, pathological changes and age, sex, lung weight and body weight have already been presented.

Anesthetized rats or hamsters were given intratracheal injections of particles suspended in saline and subsequently dispersed ultrasonically. 4 hours, 1 day or 3 days following the injection the animals were exsanguinated and the lungs excised, gas-freed, cannulated and washed 12 times. The volume of each saline wash was 5 times greater than the tissue volume. The cells in the lung washings were counted in a hemacytometer chamber. Dose-response relationships and time-response relationships were explored. In general, the increase in free cells was maximal 1 day after the injection but was also elevated from control levels at 4 hours and 3 days. Coal dust, carbon, chrysotile, iron oxide and barium sulfate all were associated with an increase in the recovery of free cells. When the particle size of the coal dust was reduced while the total mass was kept constant, the response was enhanced.

External massage of the lung was associated with increased recovery of free cells as was the absence of divalent cations from the washing medium. Data related to the importance of repeated washings is given. In addition, the volumes of saline retained by the lung during the wash procedure is discussed.

INTRODUCTION

TOXIC particulates can enter the body through the respiratory tract. The reaction of the alveolar surface to the deposition of these particles involves primarily the free cells of the lung. The term "free cells" refers to those cells that do not form part of the continuous alveolar epithelial layer, constituted principally of pulmonary surface epithelial cells (Type 1 pneumonocytes) and great alveolar cells (Type 2 pneumono-

* This investigation was supported by grant ES–00002 from the National Institute of Environmental Health Sciences and grant AP–00084 from the National Air Pollution Control Administration.

† Supported by Research Career Development Award, Environmental Health Sciences grant ES–44782.

‡ Technical assistance supplied by Mrs. Dwyn Sherry, Miss Lucinda Mowitt and Miss Dominica Paci.

cytes). Instead, free cells rest on this lining. For the most part, the pool of free pulmonary cells is composed of large mononuclear phagocytes called alveolar macrophages. Under some conditions; for example, in the presence of hemorrhagic edema or pulmonary infection; the pool may be enriched by other cell types derived from the blood. This paper describes how particles deposited in the lungs can alter the numbers of pulmonary free cells harvested by repeated lung washings; it also describes some factors related to the quantification of free cells.

Alveolar macrophages play a pivotal role in the clearance of particles of all kinds from the lungs. It is in the phagocytic and lytic potential of the alveolar macrophages that most of the known bactericidal properties of the lungs reside (GREEN & KASS, 1964). The alveolar macrophages also participate in the clearance of non-living, insoluble dust and debris from the nonciliated portions of the lung. Particles that remain on the surface of the alveoli either within free alveolar macrophages or on the fluid surface are removed to the ciliated part of the lung. The speed is determined by macrophage migration and perhaps by mouthward flow of alveolar cell secretions. LABELLE & BRIEGER (1959) showed there was a high positive correlation between the amount of dust cleared from the lungs and the number of phagocytic cells present.

Macrophages appear to play a role in the development of some diseases caused by inhaled materials. Since macrophages ingest deposited matter, they are often exposed to higher levels of toxic materials than other lung cells. KESSEL et al. (1963) showed that free silica was toxic in vitro to the macrophages of rats, mice and men. The expression of this cytotoxic effect requires the active metabolism of macrophages (OREN et al., 1963). VIGLIANI et al. (1961) have proposed that an unknown substance released by dying macrophages may be a stimulus to the formation of the fibrosis that is characteristic of silicosis. ALLISON et al. (1967) have shown that following ingestion of silica by the macrophages, lysosomal enzymes are released into the macrophage cytoplasm. These kill the macrophage. A substance released by dead macrophages attracts fibroblasts and causes an eventual fibrogenic response. HOLT et al. (1964) have suggested that the fibrogenic action of asbestos is also mediated by alveolar macrophages.

METHODS

Sprague-Dawley rats and Syrian golden hamsters were given intratracheal injections of a suspension of particles in physiological saline. At various times following the exposure, the animals were sacrificed and the population of alveolar macrophages was examined by the method of repeated lung washings. The details are as follows:

Particle suspensions (concentrations expressed on a weight per volume basis) were made up in 0·85% NaCl and sterilized in an autoclave. The flask containing the suspension was then placed in a well sonicator (Son Blaster Series 200 manufactured by the Narda Ultrasonics Corp.) for 10 min. It was stirred continuously with a magnetic stirrer until the moment of injection.

Prior to the intratracheal injection the animals were lightly anesthetized: the rats with ether (Fisher Anesthesia Grade) and the hamsters with sodium methohexital (Brevital) 50 mg per kg body weight (i.p.). The rodents were then placed on a surface 34° from the vertical, head up, and suspended by an elastic band across their teeth.

The oro-pharynx and larynx were visualized by exterior transillumination with a microscope lamp. A sterile blunt 19 gauge spinal puncture needle was inserted through the larynx a few cm into the trachea and the suspension of particles or the saline control solution was injected. Animals were kept in this nearly vertical position for 1 min before being returned to their cages. Unless otherwise stated all animals received $0·15$ cm^3 solution per 100 g of body weight.

The free cell response to these experimental treatments was analyzed in the following manner. For most particulates, two parameters were varied. First, how the response varies as a function of the magnitude of the exposure; secondly, how the response varies as a function of the time elapsed since the exposure. For each combination of parameters (a given exposure and a given time since exposure) at least six animals were used. The method employed is that of repeated lung washings and was described in detail in a recent article (BRAIN & FRANK, 1968a). The rats were sacrificed by exsanguination while anesthetized with sodium pentobarbital. The lungs were removed, rendered gas-free, and the trachea was cannulated. About one hour after exsanguination the lungs were washed internally with 12 1-min wash cycles, each using a volume of physiological saline five times that of the tissue volume. The number of cells per washing was measured with a Spencer hemacytometer chamber. Controls for experimental groups were done at the same time and were matched for age and post-mortem delay.

RESULTS

Importance of Procedural Variables

The use of lung lavage or lung washing to estimate the numbers of free cells was first used by GERSING & SCHUMACHER (1955) and used extensively by LABELLE & BRIEGER (1960, 1961). We have attempted to make the technique more sensitive and reproducible by utilizing multiple lung washings and by controlling the factors of the washing procedure (BRAIN & FRANK, 1968a, 1968b).

We have washed the lungs of dogs, rabbits, guinea pigs, hamsters, mice, rats and cats and in all cases the average yield for 12 washes falls between 3 and 15 million cells per gram of lung. In order to obtain quantitatively consistent recoveries of free cells, it is necessary to control several aspects of the harvesting procedure. We have examined the effects of gas-freeing the lungs, of the length of the postmortem delay time, wash volume, leakage, pathological changes, and of the number of washes (BRAIN & FRANK, 1968a). Another paper dealt with the effects of age, sex, lung weight and body weight of the animals on the numbers of free cells recovered (BRAIN & FRANK, 1968b). Additional observations (manuscript in preparation) deal with the effects of wash volume, osmolarity, temperature and time course of the washing cycle. Many of these factors are simply variables in the procedure that should be controlled.

Some of these investigations, however, have provided clues to more fundamental questions. For example, the experiments with varied washing-fluid compositions have yielded insights into the surface forces existing between the alveolar macrophage and the alveolar wall (BRAIN & FRANK, 1967; BRAIN, 1970). If rat lungs are washed 12 times with $0·85\%$ NaCl, $8·87 \pm 1·03$ (S.E.) $\times 10^6$ cells per g of lung are recovered. However, if a balanced salt solution containing a variety of cations and anions is used, only $2 \cdot 28 \pm 0 \cdot 49$ (S.E.) $\times 10^6$ cells per g of lung are recovered. Additional experiments showed that Ca^{++} and Mg^{++} ions were responsible for the observed differences between the balanced salt solution and the physiological saline. Apparently Ca^{++} and Mg^{++} critically influence the adhesive forces which exist between alveolar macrophages and the alveolar wall. Similar differences in free cell yield between balanced salt solution and physiological saline were also noted in hamsters, cats and rabbits (unpublished data).

Effects of Massage

Mechanical factors are also involved in the recovery of free cells from the alveolar surface and airways. In the experiment described here, the excised lungs were gently massaged with the fingertips for a 30 s period after instillation of the saline and before withdrawal. In the control lungs (shown as "30 s hold") the timing of the wash procedure was identical except the lung was suspended quietly in saline during the 30 s period.

Figures 1 and 2 show the numbers of free cells recovered by washing rat lungs with

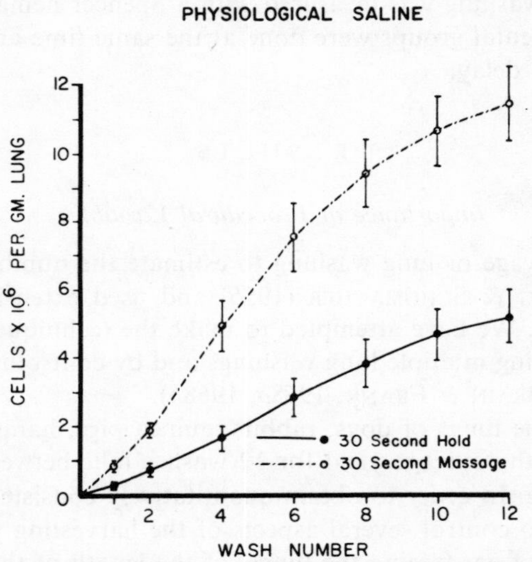

FIGURE 1. Effects of massage on free cell yield. Rat lungs washed with $0 \cdot 85\%$ NaCl. The means are shown with their standard errors.

and without massage. The total accumulated cells recovered are displayed as a function of the wash number. In Figure 1, where the washing medium was physiological saline ($0 \cdot 85\%$ NaCl), the yield of cells was more than doubled by the massage. A 3-fold increase was obtained when the lungs washed with balanced salt solution (BSS) were subjected to the massage procedure. Particularly in the BSS washed lungs, massage seemed to make the results somewhat more variable as indicated by the considerably greater standard error of the massaged lungs. Hamster lungs and cat lungs which were massaged also had cell yields which were 50 to 100% greater than their "30 s hold" counterparts. Figures 1 and 2 also illustrate the difference in cell yield which is dependent on the electrolyte composition of the washing fluids. It is to be noted that the units on the ordinate of Figure 2 are worth only half of those shown in Figure 1.

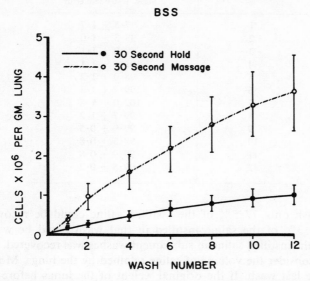

FIGURE 2. Effects of massage on free cell yield. Rat lungs washed with balanced salt solution. Note the different scale on the ordinate. The means are shown with their standard errors.

Saline Retention by the Lungs

GROSS et al. (1969) have reported that "the amount of fluid injected, but remaining in the lung, has been found to be quite variable and unpredictable". They also reported (GROSS et al., 1969) that "different amounts of fluid could be recovered by drainage from the trachea; this varied from 40% to 90%". Our experience with the recovery of intracheally injected saline washes in excised lungs has been somewhat more consistent.

It should first be emphasized that the volume of the saline wash should be selected with care. We have based our wash volumes on experiments yielding the volume-pressure relationships of rat lungs. In 10 different lungs the volume of air contained in the rat lungs at Total Lung Capacity (as defined by a transpulmonary pressure of 30 cm H_2O) was between 8 and 12 cm^3 of air per g of lung. Thus if each saline wash were 5 cm^3 per g of tissue, the lung would be adequately filled to about one-half TLC but the probability of leaks is minimized. In fewer than 5% of the rodent lungs washed with such a volume was there a leak of more than 10% of the injected saline. If more saline was injected, however, leaks became more frequent.

At the beginning of the washing procedure, saline was instilled into gas-free lungs. The lungs always retained some of the instilled saline at the end of the first wash even though a negative pressure was applied to the syringe. A variable fraction of the instilled saline could be recovered and this experiment describes that fraction. The data were taken from 15 male rats whose lungs were free of major leaks. Table I shows the percentage of instilled saline that was recovered in each wash.

TABLE I. PERCENTAGE OF INSTILLED SALINE RECOVERED

Wash number	Percentage of instilled saline recovered Mean + standard error
1	$77 \cdot 5 \pm 1 \cdot 7$
2	$98 \cdot 3 \pm 1 \cdot 0$
3	$99 \cdot 0 \pm 1 \cdot 1$
4	$101 \cdot 6 \pm 1 \cdot 1$
5	$98 \cdot 0 \pm 1 \cdot 2$
6	$99 \cdot 7 \pm 1 \cdot 3$
7	$102 \cdot 0 \pm 1 \cdot 8$
8	$99 \cdot 7 \pm 1 \cdot 2$
9	$99 \cdot 9 \pm 0 \cdot 5$
10	$98 \cdot 3 \pm 0 \cdot 8$
11	$99 \cdot 9 \pm 0 \cdot 8$
12	$99 \cdot 5 \pm 0 \cdot 2$

In the first wash only $77 \cdot 5 \%$ of the instilled saline could be recovered. By the second wash, $98 \cdot 3 \%$ of the saline instilled in that wash could be withdrawn and essentially all of the instilled saline in subsequent washes was recovered.

We may also consider the volume of saline retained by the lungs. Most lungs were weighed after the last wash. If the original weight of the lungs before washing was subtracted from the final post-wash weight, the difference equalled the weight of the saline retained at the conclusion of the lung washing procedure. To compare lungs of different weights, the saline retained was compared to the lung weight. The mean weight of saline retained in the lungs of 34 normal animals was $1 \cdot 27 \pm 0 \cdot 06$ times the lung weight. The lungs of rats that had post-mortem delay times exceeding 3 h tended to retain more saline. In 8 animals which had post-mortem delay times of 3 h or more, the mean weight of saline retained was $1 \cdot 68 \pm 0 \cdot 12$ times the lung weight. The lungs of animals which had post-mortem delay times exceeding 3 h retained 24% more saline ($P < 0 \cdot 005$).

Importance of Repeated Washings of the Lung

Our data show that the lung washing technique is made more reliable and sensitive by washing the alveolar surface more than once or twice. In more than 90% of the experimental or control groups, as the lungs were repeatedly washed the mean cumulative yield increased at a faster rate than did the standard error. Therefore, the coefficient of variation, $100 \times$ standard deviation/mean, generally decreased as a function of increasing numbers of washes. Even though individual washes often became more variable, differences tended to cancel each other so that the cumulative total yield became less variable.

Thus repeated washings make the lung-washing technique more sensitive to differences between experimental groups. In 14 different experiments (169 animals) the value of t (Student's t-test) was calculated for the difference between the control and experimental groups at each wash number. The average t-values for all 14 groups are shown in Table II with their standard errors. Also shown is the corresponding value of P, the probability of the observed difference occurring by chance (12 degrees of freedom are assumed).

TABLE II. RELATION OF REPEATED WASHINGS TO METHOD SENSITIVITY

Wash No.	Average t-value	Probability
1	2·76 ± 0·49	<0·02
2	3·32 ± 0·89	<0·01
3, 4	5·84 ± 0·74	<0·001
5, 6	6·02 ± 0·51	<0·001
7, 8	6·24 ± 0·30	<0·001
9, 10	6·55 ± 0·40	<0·001
11, 12	6·37 ± 0·42	<0·001

It is apparent that as the lung is repeatedly washed, the difference becomes increasingly significant. The data suggest that lungs should be washed at least six times in order to achieve maximum sensitivity.

In almost all experiments there was also a reduction in variability when the free cells recovered were expressed in terms of cells per g lung as compared with free cells per rat. This was true even when body weights were relatively uniform.

A final point to be made regarding procedure is that for each exposure situation, it is essential to examine control animals simultaneously. We find that groups of control animals may vary by as much as 60% within the same species. This may be due to genetic differences, seasonal rhythms, changes in humidity or temperature, or perhaps undetected disease. Controls killed at other times should not be used for comparison.

CHANGES IN THE NUMBERS OF FREE CELLS

Carbon Particles

Previous experiments using cats exposed to carbon aerosols (BRAIN, 1966) and rats exposed to tobacco smoke (unpublished data) and to a triphenyl phosphate aerosol (BRAIN, 1970) have shown that in most cases deposition of particles in the lungs is followed by increased numbers of free cells in the lung. In order to explore dose-response relationships and time-response relationships, we injected over 70 hamsters intratracheally with suspensions of carbon particles in saline. We have increasingly used hamsters since they are more resistant to lung diseases than rats and in our hands they also tolerate intratracheal injections better than rats.

Figure 3 shows the results obtained from hamsters injected intratracheally with a suspension of carbon particles 1 to 3 μm in size ultrasonically dispersed in physiological saline. All animals were killed 1 day following the intratracheal injection. Since the 1·0% (weight/volume) carbon suspension elicited a response not significantly different from the 0·5% carbon suspension, the results suggested that a maximum response had been achieved at the 0·5% dose level. The total cell yields for the animals injected with carbon (0·0625%) are significantly different ($P < 0·05$) from the controls injected with saline. All points on the curves for the 0·5% and 1·0% suspensions are significantly different from the control points at the $P < 0·005$ level.

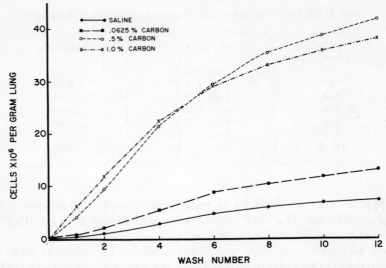

FIGURE 3. Number of free cells harvested from hamster lungs by repeated lung washings. All animals received intratracheally 0·15 cm³ of a suspension of carbon particles per 100 g body weight. The concentration of carbon was 0·0%, 0·0625%, 0·5% and 1·0%. All animals were sacrificed 1 day after the injection. All points are based on 6 or more animals.

The time-response relationships for carbon are displayed in Figure 4 for hamsters receiving the 0·5% carbon suspension. Animals were sacrificed at 4 hours, 1 day and 3 days following the intratracheal injection. Control hamsters (not shown in

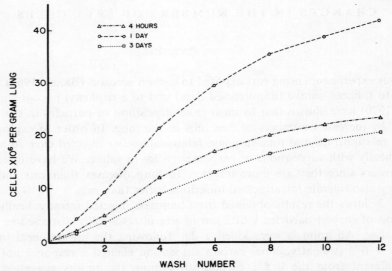

FIGURE 4. Numbers of free cells harvested from hamster lungs by repeated lung washings. All animals received intratracheally 0·15 cm³ of a 0·5% suspension of carbon particles per 100 g body weight. The times shown represent the interval between the injection and the time of sacrifice. Control hamsters were injected with 0·15 cm³ saline per 100 g body weight. All of the saline control groups (not shown) for the 3 times had total yields of less than $10·6 \times 10^6$ cells per g lung. All points are based on 6 or more animals.

Figure 4) were injected with $0 \cdot 15 \ cm^3$ saline per 100 g body weight and were sacrificed at the same three times. The total cumulative yield at the end of the 12 washes was $10 \cdot 54 \pm 1 \cdot 51$ (S.E.) $\times 10^6$ cells per g lung for the 4 h controls, $9 \cdot 35 \pm 0 \cdot 84$ (S.E.) $\times 10^6$ cells per g lung for the 1 day controls, and $8 \cdot 54 \pm 1 \cdot 31$ (S.E.) $\times 10^6$ cells per g for the 3-day controls. There are at least 8 animals in each control group. Figure 4 shows how the yield of macrophages changes as a function of time after injection. The response is maximal 1 day after the injection but it is also elevated from control levels at 4 hours and 3 days.

Coal Dust: Influence of Particle Size

In two sets of experiments the influence of particle size on the free cell response was examined. In the first experiment coal dust (supplied by the U.S. Bureau of Mines, Exp. Mine No. 1, Braceton, Pa., 99%+ through a 200 mesh screen) was taken and put through two sieves (U.S. Standard Sieve Series, Newark Wire Cloth Co., Newark, N.J., No. 60 and No. 270). When Sieve No. 60 was used only particles smaller than $0 \cdot 053$ mm were recovered. When Sieve No. 270 was used, the particles which did not go through the sieve were used and these were all larger than approximately $0 \cdot 25$ mm. In spite of the big difference in particle size, 1% suspensions of each size were made up. Since the particle diameters differed by at least a factor of 5, the number of particles per cm^3 of suspension varied by at least a factor of 125 with a somewhat smaller difference in surface area.

Table III shows the data obtained from hamsters injected, $0 \cdot 15$ cm per 100g body weight, with either the large coal particles, the small coal particles or a saline control. In all cases the animals were sacrificed 24 h after injection.

TABLE III. INFLUENCE OF PARTICLE SIZE ON LUNG FREE CELL YIELD

Wash No.	Total cells recovered. (10^6 per g of lung)		
	Coal dust $<0 \cdot 053$ mm	Coal dust $>0 \cdot 25$ mm	Controls Saline-injected
1	$4 \cdot 24 \pm 0 \cdot 71$	$2 \cdot 51 \pm 0 \cdot 38$	$0 \cdot 57 \pm 0 \cdot 17$
2	$10 \cdot 82 \pm 1 \cdot 62$	$5 \cdot 63 \pm 0 \cdot 88$	$1 \cdot 49 \pm 0 \cdot 40$
3, 4	$22 \cdot 26 \pm 3 \cdot 26$	$12 \cdot 31 \pm 1 \cdot 62$	$4 \cdot 80 \pm 1 \cdot 12$
5, 6	$30 \cdot 96 \pm 4 \cdot 51$	$17 \cdot 55 \pm 1 \cdot 98$	$7 \cdot 29 \pm 1 \cdot 54$
7, 8	$36 \cdot 64 \pm 5 \cdot 44$	$20 \cdot 53 \pm 2 \cdot 07$	$8 \cdot 65 \pm 1 \cdot 55$
9, 10	$40 \cdot 47 \pm 6 \cdot 01$	$22 \cdot 30 \pm 2 \cdot 26$	$9 \cdot 66 \pm 1 \cdot 58$
11, 12	$43 \cdot 28 \pm 6 \cdot 45$	$23 \cdot 79 \pm 2 \cdot 37$	$10 \cdot 35 \pm 1 \cdot 60$
Number of animals	10	7	9

Values are means $\pm$ standard error.

In a separate experiment, hamsters were injected with either a suspension of carbon mass mean diameter $2 \cdot 3 \ \mu m$ or with a suspension made up from carbon mass mean diameter $0 \cdot 18 \ \mu m$. Animals received $0 \cdot 15 \ cm^3$ per 100 g body weight of either the $0 \cdot 0625$% suspensions of the particles or a saline control. At the end of 12 washes, $18 \cdot 50 \pm 1 \cdot 97$ (S.E.) $\times 10^6$ cells were harvested from animals injected with the smaller particles ($P < 0 \cdot 05$ compared with controls) while the animals injected with the larger carbon particles yielded only $12\cdot58 \pm 1\cdot68$ (S.E.) $\times 10^6$ cells (not significantly different from the control values).

In this experiment and in the one with the coal dust there seems to be a clear effect of particle size. In the data in Table III the cells recovered from the $<0\cdot053$ mm coal dust hamsters are significantly higher (at the $P < 0\cdot005$ level) at every wash from the $>0\cdot25$ mm animals. Both groups of animals show cell yields significantly higher ($P < 0\cdot001$) than that of the control animals. In the carbon injected animals the animals injected with small particles had significantly more free cells than the animals injected with the large carbon particles. Thus, the increase of free cells may relate to total particle area or number rather than particle mass.

Barium Sulfate

Barium sulfate, similar to that commonly used to visualize the gastro-intestinal tract during X-ray procedures, was made up in a 1% solution which was intratracheally injected into hamsters, $0\cdot15$ cm^3 per 100 g body weight. Table IV shows the free cell yields obtained at 4 hours, 1 day and 3 days following the barium sulfate administration.

TABLE IV. INFLUENCE OF BARIUM SULFATE ON LUNG FREE CELL YIELD

Wash No.	Total cells recovered. (10^6 per g of lung)			
	1% Barium 4 h	1% Barium 1 day	1% Barium 3 days	Controls Saline-injected
1	$1\cdot08 \pm 0\cdot29$	$1\cdot77 \pm 0\cdot36$	$0\cdot57 \pm 0\cdot09$	$0\cdot67 \pm 0\cdot11$
2	$2\cdot73 \pm 0\cdot63$	$5\cdot13 \pm 0\cdot99$	$1\cdot70 \pm 0\cdot41$	$1\cdot53 \pm 0\cdot23$
3, 4	$6\cdot21 \pm 1\cdot43$	$11\cdot51 \pm 1\cdot96$	$4\cdot65 \pm 0\cdot77$	$3\cdot92 \pm 0\cdot46$
5, 6	$8\cdot12 \pm 1\cdot74$	$16\cdot49 \pm 2\cdot13$	$6\cdot85 \pm 0\cdot93$	$5\cdot95 \pm 0\cdot50$
7, 8	$9\cdot56 \pm 2\cdot11$	$19\cdot76 \pm 2\cdot33$	$8\cdot21 \pm 0\cdot90$	$8\cdot51 \pm 0\cdot53$
9, 10	$10\cdot63 \pm 2\cdot17$	$22\cdot16 \pm 2\cdot54$	$9\cdot28 \pm 0\cdot78$	$9\cdot61 \pm 0\cdot50$
11, 12	$11\cdot50 \pm 2\cdot36$	$23\cdot52 \pm 2\cdot71$	$10\cdot15 \pm 0\cdot78$	$10\cdot34 \pm 0\cdot52$
Number of animals	6	9	9	9

Values are means $\pm$ standard error.

Barium sulfate ($1\cdot0\%$) causes a significant increase ($P < 0\cdot005$) in free cells only if the lungs are washed 1 day after the injection. At 4 h and 3 days, the free cell yields do not differ significantly from the control values. The controls shown are the combined values of animals sacrificed 4 h, 1 day and 3 days following the intratracheal injection of saline.

Chrysotile and Iron Oxide

Hamsters were also given intratracheal injections of 1% chrysotile and 1% iron oxide suspensions. The chrysotile was obtained in bulk from Johns Manville Co. and pulverized in a mill for 9 min. The iron oxide was obtained from Pfizer Minerals, Pigments and Metals Division and is size No. R–2999, Lot 59. According to the manufacturer, 99% are smaller than 1 μm. All animals were given $0\cdot15$ cm^3 per

100 g body weight of the suspension and then sacrificed 1 day after the intratracheal injection. Table V shows the results obtained.

TABLE V. INFLUENCE OF CHRYSOTILE AND IRON OXIDE ON LUNG FREE CELL YIELD

Wash No.	Total cells recovered. (10^6 per g of lung)		
	1% Chrysotile	1% Iron oxide	Controls Saline-injected
1	$4 \cdot 76 \pm 1 \cdot 55$	$1 \cdot 73 \pm 0 \cdot 33$	$0 \cdot 62 \pm 0 \cdot 13$
2	$11 \cdot 02 \pm 2 \cdot 91$	$5 \cdot 24 \pm 0 \cdot 62$	$1 \cdot 57 \pm 0 \cdot 26$
3, 4	$22 \cdot 94 \pm 5 \cdot 13$	$11 \cdot 07 \pm 1 \cdot 74$	$4 \cdot 38 \pm 0 \cdot 56$
5, 6	$31 \cdot 64 \pm 6 \cdot 15$	$15 \cdot 21 \pm 2 \cdot 28$	$6 \cdot 58 \pm 0 \cdot 76$
7, 8	$38 \cdot 30 \pm 7 \cdot 04$	$18 \cdot 36 \pm 2 \cdot 87$	$7 \cdot 89 \pm 0 \cdot 80$
9, 10	$43 \cdot 11 \pm 7 \cdot 45$	$20 \cdot 38 \pm 3 \cdot 14$	$8 \cdot 74 \pm 0 \cdot 82$
11, 12	$46 \cdot 28 \pm 7 \cdot 63$	$22 \cdot 01 \pm 3 \cdot 32$	$9 \cdot 35 \pm 0 \cdot 84$

Number of
animals   6   7   9
Values are means $\pm$ standard error.

The number of cells recovered from the chrysotile-injected animals in the first wash was significantly different ($P < 0 \cdot 05$) from the control first wash. All cumulative yields for subsequent washes were significantly different from the controls at the $P < 0 \cdot 01$ level. All values in Table IV for the iron oxide animals are significantly different from the controls at the $P < 0 \cdot 01$ level. Thus, 1% solutions of both particles caused more than a doubling of free cells when the lungs were washed 1 day after exposure.

RELATION TO CELL DIVISION

Preliminary experiments deal with the relation of cell division to the particle-induced increase of lung free cells. Is the increase in free cells attributable to the release of pre-existing cells from an alveolar macrophage reservoir or is there a proliferation of new alveolar cells? The increase in free cells often seen only 4 h after the experimental treatment period suggests that there may be a release of pre-existing cells since this length of time is not adequate for appreciable cellular proliferation and differentiation.

In order to investigate whether cell division is necessary for the observed increase in free cells, we have tried to block mitosis with irradiation. Hamsters were given roentgens whole body exposure of 200 kV(peak) X-rays. The sham-irradiated controls were handled identically but received 0 roentgens. One day after the irradiation, both 0r and 800r groups were given intratracheal injections of saline or a $0 \cdot 5$% suspension of $0 \cdot 5$ to 3 μm carbon particles. One day after this injection, the numbers of free cells in the lungs were measured. The irradiated and particle injected group had $29 \cdot 11 \pm 3 \cdot 62$ (S.E.) $\times 10^6$ cells per g lung and the non-irradiated and particle injected group had $28 \cdot 01 \pm 1 \cdot 72$ (S.E.) $\times 10^6$ cells per g lung, both significantly higher ($P < 0 \cdot 005$) than saline control animals. Thus, there was no difference in the irradiated and non-irradiated animal response.

Rats were similarly treated, but they did not receive intratracheal injections until

3 days after the irradiation. Again, both irradiated and sham-irradiated animals showed significant increases in alveolar macrophages when they were given intratracheal injections of carbon particles. Although it is uncertain whether 800 roentgens immediately stops *all* cell division in alveolar macrophage precursor stem cells, these experiments do suggest that some of the new cells can come from pre-existing reservoirs of cells. It would seem reasonable, however, that if increases of free cells over long periods of time occur, increased proliferation of macrophage stem cells would be necessary. CASARETT & MILLEY (1964) measured mitotic activity with the colchicine technique after exposure to a $Fe(OH)_3$ aerosol. Rats receiving a dust load of about 10 μg showed a doubling of the alveolar cells stopped in metaphase. The peak appeared to be between 3 and 5 days after inhalation.

MORPHOLOGICAL STUDIES

Free cells recovered by lung lavage do not necessarily meet the theoretical definition of free cells discussed in the introduction. It is possible that some Type 1 and 2 pneumonocytes, airway epithelial cells, and contaminating blood cells may also be harvested. The cells recovered in the lung washings were prepared for examination by centrifuging the pooled lung washings (all 12 washes) to form a pellet. The pellet was embedded in parafin or Epon and sectioned for examination with light microscopy. Although the cells varied both in staining characteristics and in relative size, more than 80% were mononuclear. Red blood cells, polymorphonuclear leukocytes, or ciliated cells were occasionally present in the lung washings. The cells had abundant cytoplasm which was mildly eosinophilic; particles, vacuoles, and inclusion bodies were often visible.

In a few experiments, smears were made of the individual washes. Washes one and two had more non-mononuclear cells than subsequent washes. Cells recovered from bronchial or tracheal mucus have relatively low percentages of mononuclear cells and are often mixed with ciliated cells, debris and occasional red blood cells and polymorphonuclear leukocytes. We suggest that the early washes remove almost all free cells from the airways while the free cells on the alveolar surface, because of adhesive forces holding them to the alveolar wall, are recovered throughout the 12 washes. In animals exposed to particulate challenge, such as the iron oxide particles, lung washings are composed predominantly of cells containing the particulate marker. Included are a range of cells from those filled with particles to others containing only a few.

DISCUSSION

Problems in Measuring Free Cells in the Lungs

When attempting to interpret these kinds of changes in the numbers of free cells present in the lungs, it is important to be aware of some of the assumptions implicit in the lung-washing technique and hence to realize some of the limitations of the method. It is assumed that the efficiency of the harvesting technique is constant. The exact fraction of all free cells present that are recovered by 12 washes is unknown, but the fraction is assumed to be constant in controls and in experimental exposure groups. But the possibility that the experimental treatment has influenced the efficiency of recovery must always be considered. If the experimental procedure provokes an inflammatory response or atelectasis, altered efficiency may occur. GROSS *et al.* (1969) are right when they point out that severe pneumoconstriction, atelectasis, or fibrosis induced by large doses of particles can affect the efficiency of the washing procedure.

One should also remember that the pool size of free cells, like any other biological pool, is dynamically determined. The equilibrium number of cells present at a point in time is a function of the input and output history of the pool. For example, if the pool size decreased, this could represent either decreased production or recruitment of free cells or accelerated clearance of free cells from the lungs or both. If input and output of free cells both increased, the pool size could remain constant in spite of increased release of alveolar macrophages on the lung surface. Accelerated or depressed lysis of macrophages would also influence the equilibrium number of free cells.

In addition to quantifying free cells, it is also necessary to characterize the morphological and histochemical properties of the population of free cells recovered from control and exposure groups. The composition of the altered pool may depend on the stimulus used. Although lung washings from animals exposed to particulates like ferric oxide and silica contain mostly mononuclear alveolar phagocytes, highly irritating or infectious particles can produce an inflammatory reaction consisting of a local exudation of blood cells, mostly polymorphonuclear leukocytes, along with considerable numbers of red blood cells and plasma or edema fluid.

LEMON (1937) long ago pointed out that the lungs can respond to different types of foreign particles in different ways. When he injected tubercle bacilli into the lungs, he found that the alveoli rapidly filled with polymorphonuclear leukocytes which proceeded to ingest the bacilli. When silica was injected there were essentially no polymorphonuclear leukocytes; the silica was ingested almost entirely by the mononuclear alveolar phagocytes. With use of lung washing techniques in humans, PRATT *et al.* (1969) demonstrated that the free cells recovered from smokers had a higher percentage of macrophages than the free cells recovered from non-smokers. Thus, each experimental exposure may produce its own profile of cell types in the lung washing. We intend to supplement the studies reported here by a more thorough morphological examination of the cells recovered along with an investigation of their histochemical and functional properties.

INCREASES IN ALVEOLAR MACROPHAGE NUMBERS

It is not surprising that a cell system so intimately involved with the disposal of inhaled materials might respond to the quantity of particles presented to it. Fifty years ago PERMAR (1920) stated that foreign particulate material introduced into the lungs increased the rate of production of phagocytes. "The rate of the proliferative reaction depends entirely on the need for phagocytes as determined by the quantity of foreign particulate material to be removed from the air spaces. The contrast between the number of these cells appearing in the normal lung and that found after the introduction of foreign particulate matter is marked."

CARLETON (1934) gave intratracheal instillations of olive oil to dogs and rabbits and noted a swelling and release of alveolar cells. DRINKER & HATCH (1954) stated that, "within the alveoli are phagocytes, which are brought out in vast hoards by the stimulus of foreign bodies, such as dust particles, which they engulf".

More recently LABELLE & BRIEGER (1960, 1961) showed that inhalation of dust can increase the number of free cells. YEVICH (1965) reported that there is an increase in the number of rat alveolar spaces which contain macrophages after the rats are exposed to aerosols of oil or diatomaceous earth. FERIN *et al.* (1964) and FERIN (1960*a*, 1960*b*) presented indirect evidence that trypan blue and titanium dioxide can influence the numbers of macrophages in the lungs. RASCHE & ULMER (1967) reported that an aerosol of $AlCl_3$ increased the number of macrophages. BINGHAM *et al.* (1968) reported that exposure to lead sesquioxide resulted in a decrease in the number of alveolar macrophages. GROSS *et al.* (1969) reported significant increases in pulmonary macrophages following massive intratracheal injections of silicon dioxide and antimony trioxide.

What is the significance of increased numbers of free cells? Increased numbers of macrophages increase the probability that particles will be phagocytized and remain on the alveolar surface. SCHILLER (1961) maintained that only free particles can penetrate the walls of the alveoli. He found little evidence that phagocytes laden with dust can re-enter the alveolar wall. Thus, phagocytosis plays an important role in the prevention of the entry of particles into the fixed tissue of the lung. Once particles leave the alveolar surface and penetrate the fixed tissues subjacent to the air-liquid interface (Type 1 and 2 cells, interstitial and lymphatic tissue), their removal is slowed.

If the particles are within cells in the alveolar wall, their release into the alveolar space will now depend on the turnover time of the cells and the rates at which they are desquamated into the alveolar spaces or migrate into the lymphatic and circulatory system. Pathological processes, such as fibrosis, may slow the clearance of particles from this compartment. MORROW *et al.* (1964) have also emphasized the importance of the *in vivo* solubility of the particles. Thus, the probability of a particle entering a fixed tissue in which it would have a long biological half-life is reduced if the particle is phagocytized by a free cell.

Some experiments support these ideas. LABELLE & BRIEGER (1959, 1960) showed that there was a high positive correlation between the amount of dust cleared from the lungs and the number of phagocytic cells which could be counted. The fraction of the original lung burden which was excreted in the first day was related to the number of alveolar macrophages available to act as carriers. FERIN (1960*a*) has also reported that increased numbers of macrophages are correlated with an increased fraction cleared rapidly via the airways. Since increased numbers of macrophages lead to increased particle removal, these experiments suggest that macrophages prevent the penetration of particles into lymph nodes and interstitial spaces. Perhaps, it is primarily bare particles that cross the alveolar membrane, are removed via lymphatic pathways, or reside in the interstitial space.

CONCLUSIONS

There is abundant evidence indicating the central role of alveolar macrophages in the maintenance of the non-ciliated region of the lung as a clean and sterile surface suitable for gas exchange. It is essential to understand alveolar macrophages before we can understand pulmonary defenses; furthermore, knowledge of the behavior of alveolar macrophages is a central prerequisite to an understanding of pulmonary disease. New insights into the factors predisposing human populations to pulmonary disease arising from exposure to inhaled particles are required. The control of disease lies in the recognition of factors important in the defense of the organism.

REFERENCES

ALLISON, A. C., HARINGTON, J. S., BIRBECK, M. & NASH, T. (1967). In: *Inhaled particles and vapours* II. *Ed.* C. N. Davies. Oxford, Pergamon Press. pp. 121–128.

BINGHAM, E., PFITZER, E. A., BARKLEY, W. & RADFORD, E. P. (1968). *Science* **162,** 1297–1299.

BRAIN, J. D. (1966). *Clearance of particles from the lungs: alveolar macrophages and mucus transport.* Boston, Harvard University, Doctoral Thesis.

BRAIN, J. D. (1970). *Archs intern. Med.* **126,** 477–487.

BRAIN, J. D. & FRANK, N. R. (1967). *Fedn Proc. Fedn Am. Socs exp. Biol.* **26,** 498.

BRAIN, J. D. & FRANK, N. R. (1968a). *J. appl. Physiol.* **25,** 63–69.

BRAIN, J. D. & FRANK, N. R. (1968b). *J. Geront.* **23,** 58–62.

CARLETON, H. M. (1934). *Proc. R. Soc. Med.* **114,** 513–523.

CASARETT, L. J. & MILLEY, P. S. (1964). *Hlth Phys.* **10,** 1003–1011.

DRINKER, P. & HATCH, T. (1954). *Industrial dust.* New York, McGraw-Hill.

FERIN, J. (1960a). *Ann. occup. Hyg.* **3,** 1–5.

FERIN, J. (1960b). *Prac. Lek.* **12,** 397–401. (In Slovak.)

FERIN, J., VLCKOVA, A. & URBANKOVA, G. (1964). *Prac. Lek.* **16,** 202–205. (In Slovak.)

GERSING, R. & SCHUMACHER, H. (1955). *Beitr. Silikoseforsch* **25,** 31–34.

GREEN, G. M. & KASS, E. H. (1964). *J. exp. Med.* **119,** 167–176.

GROSS, P., DETREVILLE, R. T. P., TOLKER, E. B., KASCHAK, M. & BABYAK, M. A. (1969). *Archs envir. Hlth* **18,** 174–185.

HOLT, P. F., MILLS, J. & YOUNG, D. K. (1964). *J. Path. Bact.* **87,** 15–23.

KESSEL, R. W. I., MONACO, L. & MARCHISO, M. A. (1963). *Br. J. exp. Path.* **44,** 351–364.

LABELLE, C. W. & BRIEGER, H. (1959). *A.M.A. Archs ind. Hlth* **20,** 100–105.

LABELLE, C. W. & BRIEGER, H. (1960). *Archs envir. Hlth* **1,** 432–437.

LABELLE, C. W. & BRIEGER, H. (1961). In: *Inhaled particles and vapours. Ed.* C. N. Davies. Oxford, Pergamon Press. pp. 356–368.

LEMON, W. S. (1937). *Trans. Ass. Am. Physns* **52,** 278–288.

MORROW, P. E., GIBB, F. R. & LEIGH, J. (1964). *Hlth Phys.* **10,** 543–555.

OREN, R., FARNHAM, A. E., SAITO, K., MILOFSKY, E. & KARNOVSKY, M. L. (1963). *J. Cell Biol.* **17,** 487–501.

PERMAR, H. H. (1920). *J. med. Res.* **42,** 147–162.

PRATT, S. A., FINLEY, T. N., SMITH, M. H. & LADMAN, A. J. (1969). *Anat. Rec.* **163,** 497–507.

RASCHE, B. & ULMER, W. T. (1967). In: *Inhaled particles and vapours* II. *Ed.* C. N. Davies. Oxford, Pergamon Press. pp. 243–249.

SCHILLER, E. (1961). Ih: *Inhaled particles and vapours. Ed.* C. N. Davies. Oxford, Pergamon Press. pp. 342–347.

VIGLIANI, E. C., PERNIS, B. & MONACO, L. (1961). In: *Inhaled particles and vapours. Ed.* C. N. Davies. Oxford, Pergamon Press. pp. 348–355.

YEVICH, P. P. (1965). *Archs envir. Hlth* **10,** 37–43.

DISCUSSION

J. FERIN: I can confirm some of your results. For example: the need of 6 washes, the maximum response being one day after injection, and the number of free cells in rats. These results are similar to ours, which have been published. We found a rise of cells also after a subcutaneous injection of trypan blue. What kind of rats did you use, SPF rats or the usual ones?

Dr. BRAIN: The rats were not SPF rats — I wish they were. Rats may be a poor choice for experiments dealing with the lungs since the rat is quite susceptible to pulmonary infections. Increasingly, we use hamsters since they are relatively resistant to chronic murine pneumonia and other lung diseases. It is certainly desirable to carry out experiments with SPF rats if it is feasible.

In all the experiments reported on here, the lungs were examined for evidence of disease following their excision. In most instances, when the washings were completed, the lungs were sectioned, stained, and examined. If areas of infiltration, infection, or hemorrhage were found, the data were not used.

P. GROSS: Dr. Brain is to be congratulated on accomplishing a much needed task, that of outlining the steps which are necessary if reproducible reliable macrophage counts are to be obtained with the lung wash-out technique. I must admit that I am now somewhat apologetic for having condemned the method. Yet, at the time my paper was written, the lack of published necessary precautions seemed to justify this condemnation. Even now it appears that failure to adhere to directions such as outlined by Dr. Brain, would more or less guarantee unreliable results.

One hazard which may still be difficult to avoid is the presence of unsuspected pulmonary disease in the animals used.

C. R. RYLANDER: We have some information on the SPF problem. When studying guinea pigs with essentially the same technique as described in your paper, we found that SPF animals had a lower number of macrophages than ordinary animals and the deviation between animals was much smaller in the SPF group. The number of leucocytes was however only slightly smaller in SPF animals.

For the sake of standardization and to avoid such experimental errors as GROSS *et al.* (1969) have discussed, hopefully everyone working with the free lung cell method in exposure experiments will in the future use SPF animals.

A. SPRITZER: We have been studying pulmonary cells cleared and swallowed. We find that in sputum samples the number of polymorphonuclear leucocytes ranges from 5 to 15%. In our lung washings with Hanks's Balanced Salt Solution the % of these cells is significantly lower, so that there may be significant differences in the cell type and cell population obtained by these two sampling techniques. In addition our preliminary work with so-called "germ free rats" indicate no significant difference in cell type or number of cells obtained by either technique. But again there is a lower number of polmorphonuclear leucocytes using lung irrigation.

Dr. BRAIN: When we compare the cell types obtained with balanced salt solution (BSS) and physiological saline, we find that those obtained with BSS are somewhat more variable. My interpretation is that the BSS, which contains calcium and magnesium ions, does not disturb many of the younger macrophages which have good adhesive forces holding them to the alveolar surface; thus, particularly in the early washes, one recovers cells from the airways and alveoli which do not have any adhesive forces holding them to the respiratory tract surface. These cells are rounded up, contain phagocytized material, and are vacuolated. A few polymorphonuclear leucocytes and ciliated epithelial cells are also present.

When physiological saline is used as the washing medium, the same cells recovered by the BSS are also harvested. However, in addition, one also harvests alveolar macrophages which are normally held to the alveolar surface by intermolecular and electrostatic forces. As the calcium and magnesium concentration is lowered by the repeated washings of physiological saline, these adhesive forces are interrupted and the macrophages round up and are released into the washing fluid.

I do have some doubts as to whether your technique for collecting respiratory tract fluid provides the investigator with a normal representative sample of material and cells cleared up the trachea. We have utilized a similar technique (Brain, J. D., "Clearance of Particles from the Lungs: Alveolar Macrophages and Mucus Transport". Thesis. Harvard University, School of Public Health, Boston, 1966) and found that the health of the rats was seriously compromised by the surgery and by the inadequate nutrition caused by an interrupted esophagus. The other problem I encountered is that animals with cannulated esophagi did not always swallow all the material which was cleared up the respiratory tract. We found that animals tended to wipe mucus on their faces and when they inhaled radioactive material, we found increased amounts around their faces which apparently represented material which was cleared from the lungs, but not swallowed.

O. G. RAABE: You have described a very sensitive response to a dose of particles. However, it would be easier to fully evaluate your results if you would provide more details about the particles used. In particular it would be useful to know the number of particles in the exposure and the mass of these particles. To calculate this it is necessary to know the particle size distribution of the particles. Apparently, from the information you do give, the exposures involved masses of the order of hundreds of micrograms and the number of particles was of the same order as the number of additional macrophages collected. This may be a coincidence, but more information about the particles is necessary to evaluate this. Also, it would be better if the exposure were carried out by aerosol inhalation rather than tracheo-bronchial injection.

Dr. BRAIN: Our knowledge of the particles used varies a great deal. In some cases thorough microscopy has been done and we would be glad to provide a size distribution. In other cases, for example, the coal dust, our knowledge of the exact particle size distribution is relatively crude. We have done inhalation exposures to triphenyl phosphate, carbon dust, and cigarette smoke, but most of these have been previously reported (i.e. BRAIN, J. D. (1970), Free Cells in the Lungs: Some Aspects of Their Role, Quantitation and Regulation, *Archives of Internal Medicine*, **126**: 477–487). Therefore, I did not discuss them here.

M. GRUNSPAN: Why is a higher number of macrophages produced only after washing the lungs several times? What is the relationship between these washings and the surfactant factor? Did you do parallel determinations between the number of lung macrophages and the quantity of surfactant?

Dr. BRAIN: I think the question was how does the recovery of cells compare with the recovery of surfactant. It is surprising that one continues to recover macrophages wash after wash. It probably relates to the strong adhesive forces which exist between the macrophages and the alveolar wall; these forces are only gradually disrupted. The recovery of surfactant is much more rapid. If one washed a dozen times in three washes, one probably would have 80 or 90 per cent of the total recovered; thus, it is washed out much more rapidly than the cells are. With the surfactant, it is simply a matter of getting it into solution; it is not necessary to interrupt adhesive forces.

B. RASCHE: In our experiments we give marked macrophages intravenously in guinea pigs after a dust exposure. We later found these marked macrophages in the lung. This proves the hematopoetic transport of macrophages into the irritated region.

J. BRUCH: In electron microscope studies of rat lungs it can be discerned that only one part of the macrophage actually lies free in the alveolar lumen. A larger part of the macrophage on the other hand is attached to the alveolar epithelium through numerous cytoplasmic processes in closely linked union. Peroxidase, injected into the blood vessel, becomes phagocytosed within 5 minutes of passing over these macrophages, but not in the actual free alveolar macrophages. These closely linked ones can only be dissolved with more washing out. It may be presumed that these intercellular bonds are influenced by Ca and Mg-ions.

Mr. DE VIR: I should be more satisfied if you could give the number of particles as well as the mass concentration.

I think you will have to look again at the electrical charge on the particles injected. This may have a big effect. It is quite normal in the transport phenomena of the cells you are talking about that calcium and magnesium have an effect on conductivity transport. This is perhaps a partial explanation in addition to this multi-washing of yours.

Dr. BRAIN: I do not think the results with calcium and magnesium are totally surprising. There are many similar instances in biology where calcium and magnesium are known to be involved in the adhesion of cells. Apparently, the cell surface has a negative charge on it and thus adjacent cells tend to repel each other. These cations with positive charges serve as a bridge between negative charges on adjacent cell surfaces. This allows the cells to come close enough so that short range forces can become very important.

With regard to your comment about particle size, your point is well taken. We are all remiss unless we give complete and detailed information about the particles in terms of composition and size distribution.

INFLUENCE DE LA NATURE DES POUSSIERES ET DE LA CHARGE PULMONAIRE SUR L'EPURATION.[1]

L. Le Bouffant

Centre d'Etudes et Recherches des Charbonnages de France, Groupe Pneumoconiose, B.P. 27, 60 — Creil — France

Abstract — The inhalation of dusts of different kinds by rats and cats shows that lung clearance depends on the nature of the dust and varies according to the animal species.

From a reference lung clearance curve established with activated haematite, it is possible to determine the influence of various factors, such as pulmonary dust load, time since exposure or nature of particles, on the lung clearance capacity at a given time.

The inhalation of coal, even in small quantities, leads to a decrease of alveolar clearance in rats. After heavy doses of dust, the rate of alveolar clearance becomes negligibly small; moreover the clearance function does not recover appreciably. Inhaled quartz decreases the rate of lung clearance in about the same way, but the clearance activity partly recovers. After a long time following quartz inhalation, alveolar retention shows a marked reduction in consequence of a decrease in alveolar accessibility due to quartz lesions.

INTRODUCTION

Les recherches nombreuses effectuées depuis quelques années sur l'épuration pulmonaire ont déjà permis de dégager un certain nombre de constatations sur la fonction épuratrice du poumon vis-à-vis des particules inhalées, tout au moins en ce qui concerne le poumon normal. C'est ainsi qu'on a pu établir aussi bien par des études sur l'homme que par l'expérimentation animale, que l'élimination des poussières déposées dans le tractus pulmonaire obéissait à une série de lois exponentielles, dont les constantes de vitesse diffèrent selon le niveau considéré: bronches, bronchioles, alvéoles.

Les connaissances sont par contre plus fragmentaires en ce qui concerne les mécanismes exacts de l'épuration et surtout les perturbations occasionnées par des agressions diverses telles que la surcharge pulmonaire résultant d'empoussiérages répétés, l'action de substances toxiques de natures diverses et, d'une manière plus générale, par des altérations d'importance variable au niveau des cellules ou des tissus pulmonaires.

Le présent travail s'insère dans une étude d'ensemble (*cf.* communications de

[1] Travail réalisé en collaboration par le Centre d'Etudes et Recherches des Charbonnages de France* et l'Association Commissariat à l'Energie Atomique — Euratom**.

Ont participé à ce travail: Daniel, H.*; Hénin, J. P.*; Lafuma, J.**; Martin, J. C.*; Masse, R.**; Morin, M.**; Nénot, J. C.**; Skupinski, W.**

Nenot 1971; Masse 1971) visant à mesurer l'importance des modifications cinétiques apportées à l'épuration pulmonaire par ces différents facteurs et à élucider les mécanismes responsables de ces modifications, particulièrement au niveau alvéolaire.

Deux facteurs sont considérés ici: la nature des poussières et la charge pulmonaire. Dans certains cas, des comparaisons ont pu être faites entre les capacités d'épuration d'animaux d'espèces différentes. La variation de la cinétique d'épuration en fonction du temps d'évolution après l'empoussiérage a été étudiée, afin de connaître les possibilités de restauration de la fonction épuratrice.

METHODE EXPERIMENTALE

L'étude a porté sur deux espèces d'animaux: le rat et le chat. Le choix de ces deux espèces repose sur des considérations d'ordre anatomique et sur l'existence de différences marquées dans le mode d'épuration qui ont déjà été exposées à l'occasion de travaux antérieurs (Policard et al., 1965).

Deux méthodes ont été utilisées pour l'étude quantitative de l'épuration. La première consiste à sacrifier les animaux empoussiérés par groupes après des périodes d'évolution convenablement choisies et à doser la poussière pulmonaire par une méthode chimique. La courbe d'épuration peut alors être tracée à partir des moyennes des groupes, avec une précision qui dépend de l'importance du facteur de variation individuelle et du nombre d'animaux constituant chaque groupe. Cette méthode s'applique à tous les types de poussières à la seule condition qu'elles puissent être dosées chimiquement. Elle nécessite par contre l'emploi d'un nombre d'animaux relativement élevé pour maîtriser la dispersion.

L'autre méthode est dérivée de celle qui a été mise au point par Albert & Arnett (1955) pour l'étude de l'épuration pulmonaire chez l'homme. Elle consiste à faire inhaler des poussières radioactives à l'animal puis à tracer la courbe d'épuration en mesurant l'activité résiduelle des poussières intra-pulmonaires par un comptage externe. Cette méthode permet de tracer la courbe d'épuration d'un même sujet et d'étudier les variations individuelles par comparaison de plusieurs courbes. Toutefois, elle est nécessairement limitée à l'étude de particules existant sous la forme radioactive ou susceptibles d'être marquées par addition d'une substance radioactive.

Emploi de Poussières Non Marquées

Cette méthode a été utilisée pour étudier l'influence de la nature des poussières sur la capacité d'épuration. Cinq types de poussières ont été étudiés: du charbon, du quartz, de l'oxyde de titane, un oxyde de fer (hématite) et de l'amiante (chrysotile).

Les caractéristiques de ces poussières étaient les suivantes:

— Charbon: charbon lorrain et anthracite russe, constitués par des particules inférieures à 5 μm obtenues par broyage.
— Quartz: silice obtenue par broyage ("silice Ni"). Particules inférieures à 5 μm.
— Oxyde de titane: oxyde préparé par voie chimique. Particules unitaires <1 micron, groupées en agrégats inférieurs à 5 μm.
— Oxyde de fer: hématite préparée par voie chimique (qualité "rouge à polir"). Particules <1 micron groupées en agrégats inférieurs à 5 μm.

— Amiante: chrysotile broyé. Particules <1 μm groupées en agrégats inférieurs à 5 μm.

Les animaux sont exposés aux poussières dans une chambre d'empoussiérage à régulation automatique modèle Cerchar. La concentration est maintenue constante à la valeur de 300 mg/m³ pendant toute la durée de l'empoussiérage (LE BOUFFANT, 1961).

Deux séries d'essais ont été réalisées:

(a) un empoussiérage en 13 séances suivi d'un délai d'épuration de 46 jours (charbon, quartz, oxyde de titane, oxyde de fer), essai pratiqué sur le chat et sur le rat. Le taux d'épuration au bout de ce délai a été déterminé en rapportant la quantité de poussière résiduelle à la teneur au point 24 h.

(b) un empoussiérage unique de 6 h (quartz, oxyde de titane, chrysotile) sur le rat, l'épuration étant suivie pendant 56 jours.

Emploi de Poussières Marquées

La poussière est constituée par de l'oxyde de fer (rouge à polir) de la même qualité que ci-dessus. Le produit est préalablement activé sous neutrons pour obtenir une certaine quantité de Fe-59 radioactif (LEFEVRE et al., 1968; LEFEVRE, 1969).

L'aérosol est produit à partir d'une suspension de cette poussière en milieu liquide, l'inhalation ayant lieu dans des installations différentes conçues pour l'exposition individuelle dans le cas des chats ou l'exposition par groupe de 12 animaux dans le cas des rats. Chez le chat, l'inhalation a lieu sous anesthésie générale au nembutal.

La mesure de l'activité est effectuée par comptage externe au moyen d'un compteur à scintillation placé au niveau des poumons, en utilisant le rayonnement γ de 1,10 et 1,29 MeV du Fe-59. La dose moyenne par poumon est inférieure à 1 μCi.

Cette méthode a été utilisée pour les essais suivants:

— établissement des courbes-types d'épuration chez le chat et le rat.

— étude de l'action d'une charge préalable de poussière sur la capacité d'épuration. Pour réaliser cette charge, les animaux sont d'abord soumis à un empoussiérage au charbon ou à la silice pendant des laps de temps de 6 h à 3 mois selon les cas. La modification de la capacité d'épuration est ensuite mesurée en établissant une courbe-test à l'hématite marquée.

— étude de la restauration de la capacité d'épuration en fonction du temps à la suite d'un empoussiérage, les délais d'évolution s'échelonnant selon les cas entre 0 et

TABLEAU I. EPURATION COMPAREE DE DIFFÉRENTES POUSSIERES CHEZ LE CHAT ET LE RAT

		Charbon	Oxyde de titane	Oxyde de fer (hématite)	Silice (quartz)
Poussières retenues dans les poumons 24 h après la fin de l'empoussiérage (en mg par g de poumon)	Chat	7,6	9,1	6,2	2,9
	Rat	7,7	10,1	6,6	2,3
Taux d'épuration totale après 46 jours (en %)	Chat	84	70	76	45
	Rat	<5	23	55	25

18 mois. L'évolution de la capacité d'épuration est ensuite mesurée en traçant la courbe-test à l'hématite marquée.

RESULTATS

Influence de la Nature des Poussières et de l'Espèce Animale. Epuration Comparée du Charbon, du Quartz, de l'Oxyde de Titane et de l'Hématite chez le Rat et chez le Chat

Les résultats de cette comparaison portant sur un empoussiérage de 13 jours et une évolution de 46 jours sont groupés dans le Tableau I.

Rétention Pulmonaire

La quantité de poussière exprimée en milligrammes par gramme de poumon — retenue dans les poumons au bout de 24 heures, c'est-à-dire après que la plus grande partie des poussières déposées dans les voies respiratoires supérieures a été éliminée, varie notablement selon la nature de la poussière. On note en particulier que la rétention du quartz est nettement moindre que celle du charbon, de l'oxyde de titane ou de l'hématite, la rétention maximale étant observée pour l'oxyde de titane, poussière totalement inerte et insoluble. Cette différence doit cependant être corrigée pour tenir compte de l'augmentation de poids des poumons qui apparaît très nettement déjà dès la fin de l'empoussiérage dans le cas du quartz. En effet, chez le rat, le poids moyen des poumons au point 24 h est de 1,6 g avec le quartz, alors qu'il reste inférieur à 1,2 g avec les autres poussières. Ce poids continue ensuite à augmenter pour atteindre 2,27 g au bout du 46 ème jour.

Par contre, les différences de rétention entre le chat et le rat sont minimes pour une même poussière.

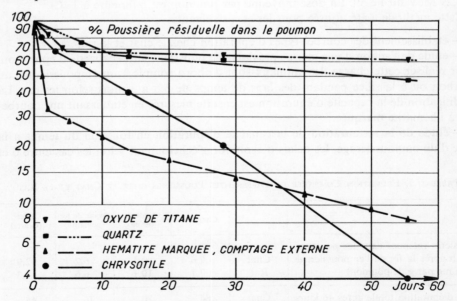

FIGURE 1. Epuration comparée de poussières de nature différente chez le rat après un empoussiérage unique.

Epuration Pulmonaire

Les taux d'épuration diffèrent également d'une façon notable selon la nature de la poussière. Chez le chat, l'épuration est maximale avec le charbon et minimale avec le quartz.

Des différences importantes apparaissent ici entre le chat et le rat: le taux d'épuration est nettement inférieur pour le rat, quelle que soit la poussière considérée. On observe en outre une anomalie remarquable, à savoir que le taux d'épuration du charbon chez le rat est très faible. Cette particularité, dont le caractère systématique a pu être vérifié, n'a pas trouvé jusqu'à présent d'explication.

Influence de la Nature des Poussières sur la Cinétique D'Epuration

La Figure 1 représente en coordonnées semi-logarithmiques les courbes d'épuration établies chez le rat avec des poussières d'oxyde de titane, de quartz ou de chrysotile, après un empoussiérage unique de 6 h. Elle comporte en outre, à des fins de comparaison, la courbe d'épuration de l'hématite marquée établie par comptage externe, l'empoussiérage ayant été réalisé dans les conditions indiquées plus haut à propos des poussières marquées. Il convient de préciser que la charge pulmonaire est nettement différente dans ces deux séries d'essai: 0,5 mg à 1 mg/g de poumon pour les empoussiérages de 6 h, de l'ordre de 50 μg/g de poumon pour l'empoussiérage à l'hématite marquée.

La forme des courbes, constituées par des tronçons de droites, confirme l'allure exponentielle du phénomène d'épuration, avec des constantes de vitesse différentes suivant le niveau du dépôt dans le poumon. En première approximation, on distingue dans ces courbes deux tronçons correspondant respectivement à l'épuration du secteur bronchique, d'allure rapide, et à celle du secteur alvéolaire, nettement plus lente. Un tronçon intermédiaire entre les précédents apparaît sur la courbe d'épuration de l'hématite marquée. Nous verrons plus loin que cette phase intermédiaire, peu différente de la phase alvéolaire longue, n'apparaît pas toujours nettement sur les courbes d'épuration de l'hématite, sauf dans les cas où elle apparaît renforcée par rapport à l'épuration alvéolaire sous l'influence d'une altération pulmonaire.

La position relative des courbes d'épuration de l'oxyde de titane, du quartz et de l'hématite correspond à celle des valeurs contenues dans le Tableau I, les différences entre les taux d'épuration étant dues aux conditions différentes de l'empoussiérage.

Enfin, le chrysotile présente une vitesse d'épuration très élevée. Cette particularité est due à la solubilité lente de ce minéral dans les tissus: il ne s'agit donc pas ici uniquement d'une épuration suivant le mécanisme mis en oeuvre pour les autres poussières mais en partie d'une élimination par dissolution.

Influence de la Charge Coniotique et du Délai D'Evolution sur la Capacité D'Epuration

La possibilité de disposer de séries d'animaux homogènes grâce aux rats SPF permet d'obtenir une faible dispersion des points expérimentaux, rendant possible des études relativement fines de l'influence de facteurs divers sur la capacité d'épuration. Il n'en est pas de même avec des chats, dont l'hétérogénéité inévitable liée à la diversité d'origine des animaux a pour conséquence une dispersion importante des résultats. C'est pourquoi l'étude systématique de l'influence de la charge pulmonaire sur la capacité d'épuration a été réalisée uniquement sur le rat dans un premier temps, les différences entre espèces pouvant être ensuite analysées en choisissant pour les facteurs étudiés les domaines de variation les plus appropriés.

Modification de la Capacité d'Epuration en Fonction de la Charge en Poussières de Charbon

La Figure 2 représente en coordonnées semi-logarithmiques les résultats du test à

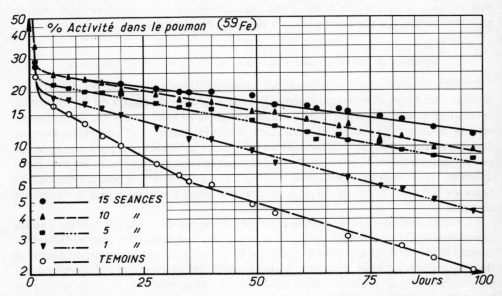

FIGURE 2. Modification de l'épuration sous l'action d'un empoussiérage préalable au charbon. Test à l'hématite marquée immédiatement après l'empoussiérage.

l'hématite marquée pratiqué immédiatement à la suite d'une série d'empoussiérages au charbon de 1, 5, 10 et 15 séances de 6 h, à la concentration de 300 mg/m³. La quantité de charbon présente dans les poumons s'échelonnait entre 2 et 8 mg par poumon.

On distingue sur les courbes deux parties, de pentes nettement différenciées, correspondant respectivement à l'épuration bronchique et à l'épuration alvéolaire. Si l'épuration bronchique ne paraît pas affectée par la présence de poussières, même au bout de quinze séances de 6 h, il n'en est pas de même de l'épuration alvéolaire qui présente un ralentissement progressif en fonction de la charge pulmonaire.

On a tenté de chiffrer l'importance de ce ralentissement ainsi que la variation de la quantité d'hématite déposée au niveau alvéolaire sous l'influence de l'empoussiérage. Pour cela, une analyse mathématique des résultats a été faite en considérant que le poumon est constitué par une série de compartiments se vidant les uns dans les autres ou à l'extérieur. Chaque compartiment pris isolément se vide suivant une loi exponentielle de type $Q = Q_0 \, e^{-kt}$ où Q_0 est la quantité initiale de poussière dans ce compartiment, Q la quantité restante à l'instant t et k la constante de vitesse pour le compartiment désiré. En faisant l'hypothèse qu'il existe 1, 2 . . . n compartiments et en considérant qu'il existe entre eux des interactions, on ajuste par approximations successives la valeur de Q_0 et k pour chaque compartiment jusqu'à l'obtention d'une courbe superposable à la courbe réelle. Au lieu de la constante de vitesse k, on peut considérer la période $\tau = \log_e 2/k$, ou temps nécessaire pour épurer la moitié de la poussière déposée dans le compartiment.

TABLEAU II. INFLUENCE DE CHARGES CONIOTIQUES CROISSANTES (CHARBON) SUR LA FONCTION EPURATRICE. MESURES EFFECTUÉES IMMÉDIATEMENT APRÈS LA FIN DE L'EMPOUSSIÉRAGE

Durée de l'exposition (nombre de séances)	1er compartiment		2ème compartiment	
	τ (jours)	Q_0 (%)	τ (jours)	Q_0 (%)
1	0,2	79,5	40	20,5
5	0,2	77	69	23
10	0,35	82,5	76	16,5
15	0,1	74	72	26
Témoins	0,2	80	22,5	19,5

Le Tableau II donne les valeurs obtenues en utilisant un schéma simplifié à deux compartiments. Il confirme que la période d'épuration bronchique reste très courte même après des empoussiérages répétés. Par contre, la période longue augmente en fonction de l'empoussiérage et se trouve déjà doublée à la suite d'un seul empoussiérage de 6 h. Quant aux proportions de poussières d'hématite déposées respectivement au niveau des bronches et des alvéoles, elles ne sont pas modifiées significativement et oscillent autour de 80% et 20% comme dans le cas des témoins, montrant qu'il n'y a pas eu de modification sensible de la dynamique de l'inhalation ou de la rétention.

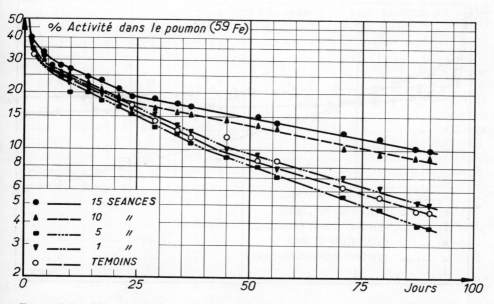

FIGURE 3. Modification de l'épuration sous l'action d'un empoussiérage préalable au charbon. Test à l'hématite marquée 6 mois après la fin de l'empoussiérage.

Restauration de la Fonction Epuratrice

Un deuxième test à l'hématite marquée a été pratiqué après une période d'évolution de 6 mois afin d'étudier les possibilités de restauration du pouvoir épurateur. Les résultats sont portés sur la Figure 3 et dans le Tableau III.

TABLEAU III. INFLUENCE DE CHARGES CONIOTIQUES CROISSANTES (CHARBON) SUR LA FONCTION EPURATRICE. MESURES EFFECTUÉES 6 MOIS APRÈS LA FIN DE L'EMPOUSSIÉRAGE

Dirèe de l'exposition (nombre de sèances)	1er compartiment		2ème compartiment	
	τ (jours)	Q_0 (%)	τ (jours)	Q_0 (%)
1	0,4	70	31	30
5	0,5	72	28	27
10	0,5	71,5	47	28
15	0,35	69,5	49	30
Témoins	0,45	69,5	30	30

La comparaison avec les témoins montre que l'épuration alvéolaire présente une récupération totale dans le cas des empoussiérages faibles, mais qu'elle reste incomplète pour les deux empoussiérages les plus forts: périodes de 47 et 49 jours contre 30 jours pour les témoins, soit une augmentation de 1,6 fois.

Altération et Restauration de l'Epuration dans le cas d'Empoussiérages Massifs au Charbon

La même étude a été effectuée en soumettant les animaux à un empoussiérage prolongé avec de la poussière de charbon, à savoir 6 h par jour à la concentration de

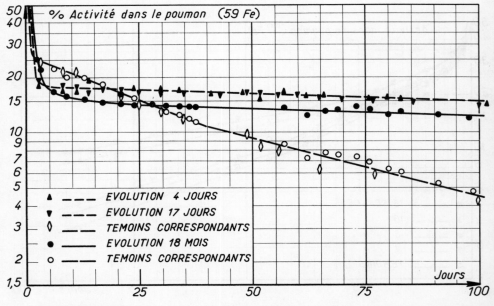

FIGURE 4. Modification de l'épuration sous l'action d'un empoussiérage au charbon de longue durée. Test à l'hématite marquée après différents délais d'évolution.

300 mg/m³ pendant 3 mois. On a ensuite testé la capacité d'épuration après l'empoussiérage, au bout de 4 jours, 17 jours et 18 mois d'évolution. Les résultats sont portés sur la Figure 4 et le Tableau IV.

TABLEAU IV. INFLUENCE D'UN EMPOUSSIÉRAGE PROLONGÉ AU CHARBON (3 MOIS) SUR LA FONCTION ÉPURATRICE, APRÈS DIFFÉRENTS DÉLAIS D'ÉVOLUTION

Délai d'évolution	1er compartiment		2ème compartiment	
	τ (jours)	Q_0 (%)	τ (jours)	Q_0 (%)
4 jours	0,5	85	365	17
17 jours	0,5	84	331	18
18 mois	0,7	90	277	12
Témoins	0,5	78,5	42	23,5

Il apparaît que l'altération de la capacité d'épuration alvéolaire observée précédemment avec des empoussiérages courts continue à s'aggraver à mesure qu'on augmente la durée d'exposition aux poussières. A la fin de l'empoussiérage, la période du compartiment 2 est de 365 jours, ce qui correspond à un allongement de 8,7 fois. En outre, la restauration reste très faible puisque la période est encore de 277 jours au bout de 18 mois. Il est à noter par ailleurs que la part de la rétention alvéolaire diminue notablement en fonction du temps chez les animaux empoussiérés: elle est réduite de moitié dans le cas d'une évolution de 18 mois.

Modification de la Capacité d'Epuration sous l'Influence d'un Empoussiérage au Quartz

L'essai a été réalisé dans les mêmes conditions d'empoussiérage que ci-dessus:

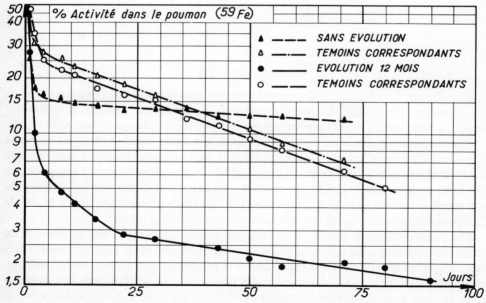

FIGURE 5. Modification de l'épuration sous l'action d'un empoussiérage au quartz de longue durée. Test à l'hématite marquée après différents délais d'évolution.

3 mois d'exposition à une poussière de quartz à la concentration de 300 mg/m^3. Le test à l'hématite marquée a ensuite été réalisé immédiatement après l'empoussiérage et au bout d'une évolution de 12 mois.

La Figure 5 et le Tableau V montrent que la capacité d'épuration alvéolaire, ici encore, est fortement réduite par l'empoussiérage, la période passant de 28 jours pour les témoins à 261 jours pour les animaux empoussiérés et testés immédiatement après. Parallèlement le taux de rétention alvéolaire est réduit de près de moitié.

Quant à la restauration, elle diffère nettement de celle qu'on observe avec le charbon, puisque la période retombe à 41 jours au bout de 12 mois, alors qu'elle est encore de 277 jours au bout de 18 mois dans le cas du charbon. Par contre, le taux de rétention alvéolaire continue à diminuer très fortement et ne représente plus que 5 % de la rétention pulmonaire totale après le délai de 12 mois. On remarquera par ailleurs que la courbe d'épuration correspondant à ce même délai présente entre la partie bronchique et la partie alvéolaire un tronçon nettement différencié correspondant à une vitesse d'épuration intermédiaire. Il n'en a pas été tenu compte dans la détermination des valeurs du Tableau V qui correspondent à un schéma en deux compartiments. Une analyse plus poussée ferait apparaître une phase intermédiaire à période relativement courte, de l'ordre de 15 jours, la période du dernier tronçon étant majorée de ce fait, mais les tendances indiquées ne seraient pas modifiées.

Tableau V. Influence d'un Empoussiérage Prolongé à la silice (3 mois) sur la Fonction Épuratrice après Différents délais d'Évolution

Délais d'évolution	1er compartiment		2ème compartiment	
	τ (jours)	Q_0 (%)	τ (jours)	Q_0 (%)
0	0,35	85,5	261	14,5
12 mois	0,5	94,5	41	5,2
Témoins	0,5	79	28	23

DISCUSSION

Il se dégage des résultats précédents un certain nombre de points marquants en ce qui concerne l'influence des trois facteurs suivants sur la capacité d'épuration: structure pulmonaire liée à l'espèce, nature des poussières, charge pulmonaire.

Une même poussière n'est pas éliminée avec une égale rapidité chez des animaux d'espèce différente. C'est ainsi que le chat épure ses poumons nettement plus vite que le rat, quel que soit le type de poussière considéré. Cette observation est recoupée par des observations histologiques qui montrent de façon constante que les alvéoles du rat contiennent des quantités importantes de particules longtemps après la fin de l'empoussiérage, alors qu'ils sont rapidement nettoyés chez le chat.

Ces résultats sont à mettre, au moins en partie, au compte des différences de structure pulmonaire de ces deux animaux, le chat disposant de glandes bronchiques beaucoup plus développées que celles du rat et présentant par ailleurs une circulation lymphatique différente. On observe que les poussières qui passent dans l'interstitium chez le chat sont localisées principalement dans les gaines péribronchiolaires et périvasculaires, tandis que chez le rat on les retrouve surtout dans les ganglions trachéobronchiques. Par ailleurs, il est probable, mais ceci reste à démontrer, que le nombre et la mobilité des cellules à poussière jouent également un rôle important dans les différences observées.

La vitesse d'épuration des poussières dépend de leur nature chimique. Toutefois, les résultats obtenus ne permettent pas d'établir une relation entre le type de poussière et leur vitesse d'épuration. Chez le chat, l'épuration des poussières atoxiques comme le charbon, l'oxyde de titane, l'hématite s'effectue nettement plus vite que celle du quartz, la vitesse la plus grande étant observée pour le charbon. Mais cet ordre n'est plus le même dans le cas du rat, chez lequel l'oxyde de titane et le quartz s'éliminent à peu près de la même façon, tandis que le charbon ne s'élimine pratiquement pas. Aucune explication n'a été trouvée à cette anomalie jusqu'à présent. Quant au chrysotile, dont l'épuration est beaucoup plus rapide, il entre dans la catégorie des substances solubles dont la vitesse d'élimination peut être décomposée en deux termes: un terme d'épuration et un terme de dissolution.

Enfin, la charge pulmonaire modifie de manière importante la capacité d'épuration du poumon. Chez le rat, cette modification apparaît déjà pour des empoussiérages faibles, correspondant à une surcharge pondérale de l'ordre de un pour mille. Elle se produit aussi bien avec des poussières inertes qu'avec des poussières toxiques. Une seule séance d'empoussiérage de 6 h avec du charbon à la concentration de 300 mg/m³ suffit pour réduire de moitié la vitesse d'épuration alvéolaire, un empoussiérage de 3 mois la rend voisine de zéro. De plus, il apparaît que la rétention alvéolaire varie dans de larges proportions en fonction du temps dans le cas du quartz, le rapport rétention alvéolaire/rétention bronchique passant de 29 % à 5 % au bout de 3 mois d'empoussiérage suivis de 12 mois d'évolution, ce qui traduit une diminution considérable de l'accessibilité alvéolaire sous l'influence du développement des lésions.

Quant à la restauration de la vitesse d'épuration, elle est variable suivant la nature de la poussière, tout au moins chez le rat. Négligeable dans le cas du charbon, elle est nette dans le cas du quartz, mais la vitesse d'épuration n'a cependant pas encore atteint sa valeur normale au bout d'un an. Il est probable que les constatations seraient différentes chez le chat, dont nous avons vu que l'épuration alvéolaire était rapide vis-à-vis du charbon. L'intérêt d'une étude parallèle sur le chat apparaît ici clairement, car elle permettrait, compte tenu des analogies existant entre le poumon du chat et le poumon humain, d'apporter des indications précieuses sur l'évolution de la fonction épuratrice chez l'homme sous l'effet d'empoussiérages prolongés et sur les possibilités de restauration de cette fonction.

REFERENCES

ALBERT, R. E. & ARNETT, L. C. (1955). *A.M.A. Archs ind. Hlth* **12**, 99–106.

LE BOUFFANT, L. (1961). In: *Inhaled particles and vapours*. Ed. C. N. Davies. Oxford, Pergamon Press. pp. 369–383.

LEFEVRE, G. (1969). Thèse. Paris.

LEFEVRE, G., NENOT, J. C., LAFUMA, J., COLLET, A. & CHARBONNIER, J. (1968). *Archs Mal. prof. Méd. trav.* **29**, 669–678.

MASSE, R. (1971). This symposium, pp. 247–257.

NENOT, J. C. (1971). This symposium, pp. 239–246.

POLICARD, A., COLLET, A. & NORMAND-REUET, C. (1967). In: *Inhaled particles and vapours* II. Ed. C. N. Davies. Oxford, Pergamon Press. pp. 3–7.

DISCUSSION : See pp. 258–259.

ETUDE DE L'INFLUENCE DE L'IRRADIATION SUR L'EPURATION PULMONAIRE [(1)]

J. C. Nenot

*Commissariat à l'Energie Atomique, Département de la Protection Sanitaire,
B.P. N° 6, 92 — Fontenay-aux-Roses, France*

Summary — The influence of radiation exposure on lung clearance in rats was studied from a functional point of view. Exposure was delivered in two ways: either external exposure at L.D. 50 or internal exposure with ^{239}Pu aerosols at different concentrations. Three levels of alveolar contamination in α emitters were studied: 1, 0·1 and 0·007 μCi/g of lung. Lung clearance was then tested 10 days after exposure, with ^{59}Fe oxide insoluble particles administered to the animals by inhalation. External exposure did not modify either retention or clearance rate, whereas internal exposure to α particles largely modified clearance kinetics. This study will be carried on with an investigation of cellular mechanisms.

INTRODUCTION

Les risques professionnels inhérents à l'industrie nucléaire sont liés aux dangers de l'irradiation; ils sont très différents dans leurs conséquences suivant qu'ils relèvent de l'irradiation externe ou de l'irradiation interne. Schématiquement, la première constitue un risque aigu, mettant en cause soit l'organisme entier soit certains organes. La seconde représente au niveau du poumon un risque d'irradiation locale chronique, que ce soit au niveau des tissus pour les émetteurs β et γ, ou au niveau des cellules pour les émetteurs α. Les natures d'émissions représentent des paramètres bien individualisés; dans cette étude l'irradiation externe a été pratiquée à l'aide du rayonnement γ du cobalt, l'irradiation interne à l'aide du rayonnement α du plutonium.

En collaboration avec les laboratoires du Cerchar (Lefevre *et al.*, 1968), nous avons mis au point une technique permettant l'étude dynamique de l'épuration pulmonaire sur animal vivant. Cette méthode permet de suivre l'élimination d'un radionucléide administré par voie aérienne, grâce à des mesures externes à l'animal. Ses avantages sont doubles: outre la standardisation de sa méthodologie, dans laquelle le type d'émetteur ne joue aucun rôle, elle permet de tester l'épuration au moment choisi par l'expérimentateur, de la répéter sur le même animal placé dans des conditions expérimentales identiques ou non.

La méthode générale consiste à comparer l'épuration pulmonaire d'animaux témoins et d'animaux du même lot ayant subi une irradiation préalable, externe ou interne.

[1] Travail réalisé en collaboration avec l'Association Euratom-Cea** et le Centre d'études et de Recherches des Charbonnages de France* (Cerchar) Ont participé: J. P. Henin*, J. Hercouet**, J. Lafuma**, L. Le Bouffant*, R. Masse**, M. Morin**, W. Skupinski**.

L'irradiation externe permet de connaître la dose délivrée à l'organisme avec exactitude, mais cause des dommages à des tissus très différents dans leurs fonctions, et soumet l'animal à une agression importante. La contamination pulmonaire par émetteur α délivre l'irradiation directement aux constituants de l'alvéole; l'effet cytotoxique de l'émission α, en modifiant les populations cellulaires, permet de faire la part des mécanismes cellulaires dans l'épuration pulmonaire. Par contre la dose délivrée au poumon profond n'est connue qu'avec approximation.

Il est ainsi possible de mener parallèlement, avec les mêmes moyens, des études différentes dans leurs essences, telles que l'étude des mécanismes de l'épuration pulmonaire et l'étude du seuil des sensibilités fonctionnelle et cellulaire, décrite par MASSE (1971). Ces études ont un point commun: elles ne se préoccupent que du problème fonctionnel.

TECHNIQUES

Pour répondre au double impératif de disposer de lots représentatifs d'animaux, placés exactement dans les mêmes conditions expérimentales, et de placer l'expérimentateur dans les meilleures conditions de sécurité possibles imposant le travail en boîtes à gants, nous n'avons utilisé que des rats dans les expériences décrites; le critère de ce choix est basé essentiellement sur la taille de l'animal. Les rats sont rassemblés par lots de 12, ce qui représente la capacité moyenne du matériel de contamination respiratoire. Cette contamination se fait sur animaux non anesthésiés, respirant librement l'atmosphère d'une enceinte étanche, remplie par l'aérosol radioactif fourni par le générateur directement branché sur cette enceinte. Les données numériques des activités pulmonaires sont obtenues par comptage global journalier des rats, après qu'ils aient subi l'inhalation de ^{59}Fe, sous forme de poussières d'oxyde de fer, insoluble en milieu biologique. La charge pulmonaire des rats après l'inhalation est de l'ordre de 50 μg/g de poumon, ce qui correspond à une activité inférieure à 1 μCi/g de poumon. Cette activité est suffisante pour pouvoir poursuivre les mesures pendant 3 à 6 mois.

Les courbes d'épuration et leur analyse par compartiments sont obtenues par une méthode de Monte Carlo, décrite par BAZIN *et al.* (1968); les coefficients des exponentielles sont tirés au hasard, permettant de recalculer les valeurs théoriques, et de les comparer aux points expérimentaux, et d'obtenir une certaine somme des carrés des écarts caractérisant l'ajustement avec un processus de convergence. Chaque nouveau tirage fournit de nouvelles valeurs. On obtient ainsi une courbe de distribution des coefficients tels que l'ajustement de la courbe conserve la même précision. Le programme d'analyse permet l'ajustement de N compartiments; si un de ceux-ci disparaît, le programme confond deux compartiments et répartit les résultats, pourcentages et périodes, de manière identique. Ceci permet de tester la validité du modèle.

RESULTATS

Epuration Pulmonaire Normale

L'épuration pulmonaire de rats conventionnels se fait suivant un modèle à trois compartiments. Le premier s'épure très rapidement, avec une période toujours inférieure à 24 h; il exprime les remontées mécaniques au niveau de la trachée, des bronches et du nasopharynx, avec peut-être déjà une faible composante pulmonaire. Les deux autres compartiments sont en rapport avec l'épuration alvéolaire mais sont très dissemblables entre eux: l'un représente l'élimination vers l'extérieur par remontée cellulaire, avec élimination totale de l'organisme; sa période est d'environ 4 semaines. Le dernier compartiment correspond à l'épuration de la fraction qui a traversé la paroi alvéolaire; la période de ce troisième compartiment est très longue par rapport à celles des deux premiers, de l'ordre de grandeur d'un an. Les pourcentages de ces trois compartiments sont différents. Le premier représente 65 à 85% de la quantité totale déposée. Le reste est partagé entre les deuxième et troisième dans des proportions variables. La répartition peut se faire à parties égales chez des rats conventionnels. Le passage septal est d'autant plus important qu'il existe une modification pathologique antérieure, telle qu'une infection pulmonaire chronique, même sans manifestations cliniques décelables.

Cette effraction de la paroi alvéolaire est extrêmement réduite chez les rats S.P.F., ce qui se traduit par l'augmentation du deuxième compartiment. La représentation de l'épuration pulmonaire des rats S.P.F. peut alors être donnée par un modèle à deux compartiments; le troisième est négligeable en pourcentage et sa période est très longue en regard de la durée des expériences. Toutes les expériences ont été pratiquées avec des rats S.P.F. (souche Sprague Dawley), fournis par un élevage gnotobiotique. La rétention alvéolaire peut être variable d'un lot d'animaux à un autre, puisque fonction des caractéristiques physiques de l'aérosol, comme sa granulométrie, et de paramètres respiratoires conditionnés par les modalités expérimentales.

Modifications dues à l'Irradiation Externe

L'irradiation externe, globale, est délivrée par le rayonnement γ du ^{60}Co avec un flux de $18 \cdot 5$ rad/min. Les doses sont de 777 rads pour les rats mâles de 250 g et de 592 rads pour les rats femelles de 200 g, ce qui correspond à la D.L.50 à 1 mois pour la souche utilisée. Des délais variables séparent l'irradiation et le test d'épuration: celui-ci est pratiqué 1 jour, 2 jours, 4 jours ou 11 jours après l'irradiation.

Dans aucune de ces expériences on ne constate de modifications de l'épuration, si ce n'est un taux de rétention immédiate plus petit chez les rats irradiés que chez les

TABLEAU I. RÉPARTITION ET PÉRIODE BIOLOGIQUE DE L'AÉROSOL INSOLUBLE DE ^{59}Fe, APRÈS IRRADIATION EXTERNE À D.L.50. (MOYENNES DES LOTS; LES ÉCARTS MAXIMUM PAR RAPPORT À LA MOYENNE SONT INFÉRIEURS À 15%).

Délai entre l'irradiation et le test	Compartiments			
	1		2	
	%	Période	%	Période
1 jour	81	15 h	19	29 jours
2 jours	83	20 h	17	32 jours
4 jours	78	12 h	22	33 jours
11 jours	82	8 h	18	31 jours
Témoins	83	10 h	17	33 jours

témoins et un léger retard vers le quatrième jour chez les irradiés; ces deux phénomènes sont transitoires et disparaissent vers le huitième jour. A partir de cette
date, il est impossible de différencier les rats irradiés des témoins (Tableau I). Une
dose aussi importante que la D.L. 50 n'a donc aucune influence sur la fonction
épuratrice du poumon; cette dernière ne pourrait être perturbée que par des doses
encore plus élevées.

Modifications dues à l'Irradiation Interne

L'irradiation interne est délivrée par l'émission α du plutonium 239. Celui-ci est
administré aux animaux grâce à un matériel identique à celui qui sert pour le test au
^{59}Fe, sous forme d'aérosol de nitrate de ^{239}Pu en solution nitrique $0\cdot5$ N; le volume
de départ de la solution à nébuliser est de 5 ml. L'emploi d'une solution permet
d'obtenir une grande homogénéité des charges alvéolaires, très supérieure à celle que
l'on pourrait avoir avec des particules solides, comme celles d'oxyde de plutonium.
Le ^{239}Pu s'insolubilise lors de son introduction dans les voies respiratoires, et se
comporte dans le poumon profond comme une poussière. La concentration alvéolaire étant directement en rapport avec la concentration de la solution à partir de
laquelle est issu l'aérosol et avec le temps d'exposition, il est facile de faire varier à
volonté la charge pulmonaire en ^{239}Pu, donc l'irradiation cellulaire (Tableau II).
Nous avons pris pour bases de recherche différents niveaux de toxicité donnés par
BAIR (1970). Nous avons arbitrairement choisi des valeurs proches de celles responsables de:

(1) mort par asphyxie dans les mois suivant la contamination respiratoire (1 μCi/g
de poumon);
(2) mort par insuffisance respiratoire chronique en quelques années ($0\cdot05$ μCi/g de
poumon);
(3) mort par cancer pulmonaire dans des délais variables ($0\cdot01$ μCi/g de poumon).
Nous disposons ainsi de trois séries d'animaux dont les concentrations en ^{239}Pu dans
le poumon profond sont respectivement de $1\cdot0$, $0\cdot10$ et $0\cdot007$ μCi/g de poumon frais.

TABLEAU II. CORRESPONDANCE DES CONDITIONS EXPÉRIMENTALES ET DES
CONCENTRATIONS ALVÉOLAIRES APRÈS INHALATION DE ^{239}Pu

| | Concentration dans la solution | | Concentration dans l'alvéole |
	(mg/ml)	(mCi/ml)	(μCi/g)
Série I	20	$1\cdot26$	1
Série II	$2\cdot88$	$0\cdot18$	$0\cdot1$
Série III	$0\cdot88$	$0\cdot055$	$0\cdot007$

Le délai entre l'inhalation de ^{239}Pu et le test d'épuration est fixe pour toutes les
expériences et égal à 10 jours. Il a été vérifié préalablement que l'administration d'un
aérosol acide délivré dans les mêmes conditions expérimentales que le ^{239}Pu ne
modifiait pas la réponse cellulaire.

A la différence de l'irradiation externe, la présence de plutonium dans le milieu
alvéolaire se traduit par des modifications très importantes des courbes d'épuration.

Les rats de la série I (1 μCi/g de poumon) ont une épuration très ralentie (Figure 1). Trois mois après le test, la charge pulmonaire se situe aux environs de 15% de la charge initiale et décroît très lentement, alors que celle des témoins est inférieure à 5%. L'analyse par compartiments montre que l'élimination des particules se fait suivant un modèle à deux compartiments, mais que la nature de ces compartiments est très différente de celle des compartiments des témoins (Tableau III). Le premier demeure normalement inchangé. Le second disparaît, et est remplacé par un compartiment de période longue, supérieure à 4 mois, qu'il est possible d'identifier au troisième compartiment des animaux témoins, tel qu'il a été décrit plus haut. Cela signifie la prédominance de l'épuration vers les ganglions, après passage septal, sur l'épuration par remontée cellulaire, ainsi qu'en font foi les comptages des ganglions trachéo-

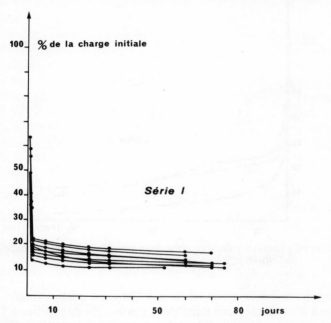

FIGURE 1. Epuration pulmonaire de ^{59}Fe après inhalation de ^{239}Pu (1 μCi/g de poumon).

TABLEAU III. RÉPARTITION ET PÉRIODE BIOLOGIQUE DE L'AÉROSOL INSOLUBLE DE ^{59}FE APRÈS INHALATION DE NITRATE DE ^{239}PU. (MOYENNES DES LOTS; LES ÉCARTS MAXIMUM PAR RAPPORT À LA MOYENNE SONT INFÉRIEURS À 10%)

Série	^{239}Pu concentration dans l'alvéole (μCi/g)	Compartiments			
		1		2	
		%	Période	%	Période
I	1	83	14 h	17	150 jours
II	0·1	74	9 h	26	95 jours
III	0·007	70	9 h	30	30 jours
Témoins	0	83	10 h	17	33 jours

bronchiques. Ce phénomène s'explique par l'effet hautement cytotoxique des particules α.

Les rats de la série II (0·10 μCi/g de poumon) se situent entre ceux de la série I et les témoins. La validité des résultats donnés pour la période du deuxième compartiment n'est pas absolue. La durée de l'expérience — 3 mois — n'est pas suffisante pour permettre à un éventuel troisième compartiment de s'extérioriser; la Figure 2,

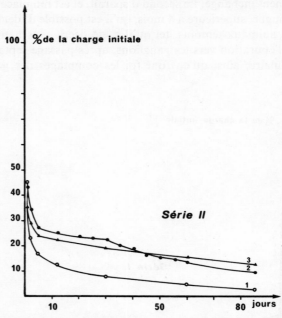

FIGURE 2. Epuration pulmonaire de ⁵⁹Fe chez deux rats (2 et 3), après inhalation de ²³⁹Pu (0·10 μCi/g de poumon). Rat 1 = témoin.

comparant deux des animaux ayant inhalé le ²³⁹Pu et un animal témoin, montre qu'i existe à ce niveau d'irradiation cellulaire deux possibilités de réactions. Le comportement du rat 3 de la figure correspond à la moitié des courbes d'épuration des rats de la série II; son épuration est lente, mais régulière. A l'inverse, le rat 2, représentatif de l'autre moitié des animaux, montre au 30e jour une restauration fonctionnelle: la vitesse de son épuration augmente et devient comparable à celle des rats témoins au 10e jour. Ce fait doit être lié aux différences de sensibilité des animaux ou à des niveaux de contamination alvéolaire légèrement différents.

L'irradiation cellulaire par particules α à raison de 0·10 μCi/g de poumon constitue donc une limite au-dessous de laquelle une restauration fonctionnelle est possible.

Les rats de la série III (0·007 μCi/g de poumon) sont très homogènes, et ne sont pas différents des témoins (Tableau III, Figure 3). Leur niveau de contamination représente une limite inférieure aux possibilités d'exploration fonctionnelle de la méthode.

Les courbes telles qu'elles sont tracées sur les Figures 1, 2 et 3 sont difficiles à comparer entre elles, soit dans le cadre de la même série, soit entre les séries, car le pourcentage épuré par voies aériennes hautes durant les premiers jours est grand par rapport à l'activité initiale et est variable d'un animal à un autre. L'intercomparaison est plus aisée en prenant comme origine des temps le troisième jour après le test et en appelant 100% l'activité présente dans l'animal à ce jour. Cette activité correspond alors à celle réellement déposée dans le poumon. Il s'agit d'un choix arbitraire, mais l'erreur ainsi faite est inférieure à celle qui consiste à rapporter toutes les activités des

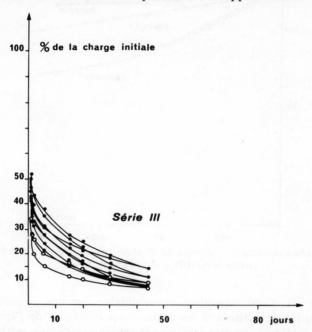

FIGURE 3. Epuration pulmonaire de ^{59}Fe après inhalation de ^{239}Pu (0·007 μCi/g de poumon). En blanc: Témoins.

animaux aux activités initiales, sans préjuger des niveaux de dépôts. Il apparaît alors (Figure 4) que la série III se comporte strictement comme les témoins, à l'encontre des séries I et II.

CONCLUSION

L'irradiation aiguë par les rayons γ du cobalt modifie très peu l'épuration pulmonaire. Il semble peu intéressant d'améliorer la méthode d'irradiation en focalisant cette dernière sur les champs respiratoires, étant donné la disproportion entre les doses et les effets.

L'irradiation chronique interne, délivrée directement aux cellules, a des effets liés aux doses. Des doses moyennes permettent une restauration de l'épuration; le problème posé réside dans l'élucidation des mécanismes cellulaires sur lesquels elle repose. Cette restauration n'existe pas lors de contaminations massives; le phénomène observé est alors en tous points comparable à celui constaté par LE BOUFFANT (1971) chez des rats empoussiérés par des poussières inertes comme le charbon ou toxiques comme la silice. Les mécanismes qui sont perturbés, modifiés ou supprimés siègent au niveau de l'alvéole, et ne peuvent être étudiés qu'au niveau de la cellule elle-même. Par ailleurs, la méthode décrite possède une limite de sensibilité correspondant aux

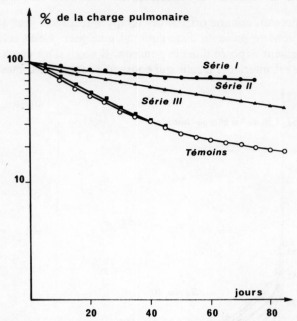

FIGURE 4. Epuration pulmonaire comparée du ^{59}Fe des rats des séries I, II et III; moyenne de chaque série. 100% = activité au 3e jour.

rats de la série III. Il est cependant vraisemblable que des quantités encore plus faibles de ^{239}Pu inhalé perturbent les mécanismes cellulaires de l'épuration pulmonaire. Ces perturbations pour être décelées nécessiteraient d'autres méthodes d'analyse.

BIBLIOGRAPHIE

BAIR, W. J. (1970). 2nd Int. Cong., Int. Radiol. Protection Ass., Brighton.
BAZIN, J. P., MARCHADIER, B. & LAFUMA, J. (1968). *Traitement mathématique de données métaboliquse liées à la théorie des compartiments.* 1er Congrès Européen de Radio-protection, Menton, France.
LE BOUFFANT, L. (1971). *Influence de la nature des poussières et de la charge pulmonaire sur l'épura-tion.* This Symposium, pp. 227–237.
LEFEVRE, G. (1969). *Thèse*, Conservatoire des Arts et Métiers, Paris.
LEFEVRE, G., NENOT, J. C., LAFUMA, J., COLLET, A. & CHARBONNIER, J. (1968). *Archs Mal. prof. Méd. trav.* **29**, 669–678.
MASSE, R. (1971). *Etude cytologique comparée de l'influence du plutonium et de la silice inhalés sur le comportement du macrophage alvéolaire.* This Symposium, pp. 247–257.

DISCUSSION : See pp. 258–259.

ETUDE CYTOLOGIQUE COMPAREE DE L'INFLUENCE DU PLUTONIUM ET DE LA SILICA INHALES SUR LE COMPORTEMENT DU MACROPHAGE ALVEOLAIRE[1]

R. MASSE

Commissariat à l'Energie Atomique, Départment de la Protection Sanitaire, Section de Tocicologie Nucléaire, B.P. N° 6, 92 — Fontenay-aux-Roses, France

Summary — Comparison of the results of cytological observations and kinetic analysis of lung clearance in rats poisoned by plutonium and silica has enabled the part played by the different parameters to be established. Plutonium showed a cytotoxic and cytostatic action and inhibited the bronchial excretion of macrophages. Silica showed a cytotoxic action, enhanced cellular production and inhibited the bronchial excretion of macrophages. Plutonium action appeared as a threshold mechanism; below a limiting dose cytological changes were compensated and did not result in any trouble of excretion. The determining factor in the blockage of alveolar clearance seemed to be a trouble of cellular mobilization or motility depending on the cell itself and its environment.

INTRODUCTION

L'ÉVALUATION de la toxicité d'un gaz d'un aérosol ou d'un empoussiérage pour le poumon repose essentiellement sur des modifications tradives ventilatoires radiologiques ou histopathologiques. L'intérêt d'un test d'analyse cinétique de l'épuration pulmonaire réside dans le fait qu'il permet dans des délais raisonnables de s'assurer de l'intégrité de la fonction antixénique non spécifique. Les altérations de cette fonction entrainent la stase des toxiques non dégradés et favorisent le passage septal, elles permettent aussi l'accumulation intra alvéolaire des agents nocifs de toute nature continuellement inhalés.

L'analyse que nous présentons ici a pour but de fournir les bases de physiopathologie cellulaire qui permettront de dégager les mécanismes conditionnant le ralentissement de la clearance alvéolaire par remontée bronchique. Deux types de toxiques ont été étudiés: le plutonium 239 et la silice, qui provoquent aux doses convenables (NENOT, 1971; LE BOUFFANT, 1971) une alteration comparable de la clearance alvéolaire mise en évidence par la technique précédemment décrite (LEFEVRE *et al.*, 1968).

[1] Travail réalisé en collaboration par l'association Commissariat à l'Energie Atomique* — EURATOM** et le Centre d'Etudes et de Recherches des Charbonnages de France.***

Ont participé à ce travail, CARON, L.*** — DANIEL, H.*** — HENIN, J. C.*** — LAFUMA, J.* — LE BOUFFANT, L.*** — L'HULLIER, I.* — MARTIN, J. C.***—MORIN, M.** — NENOT, J. C.** — SEDAGHAT, B.* — SKUPINSKI, W.**

MATERIELS ET METHODES

Générateurs d'Aérosols et d'Empoussiérage

Le plutonium en solution nitrique 0,5 N et l'hématite en suspension aqueuse ont été mis en aérosols selon les techniques précédemment décrites (Nenot, 1971). La silice a été mise en suspension dans la chambre d'empoussiérage modèle Cerchar :

Tous les animaux utilisés sont de race Sprague Dowley SPF. Soixante seize rats ont inhalé l'hématite activée et ont subi le comptage γ global.

Vingt quatre rats ont respiré pendant 1h30 un aérosol produit par une solution à 0,18 mCi/cm³ de ²³⁹Pu dans le générateur.

Vingt quatre rats ont respiré pendant le même temps un aérosol produit par une solution à 0,055 mCi de ²³⁹Pu/cm³.

Tableau 1. Modifications Cytologiques

Conditions expéri-mentales	Nombre de macrophages extraits par rinçage (10⁶)	Macro-phages/cellules extraites (%)	Macrophages en phase S/Macrophages totaux (⁰/₀₀)	Indice de réactivité cytoplasmique	Nombre de Macrophages excrétés par 24h calculé sur courbe d'épuration (10⁶)
Rats témoins mâles en période d'hiver	8,03 ± 1,46	94,5 ± 2,13	42,60 ± 11,40	35,22 ± 3,7	0,70 ± 0,17
Rats mâles après inhalation de ²³⁹Pu 0,18 mCi/cm³ Hiver	3,05 ± 0,79	87,12 ± 7,88	1,00 ± 0,86	10,10 ± 5,90	0,185 ± 0,067
Rats mâles après inhalation de ²³⁹Pu 0,055 mCi/cm³ Hiver	6,02 ± 0,74	90,32 ± 3,6	19,75 ± 8,28	34,55 ± 12,22	0,481 ± 0,129
Rats témoins femelles en période d'été	13,76 ± 4,97	93,75 ± 2,36	45,83 ± 13,93	26,83 ± 12,28	1,57 ± 0,49
Rats femelles après inhala-tion de Silice en période d'été. 10 em-poussiérages à 300 mg/m³	26,5 ± 10,73	63,41 ± 16,83	98,33 ± 19,69	5,00 ± 2,98	1,12 ± 0,45

Six rats ont subi dix séances d'empoussiérage de silice à la concentration de 300 mg/m³.

Douze rats en outre, non testés à l'hématite, ont inhalé pendant 2 h un aérosol produit par une solution nitrique 0,5 N de façon à éliminer les réactions cellulaires non spécifiques du plutonium. Les expérimentations se sont déroulées à différentes périodes de l'année, sur des sujets mâles pour le plutonium, femelles pour la silice. De fortes variations saisonnières ont été observées sur les animaux de notre élevage dans la population cellulaire du poumon en l'absence de toute expérimentation par aérosol, nous en avons donc tenu compte pour l'expression des résultats (Tableau 1 et 2).

TABLEAU 2. HÉMATITE EXTRACTIBLE, INDICE DE PHAGOCYTOSE

Conditions expérimentales	Durée de l'experience après inhalation d'hématite (Jours)	Activité ^{59}Fe extraite par rinçage/ Até totale pulmonaire (%)	Aptitude à la phagocytose Cellules à in- inclusion d'héma- tite/Macrophages totaux (%)
Rats témoins mâles	2. 10	30,65 ± 8,78	76,5 ± 6,69
Rats mâles après inhalation ^{239}Pu 0,18 mCi/cm³	2. 10	24,88 ± 6,1	53,21 ± 3,74
Rats témoins mâles	15. 20	41,7 ± 10,6	88,5 ± 6,7
Rats mâles après inhalation ^{239}Pu 0,055 mCi/cm³	15. 20	35,45 ± 6,6	92,4 ± 5,6
Rats témoins femelles	15. 20	39,33 ± 12,58	86,5 ± 6,63
Rats femelles après em- poussiérage de Silice	15. 20	33,66 ± 6,3	53 ± 5,17

Réalisation et Prélèvements des Echantillons

Selon des délais variables après les séances d'aérosols et d'empoussiérage les animaux sont anesthésiés au Nembutal et sacrifiés par section de l'aorte postérieure. Les poumons sont prélevés pour extraction des cellules alvéolaires selon la technique de GERSING & SCHUMACHER (1955) modifiée par BRAIN & FRANCK (1968). Les poumons isolés sont incubés à 37° pendant 20 min après instillation intratrachéale de 5 cm³ d'une solution de Mac Coy enrichie à 10% de Serum de Veau et contenant 10 μCi de Thymidine tritiée par cm³, de manière à déterminer le nombre de macrophages en phase de Synthèse (MASSE et al., 1970). Après élimination du liquide nutritif, le lobe Azygos est ligaturé par son pédicule et des fragments de 2 à 3 mm de côté sont fixés dans le glutaraldéhyde à 2,5%, post fixés dans l'acide osmique et inclus dans l'Epon. Douze rinçages du poumon sont alors effectués par fraction de 5 cm³. Le premier rinçage contient 5 mg de Thymidine dans la solution physiologique.

Le liquide de Mac Coy recueilli et le premier rinçage sont traités isolément, les 11 autres fractions sont homogénéisées et les cellules recueillies sont dénombrées par comptage direct à l'hématimètre. Un prélèvement aliquote est recueilli pour évaluation de la radioactivité du ^{59}Fe, éventuellement du ^{239}Pu.

Le poumon après rinçage est recueilli pour comptage γ et x.

Les cellules contenues dans le liquide de rinçage sont centrifugées à 50 g pendant 6 mn dans une microcentrifugeuse. Les culots obtenus sont étalés sur lame. Une fraction aliquote du surnageant est réservée pour contrôle de l'activité de ^{59}Fe et ^{239}Pu non centrifugeable.

Les frottis obtenus sont fixés dans l'alcool-éther pendant 20 min minimum puis, soit colorés directement à l'éosine -azur en solution aqueuse, soit exposés 8 jours après autoradiographic avec l'émulsion en gel Ilford K$_2$.

La remontée bronchique des macrophages alvéolaires est évaluée de différentes manières: dix animaux ont subi le sondage gastroesophagien par fistule externe selon la technique décrite par SPRITZER & WATSON (1964). Les cellules et le mucus bronchique déglutis sont recueillis dans une bouteille de P.V.C. fixée sur le flanc. On évalue le nombre de cellules, d'une part en mesurant la radioactivité due au ^{59}Fe et en là rapportant à la radioactivité des macrophages obtenus pour rinçage pulmonaire, d'autre part en dénombrant directement ces cellules après analyse cytologique. Dans ce dernier cas les cellules sont fixées directement dans la bouteille par de l'alcool éthylique et filtrées sur filtre millipore 0,8 μm. Les filtres sont séchés, pesés et un fragment aliquote est coloré rapidement au Noir Amide, différencié puis éclairci au propanolxylène. Seules sont dénombrées les cellules présentant des inclusions d'hématite. On revient au nombre total de cellules excrétées après avoir déterminé sur frottis le pourcentage de ces cellules par rapport aux macrophages totaux.

Enfin le nombre de cellules subissant la remontée bronchique par jour est appréciée par extrapolation directe des courbes obtenues par le test à l'hématite. Dans ce cas la portion de courbe comprise entre le 5 e et le 20 e jour est traitée comme une simple exponentielle. On en détermine la période et la valeur $A_0 - A$ pour $t = 1$j en donnant à A_0 la valeur 100%. Les mesures obtenues après rinçage du poumon permettent d'exprimer l'activité pour N macrophages extraits en % de l'activité totale du rat ce qui permet de calculer le nombre théorique de macrophages qui devront quitter le poumon pour assurer la décroissance $A_0 - A$.

Examens Pratiques et Expression des Résultats

Les différentes fractions aliquotes des prélèvements définis précédemment sont comptées par scintillation d'un cristal à iodure de sodium pour l'évaluation de l'activité γ du ^{59}Fe et x du ^{239}Pu.

Les poumons rincés sont comptés de la même manière ce qui permet, sans correction de géométrie, de mesurer l'activité totale pulmonaire qui représente la somme des activités du liquide de rinçage et de l'activité résiduelle du poumon.

Sur les frottis de cellules pulmonaires colorés on apprécie:

— Le pourcentage de macrophages par rapport aux cellules totales extraites en tenant compte uniquement de critères morphologiques.

— Le pourcentage de macrophages chargés d'hématite par rapport aux macrophages totaux.

— Le pourcentage de macrophages ayant incorporé la thymidine tritiée et présentant après autoradiographie au moins 10 grains d'argent au dessus du noyau.

Les prélèvements inclus dans l'Epon sont coupés en section de 0,5 μm et colorés à l'azur II à 0,2 %. Certaines coupes sont exposées en autoradiographie pour un contrôle topographique (Figure 1). Les conditions d'incubation et de prélèvement des

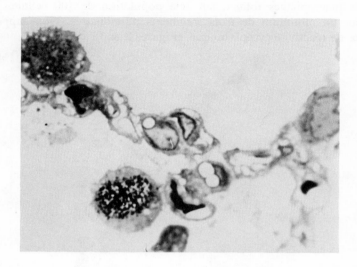

FIGURE 1. Macrophage alvéolaire après incorporation de thymidine tritiée. Autoradiographie sur coupe semi-fine — Coloration à l'Azur II.

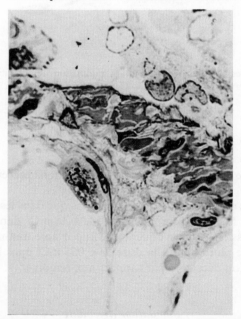

FIGURE 2. Macrophage étalé. Noter quelques prolongements cytoplasmiques et l'aspect hyalin du cytoplasme au contact de la paroi. Coupe semi-fine — Coloration Azur II.

échantillons modifient l'aspect morphologique des macrophages pulmonaires. Un certain nombre d'entre eux présentent des expansions nettes du hyaloplasme qui occupe différentes portions de la périphérie cellulaire selon les incidences de coupe. Les granulations spécifiques du cytoplasme apparaissent alors groupées, soit en couronne autour du noyau, soit selon un croissant polaire. On détermine le pourcentage des cellules dont le voile représente au moins 20 % du diamètre cellulaire par rapport aux macrophages totaux, sur une population de 100 cellules au moins, comptées sur un minimum de trois fragments pulmonaires. Nous appelons cette valeur indice de réactivité cytoplasmique. (Figures 2 & 3).

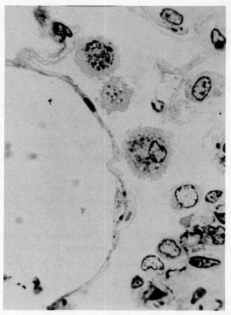

FIGURE 3. Macrophages alvéolaires montrant la répartition des particules et inclusions par rapport au cytoplasme hyalin — Coupe semi-fine colorée à l'Azur II.

RESULTATS

Test à l'Hématite

Les résultats ont été présentés dans les communications précédentes (NENOT, 1971; LE BOUFFANT, 1971).

Pour en résumer les conclusions, nous retiendrons que dans les séries d'animaux que nous avons étudiées, le plutonium à la dose de 0,18 mCi dans le générateur et la silice après 10 empoussiérages provoquent une importante diminution de la clearance alvéolaire alors que le plutonium à la dose de 0,055 mCi dans le générateur ne provoque aucune altération décelable par rapport aux témoins.

Population Alvéolaire

Le Tableau 1 permet d'apprécier l'influence des toxiques sur les différents paramètres mesurés. Le plutonium même à dose faible diminue de manière très sensible le nombre de macrophages extraits du poumon. Cette variation ne peut s'expliquer par une rétention cellulaire puisque la fraction d'hématite extraite ne varie que faiblement dans les deux séries: Tableau 2. L'aptitude à la synthèse d'ADN disparaît presque totalement aux fortes doses de plutonium, décroît de plus de la moitié de sa valeur pour les faibles doses. Les modifications ne s'accompagnent pas de l'apparition notable de cellules inflammatoires en dehors de quelques lymphocytes. L'influence de la silice est entièrement différente: la population alvéolaire est nettement augmentée, les cellules en phase de synthèse sont nombreuses et des polynucléaires apparaissent dans l'alvéole.

Modifications Fonctionnelles

Ces modifications apparaissent dans les Tableaux 1 et 2. Le plutonium à forte dose et la silice entrainent une importante diminution du nombre de macrophage capables de phagocyter l'hématite et une chute de l'indice de réactivité cytoplasmique. On n'observe pas de modification de ces paramètres avec le plutonium à faible concentration.

TABLEAU 3. COMPARAISON DES METHODES D'EVALUATION DE LA REMONTÉE BRONCHIQUE

Conditions expérimentales	Durée de l'expérience depuis l'inha-lation de Fer (Jours)	Nombre de macrophages mesuré sur filtre excr. par 24 h (10^6)	Nombre de macrophages calculé d'après l'activité du Fer 59 dans les prélèvements (10^6)	Indice d'incorporation de Thymidine $(^o/oo)$
Témoin	3	0,63	0,75	9,5
Témoin	6	0,35	0,37	5,5
Témoin	7	0,75	0,74	10,5
Témoin	8	0,21	0,46	18,5
Témoin	8	0,22	0,48	10,5
^{239}Pu forte concentration	1	0,18	0,80	—
^{239}Pu forte concentration	2	0,10	0,75	—
^{239}Pu forte concentration	3	0,11	0,28	—
^{239}Pu forte concentration	7	0,09	0,1	—
^{239}Pu forte concentration	7	0,15	0,1	—

Remontée Bronchiques des Macrophages

L'évaluation de ce paramètre apparaît dans les Tableaux 1 et 3.

Dans le Tableau 3 qui représente des mesures individuelles, la corrélation entre la valeur théorique de la remontée bronchique calculée sur l'excrétion du Fer 59 et le nombre de macrophages retrouvés, est nettement mise en défaut pour les mesures effectuées les premiers jours après l'inhalation chez les animaux intoxiqués au plutonium, malgré les corrections effectuées en tenant compte de l'indice de phagocytose. Toutes les valeurs observées sont plus faibles que celles calculées sur les courbes (Tableau 1). A titre d'information nous avons fait figurer l'indice d'incorporation de thymidine tritiée chez les témoins ayant subi l'intervention de Spritzer qui montre des valeurs anormalement basses par rapport aux témoins figurant dans le Tableau 1. Les valeurs calculées sur les courbes montrent dans tous les cas d'inhalation de toxique une diminution du nombre de macrophages excrétés.

Restauration

Six rats ayant inhalé le plutonium à forte concentration ont été sacrifiés du 45e au 85e jours après l'inhalation du toxique. Le Tableau 4 montre l'évolution des différents paramètres. Cette évolution se fait nettement dans le sens d'une restauration; toutefois on remarque une diminution importante de l'hématite extractible. Il n'a pas été observé de corrélation nette entre la restauration cellulaire et la restauration de l'excrétion du Fer 59.

TABLEAU 4. RESTAURATION CELLULAIRE

Conditions expérimentales	Depuis l'inhalation de plutonium (Jours)	Nombre de Macrophages (10^6)	Ilématite extractible (%)	Indice d'incorporation Thymidine (°/oo)	Indice de phagocytose (%)	Réactivité cytoplasmique
Plutonium forte concentration	46	9,5	29,2	32	23,2	12
,, ,, ,,	46	4,5	22,3	30	21	17
,, ,, ,,	67	6,2	10,3	15	42	26
,, ,, ,,	68	18,5	13,2	21	36	28
,, ,, ,,	85	9,3	30,3	31	49	—
,, ,, ,,	85	5,4	18,4	9	53	—

DISCUSSION

Interprétation des Résultats

L'homéostasie de la population alvéolaire dépend d'au moins trois facteurs essentiels: l'apparition des cellules nouvelles, l'élimination par remontée bronchique, la mort cellulaire *in situ*. L'origine du macrophage alvéolaire est controversée et vraisemblablement multiple. Les expériences de PINKETT et al. (1966); VAN FURTH et al. (1968); VIROLAINEN (1968); NICOL et al. (1967); BOWDEN et al. (1969) mettent en évidence que le lymphocyte, le monocyte, les cellules de Kupffer, des cellules interstitielles, peuvent être à l'origine des macrophages alvéolaires. Certains auteurs dont CASARETT (1967) soutiennent en outre la filiation entre les pneumocytes II de BERTALANFFY (1964) et les macrophages alvéolaires. Les expériences que nous avons menées (MASSE et al., 1970) ont montré que les macrophages alvéolaires avaient un potentiel de division non négligeable. Les recherches en cours (SEDAGHAT, 1971) permettent de penser que cette source de cellules nouvelles assure la part la plus importante de la population alvéolaire. Il est assez remarquable de constater que des macrophages très évolués, chargés de particules d'hématite ou de silice conservent cette aptitude. Dans le cas du plutonium la restauration de l'aptitude à la synthèse est précédée de l'apparition de petits macrophages lympocytiformes dont COLLET et al. (1966) avaient souligné la parenté morphologique avec les cellules évoluées. Ces cellules ont un indice d'incorporation très faible. Leur présence coïncide avec celle d'une population de macrophages typiques pratiquement dépourvus d'hématite et de plutonium qui sont par contre fréquemment marqués en autoradiographie. Il paraît ainsi vraisemblable qu'il existe une source extra alvéolaire de cellules dont le rôle est le remplacement des cellules souches. Cette interprétation n'est pas en opposition avec les résultats des auteurs précédemment cités.

Notre estimation de la remontée bronchique des cellules intra alvéolaires ne concorde pas avec celle obtenue par SPRITZER et al. (1968). Le nombre total de cellules mononucléées que nous observons sur filtre conduit à une estimation supérieure à 10^6 cellules dégluties par heure, cependant il nous semble que seule une fraction des cellules excrétées est d'origine alvéolaire. Il faudrait en effet qu'au moment où plus de 80% des macrophages du poumon sont chargés d'hématite, moins de 5% des cellules excrétées ne le soient.

Compte tenu du pourcentage très faible de particules libres retrouvées sur filtre 0,8 μm et d'une corrélation satisfaisante entre le nombre théorique et le nombre de macrophages mesurés sur filtre, il semble que pour l'essentiel l'épuration des particules d'hématite se fasse par les macrophages jusque dans l'oesophage. Le mécanisme est différent pour les animaux sacrifiés peu de temps après l'inhalation, ce qui s'explique par le fait que l'on observe à ce moment l'épuration des voies aériennes hautes où les particules ne sont pas phagocytées.

L'utilisation des courbes d'épuration pour le calcul du nombre de macrophages excrétées paraît offrir plus de garantie d'intégrité physiologique que la technique chirurgicale dont l'influence sur la population alvéolaire a été signalée. Elle suppose un certain nombre d'hypothèses que l'expérience n'a pas encore contredites: l'homogénéité de la répartition des particules dans les macrophages, la possibilité de négliger quantitativement le passage septal, la phagocytose complète des particules à partir du 5e jour, l'absence d'un autre territoire de rétention que le macrophage alvéolaire.

L'importance de la mort cellulaire n'a pu être quantifiée dans notre expérimentation. Elle est cependant à l'origine du continuel brassage de particules qui ne concourt pendant le mois qui suit l'inhalation, qu'à des modifications minimes du nombre de macrophages chargés d'hématite, de sorte que la répartition des poussières demeure grossièrement homogène dans la population de macrophages. Elle participe vraisemblablement aussi à l'accumulation de figures myéliniques (alvéolite lipidique) observée après inhalation du plutonium et de silice.

Dans les conditions physiologiques ces différents paramètres sont coordonnés et la population cellulaire varie peu (BRAIN & FRANCK, 1968). L'inhalation de plutonium à faible dose provoque des modifications qui sont compensées. La population décroît, le nombre de macrophages excrétés décroît de façon proportionelle et la cinétique d'épuration n'est pas altérée. Le plutonium à forte concentration provoque une diminution de l'excrétion cellulaire plus importante que la chute du nombre total des macrophages dans le poumon.

La silice provoque une augmentation du nombre des macrophages qui n'est pas compensée par l'augmentation de l'excrétion.

Ces observations permettent d'affirmer que le nombre des cellules alvéolaires n'est pas le facteur essentiel de l'épuration. L'examen histologique des tissus et la valeur du taux d'hématite extractible permettent d'éliminer l'influence d'une réorganisation tissulaire constituant un obstacle à l'épuration. Il semble donc qu'on doive rechercher dans des troubles de la mobilité ou de la mobilisation cellulaire le facteur déterminant. Les variations de l'"indice de réactivité cytoplasmique" que nous présentons sont un argument en cette faveur: FAUVE et al. (1968) ont montré en effet une étroite corrélation entre la mobilité et l'aptitude à l'étalement des macrophages; il serait néanmoins souhaitable de disposer pour le macrophage alvéolaire d'un test de mobilité authentique. Il est également probable que les modifications biochimiques interviennent dans ce mécanisme, le drainage du fluide alvéolaire paraît fortement diminué (alvéolite lipidique) or ce mécanisme est retenu par HEPPLESTON (1967) comme favorisant la migration des macrophages. Enfin les modifications de taille cellulaire peuvent constituer un obstacle non négligeable. Aussi bien dans le cas de la silice que dans celui du plutonium des cellules extrêmement volumineuses apparaissent et on peut douter qu'elles puissent franchir les bronchioles respiratoires.

La restauration cellulaire précède la restauration de l'excrétion du Fer 59. Toute fois les conditions dans lesquelles nous avons pu observer le phénomène, c'est à dire de 45 à 85 jours après l'inhalation du plutonium à forte activité ne permettent pas d'établir une relation entre les deux restaurations. Ceci peut s'expliquer par la diminution de l'hématite extractible et par l'examen histologique. De nombreuses cellules ont gagné les parois et les gaines et la fraction disponible pour l'excrétion ne représente qu'un faible pourcentage de l'activité totale pulmonaire.

BIBLIOGRAPHIE

BERTALANFFY, F. D. (1964). Respiratory tissue: structure — histophysiology — cytodynamics. Part I. — Reviews and basic cytomorphology. *Int. Rev. Cytol.* **16**, 233–328.
BOWDEN, D. H., ADAMSON, I. & WYATT, J. P. (1969). *Am. J. Path.* **55**, 44a.
BRAIN, J. D. & FRANCK, N. R. (1968). *J. Geront.* **23**, 58–62.
COLLET, A., MARTIN, J. C., NORMAND-REUET, C. & POLICARD, A. (1967). In: *Inhaled particles and vapours II.* Oxford, Pergamon Press. pp. 155–165.
FAUVE, R. M. & DEKARIS, D. (1968). *Science* **160**, 795–796.
GERSING, R. & SCHUMACHER, H. (1955). *Beitr. Silikoseforsch.* **25**, 31–34.
HEPPLESTON, A. G. (1967). *Poumon Coeur* **23**, 1213–1285.
LE BOUFFANT, L. (1971). *Dans ce congrès.* pp. 227–237.
LEFEVRE, G., NENOT, J. C., LAFUMA, J., COLLET, A. & CHARBONNIER, J. (1968). *Archs. Mal. prof. Méd. trav.* **29**, 669–678.
MASSE, R., MARTIN, J. C., ZAGORCIĆ, A., LAFUMA, J. & LE BOUFFANT, L. (1970). *C.r. hebd. Séanc. Acad. Sci. Paris* **270**, 245–248.

NENOT, J. C. (1971). *Dans ce congrès*. pp. 239–246.
PINKETT, M. O., COWDREY, C. R. & NOWELL, P. C. (1966). *Am. J. Path.* **48**, 859–867.
SEDAGHAT, B. (1971). *A paraître Thèse de Sciences*.
SPRITZER, A. A. & WATSON, J. A. (1964). *Hlth. Phys.* **10**, 1093–1097.
SPRITZER, A. A., WATSON, J. A., AULD, J. A. & GUETTHOFF, M. (1968). *Archs. envir. Hlth.* **17**, 5, 726–730.
VAN FURTH, R. V. & COHN, Z. A. (1968). *J. exp. Med.* **128**, 415–435.
VIROLAINEN, M. (1968). *J. exp. Med.* **127**, 943–952.

DISCUSSION OF PAPERS PRESENTED BY LE BOUFFANT (p. 227), NENOT (p. 239) AND MASSE (p. 247).

M. GRÜNSPAN: I congratulate the authors on their experiment; however, I would like to make some comments and criticisms.

You have used groups of animals including both males and females and compared the action of two toxic agents: plutonium and silica. Nicol and Bilbey have demonstrated the role of oestrogens on macrophage mobility. Moreover, the number of cells you extracted from the lung, using the same technique, was not the same in your male and female controls. You cannot, therefore, compare the action of silica and plutonium on your animals; you need a group of males poisoned by silica and a group of females poisoned by plutonium.

As for the study of cellular mobility, why did you not use a reversible blockade of the Krebs' cycle?

Dr. MASSE: Brain and Franck have shown that the number of macrophages extracted by lung lavage varied according to a number of experimental parameters such as age, sex or strain. Our results agreed with these conclusions.

One effect of ostrogens is, indeed, to increase macrophage mobility. In our experimental conditions, however, both in males and females, we noticed a blockage of alveolar clearance following poisoning. Such a blockage is not the indication of an increase but rather of a loss of cellular mobility due to the cell itself or its environment.

Moreover, each group of poisoned animals was compared to a group of controls of the same sex, and the experimental data showed very clear changes of the measured parameters. In such conditions, I do not think that sex is a determining factor of the different behaviour of macrophages in our groups of animals poisoned by silica and plutonium respectively.

Your suggestion to study cellular mobility by a reversible blockade of Krebs' cycle is very interesting. In the work we have presented here, however, we intended to study the mechanisms which could explain the loss of alveolar clearance as measured by the test of ferric oxide inhalation and analysed in both Messrs. Le Bouffant and Nenot's papers in the case of silica and plutonium poisoning. Rather than study cellular mobility we intend to demonstrate by a number of arguments that decreased macrophage mobility inside the alveoli can account for the observed processes.

R. RYLANDER: You have used a test of cellular mobility. Do you not think that the study of bacterial viability in the presence of macrophage is an outstanding indicator of the physiological integrity of macrophages?

Dr. MASSE: It certainly seems more important to look for changes in cellular physiology after the action of different poisons than for changes in the number of cells in the alveoli. As Mr. Brain said, the alveolar population results from a balance between both cellular uptake and excretion, its variations resulting, as we have shown, from either factor.

R. RYLANDER: For the discussion I would like to add the following information concerning results from our own studies where we studied the pulmonary clearance of viable bacteria in guinea-pigs. Animals who had been exposed to carbon black dust, inhaled from an atmosphere containing 15 mg/m^3 for 4 weeks, showed a marked depression of the bacteria clearing capacity 3 hours after exposure to an aerosol of viable bacteria. This could be taken to indicate that a depression of the bacteriocidal effect of the phagocytes could be an indication of decreased pulmonary clearance from the alveolar region.

K. ROBOCK: Is it possible that the cytotoxicity of plutonium 239 is based on an action of the α-radiation of the particles to the electron-transfer-chair of the biologically important cell reactions? What is your opinion?

Dr. MASSE: The cytotoxicity of plutonium can be direct or indirect. An α particle reaching any point of the cell will lead to cell death more or less quickly. Besides, the vascular injuries observed in lungs poisoned by plutonium can be shown by a change of the alveolar environment. Although experimental verification is lacking I think that the loss of cellular mobility is due to an environmental change, perhaps the accumulation of lipids in the alveoli, which is found both with plutonium and silica poisoning.

We have no experimental data allowing us to appreciate the direct part played by α exposure on one particular point of the electron transfer chain. The consequences of such processes on some important functions of cells should be studied in vitro.

K. ROBOCK: In the study presented by M. Le Bouffant (page 227), what was the quartz and ash content of the coal samples?

Dr. L. LE BOUFFANT: The coal used contained only traces of quartz — less than 1%. The ash content was of the order of 5%.

THE EFFECTS OF DURATION AND INTER-MITTENCY OF EXPOSURE ON THE ELIMINATION OF AIR-BORNE DUST FROM HIGH AND LOW RANK COAL MINES

A. G. HEPPLESTON, G. W. CIVIL and A. CRITCHLOW*

Department of Pathology, University of Newcastle upon Tyne, England

Summary — The elimination by rats of air-borne dust from high and low rank coal mines has been compared after exposure to different environmental conditions. Overall, the long-term clearance of low rank dust tended to be greater than in the case of high rank, although a peculiar macrophage reaction to low rank dust may have affected its removal from the lung. Only with high rank dust was there an indication that clearance after short or intermittent inhalations was better than after long or continuous ones.

ON the basis of an extensive survey of South Wales coal workers, HART & ASLETT (1942) found that the incidence of simple and complicated pneumoconiosis was higher in men employed in anthracite mines, especially as face workers, than in steam or bituminous mines. They concluded that the rank of coal (N.C.B., 1964) mined appeared to be the most important characteristic related to the observed differences. Similarly in the National Coal Board survey of selected collieries in Great Britain (HICKS *et al.*, 1961) the prevalence of simple and complicated pneumoconiosis was greater in high than in low rank pits, but it was not possible to say how far the differences were determined by rank or by atmospheric dust concentrations. Studying parts of the South Wales coal field, COCHRANE (1962) showed that the attack rate of the complicated form of the disease was much higher in men with radiological category 2 or 3 than category 1 simple pneumoconiosis. The quantity of coal retained in the lungs evidently has an important bearing on the development of both forms of coal workers' pneumoconiosis. Although the general prevalence of the disease is declining in Britain it has not been eliminated and the problem is currently a major concern in the U.S.A.

Accordingly the environmental factors which determine dust retention in the lung still merit attention. In addition to rank of coal we have examined quantitatively the influence of overall duration of inhalation, in conjunction with its continuity or intermittency, on the subsequent elimination of the dust. For these purposes rats are particularly suitable, but the chronic respiratory disease which not infrequently affects this species must be avoided by employing specific pathogen-free (SPF) animals.

---

* Ministry of Technology, Safety in Mines Research Establishment, Sheffield.

METHODS

Airborne Dusts

These were collected over prolonged periods by means of suction filters placed in the return airways of actively-worked faces. The dusts were then passed through a 60-mesh sieve to remove coarse material. Ffaldau colliery (South Wales) was the source of the high rank (N.C.B. Coal Rank Code 204/301) dust and Lea Hall (Staffordshire) that of the low rank (Code 902), both being provided by courtesy of the National Coal Board. In this account the term "coal" refers to airborne dust.

Exposures

SPF rats were exposed in dust chambers, based on WRIGHT's (1957) design, for 16 h per day on 5 days each week. For each dust four experiments were carried out in parallel, two exposures lasting 480 h each and two 960 h. For each duration one exposure was given continuously, i.e. over 6 or 12 consecutive weeks, and the other exposure intermittently, i.e. in three periods of 160 h (2 weeks) or 320 h (4 weeks) separated by intervals of 4 weeks in the normal atmosphere. The exposures were accordingly designated short continuous (SC), long continuous (LC), short intermittent (SI) and long intermittent (LI). Dust concentrations in the chambers were measured frequently by gravimetric thermal precipitator (GTP) fitted with an elutriator that excluded particles above 7 μmUDS and sampling at a rate of 100 ml/min. On completion of the exposures, animals survived under the usual barrier conditions for periods that varied from 2–5 days to 20 weeks.

Dust Analyses

Rats were killed in groups by gassing and the thoracic contents excised and fixed intact. The lungs were then detached and all the hilar lymph nodes removed. The lungs and the nodes of each rat were analysed separately for coal content, the extraction procedure being a modification of that used by RIVERS et al. (1963). A correction was applied to individual estimations of coal content to compensate for changes in the ash percentage of the samples during extraction. The corrections were based upon the analyses of the pooled GTP samples.

RESULTS

Linear regression analysis was applied to values for lung and node burdens of rats killed at different times after exposure. The regression coefficients thus obtained permitted estimation, for each experiment, of the lung and node burdens at the end of exposure, and of the rates of subsequent elimination (in μg/week). The rate of bronchial elimination was obtained by difference between the total elimination rate (regression of lung burdens) and the lymphatic elimination rate (regression of node burdens). Correction of the dust recoveries for average body weight during exposure by covariance analysis did not significantly increase the precision in any group.

Two series of experiments were performed with Ffaldau dust and one with Lea Hall. The results have been studied from two aspects. Firstly, the effects of different types of exposure for each dust were compared and, secondly, the response of rats to different dusts was analysed for each type of exposure. The conditions of exposures are given in Table I.

TABLE I. CONDITIONS OF THE EXPOSURES

Dust	Exposure	No. and sex	Mean dust concentration (mg/m³)			
			First period	Second period	Third period	Overall
Ffaldau 1	SC	13 M				9·3
(GTP Ash	SI	15 M	8·7	11·5	11·0	10·4
=34·8%)	LC	14 M				12·6
	LI	16 M	12·3	12·0	10·6	11·7
Ffaldau 2	SC	16 F				10·8
(GTP Ash	SI	15 M	8·8	12·0	8·5	9·5
=34·8%)	LC	14 F				9·5
	LI	13 M	10·5	12·0	10·6	10·9
Lea Hall	SC	16 M				19·9
(GTP Ash	SI	15 M	11·1	22·7	16·9	17·8
=67%)	LC	16 M				11·4
	LI	16 M	21·7	11·4	17·8	17·1

Comparison of Exposures

Ffaldau 1

The mean dust burdens of the lungs and lymph nodes at different times after completion of the exposures, and their regression lines, are shown in Figure 1. The elimination rates (μg/week $\pm$ SE) were as follows:

	Bronchial	Lymphatic	Total
SC	17 $\pm$ 171	34 $\pm$ 25	51 $\pm$ 170
SI	292 $\pm$ 95	39 $\pm$ 28	331 $\pm$ 91
LC	−117 $\pm$ 140	195 $\pm$ 20	78 $\pm$ 139
LI	28 $\pm$ 156	148 $\pm$ 37	176 $\pm$ 151

The negative mean value for LC bronchial elimination is evidently a result of very low clearance by this route coupled with high variation between individual lung burdens. However, elimination via the bronchial tree was apparently favoured following short rather than long, and intermittent rather than continuous exposure. Lymphatic removal of coal was greater after the longer periods of inhalation whether continuous ($P < 0·001$) or intermittent ($P < 0·05$), despite the fact that lung burdens were not increased proportionately. The intermittency of exposure had no apparent effect. Calculated as the percentage of the initial lung burden eliminated per week, lymphatic clearance for LC was significantly higher than SC ($P < 0·001$) and LI ($P < 0·05$).

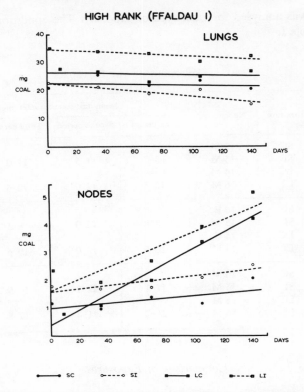

FIGURE 1. Regression lines shown in relation to mean values of lung and node burdens for a high rank dust (first experiment).

Ffaldau 2

The dust burdens and regression lines are shown in Figure 2.

In these experiments the dust concentrations were closely comparable, as in Ffaldau 1, and the rates of clearance (μg/week $\pm$ SE) were:

	Bronchial	Lymphatic	Total
SC	151 $\pm$ 77	49 $\pm$ 7	200 $\pm$ 77
SI	421 $\pm$ 99	63 $\pm$ 16	484 $\pm$ 98
LC	-120 ± 199	74 $\pm$ 14	-46 ± 119
LI	223 $\pm$ 134	125 $\pm$ 29	349 $\pm$ 130

These figures suggest that bronchial elimination is more effective after intermittent than continuous inhalation and also after short rather than long exposure, the overall disposal showing a similar trend. However, only SI > SC (total and bronchial) and LI > LC (total) achieved significance at the 0·05 level. The rate of lymphatic removal also appears to have been greater after intermittent than after continuous exposures but long exposures tended to be more effective than short; statistical significance was not however attained.

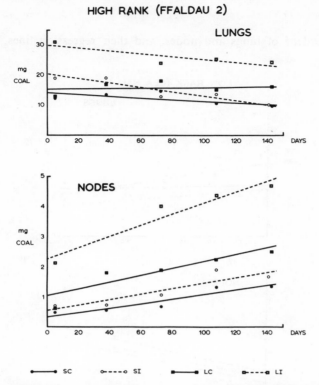

FIGURE 2. Regression lines shown in relation to mean values of lung and node burdens for a high rank dust (second experiment).

Female rats were used for the continuous experiments so the post-exposure lung burdens were probably smaller than they would have been had the heavier male animals been available as for the intermittent exposures. The percentage retention of particles was therefore derived by relating the measured lung burdens of individual rats to the estimated weight of dust they inspired during the exposure. This latter figure was calculated from the dust concentrations, the duration of the exposures, and the minute volumes as derived from GUYTON's (1947) formula using mean weights of individual rats during exposure. Regression analysis revealed remarkable similarities in the percentage retention at the end of exposure between the short exposures (SC, female $= 32 \cdot 9 \pm 1 \cdot 3 \%$: SI, male $= 32 \cdot 2 \pm 1 \cdot 1 \%$) and also between the long exposures (LC, female $= 20 \cdot 5 \pm 1 \cdot 0 \%$: LI, male $= 20 \cdot 7 \pm 0 \cdot 7 \%$). The use of both sexes does not therefore appear to have complicated the issues unduly in this series of experiments.

Working on this same basis of percentage retention, significant regression coefficients of slope for total elimination were found for SI ($P < 0 \cdot 001$) and SC ($P < 0 \cdot 02$), but not for LC or LI. In comparing the regression coefficients the effect of duration of exposure was seen with SC > LC ($P < 0 \cdot 05$) and SI > LI ($P < 0 \cdot 005$), but there were no significant differences which could be attributed to the intermittency of exposure.

Lea Hall

The dust burdens of lungs and nodes, and their regression lines, are shown in Figure 3.

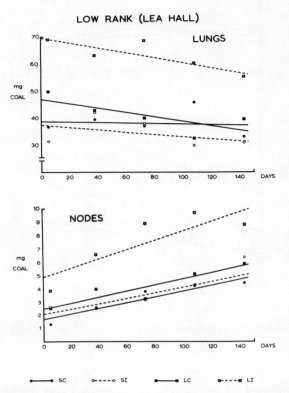

FIGURE 3. Regression lines shown in relation to mean values of lung and node burdens for a low rank dust.

Three of these experiments had dust concentrations that were higher than previously obtained but all post-exposure pulmonary dust contents were greater than with the high rank dust. The elimination rates (μg/week $\pm$ SE) were:

	Bronchial	Lymphatic	Total
SC	-63 ± 237	146 ± 21	83 ± 237
SI	146 ± 273	137 ± 47	283 ± 269
LC	433 ± 166	153 ± 27	586 ± 164
LI	418 ± 360	233 ± 73	651 ± 353

Probably due to the larger variance as compared with Ffaldau 2, significant differences between the four experiments were not obtained. Expression of the results as a percentage of the initial lung burden likewise failed to demonstrate significant alterations in the elimination rates, whether total, bronchial or lymphatic, between any of the experiments. The lung retention at the end of the exposure, when expressed as a percentage of the amount of coal estimated as inhaled, was similar for all four experiments (SC = $35\cdot9 \pm 1\cdot4\%$: SI = $38\cdot7 \pm 2\cdot1\%$: LC = $35\cdot3 \pm 0\cdot6\%$: LI = $32\cdot8 \pm 1\cdot2\%$). The percentage retention values regressed significantly ($P < 0\cdot001$) following the LC exposure, but although regressions of similar magnitude were found for SI and LI, they did not achieve significance. The only comparison to do so was LC> SC ($P < 0\cdot05$).

The advantages in overall and bronchial elimination rates shown with a high rank dust in short as against long and intermittent over continuous exposures are thus not reflected in the corresponding rates for a low rank dust. With the latter the only significant finding, that total LC elimination rate was superior to SC, was anomalous.

Comparison of Rank

In the following four tables the probability values are given in brackets and apply to comparisons of figures immediately above and below.

Short Continuous Exposure

Dust	Lung burden at end of exposure (mg)	Clearance rates (μg/wk)		% retention of inhaled particles	
		Bronchial	Lymphatic	At end of exposure	Regression
Ffaldau 1	$22\cdot9 \pm 1\cdot2$	17 ± 171	34 ± 25	—	—
	$(0\cdot001)$	(N.S.)	(N.S.)		
Ffaldau 2 (females)	$14\cdot1 \pm 0\cdot6$	151 ± 77	49 ± 7	$32\cdot9 \pm 1\cdot3$	$-0\cdot072 \pm 0\cdot025$
	$(0\cdot001)$	(N.S.)	$(0\cdot001)$	(N.S.)	$(0\cdot05)$
Lea Hall	$38\cdot9 \pm 1\cdot7$	-63 ± 237	146 ± 21	$35\cdot9 \pm 1\cdot4$	$0\cdot008 \pm 0\cdot028$

The use of female rats in Ffaldau 2 led to a significantly smaller accumulation of dust than in males of Ffaldau 1 but the bronchial and lymphatic clearance rates though higher in the females were not significantly so. The higher dust concentration in the Lea Hall experiment presumably accounts for the larger pulmonary accumulation of dust, bronchial elimination being highly variable but not clearly different from Ffaldau 2 whilst lymphatic disposal was definitely more effective with Lea Hall. The post-exposure retention percentages do not differ but the regression of this parameter is greater for Ffaldau 2.

Short Intermittent Exposure

Dust	Lung burden at end of exposure (mg)	Clearance rates (μg/wk)		% retention of inhaled particles	
		Bronchial	Lymphatic	At end of exposure	Regression
Ffaldau 1	$22\cdot7 \pm 0\cdot6$	292 ± 95	39 ± 28	—	—
	$(0\cdot01)$	(N.S.)	(N.S.)		
Ffaldau 2	$19\cdot9 \pm 0\cdot7$	421 ± 99	63 ± 16	$32\cdot2 \pm 1\cdot1$	$-0\cdot105 \pm 0\cdot023$
	$(0\cdot001)$	(N.S.)	(N.S.)	$(0\cdot02)$	(N.S.)
Lea Hall	$37\cdot3 \pm 1\cdot9$	146 ± 273	137 ± 47	$38\cdot7 \pm 2\cdot1$	$-0\cdot047 \pm 0\cdot043$

Despite the higher lung burden in Ffaldau 1, neither of the clearance rates differed significantly in the two experiments with higher rank coal. The particle concentration during exposure and the dust burden were greater for Lea Hall than Ffaldau 2 as was the degree of retention, but the regressions of the latter parameter did not differ. Though the mean bronchial clearance rate is lower for Lea Hall than Ffaldau 2, no significance can be attached due to the magnitude of the errors in estimating the elimination of Lea Hall.

Long Continuous Exposure

Dust	Lung burden at end of exposure (mg)	Clearance rates (μg/wk)		% retention of inhaled particles	
		Bronchial	Lymphatic	At end of exposure	Regression
Ffaldau 1	26·7 ± 1·0 (0·001)	−117 ± 140 (N.S.)	195 ± 20 (0·001)	—	—
Ffaldau 2 (females)	15·3 ± 0·8 (0·001)	−120 ± 199 (0·05)	74 ± 14 (0·02)	20·5 ± 1·0 (0·001)	−0·006 ± 0·020 (0·05)
Lea Hall	47·2 ± 1·2	433 ± 166	153 ± 27	35·3 ± 0·6	−0·057 ± 0·013

Dust concentrations were comparable throughout these experiments. A significantly smaller lung burden was again present in female as opposed to male rats inhaling high rank coal, but bronchial clearance though variable appeared low and comparable in both experiments. Lymphatic elimination was more rapid in males with the larger lung burdens. There was a much greater pulmonary accumulation of Lea Hall than Ffaldau dust. Bronchial removal was also higher for Lea Hall, but its lymphatic disposal, though better than Ffaldau 2 (females) did not differ from Ffaldau 1 (males). Retention as a percentage and its regression were greater for the low rank coal.

Long Intermittent Exposure

Dust	Lung burden at end of exposure (mg)	Clearance rates (μg/wk)		% retention of inhaled particles	
		Bronchial	Lymphatic	At end of exposure	Regression
Ffaldau 1	34·6 ± 1·1 (0·01)	28 ± 156 (N.S.)	148 ± 37 (N.S.)	—	—
Ffaldau 2	30·0 ± 1·0 (0·001)	223 ± 134 (N.S.)	125 ± 29 (N.S.)	20·7 ± 0·7 (0·001)	−0·019 ± 0·014 (N.S.)
Lea Hall	69·7 ± 2·5	418 ± 360	233 ± 73	32·8 ± 1·2	−0·039 ± 0·023

Although more Ffaldau 1 dust accumulated in the lung than Ffaldau 2, bronchial and lymphatic elimination rates were not significantly different despite a suggestion of better bronchial clearance with Ffaldau 2. The higher dust concentration of Lea Hall again presumably contributed to the larger lung burden, though the percentage retention of this dust was also significantly higher. Bronchial and lymphatic clearance rates tend to be higher for Lea Hall but not significantly so. Regression of the percentage retention parameter, though apparently higher for Lea Hall, also shows no significant difference from Ffaldau.

The larger lung burdens of low rank coal immediately after exposure render difficult the inter-dust comparisons of elimination. Thus percentage retention of inhaled particles is greater for low rank dust in all four experiments and significantly so in three, but there is no apparent connection with atmospheric dust concentration. Regression of the percentage retention parameter tends to be greater for high rank dust with short exposures, but for low rank dust with LC and possibly with LI. Bronchial elimination does not follow a clear pattern but may be more effective with high rank coal in short exposures and with low rank dust in long ones. Removal by the lymphatic system is more readily accomplished with low rank dust, significantly so after the continuous exposures. However, some dependence on lung burden is also indicated.

COMMENT

Reduced to terms which may be oversimplified, it may be said that, in so far as total and bronchial elimination are concerned, the advantage lies with high rank dust after short exposures whether continuous or intermittent and with low rank dust following long exposures.

In the production of these differences a non-environmental factor may play a part, namely the pulmonary reaction to the dusts. From the left lung of one rat in each group killed at a particular interval, three 5 μm sections were taken and the remaining tissue conserved for chemical extraction. Histologically, the reaction to low rank dust differed from that to the high rank in that the macrophages occupied larger areas of alveolar tissue and were distinctly more distended and foamy in appearance. Initially such a state may lead to delay in bronchial disposal but as exposure is prolonged the turnover of cells may become greater and induce more effective elimination by this route. The same factor may, in combination with the greater lung burden, underlie the better lymphatic removal of the low rank dust at least under continuous conditions of inhalation.

On the other hand, environmental conditions influenced the clearance of high rank dust, especially via the bronchial route, in that it is removed more readily when inhalation is brief and intermittent rather than long and continuous. It is possible that the macrophage response obscured the interplay of these environmental factors in the case of low rank dust.

Further experiments prompted by these preliminary findings will examine the influence of dust concentration during exposure on elimination and include other dusts in an attempt to assess the importance of the macrophage-particle reaction. At this stage it is not possible to correlate our observations with those of SKIDMORE et al. (1965), who found no differences in uptake and retention of high and low rank coals, but it should be noted that they employed standard rats which showed a high incidence of pulmonary infection.

Acknowledgements — This study was supported by the National Coal Board and the Medical Research Council.

REFERENCES

COCHRANE, A. L. (1962). *Br. J. ind. Med.* **19**, 52–64.
GUYTON, A. C. (1947). *Am. J. Physiol.* **150**, 70–77.
HART, P. D'A. & ASLETT, E. A. (1942). *Spec. Rep. Ser. med. Res. Coun.* (243).

270   A. G. Heppleston, G. W. Civil and A. Critchlow

Hicks, D.; Fay, J. W. J., Ashford, J. R. & Rae, S. (1961). *The relation between pneumoconiosis and environmental conditions.* London, National Coal Board.
N.C.B. (1964). *The coal classification system used by the National Coal Board.* London, National Coal Board.
Rivers, D., Morris, T. G. & Wise, M. E. (1963). *Br. J. ind. Med.* **20**, 13–23.
Skidmore, J. W., Morris, T. G., Nagelschmidt, G. & King, E. J. (1965). *Ann. occup. Hyg.* **8**, 183–192.
Wright, B. M. (1957). *Br. J. ind. Med.* **14**, 219–228.

DISCUSSION

J. W. SKIDMORE: (i) You have a significant quantity of ash in each dust cloud; have you observed any difference in elimination rates of the coals and non-coals? (ii) Can you be sure that your different elimination rates are not related to the non-coal component?

Mr. CIVIL: (i) This has not yet been determined in regard to bronchial clearance. However, the ash content of dust extracted from lymph nodes tended to be higher than that extracted from lungs, so there may be some selective lymphatic elimination of the ash material. (ii) It is not yet possible to be certain, since the exposures were to air-borne dust collected from the respective mines.

K. ROBOCK: (i) Why do you use higher dust concentrations for the low rank coal than for the high rank coal? (ii) Have you determined the quartz content of the samples?

Mr. CIVIL: (i) It does not seem likely that dust concentration has affected the results. None of the clearance rates can be related to differences in dust concentration. (ii) The air-borne dust collected from the high rank coal mine contained approximately $3 \cdot 3\%$ quartz, and that from the low rank mine $8 \cdot 5\%$ quartz.

D. F. C. MUIR: Was there any difference in the size distribution of particles in the respirable range for the high and low rank coals?

Mr. CIVIL: We have size distribution figures for the respirable portion of both dusts and they are comparable.

LONG-TERM STORAGE, MIGRATION AND ELIMINATION OF DUST IN THE LUNGS OF ANIMALS, WITH SPECIAL RESPECT TO THE INFLUENCE OF POLYVINYL-PYRIDINE-N-OXIDE

W. Klosterkötter and F. Gono

Institut für Hygiene und Arbeitsmedizin, Klinikum Essen der Ruhr-Universität Bochum, W. Germany

Abstract — The paper describes three test series with rats. (1), long-term inhalation of quartz (concentration: 1 mg/m³; duration of exposure: 1 year, 5 hours per day, 5 days per week). This type of exposure causes a typical silicosis. The elimination three and six months after termination of the exposure is very low. (2), long-term inhalation of TiO_2 only, of TiO_2 plus quartz, of TiO_2 plus quartz plus polyvinyl-pyridine-N-oxide (PNO), of TiO_2 plus PNO. Quartz increases significantly the retention and penetration of TiO_2. This quartz effect is suspended by the inhalation of PNO. The elimination of TiO_2 is not promoted by PNO. (3), long-term elimination test after inhalation of quartz; (a) 3 × 5 hours, 30 mg/m³; (b), 10 × 5 hours, 30 mg/m³ The retention, elimination and penetration were observed for 15 months after exposure. The biological half-life value was about 3 months. The further development of the elimination curve differed essentially from the curve for the exponential half-life time. The initial dust load of the lungs influences the retention and the elimination.

INTRODUCTION

As known from several experimental investigations, inhaled quartz dust migrates in considerable quantities, contrary to inert dusts, into the extrapulmonary mediastinal lymph nodes. It can be concluded therefrom, that a considerable portion of the quartz dust deposited in the alveolar region penetrates into the lung interstice. We attribute this penetration to the cytotoxic effect of quartz which leads to the destruction of the alveolar phagocytes, and we think that quartz particles penetrate mostly in a free condition (Klosterkötter, 1963; Klosterkötter & Einbrodt, 1965a). Our opinion is supported by the fact that penetration into the interstice and migration into the mediastinal lymph nodes are essentially checked by application of polyvinyl-pyridine-N-oxide (PNO) (subcutaneous injection, inhalation) and that bronchial alveolar clearance is promoted (Schlipköter & Brockhaus, 1965; Klosterkötter & Einbrodt, 1965b; Pott et al., 1968; Klosterkötter & Gono, 1969). We consider it a further proof of our thesis that the penetration of an inert dust and the migration into the extrapulmonary lymph nodes are considerably enhanced by quartz (3 to 5% in the lung dust) (Klosterkötter & Einbrodt, 1965c;

273

Klosterkötter, 1967). We must assume that this observation will also be relevant to industrial conditions; e.g. in coal mines where the dust contains much inert material and up to a few percent quartz. We suggest that the results of these animal experiments ought to be taken into consideration in the compilation of MAC-values for dusts.

As observed in previous investigations, the elimination of quartz dust takes place exponentially, slowly and incompletely. There are big differences in lung clearance with time and with quantity, and according to whether the dust load of the lungs has been built up by high doses over short periods or by low doses over a long time. This is understandable as, in the first case, there is more quartz in the alveoli while, in the latter, the quartz percentage in the lung interstice is higher, thus reducing the chance of elimination. Thus, we must expect that the quartz deposits, built up in the lungs over a long time, will be very stable, resulting in a long-time local cytopatho-genous effect.

In the last two years, we have carried out a series of new inhalation experiments with rats, the results of which are the subject of this paper. The aim has been to obtain a better understanding of lung clearance, and to provide fundamental knowledge for determining MAC-values.

STORAGE, PENETRATION AND ELIMINATION OF QUARTZ AFTER LONG-TERM INHALATION

Methods

One hundred female rats inhaled quartz for periods of up to one year in a Polley dust tunnel. The dust concentration was 1 mg/m³. This was controlled by the Gravi-metric Dust Sampler (Casella) and by a recording Tyndalloscope (Sigrist). Groups of approximately equal numbers of animals were killed, 3 months (57 exposures) and 12 months (240 exposures) after beginning the inhalations, and also 3 months and 6 months after termination of the inhalations. The lungs and mediastinal lymph nodes were analysed for SiO_2 according to the method of Stegemann & Fitzek (1956). Some lungs were histologically investigated after the end of the tests. The lung retention was calculated in percent of the total dust offered, assuming a minute volume of 100 ml.

Results

After killing the rats, the following macroscopic observations were made: 3 months after beginning the inhalations, we found individual small white dust foci, the mediastinal lymph nodes were not enlarged. Twelve months after beginning the inhalations, we found a moderate number of grey dust foci, the mediastinal lymph nodes had been enlarged moderately to strongly and showed a grey-blackish colour. Three months and 6 months after the termination of exposure, a rather large number of dust nodules and much enlarged mediastinal lymph nodes of a grey-blackish colour were found.

Table I gives the results of the chemical analyses and the retention data in percent of the dust offered (L = lungs; LN = mediastinal lymph nodes; R(%) L = percent retention (of the total dust offered) in the lungs; R(%) L + LN = percent retention in the lungs and lymph nodes).

TABLE I. QUARTZ CONTENT IN THE LUNGS AND LYMPH NODES AND RETENTION IN PERCENT OF TOTAL
DUST OFFERED

Time	L (mg SiO$_2$)	LN (mg SiO$_2$)	R(%)L	R(%)L + LN
Exposure, 3 months	0·165	0·005	9·6	9·9
Exposure, 12 months	0·350	0·034	4·9	5·3
3 months after exposure	0·350	0·084	4·9	6·0
6 months after exposure	0·315	0·104	4·4	5·8

The histological investigation of the lungs after termination of the tests showed a
moderate number of typical silicotic nodules of the grade II to III according to Belt
and King.

Discussion

The one-year inhalation of a small quartz concentration (1 mg/m³) leads, in the
case of rats, to the building up of a siliceous dust deposit in the lungs. The increase
in retention is not linear, due to the effects of lung clearance. From the third to the
twelfth month of exposure, the final retention, relative to the total dust offered,
decreased by about 50%, i.e. from 9·6% to 4·9%. During a phase of 6 months after
the exposure, only a little quartz was eliminated, but there was a marked migration
into the mediastinal lymph nodes. This indicates that most of the retained dust was
in the lung interstices at the termination of exposure.

It appears instructive to carry out long-term inhalation and elimination tests with
different dusts and also with lower concentrations, as this will provide better experimental support for MAC values than short-term tests as carried out by most authors.
The final retention value in percent of the total dust offered has a high informative
value.

THE INFLUENCE OF QUARTZ AND PNO ON THE RETENTION,
PENETRATION AND ELIMINATION OF TiO$_2$ IN LONG-TERM
INHALATION TESTS

Introduction

Titanium dioxide (TiO$_2$) is a so-called inert dust. It has no cytopathogenous effect
in vitro and no fibrogenic effect *in vivo*. We prefer to use TiO$_2$ in animal experiments
instead of coal dust, as TiO$_2$ can easily be assayed chemically in very small quantities.

In previous investigations (KLOSTERKÖTTER & EINBRODT, 1965b; KLOSTERKÖTTER,
1967), we were able to show that the elimination of TiO$_2$ is reduced and slowed down
by quartz, and that retention and penetration are much intensified. We attribute this
to the fact that the TiO$_2$-phagocytes are destroyed by the simultaneous absorption of
quartz, which causes the TiO$_2$ particles to become free and, if they are not phagocytized again, to penetrate into the interstices.

The tests described in the following were made in order to clarify to what extent
quartz influences the retention, penetration and elimination of TiO$_2$ in long-term

inhalation tests, and whether the unfavourable effect of quartz can be reduced or even annulled by the inhalation of PNO.

Methods

Two hundred female rats, each weighing between 160 and 180 g, were used, divided into 4 groups of 50 rats each. All 4 groups inhaled TiO_2 simultaneously for periods up to 1 year (4 times per week, 5 hours per day) in the Polley dust tunnel. The average concentration was $21 \cdot 1$ mg/m³, controlled by the Gravimetric Dust Sampler (Casella) and a recording Tyndalloscope (Sigrist). Except for this TiO_2 inhalation, the Group I rats received no further treatment. Group II inhaled quartz additionally (1 day per week, 4 hours per day). Group III inhaled, simultaneously with the Group II, quartz and additionally PNO (1 day per week, 1 hour per day; concentration: $2 \cdot 5$ mg/m³). The average quartz concentration in these tests amounted to 10 mg/m³; it was controlled by the Gravimetric Dust Sampler and a Tyndalloscope. Group IV inhaled (in addition to the TiO_2 exposure) PNO once a week for one hour at a concentration of $2 \cdot 5$ mg/m³. Within one year, 200 TiO_2 exposures and 50 quartz and/or PNO exposures were carried out.

After 9 months, after 12 months, and 3 months after termination of the inhalations, up to 10 rats of each group were killed. Their lungs and mediastinal lymph nodes were analyzed for TiO_2 by the method of KLOSTERKÖTTER & EINBRODT (1965c). The rats of the Groups II–III were additionally analysed for SiO_2 according to the method by STEGEMANN & FITZEK (1956). The moist weights of the lungs were also determined during the sectioning of the animals.

Results

Tables II to V show the results of the long-term inhalation tests. (L = lungs, LN = lymph nodes, LW = moist weights of lungs.)

TABLE II. GROUP I: TiO_2-INHALATION

Time	L		LN		LW (g)
	(mg TiO_2)	(mg SiO_2)	(mg TiO_2)	(mg SiO_2)	
9 months, 150 exposure	4·43	—	0·10	—	2·13
12 months, 200 exposure	6·69	—	0·12	—	2·25
3 months after exposure	6·54	—	0·25	—	2·92

TABLE III. GROUP II: TiO_2 + QUARTZ-INHALATION

Time	L		LN		LW (g)
	(mg TiO_2)	(mg SiO_2)	(mg TiO_2)	(mg SiO_2)	
9 months, 150 + 38 exposures	6·42	0·39	0·27	0·08	2·83
12 months, 200 + 50 exposures	8·88	0·46	0·47	0·11	3·38
3 months after exposure	8·80	0·49	0·67	0·13	4·26

TABLE IV. GROUP III: TiO_2 + QUARTZ + PNO-INHALATION

Time	L		LN		LW
	(mg TiO_2)	(mg SiO_2)	(mh TiO_2)	(mg SiO_2)	(g)
9 months, 150 + 38 exposures	5·17	0·36	0·19	0·02	2·27
12 months, 200 + 50 exposures	7·01	0·44	0·11	0·02	2·30
3 months after exposure	6·52	0·51	0·19	0·06	3·06

TABLE V. GROUP IV: TiO_2 + PNO-INHALATION

Time	L		LN		LW
	(mg TiO_2)	(mg SiO_2)	(mg TiO_2)	(mg SiO_2)	(g)
9 months, 150 + 38 exposures	4·14	—	0·09	—	2·03
12 months, 200 + 50 exposures	6·74	—	0·13	—	2·19
3 months after exposure	6·51	—	0·14	—	2·70

Discussion

When comparing the four test series, it can be clearly seen that the retention and penetration of TiO_2 is promoted by an additional inhalation of quartz and that the elimination of this inert dust deteriorates under the influence of quartz. The differences found are significant. The negative influence of quartz is nearly completely suspended by an inhalation of PNO for one hour per week. This is quite remarkable, if it is taken into consideration that, related to a minute volume of 100 ml, the rats were offered only 0·015 mg PNO per exposure, of which probably less than half was deposited and absorbed in the alveolar region.

When comparing the results of Group I with those of Group IV, there is no indication of a promotion of lung clearance by inhalation of PNO. This was not to be expected theoretically for an inert dust, on the thesis that PNO promotes elimination only because it checks the cytotoxic effect of quartz. The difference in the retention values in the mediastinal lymph nodes was not significant at the end of the tests (Group I by 0·11 mg higher than Group IV) because of the wide scatter of the individual values. It should be further examined, however, by inhalation tests, whether PNO also reduces the penetration of an inert dust.

It remains of interest to compare the final TiO_2 retention as a percentage of the total dust offered. The values were calculated on the basis of a minute volume of 100 ml (R(%) = retention in % of the total dust offered, L = lungs, L + LN = lungs plus mediastinal lymph nodes) (Table VI).

I suggest that the final retention values in percent of the total dust offered also be included in future long-term inhalation studies, as they can supply important information concerning the comparative assessment of dusts and the influence of concentration.

LONG-TERM RETENTION, PENETRATION AND ELIMINATION OF QUARTZ

Most authors have not tried so far to follow up the retention, penetration and elimination of quartz over a longer period. A prediction of the development of a

TABLE VI. FINAL RETENTION IN PERCENT OF TOTAL DUST OFFER

Time	TiO₂–R(%)			
	Group I	Group II	Group III	Group IV
L: 12 months exposures	5·3	7·0	5·6	5·3
L: 3 months after exposure	5·2	7·0	5·2	5·2
L + LN: 12 months exposures	5·4	7·4	5·6	5·5
L + LN: 3 months after exposure	5·4	7·5	5·3	5·3

pneumoconiosis, however, is always a long-term balance problem. In order to close an experimental gap, we carried out inhalation tests with quartz dust inhaled by rats and followed up the retention, penetration and elimination for the subsequent 15 months. As two test series with different quartz deposition were run, information could be also obtained on the influence of the lung burden.

Methods

Group A: 100 female rats (weight 180 to 200 g) inhaled quartz at a concentration of 30 mg/m³ for 3 days, 5 hours per day. The concentration was controlled by the Gravimetric Dust Sampler. The dust offered, calculated on the basis of a minute volume of 100 ml, amounted to 2·7 mg. In order to determine the primary alveolar deposition, 10 rats were killed 24 hours after the termination of inhalation. After this time, the primary bronchial clearance had ended, so that it can be supposed that the measured dust had been deposited in the alveolar region. Further rats were killed 3 months, 9 months and 15 months after termination of inhalation. Lungs and mediastinal lymph nodes were analysed for SiO₂ according to the method of STEGEMANN & FITZEK (1956).

Group B: 100 female rats (weight 180 to 200 g) inhaled quartz at a concentration of 30 mg/m³ for 10 days, 5 hours per day. The calculated dust offered was 9 mg for this mode of experiment. The times of killing and the methods of investigation were the same as for Group A.

Results

The results of the two test series are summarized in Table VII. The letters mean:

L = lungs,
LN = lymph nodes,
L + LN = retention in lungs + lymph nodes,
R(%) L = retention in the lung in percent of the total dust offered,
R(%) L + LN = retention in lungs and lymph nodes in percent of the total dust offered.

Discussion

As the results in Table VII show, the biological half-life time (TASK GROUP ON LUNG DYNAMICS, 1966) of quartz amounts to about 3 months for this mode of

TABLE VII. LONG-TERM RETENTION, PENETRATION AND ELIMINATION OF QUARTZ

Time after exposure	L (mg)	L (%)	LN (mg)	L + LN (mg)	L + LN (%)	R(%)L	R(%)L + L
			Group A				
24 hours	0·39	100	0·004	0·4	100	14·6	14·7
3 months	0·18	44·7	0·032	0·21	52·3	6·5	7·7
9 months	0·11	26·6	0·079	0·18	46·3	3·9	6·8
15 months	0·05	12·7	0·034	0·08	21·1	1·9	3·1
			Group B				
24 hours	1·06	100	0·008	1·07	100	11·6	11·8
3 months	0·57	53·7	0·128	0·68	65·3	6·3	7·7
9 months	0·33	31·3	0·277	0·61	57·0	3·7	6·8
15 months	0·30	28·5	0·249	0·55	51·7	3·4	6·1

experiment. The further development of elimination, however, does not correspond to the exponential curve for the elimination of radioactive substances. We thought it necessary to point this out in order to avoid a misunderstanding of the term "biological half-time".

Comparing the data of Groups A and B, it will be seen that the initial lung burden obviously influences the development of elimination. This is significant after 15 months for retention in the lungs and, above all, for retention in lungs plus lymph nodes; also for the final retention in percent of the total dust offered.

It is worth mentioning that, for both Groups, the quartz contents in the lymph nodes did not increase in the period from the 9th to the 15th month of elimination, but diminished. It can be supposed that the processes of cell decomposition taking place also in lymph nodes, due to the cytotoxic effect of quartz, make these lymph nodes somewhat permeable to the dust particles.

Comparing the data of Table I with those of Group A in Table VII, it is evident that the biological half-time of dust deposits depends decisively on whether these were built up by short-term exposures or by long-term exposures. With a comparable lung burden, we actually find no elimination within 3 months of long-term exposures while, in short-term exposures, 55·3% of the lung burden was eliminated from the lungs within 3 months. As the authors of the Task Group on Lung Dynamics showed, the hazard of multiple exposures can be much underestimated if based only on the biological half-times of individual or short-term exposures. It thus appears desirable to carry out more experiments in this field.

REFERENCES

KLOSTERKÖTTER, W. (1963). Beitr. Silikoseforsch. S-Bd. *Grundfragen Silikoseforsch.* **5**, 417.
KLOSTERKÖTTER, W. (1967). *Silikosebericht Nordrhein-Westfalen* **6**, 69.
KLOSTERKÖTTER, W. & EINBRODT, H. J. (1965a). *Arch. Hyg. Bakt.* **149**, 367.
KLOSTERKÖTTER, W. & EINBRODT, H. J. (1965b). *Silikosebericht Nordrhein-Westfalen* **5**, 87.
KLOSTERKÖTTER, W. & EINBRODT, H. J. (1965c). *Silikosebericht Nordrhein-Westfalen* **5**, 101.
KLOSTERKÖTTER, W. & GONO, F. (1969). *Silikosebericht Nordrhein-Westfalen* **7**, 159.
POTT, F., SCHLIPKÖTER, H. W. & BROCKHAUS, A. (1968). *Dtsch. med. Wschr.* **51**, 2479.

Schlipköter, H. W. & Brockhaus, A. (1965). *Silikosebericht Nordrhein-Westfalen* 5, 79.

Stegemann, H. & Fitzek, F. J. (1956). *Aus der deutschen Forschung der letzten Dezennien*, 417, Stuttgart.

Task Group on Lung Dynamics (1966). Deposition and retention models for internal dosimetry of the human respiratory tract. *Hlth Phys.* 12, 173–207.

DISCUSSION

P. B. Meyer: Can you extrapolate the results of your investigations (PNO and biological half times) to "quartz-inert" dust mixtures?

Prof. Klosterkötter: I regret we cannot do this.

A. L. Reeves: In our experiments with soluble beryllium, we have found a plateau effect after about three months of inhalation, i.e. continued inhalation after that made no further net contribution to the total lung load. Did you find a similar result with quartz dust?

Prof. Klosterkötter: With low concentrations of quartz we always found a real plateau effect after about six months. With high concentrations of quartz after nine months there was only a tendency to a plateau, but not a real plateau effect. With highly dispersed amorphous SiO_2 dusts (specific surface 150 m^3/g and more) we found plateau effects after three to six months.

A. G. Heppleston: In our inhalation experiments the calculation of lung retention from the minute volume was based on the body weight of individual rats. To apply a uniform minute volume of 100 ml might introduce error, especially with low concentration of dust.

Prof. Klosterkötter: We did not take the minute volume individually. We used data from the literature.

W. Weller: We measured the breathing minute volume of rats and found values of 150–180 ml per minute. Thus, alveolar ventilation of about 100 ml per minute can be assumed.

P. C. Pratt: Curves drawn on the board during the discussion indicated plateauing of the silica content of experimental animal lungs as the exposure time increased.

Was the silica content determined in weight of SiO_2 per lung, or in percentage concentration? I would also like to know what time interval is represented?

In an experiment of mine, reported in about 1953, there was a continuous, almost linear, increase in SiO_2 content of lungs during a 21-month period of exposure. Dr. Klosterkötter's experience seems to differ from this.

Prof. Klosterkötter: The curves drawn on the board are not quite correct. I would refer Dr. Pratt to my answer to Dr. Reeves.

The silica content has been determined by weight of SiO_2 per lung.

H.-W. Schlipköter: The investigations reported by Prof. Klosterkötter into the elimination rates in long term studies may be applied to other types of animals since, according to my own earlier experiments, there are no real differences in the dust elimination mechanism between rats, mice, rabbits and guinea pigs. One of our recently completed long term studies, in which rats inhaled argillaceous mineral dust with a 16% natural quartz content, demonstrated that 2 years after the commencement of inhalation dust penetration was inhibited by PVNO. The dust content in the lymphatic ganglion of the PVNO treated rats was reduced compared with that observed in a duplicate group of untreated animals.

Prof. Klosterkötter: Thank you, that is in accordance with the values I gave for titanium.

EMPHYSEMA IN RATS AND CLEARANCE OF DUST PARTICLES

J. FERIN

Department of Radiation Biology & Biophysics, School of Medicine and Dentistry, University of Rochester, Rochester, New York, U.S.A.

Abstract — The retention of TiO_2 particles in rat lungs was used to test the influence of experimental emphysema, induced by papain, on the physiological clearance mechanism. Lung clearance after a single exposure was found to be a function of the initial lung burden. After a multiple exposure, the retention of particles at the 25th day expressed as percent of deposition, is similar to that after a single exposure; however, the retention at the 8th day is markedly higher. For a sensitive test, one should use more than one determination of retention after the exposure. Papain-treated rats have a decreased clearance of TiO_2 particles from the lungs. It remains to be seen which factor of the papain model interferes with the clearance mechanism, and how it is related to human emphysema.

METHODS

THE methods used have been described by FERIN (1970). Only a brief recapitulation will be given here. Male Long–Evans rats ($\sim$200 g) were used. Each experimental group consisted of 9–10 rats. The animals inhaled anhydrous titanic oxide in an exposure chamber. The mass median aerodynamic diameter of the particles was 1·48 μm with σ_g of 3·26. The TiO_2 retained in the lungs was determined by a photometric method using 4,4-diantipyrylmethane monohydrate. In experiments with multiple exposures, the exposures were repeated 2 or 4 times, the interval between exposures was 1 or 2 days except in experiment No. 12 where it was 8 days. The experimental emphysema was produced by two intratracheal injections of 0·5 mg of papain or by repeated exposure to an aerosol of papain, produced from a 0·5% water solution.

RESULTS AND DISCUSSION

We have chosen titanic oxide to test the capacity of lung clearance in rats with inflicted pathologies because it is non-toxic, inert, and has a very low solubility. The deposition of the TiO_2 aerosol in the lungs of mice, rats, hamsters, guinea pigs, and rabbits can be computed as we have shown (FERIN, 1970), using the empirical equation:

$$D = 2\cdot02\ C^{0.84}\ T^{0.82}\ W^{0.73}$$

where D = deposition (μg/rat), C = exposure concentration of TiO_2 in the air (mg/m^3), T = exposure time (h), and W = wet lung weight (g).

Following a single TiO_2-exposure, using an optical microscope, one can see these processes in the rat lung. After five minutes from the starting of the exposure few particles are seen in the alveoli (Figure 1), so one may not make a good judgement about their disposal. Following a 30 min inhalation, the particles are numerous, and located not only on the alveolar walls, but also intracellularly (Figure 2), and some of the alveolar macrophages laden with particles are at that time already carried on the "ciliary escalator" (Figure 3). We assume that the phagocytosis of these particles has taken place in the alveoli, which would mean that alveolar clearance starts very early after the beginning of exposure. Two days after commencing the 7 h exposure, most particles are located intracellularly (Figure 4). In the center area of Figure 4 and at larger magnification in Figure 5, one can see an alveolar macrophage laden with particles, as it moves from one into an adjacent alveolus, presumably through a pore

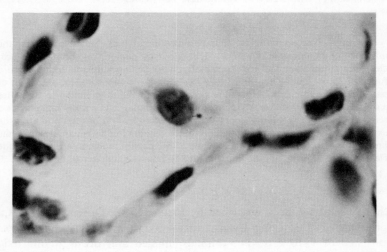

FIGURE 1. Rat lung after a 5 min TiO_2 exposure. Alveolar macrophage with a particle. Hematoxylin-eosin, from $\times$ 250.

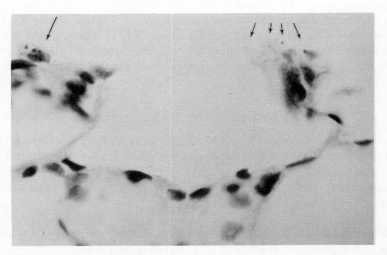

FIGURE 2. Rat lung after a 30 min TiO_2 exposure. Single arrow: macrophage with particles: multiple arrows; extracellular particles. Hematoxylin-eosin, from $\times$ 250.

of Kohn. Trapped in this position at the moment of fixation, this cell retained the shape of a moving macrophage and is not so rounded as the other phagocytes. The more rounded shape of the other "dust cells" may be an artefact due to the fixation technique used. In the same lung, one can find (Figure 6) a few particles which already passed into the interstitial space.

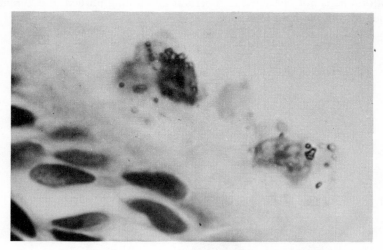

FIGURE 3. The same as Figure 2. Two "dust cells" on the "ciliary escalator".

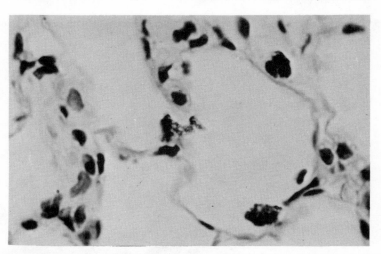

FIGURE 4. Rat lung 2 days after commencing of the 7 h TiO_2 exposure. Alveolar macrophages with many phagocytosed particles. Hematoxylin-eosin, from × 250.

In a pilot experiment, we determined the content of TiO_2 in different organs (Figure 7) during and after a 2 h exposure. We could not find TiO_2 in the blood, heart, liver, kidney or the spleen. The amount in the gastrointestinal tract is influenced also by the TiO_2 content of the rat food, which we estimate as 30 $\mu g/g$ of food. From these results, one can conclude, that due to the low solubility of the particles used, the lung clearance of the particles at this time take place mostly *via* the airways.

In normal rats, the clearance rate after a single exposure (Table I) is proportional to the initial lung burden, at least in the range from 44 through 350 μg TiO$_2$/rat. Within these limits, the relation between retention and initial lung burden is linear, so that the retention for a given time, expressed as percent of deposition, is practically the same in normal rats. That would mean that by expressing the retention in percent of deposition one is not restricted to a certain initial lung burden in different experiments when testing the lung clearance.

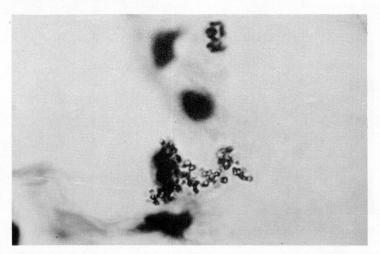

FIGURE 5. The same as Figure 4, from × 650. Alveolar macrophage with particles, moving from one into an adjacent alveolus.

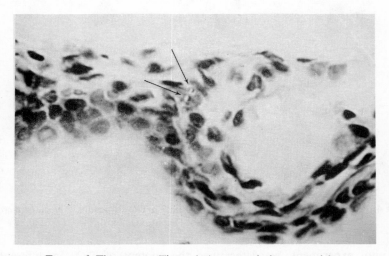

FIGURE 6. The same as Figure 4. Arrows pointing at particles.

The retention values at the 25th day after the last exposure are similar for single (Table I) or multiple (Table II) exposures. However, at the 8th day after multiple exposures the average retention of 93 % is significantly higher than the value of 74 %

obtained after single exposure. Let us compare 2 experiments having practically identical initial lung burdens (No. 5 and No. 13). The initial lung burdens are 350 and 353 μg TiO$_2$/rat, the 8th day retentions 77% and 92%, respectively. In the first case the rats were exposed once (50 mg/m^3, 7 h), in the second case, 4 times (15 mg^3, 7 h). Obviously, there is a difference in the exposure concentrations. Could this not be the cause for the difference in retention? Let us see another pair. In experiment No. 3 the animals were exposed at 15 mg/m^3 for 7 h, in experiment No. 4, at 61 mg/m^3 for 2 h. In both experiments one exposure was performed. The initial lung burdens are

TABLE I. RETENTION OF TiO$_2$ IN THE LUNGS AFTER A SINGLE EXPOSURE

Days after Exposure	1	8	25
Experiment	Deposition μg/rat	Percent of Deposition	
1	44 $\pm$ 10	80	64
2	54 $\pm$ 6	74	69
3	125 $\pm$ 21	66	58
4	134 $\pm$ 14	72	62
5	350 $\pm$ 59	77	58
Average		74	62

TABLE II. RETENTION OF TiO$_2$ IN THE LUNGS AFTER A MULTIPLE EXPOSURE (2 − 4x)

Days after Exposure	1	8	25
Experiment	Deposition μg/rat	Percent of Deposition	
11	96 $\pm$ 24	92	57
12	328 $\pm$ 65	97	60
13	353 $\pm$ 25	92	64
14	427 $\pm$ 53	97	57
15	1280 $\pm$ 146	88	68
Average		93	61

125 and 134 μg TiO$_2$/rat, the 8th day retentions 66% and 72%, respectively. This difference is not significant. A comparable pair with the same exposure time is experiment No. 3 (15 mg/m^3, 7 h) and experiment No. 5 (50 mg/m^3, 7 h) where the difference in 8th day retention is also not significant.

From these and the values of the listed 10 experiments in Tables I and II, performed on more than 300 rats, one can conclude that the number of exposures is relevant to the higher retention at the 8th day. For a sensitive test, one should determine retention at more than one time after exposure.

MORROW et al. (1966) have compared the clearance of uranium dioxide from the lung following single and multiple inhalation exposures in dogs. The clearance differed markedly, namely, 180 and 340 days for the respective biological half-times. The single exposures were brief, 1 h exposures. In the multiple exposure programme, the animals were exposed 6 h/day, 5 days a week for up to 5 years. DOWNS et al. (1967) studied the lung clearance of UO_2 in rats. The biological half-times were 141, 169, 239, and 289 days for exposure times of 17, 20, 58, and 140 days, respectively. From these experiments one conclusion can be made: With more exposures the biological half-time of lung clearance gets longer. The fact that the single and multiple exposure groups appear to have distinctly different clearance rates is not explicable by the physiochemical properties of the dust. MORROW et al (1966) hypothesized that the difference is due to one or more of the following effects described as: (a) *Compartment effect* — by repeated exposures sufficient material appears in a compartment which is relatively

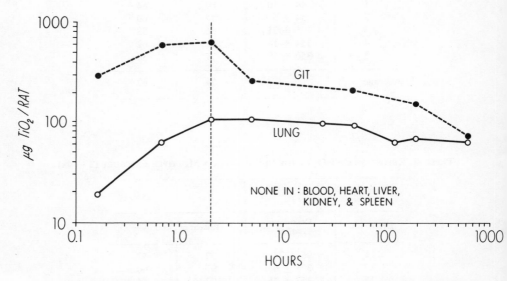

FIGURE 7. TiO_2 in organs of rat during and after 2 hour exposure of 57 mg/m³.

inaccessible to dust and more slowly cleared. (b) *Carrier or mass effect* — the absolute amount of material deposited in the pulmonary region affects its subsequent clearance. (c) *Adaptive effect* — wherein the "stimulatory" effect of dust exposure (macrophage response?) may be diminished or lost after a prolonged series of exposures.

The multiple exposures in our experiments have been performed 2–4 times, compared to the 17 or more exposures in the papers mentioned. We did not find a definitive slow-down in the clearance rate after multiple exposures. The impeded clearance at the 8th day after exposure was not influenced by the initial lung burden. We believe the repetition of exposures *per se* influences part of the lung clearance mechanism which is connected with the phagocytosis of the particles and which, depending on the circumstances, can decrease or increase the dust removal. During the process of particle elimination one could expect to find both of those effects as a part of the adaptive response of the organism. If we can extrapolate from the experiments mentioned one would expect a definite slowdown of clearance after a number of exposures which could be anywhere between 4 and 17.

In testing the lung clearance rate in rats with inflicted pathologies, we determined only the retention at day 25. However, the papain-induced changes were so severe that we found deviations from normal clearance rates (Figure 8). Papain has been used for inducing experimental emphysema by GROSS *et al.* (1965), PARK *et al.* (1969) and most recently by GILES *et al.* (1970). In our first experiment (No. 21, Table III) we related the

TABLE III. RETENTION OF PARTICLES IN NORMAL AND PAPAIN TREATED RATS AFTER
A SINGLE TiO₂ EXPOSURE

Experiment	Administration of Papain	Deposition μg/rat	The 25-day retention % of deposition	p
21	None	401	50	—
	2x i. trach.	Not determ.	31(?)	
22	None	327	49 ± 13	0·001
	2x i. trach.	165	82 ± 12	
23	None	376	49 ± 11	0·05
	26x 4 h. aeros.	438	61 ± 9	
24	None	326	49 ± 7	0·01
	6x 6 h. aeros.	293	66 ± 13	
25	None	139	57 ± 6	0·001
	4x 4,5 h. aeros.	121	77 × 10	

25-day retention in normal as well as papain-treated rats to the initial lung burdens of normal rats, and we got the surprising value of 31 % for the papain-treated group, which would represent a very rapid clearance rate. We repeated the experiment (No. 22), adding a papain-treated group of rats for the initial lung burden determination. We found a much lower deposition, 165 μg TiO₂, compared to 327 μg TiO₂ in the control rats. Thus the effect was quite the opposite; the clearance rate was markedly decreased, not increased. In experiments 23, 24, and 25 the papain was administered as an aerosol. The deposition was practically the same in both control and papain-treated rats. However, the clearance rate of TiO₂ particles decreased in the papain-treated groups. It remains to be seen which factor of the papain model interferes with the clearance mechanism, and how it is related to human emphysema.

Acknowledgements — This study was supported partially by research grant ECOO 384–01 of the Public Health Service and partially by the contract with the U.S. Atomic Energy Commission at the University of Rochester Atomic Energy Project and has been assigned Report No. UR-49-1334.

Technical assistance was provided at various times by H. Flachsbart, Ingrid Wönne and T. Wojtalak. The exposures of animals to titanic oxide were performed under the supervision of L. Leach and technical assistance of G. Sylvester.

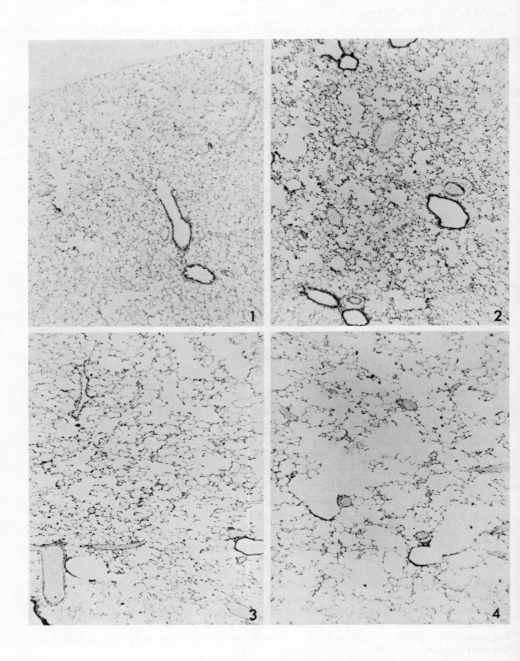

FIGURE 8. Rat lung after an intratracheal injection of 0·5 mg papain. 1 = normal; 2 = 1 day, 3 = 2 days, 4 = 4 days after injection. Hematoxylin-eosin, from × 40.

REFERENCES

DOWNS, W. L., WILSON, H. B., SYLVESTER, G. E., LEACH, L. J. & MAYNARD, E. A. (1967). *Hlth Phys.* **13**, 445–453.

FERIN, J. (1971). *Am. ind. Hyg. Ass. J.* (In Press).

GILES, R. E., FINKEL, M. P. & LEEDS, R. (1970). *Proc. Soc. exp. Biol. Med.* **134**, 157–162.

GROSS, P., PFITZER, E. A., TOLKER, E., BABYAK, M. A. & KASCHAK, M. (1965). *Archs. envir. Hlth* **11**, 50–58.

MORROW, P. E., GIBB, F. R. & LEACH, L. J. (1966). *Hlth Phys.* **12**, 1217–1223.

PARK, S. S., GOLDRING, I. P., SHIM, C. S. & WILLIAMS, M. H. (1969). *J. appl. Phys.* **26**, 738–744.

DISCUSSION

P. GROSS: I have often encountered papain which produced a chronic pneumonitis in addition to emphysema, generally in regions where there was no emphysema.

I would like to think there is the possibility of explaining the impairment of clearance on the basis of existing pneumonitis, as a secondary element.

Dr. FERIN: I cannot exclude this possibility.

A. A. SPRITZER: Were your calculations of clearance based on clearance ratio, i.e., what remained in the lung divided by what you originally deposited in the lung?

Dr. FERIN: No. The clearance was determined as follows: $E = D - R_t$. D is the lung burden 24 hours after exposure, R_t is the lung burden at t-time after exposure, for example 25 days. The difference E is the amount eliminated.

A. A. SPRITZER: Is it the basic assumption in this approach that whatever remains at day 25 gives you a compartment about which you can make your clearance estimate?

Would your clearance rate be changed if the material remaining in the lung has a sequestered component not acted upon by clearance mechanism?

Dr. FERIN: That could be correct. We compared in different experimental groups the amount of particles retained at a given time. I believe we can do this because under defined circumstances the determination of the cleared material is reproducible.

P. C. PRATT: This observation of decreased clearance of dust in rats with experimental emphysema fits very well an inference we have made in human lungs with centrilobular emphysema. Such lungs are consistently more heavily pigmented than normal and close observation shows that most of the excess pigment is located in the lesions of emphysema. In about 1965, we presented evidence suggesting that this pigmentation is the result of decreased clearance of dust from the lesions. Have you examined the lungs of your animals to ascertain whether more TiO_2 is retained in areas of papain damage than in normal areas?

Dr. FERIN: I think you could not quantitate microscopically the difference at 25 days. That is possible only by working with a large group of animals and comparing normal and pathologically treated animals by a quantitative method.

Maybe the difference would be more marked after a longer time, and even detectable microscopically.

INFLUENCE OF BCG ON LYMPHATIC LUNG CLEARANCE IN RATS

CARL-JOHAN GÖTHE and ÅKE SWENSSON

Department of Occupational Medicine, Karolinska sjukhuset, Stockholm, Sweden

Abstract — Intravenously injected BCG retards the elimination of mineral particles from the lungs and from the whole lung-hilar lymph node system, when the particles are injected through the trachea in a suspension in saline. BCG also retards the translocation of particles from the lungs to the regional lymph nodes. This applies to all types of mineral particles studied irrespective of the particle dosage, the fibrogenicity of the particles and whether the particles contain SiO_2 or not.

INTRODUCTION

ALTHOUGH it was observed as early as the nineteenth century that mineral particles could be eliminated from the lungs *via* the lymphatics (RUPPERT, 1878; ARNOLD, 1890), it was not until the last two decades that the lymphatic lung clearance mechanisms were examined in a more systematic manner (ATTYGALLE, 1956; PAVLOVA, 1961; POLICARD *et al.*, 1961; KLOSTERKÖTTER & EINBRODT, 1965; GÖTHE, 1970). However, our knowledge of the function and significance of lymphatic lung clearance is still incomplete.

The purpose of the present work was to study, in an experimental model, how infection with low-virulent tubercle bacilli (BCG) affects the translocation of mineral particles from the lungs to the hilar lymph nodes and the elimination from the lung-hilar lymph node system.

MATERIAL AND METHODS

A detailed description of the experimental technique has been given earlier (GÖTHE *et al.*, 1968; GÖTHE, 1970).

Inbred female albino rats of the Sprague-Dawley strain were used as experimental animals. Housing, cageing, feeding, etc. were standardized.

The mineral particles were suspended in physiological saline to the desired concentration. Each animal was injected intratracheally with 1 ml of the suspension under shallow ether anesthesia. The following types of mineral particles have been studied:

P 2:   Quartz particles produced by sedimentation in water of ground quartz containing 98 % of quartz. The mean diameter of the particles was 0·4 μm, and about 85 % of the particles were smaller than 0·5 μm.

P 9:   Quartz particles from the same batch as P 2. The mean diameter of the particles was 1·2 μm and nearly all particles were below 3 μm.

P 12:   Quartz particles from the same batch as P 2. The mean diameter of the
        particles was $3 \cdot 9$ μm and nearly all particles were between 3 and 9 μm.
P 310: Pure titanium dioxide. The mean diameter $0 \cdot 6$ μm.
P 501: Diatomaceous earth. Most of the particles were smaller than 5 μm. No
        crystalline SiO_2 was demonstrable with X-ray diffraction analysis.
P 503: Diatomaceous earth from the same batch as P 501. Heated to 400° C for 24 h.
        No crystalline SiO_2 demonstrable.
P 505: Diatomaceous earth from the same batch as P 501. Heated to 800° C for 24 h.
        No crystalline SiO_2 demonstrable.

The BCG (Gothenburg strain), a low-virulent strain of bovine tubercle bacilli,
was supplied as a suspension with a concentration of 20 mg of bacilli per ml. One
milligram contained about 3×10^7 "viable units". Each BCG-treated rat received
5 mg of BCG ($0 \cdot 25$ ml of the suspension) by intravenous injection into the femoral
vein after exposing the vein under shallow ether anesthesia.

The content of SiO_2 in the lungs and their regional lymph nodes was determined
with a slight modification (SWENSSON & ULFVARSON, 1969) of the method described
by KING *et al.* (1955).

RESULTS AND COMMENTS

Elimination and Translocation of Dust in Animals not Treated with BCG

In Figure 1 data have been collected from SWENSSON (1964) and GLÖMME (1967)
to demonstrate the elimination and translocation of P 9 within one month of intra-

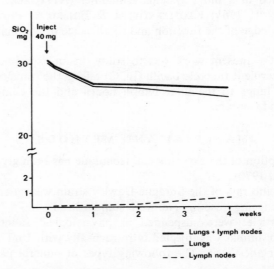

FIGURE 1. Translocation of quartz dust (P9) from lungs to hilar lymph nodes during the first
month after intratracheal dust injection (rats).

tracheal administration to rats not treated with BCG. During the first week after the
administration there is a rapid decrease in the SiO_2 content of the lungs, but a
considerably smaller increase in the SiO_2 content of the hilar lymph nodes. After the

first week there is only a very slow elimination of SiO_2 from the lung-hilar-lymph-node system, and the particles eliminated from the lungs are mainly translocated to the hilar lymph nodes.

After one month from the time of administration, practically all particles eliminated from the lungs are translocated to the lymph nodes and the elimination from

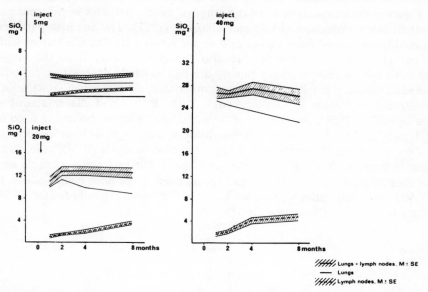

FIGURE 2. Translocation of quartz dust (P9) from lungs to hilar lymph nodes after intratracheal injection of different quartz doses (rats).

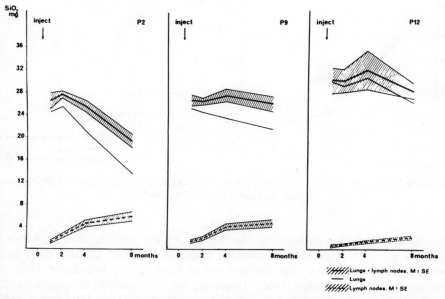

FIGURE 3. Effect of particle size on translocation of quartz dust from lungs to hilar lymph nodes (rats).

the lung-hilar lymph node system is negligible (SWENSSON, 1964; GLÖMME, 1967). The same phenomenon is observed after intratracheal injection of small as well as large doses of P 9: Figure 2.

Thus, there is a definite elimination of SiO_2 from the lung-hilar lymph node system during the first week after intratracheal injection of quartz particles, but later the SiO_2 eliminated from the lungs is mainly translocated to the hilar lymph nodes.

In Figure 3 the elimination from the lungs of quartz particles of different sizes is compared, from SWENSSON (1964) and GLÖMME (1967). The smallest particles are more readily eliminated from the lungs than the larger particles. Compared with the large particles, the small particles are also transported away from the lung-hilar lymph node system comparatively rapidly during the whole observation period.

The elimination of particles of minerals, other than quartz, which contain SiO_2, is demonstrated in Figure 4. Diatomaceous earth, P 501, and diatomaceous earth heated to 400° C, P 503, are eliminated from the lungs without becoming fixed in the hilar lymph nodes. After more intense heating, although without occurrence of crystalline structures detectable by X-ray diffraction analysis (P 505), the dust was eliminated from the lungs at about the same speed, but here a considerable amount of the dust transported from the lungs became fixed in the hilar lymph nodes. P 501 and P 503 are comparatively inert, while the variety most strongly heated (P 505) is definitely fibrogenetic (SWENSSON, 1967).

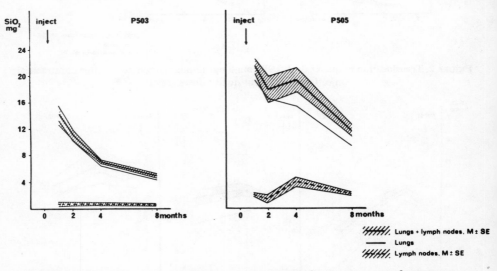

FIGURE 4. Translocation of diatomaceous earth heated to 400°C (P503) and 800°C (P505) from lungs to hilar lymph nodes (rats).

The observation, that increase in fibrogenicity of the particles also increases the propensity of mineral particles eliminated from the lungs to become fixed in the lymph nodes, is in keeping with the findings of *inter alia* LE BOUFFANT (1961) and KLOSTERKÖTTER & EINBRODT (1965). However, the translocation of quartz particles from the lungs to their regional lymph nodes seems to be very little influenced by silicotic fibrosis (SWENSSON *et al.*, 1968).

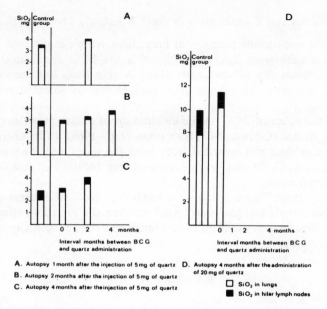

A. Autopsy 1 month after the injection of 5 mg of quartz
B. Autopsy 2 months after the injection of 5 mg of quartz
C. Autopsy 4 months after the injection of 5 mg of quartz

D. Autopsy 4 months after the administration of 20 mg of quartz

☐ SiO₂ in lungs
■ SiO₂ in hilar lymph nodes

FIGURE 5. Effect of BCG on translocation of quartz dust from lungs to hilar lymph nodes (rats).

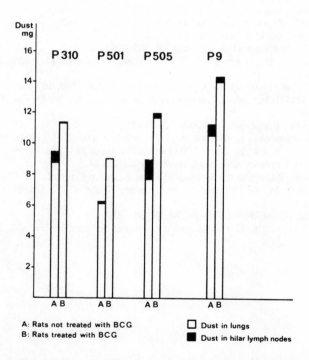

A: Rats not treated with BCG
B: Rats treated with BCG

☐ Dust in lungs
■ Dust in hilar lymph nodes

FIGURE 6. Effect of BCG on translocation of titanium dioxide (P310), unheated diatomaceous earth (P501), heated diatomaceous earth (P505) and quartz (P9) from lung to hilar lymph nodes.

Elimination and Translocation of Dust in Animals Treated with BCG

BCG causes a measurable reaction in lung, hilar lymph nodes and other organs, which reaches a peak from 2 to 4 months after the BCG administration and then successively decreases (SWENSSON *et al.*, 1968). Viable BCG has been demonstrated in different organs up to 12 months after the intravenous administration to the rat (to be published).

In Figure 5 the effect of BCG on the elimination of quartz particles (P 9) from the lungs is demonstrated (GÖTHE, 1968; SWENSSON *et al.*, 1968). In BCG-treated animals the elimination of dust was retarded from both the lungs and the whole lung-hilar lymph node system. There was also a decreased translocation of dust from the lungs to the hilar lymph nodes.

As is apparent from Figure 6, the same applied to types of mineral particles other than quartz. No correlation has been found between the retarding effect of BCG on the lymphatic clearance mechanism of the lungs and the fibrogenicity of the particles injected into the lungs.

REFERENCES

ARNOLD, J. (1890). *Beitr. path. Anat.* **8**, 1.
ATTYGALLE, D., KING, E. J., HARRISON, C. V. & NAGELSCHMIDT, G. (1956). *Br. J. ind. Med.* **13**, 41–50.
BRUNDELET, P. J. (1965). *Acta path. microbiol. scand. Suppl.* 175.
GLÖMME, J. (1967). *Evaluation of the relative fibrogenetic tendency of mineral particles in animal experiments.* Oslo, Universitetsforlaget.
GÖTHE, C.-J. (1968a). *Scand. J. resp. Dis.* **49**, 227–235.
GÖTHE, C.-J. (1968b). *Scand. J. resp. Dis.* **49**, 271–283.
GÖTHE, C.-J. (1968c). *Scand. J. resp. Dis.* **49**, 291–300.
GÖTHE, C.-J. *et al.* (1968). *Scand. J. resp. Dis.* **49**, 207–226.
KING, E. J., STACY, B. D., HOLT, P. F., YATES, D. M. & PICKLES, D. (1955). *Analyst, Lond.* **80**, 441–453.
KLOSTERKÖTTER, W. & EINBRODT, H. J. (1965). *Arch. Hyg. Bakt.* **149**, 367–384.
LE BOUFFANT, L. (1961). In: *Inhaled particles and vapours.* Ed. C. N. Davies. Oxford, Pergamon Press, pp. 369–383.
PAVLOVA, I. V. (1961). *Gig. Truda prof. Zabol.* **5**, 21–24.
POLICARD, A., CHARBONNIER, J., COLLET, A. & DANIEL-MOUSSARD, H. (1961). In: *Inhaled particles and vapours.* Ed. C. N. Davies. Oxford, Pergamon Press, pp. 384–397.
RUPPERT, H. (1878). *Virchows Arch. path. Anat. Physiol.* **72**, 14.
SWENSSON, Å. (1964). Report to the Swedish Medical Research Council.
SWENSSON, Å. (1967). In: *Inhaled particles and vapours* II. Ed. C. N. Davies. Oxford, Pergamon Press, pp. 95–102.
SWENSSON, Å. *et al.* (1968). *Scand. J. resp. Dis.* **49**, 301–310.
SWENSSON, Å. & ULFVARSON, U. (1969). *Studia Laboris et Salutis, Stockholm.* **2**, 1–12.

DISCUSSION

P. GROSS: Is the retardation of clearance in the animals treated with BCG due to localized inflammation within the lung, or a systemic effect?

Dr. SWENSSON: We have a systemic effect as we inject BCG, and we have seen the reaction in different organs.

There is a small inflammatory response in the lung, which reaches a maximum in two months, after which it decreases. In lymph nodes there is a considerable increase in weight, with a maximum in about two months, and after that there is a decrease in weight. The spleen increases to about 5–6 times the initial weight. After six months there is a decrease again.

I do not know the mechanism of the effect on the translocation of dust.

A. M. COETZEE: Have you studied the elimination of silica from the lungs after the temporary retarding effect of BCG can be expected to have worn off? Our experience in gold miners indicates that BCG vaccination is harmless.

Has any increased susceptibility to silicosis been noticed in laboratory animals treated with BCG prior to quartz inhalation?

Dr. SWENSSON: It is difficult to say.

As to application to human beings, our experimental model is quite different. We injected an enormous amount of BCG, which would have an inflammatory action on all the organs of the body. With BCG vaccination in practice, you get a much smaller reaction; I am not sure whether it is of importance or not, but it cannot be excluded.

R. MASSE: Have you been able to observe a multiplication of BCG?

Dr. SWENSSON: We have not followed that.

ASPECT BIOCHIMIQUE DE LA RÉTENTION ALVÉOLAIRE PRÉCOCE DES AÉROSOLS LIQUIDES DE TERRES RARES

Ch. Pasquier, J. C. Lefebvre and J. C. Ehrhart

Groupe de Recherches du Service de Santé des Armées auprès du Commissariat à l'Energie Atomique Département de la Protection Sanitaire BP n° 6, 92 — Fontenay aux Roses, France

Summary — A lipoprotein typical of the alveolar lining was isolated from endo-bronchial washing liquids obtained from rats and monkeys; this lipoprotein rich in glycolipids and free fatty acids had a lipidic composition widely different from the whole alveolar film. The part it played in the retention of unpolymerized lanthanum was demonstrated *in vitro* by polyacrylamide disc electrophoresis and *in vivo* by combined continued paper chromatography and electrophoresis.

The stability of the lanthanum-lipoprotein complex was tested by DTPA and its contribution in respiratory contamination discussed.

INTRODUCTION

En 1955, avec Pattle a commencé l'étude du revêtement endo-alvéolaire. Les premiers travaux furent consacrés à ses propriétés tensio-actives, afin d'expliquer la stabilité et l'élasticité pulmonaires; puis les investigations biochimiques, comme celles de Watkins (1968) ont permis de relier les phénomènes de surface alvéolaires à un groupe de phospholipides parmi lesquels la lécithine dipalmitique représente le constituant majeur. Ces analyses biochimiques étaient effectuées le plus souvent sur des extraits de broyats pulmonaires, ou plus récemment par Morgan *et al.* (1965), par Scarpelli *et al.* (1967), par Pfleger & Thomas (1969) sur des liquides de lavages endo-trachéaux. Toutes ces recherches dont l'historique a été rappelé par Scarpelli (1967), visaient l'aspect tensio-actif ou surfactant du liquide alvéolaire et étaient consacrées à l'identification des divers constituants lipidiques et à la mesure de leur tension superficielle.

Mais le rôle de ces constituants dans la fixation des polluants atmosphériques n'a pas encore été abordé, malgré l'importance qu'ils peuvent revêtir dans les phénomènes précoces qui suivent l'inhalation d'un élément radioactif ou non.

Dans ce travail, nous avons choisi d'étudier le devenir du lanthane 140 dans l'alvéole, à cause de l'importance de ce radioélément parmi les produits de fission dans les retombées radioactives, et aussi parce que première terre rare, il permet de prévoir le comportement des autres lanthanides et des actinides.

Lorsqu'une gouttelette d'une solution aqueuse de chlorure de lanthane se dépose dans l'avéole, elle rencontre d'abord l'interface air-liquide constitué essentiellement de lécithine dipalmitique. Les conditions de tension superficielle et de mouillabilité vont empêcher la goutte de s'étaler et favoriser sa pénétration dans la sous-phase. Ce phénomène peut être aisément déduit des lois théoriques qui décrivent l'étalement des gouttes en fonction des forces interfaciales; on peut aussi le vérifier expérimentalement avec un système simplifié constitué d'une couche de lécithine sur liquide calme. Ainsi, bien que la lécithine étalée en surface soit le premier constituant rencontré, et malgré son aptitude à fixer certains cations, elle ne sera pas nécessairement responsable de la capture du lanthane. Aussi, avons-nous cherché dans le film alvéolaire si un autre constituant était susceptible de fixer le radiocontaminant.

Nous exposerons brièvement les techniques utilisées, avant de rapporter les résultats et de les discuter.

MATÉRIEL ET MÉTHODES

Animaux

Nous avons utilisé deux types d'animaux: des rats de souche Wistar pesant de 200 à 250 g et des singes macaques de 4 à 5 kg.

Lavage pulmonaire

Les rats sont anesthésiés avec 0,8 mg.100 g^{-1} de Nembutal par voie intra-péritonéale, les singes avec 2 mg.kg^{-1} de Phencyclidine (Sernyvet de Parke Davis).

On perfuse l'ensemble cœur-poumons par le circuit veine cave inférieure — aorte abdominale avec du sérum physiologique à 4°C, le débit étant de 25 ml.mn^{-1} pour le rat, de 1100 ml.mn^{-1} pour le singe. Le liquide de perfusion ne contient ni novocaïne qui modifie la perméabilité alvéolo-capillaire, ni héparine qui selon Burnstein & Morfin (1969) altère les mobilités électrophorétiques.

La technique de Myrwick et al. (1961) est utilisée pour le lavage du tractus respiratoire. Par lot de 6 rats, on procède à trois lavages de 3 ml de sérum physiologique glacé, et pour 1 singe, à six lavages de 50 ml de sérum physiologique glacé. Les liquides obtenus sont centrifugés à 3000 g pendant 10 min. Le surnageant est concentré environ 20 fois par dialyse contre du saccharose à 4°C pendant 16 h. Le pH est alors ajusté par dialyse contre le tampon d'électrophorèse à 4°C.

Électrophorèses

Electrophorèse en gel de polyacrylamide

Le seul gel utilisable est le gel à 7,5% en acrylamide et pH 8,8 (migration pH 9,5) constitué selon la technique d'Ornstein (1964). On dépose 60 à 80 μl de lavage pulmonaire concentré (100 à 150 μg de protéines) contenant après dialyse, environ 40% de saccharose.

La prémigration nécessite 1 mA par tube pendant 10 min, la migration est effectuée à raison de 2,5 mA par tube pendant 1 h. Le protéinogramme est obtenu par coloration pendant 30 min dans une solution d'Amidoschwarz 10 B à 0,5% dans l'acide acétique à 7%. La décoloration est réalisée dans un appareil Shandon (transverse Disc Destainer) avec un bain de CH$_3$COOH à 7% et 0,5–0,6 A pendant 15 min (le bain est renouvelé une ou deux fois). Le lipidogramme est obtenu par coloration pendant 24 h dans une solution saturée d'Oil Red O dans le mélange: méthanol-acide trichloracétique à 20 % (1:1, v/v). La décoloration est réalisée avec une solution méthanol-eau (1:4 v/v) pendant 48 à 72 h.

L'étude de la fixation du lanthane ne pouvant être menée sur ce gel à pH 8,8 qu'après migration du matériel protéique, on introduit les gels dans une solution de lanthane (5.10^{-4}M, pH 5,4, 20°C, 40 μC.ml^{-1}) pendant 1 h. Après lavage à l'eau bidistillée, chaque gel est sectionné en 13 cylindres de 5 mm de longueur, un gel coloré servant de témoin. Si nécessaire, le sel trisodique monocalcique de l'acide Diéthylène Triamino PentAcétique (DTPA) utilisé en solution à 5 % est alors ajouté pendant 30 min. Les sections sont ensuite lavées dans un bain renouvelé d'eau bidistillée pendant 20 h. Le comptage est effectué à l'aide d'un compteur à scintillation à cristal de NaI (Tl).

Électrophorèse en rideau

On utilise l'appareil ELPHOR, combinant une chromatographie verticale et un$l$ électrophorèse horizontale, le papier Schleiber et Schull n° 604 L, un tampon véronae (pH 7,4, 20°C, la force ionique $\mu = 0,025$) et un champ électrique de 18 V.cm^{-1}. Le lavage pulmonaire concentré (environ 10 mg.ml^{-1} de protéines) et marqué (environ 10 μC.ml^{-1}) est injecté avec un débit de 60 μl.h^{-1}. La migration peut être limitée à 6 h. Le papier est mis en contact avec un film AFGA-GEVAERT D8 pendant 48 h. On utilise le révélateur DIAFINE et le fixateur ILFORD. Le protéinogramme est obtenu par coloration à l'Amidoschwarz à 6‰ dans le mélange $CH_3OH — CH_3COOH — H_2O$ (4,5:1:4,5, v/v/v) pendant 5 min, puis décoloration dans le même mélange de solvants pendant 2 h.

Analyse lipidique de la lipoprotéine

Isolement

On pratique une électrophorèse préparative sur gel de polyacrylamide à 7,5 %, pH 9,5, gel réfrigéré de 2,5 cm de diamètre et de 10 cm de longueur. La concentration est obtenue avec 10 mA pendant 10 min, la migration nécessite environ 2 h sous 18 mA. La bande (environ 300 μg de lipoprotéine) est recueillie dans un sac à dialyse contenant 3–4 ml de tampon, sac préalablement traité par le mélange $CHCl_3 — CH_3OH$ (2:1, v/v) pendant 1 h, à la température ambiante, puis par l'eau bidistillée pendant 1 h, à 70°C et sous agitation magnétique.

Extraction des lipides

On utilise 20 volumes de $CHCl_3 — CH_3OH$ (2:1, v/v) et on laisse en contact 1 h à la température ambiante. Après centrifugation, le culot est repris deux fois dans 5 ml de chloroforme-méthanol. Les trois extraits réunis sont lavés suivant la méthode de FOLCH et al. (1957). Le lavage est répété trois fois.

La phase inférieure est évaporée à sec, sous vide et à 30°C. Séchée à l'éthanol absolu, elle est reprise dans 1 ml de chloroforme-méthanol.

Caractérisation

Le fractionnement est réalisé selon la technique de WILLIAMS et al. (1960). Pour les lipides neutres, on utilise les chromato-plaques de silicagel (MERCK) de 0,25 mm d'épaisseur (éluant: pentane — éther éthylique - acide formique) (90:30:1, v/v/v). L'identification est réalisée à l'aide de témoins, après exposition aux vapeurs d'iode. On utilise aussi la réaction de caractérisation des glycérols α substitués par le périodate et le réactif de Schiff.

Phospholipides

L'adsorbant est du silicagel G ou HR, le fractionnement sur HR est réalisé avec l'éluant: $CHCl_3$ — CH_3OH — CH_3COOH — H_2O (50:30:13:5, v/v/v/v).

Avec G, on utilise le mélange $CHCl_3$ — CH_3OH — H_2O (75:25:4, v/v/v).

La nature phospholipidique des constituants est vérifiée par vaporisation du réactif de DITTMER et al (1964). Les lipides à choline sont recherchés avec le réactif de DRAGGENDORF. Les lipides à fonction amine libre sont révélés avec le réactif à la ninhydrine. Les glycolipides sont identifiés avec le réactif à l'anthrone. Les glycérols α substitués sont recherchés selon la technique au périodate-Schiff.

RÉSULTATS EXPÉRIMENTAUX

Électrophorèse annulaire

L'électrophorèse annulaire en gel de polyacrylamide a été choisie pour son haut pouvoir de résolution et sa possibilité d'utilisation en électrophorèse préparative.

En pratiquant la perfusion de la circulation pulmonaire sans surpression, il est possible de minimiser le passage des constituants du plasma vers l'alvéole; mais malgré ces précautions, les électrophorégrammes du liquide alvéolaire montrent toujours des traces plus ou moins importantes de contamination plasmatique. Le premier cliché permet de comparer après coloration à l'amidoschwarz les électrophoregrammes du plasma et du film alvéolaire. Dans ce dernier, deux bandes sont constantes: la première due aux albumines, en quantité importante même lorsque la contamination plasmatique est minimale; la deuxième très nette, située en avant de l'emplacement normal des préalbumines, n'est retrouvée que dans le liquide alvéolaire. Le présence de cette protéine a été vérifiée dans le poumon de plusieurs espèces animales: rats, lapins, singes. Toutes les autres bandes sont identiques à celles du plasma. Sur le deuxième cliché, la coloration à l'Oil Red O pour identifier les lipides, révèle deux bandes, une dans les albumines due vraisemblablement aux acides gras libres qu'elles transportent, une très nette correspondant à la bande protéique alvéolaire signalée ci-dessus.

La comparaison avec le plasma prouve que cette lipoprotéine est strictement alvéolaire.

Analyse de la lipoprotéine

Les chromatographies en couche mince révèlent des différences importantes entre la composition de cette lipoprotéine alvéolaire et celle de l'extrait lipidique du film entier; ainsi, les constituants majeurs de ce dernier, lécithines et céphalines disparaissent totalement.

La fraction lipoprotéique est caractérisée sur le plan des phospholipides (Figure 1) par une tache supérieure glycolipidique, se colorant en rouge avec l'anthrone, et par une double tache située sur les plaques G ou HR entre glycolipides et phosphatidyl éthanolamine. Sur la plaque G, le Rf de ces taches est de 0,66 et 0,60. Leur identification est en cours, mais elles ne prennent pas la coloration bleue caractéristique du phosphatidyl glycérol signalé par PFLEGER & THOMAS (1969) dans les liquides des lavages alvéolaires. L'identification des lipides neutres sur plaque G (Figure 2) montre

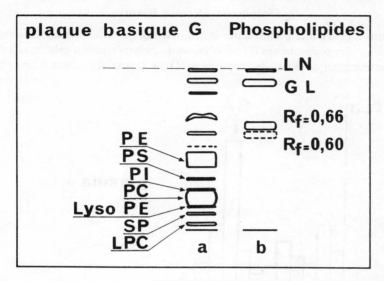

FIGURE 1. Chromatographie en couche mince de lécithine d'œuf (a) et de lipoprotéine alvéolaire (b) en milieu de migration chloroforme-méthanol-eau (75 : 25 : 4). Révélation à l'iode et à l'anthrone pour les glycolipides.

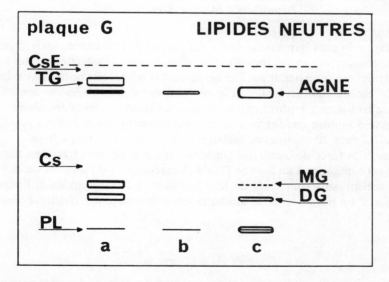

FIGURE 2. Chromatographie en couche mince de lipoprotéine alvéolaire (c) avec témoins de trioléine (a) et d'acides gras libres (b), en milieu de migration pentane - éther éthylique - acide formique (90 : 30 : 1). Révélation à l'iode et avec $Na10_4$ (SO_2)-Schiff pour les monoglycérides α.

à côté d'un témoin de trioléine, une tache importante d'acides gras libres, quelques monoglycérides colorables en bleu par le périodate-schiff, et une tache inférieure de diglycérides. Les taches de cholestérol libre ou estérifié mises en évidence dans l'extrait total du film ne sont pas retrouvées dans la lipoprotéine.

Fixation du lanthane in vitro

Rappelons que la contamination par le radioélément est effectuée après la migration dans le gel, car les phénomènes d'hydrolyse et de polymérisation inhérents aux terres rares les arrêtent en début d'électrophorèse. Dans le cas du plasma (Figure 3), la

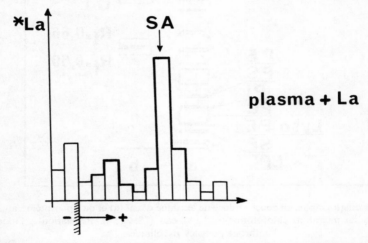

FIGURE 3. Répartition du lanthane radioactif sur les constituants du plasma obtenus par électrophorèse en gel de polyacrylamide.

contamination la plus importante se fait au niveau de l'albumine, mais il faut noter un pic de radioactivité moins important au niveau de la transferrine ou des α_1 globulines. La transferrine ne paraît pas être en cause, car isolée, elle ne fixe pas le lanthane.

Dans le cas du film alvéolaire (Figure 4), à ces deux bandes de contamination s'ajoute un troisième pic plus important, celui de la lipoprotéine alvéolaire.

La Figure 5 montre que ces pics de fixation disparaissent quand les protéines ont été délipidées dans 20 volumes de mélange acétone-eau (1:9, v/v) à froid.

Pour tester la force de liaison du lanthane sur ces différentes fractions, nous avons soumis le gel contaminé à un bain de DTPA. Les résultats sont illustrés sur la Figure 4. Tous les constituants sont lavés de leur lanthane, à l'exception de la lipoprotéine, dont la force de liaison avec le lanthane est suffisante pour résister à l'action du chélateur.

Fixation du lanthane in vivo

Nous avons contaminé des singes et des rats avec des aérosols liquides de chlorure de lanthane, pour vérifier si les résultats de fixation ci-dessus persistent lorsque les phénomènes se produisent dans l'alvéole. Les liquides de lavage pulmonaire obtenus sont analysés par électrophorèse en rideau, préconisée par JOVANOVIC & SIMONOVIC (1967); celle-ci ne permet pas d'obtenir la résolution de l'électrophorèse annulaire, néanmoins, les albumines et la lipoprotéine qui nous préoccupent sont nettement individualisées et le lanthane entrainé est repéré par autoradiographie.

Le troisième cliché superposant l'électrophorégramme et l'autoradiographie montre la fixation du lanthane par ces deux fractions. La même image est obtenue avec du ^{40}Ca. Lorsque après la contamination par le lanthane les animaux sont soumis à un aérosol de DTPA en excès, une nouvelle bands apparaît sur l'autoradiographie, celle

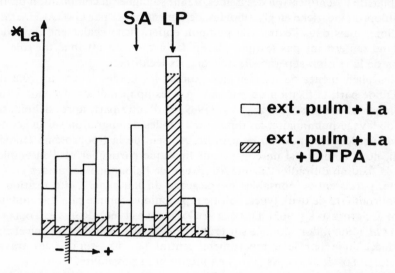

FIGURE 4. Répartition du lanthane sur les constituants du film alvéolaire avant et après trempage du gel dans une solution de DTPA.

du complexe DTPA-La (4 ème cliché). Si l'albumine est dans ce cas parfaitement débarrassée du lanthane qu'elle transportait, des traces de radioactivité persistent sur la bande lipoprotéique. Cette résistance au DTPA est cependant moins probante qu'*in vitro*.

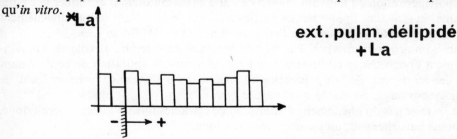

FIGURE 5. Répartition du lanthane après délipidation du liquide alvéolaire par le mélange acétone-eau (1: 9).

DISCUSSION

ABRAMS (1966) a déjà isolé une lipoprotéine de poids moléculaire $2,4 \pm 0,5.10^5$, migrant comme une α globuline en électrophorèse sur agar. Mais, cette lipoprotéine fut obtenue à partir d'un broyat de poumon et Scarpelli (1967) pense qu'il s'agit d'une globuline plasmatique. Elle pourrait correspondre à la première bande de fixation que nous obtenons au voisinage de la transferrine et que nous attribuons aussi à un composant plasmatique. Celle que nous avons mis en évidence est différente et bien individualisée par l'électrophorèse en polyacrylamide où elle migre loin en avant des albumines. Par ailleurs, en chromatographie sur gel Séphadex G_{50}, cette lipoprotéine étant exclue de la colonne, son poids moléculaire doit être supérieur à 30.000. Une étude sur Séphadex G_{200} nous permettra de mieux le cerner.

Sur le plan de l'identification des lipides, il faut souligner la composition particulière de cette lipoprotéine, riche en glycolipides, déjà mentionnés par Gallai-Hatchard & Gray (1966), mais dans l'extrait de poumon entier, riche également en acides gras libres, et ne renfermant pas les phospholipides à qui l'on attribue un rôle dans la régulation de la tension superficielle, tels que les lécithines.

Dans les phénomènes de fixation des cations, les lipides jouent un rôle prépondérant. D'une part, la fixation du lanthane par les lipoprotéines alvéolaires totales a déjà été montrée par Pasquier & Agid (1969) et d'autre part, après délipidation des liquides de lavage pulmonaire, les différentes bandes de migration sur le gel de polyacrylamide perdent leur pouvoir de capture. Au sein de la lipoprotéine étudiée dans ce travail, nous ignorons si un constituant lipidique particulier ou l'ensemble est la cause de la fixation du radioélément. Au niveau de l'albumine, les acides gras qu'elle transporte, paraissent responsables du piégeage du lanthane. Cette fixation sur les lipides pourrait être de deux types, soit de type ionique comme plusieurs auteurs, tels que Shah & Schuhman (1965), Deamer & Cornwell (1966), Rojas & Tobias (1965), Hauser et al. (1969), l'ont étudiée sur les phospholipides, soit du type micellaire avec capture mécanique par le compartiment central aqueux, comme les travaux de Papahadjopoulos & Watkins (1967) en montrent la possibilité.

Ainsi, comme nous le suggérions dans l'introduction, deux fonctions physiologiques, l'une attachée aux phénomènes de surface, l'autre à la fixation des cations seraient reliées à deux espèces lipidiques ou lipoprotéiques différentes.

Quel est le rôle de cette lipoprotéine dans les contaminations respiratoires?

Ducousso et al. (1970) ont montré qu'après inhalation de [140]La, le DTPA en aérosol administré précocement n'en épure qu'une fraction. La capture macrophagique et la polymérisation du lanthane étant à ce stade insuffisantes pour expliquer la charge restante, la structure lipoprotéique particulière, par le fait d'une liaison difficilement réversible, pourrait expliquer une limitation d'action du DTPA in vivo.

Ainsi, immédiatement après l'arrivée du lanthane dans le film alvéolaire, un compartiment lipoprotéique relativement stable se constitue. L'épuration du contaminant sera liée au devenir de la lipoprotéine elle-même, qu'il s'agisse de turnover local, de phagocytose ou de remontée mucociliaire.

Le premier pas du phénomène d'épuration de certaines formes ioniques serait donc, au moins partiellement, un piégeage lipoprotéique.

BIBLIOGRAPHIE

Abrams, M. E. (1966). *J. appl. Physiol.* **21**, 718–720.
Burstein, M. & Morfin, R. (1969). *Nouv. Revue fr. Hémat.* **9**, 365–374.
Deamer, D. N. & Cornwell, D. G. (1966). *Biochim. biophys. Acta* **116**, 555–562.
Dittmer, J. C. & Lester, R. L. (1964). *J. Lipid Res.* **5**, 126.
Ducousso, R., Bereziat, G., Perrault, G. & Pasquier, Ch. (1970). In press.

FOLCH, J., LEES, M. & SLOANE-STANLEY, G. H. (1957). *J. biol. Chem.* **226,** 497–509.
GALLAI-HATCHARD, J. J. & GRAY, G. M. (1966). *Biochim. biophys. Acta* **116,** 532–542.
HAUSER, H., CHAPMAN, D. & DAWSON, R. M. C. (1969). *Biochim. biophys. Acta* **183,** 320–333.
JOVANOVIC, V. & SIMONOVIC, I. (1967). *Arh. Hig. Rada* **18,** 147–153.
MORGAN, T. E., FINLEY, T. N. & FIALKOW, H. (1965). *Biochim. biophys. Acta* **106,** 403–413.
MYRVICK, Q. N., LEAKE, E. S. & FARISS, B. (1961). *J. Immun.* **86,** 128–132.
ORNSTEIN, L. (1964). *Ann. N. Y. Acad. Sci.* **121,** 321.
PAPAHADJOPOULOS, D. & WATKINS, J. C. (1967). *Biochim. biophys. Acta* **135,** 639—652.
PASQUIER, CH. & AGID, Y. (1969). *C.r. hebd. Séanc. Acad. Sci., Paris* **268,** 1129–1132.
PATTLE, R. E. (1955). *Nature* **175,** 1125.
PFLEGER, R. C. & THOMAS, H. G. (1969). In: Fission Product Inhalation Program, Annual Report, 1968–1969. Albuquerque (N.M.), Lovelace Foundation for Medical Education and Research. pp. 153–160.
ROJAS, E. & TOBIAS, J. M. (1965). *Biochim. biophys. Acta* **94,** 394–404.
SCARPELLI, E. M. (1967). *J. Colloid Interface Sci.* **25,** 90–96.
SCARPELLI, E. M., CLUTARIO, B. C. & TAYLOR, F. A. (1967). *J. appl. Physiol.* **23,** 880–886.
SHAH, D. O. & SCHUHMAN, J. H. (1965). *J. Lipid Res.* **6,** 341–349.
TURNER, G. A. & TAYLOR, D. N. (1968). *Radiat. Res.* **36,** 22–30.
WATKINS, J. C. (1968). *Biochim. biophys. Acta* **152,** 293–306.
WILLIAMS, J. A., SHARMA, A., MORRIS, L. J. & HOLMAN, R. T. (1960). *Proc. Soc. exp. Biol. Med.* **105,** 192–195.

DISCUSSION

N. KAVOUSSI: I would like to congratulate you on this brilliant paper.

Could you give more details about the washing techniques?

Dr. PASQUIER: In the rat as in the monkey we have used a method similar to the one mentioned for the collection of macrophages. However, care should be taken, first, to wash the lung circulation in order to avoid any contamination of the alveolar liquid by blood and, secondly, to use iced liquid because of the fragility of lipoproteins.

The whole of the alveolar liquid is not collected with the first washings, some is still collected after ten successive washings.

N. KAVOUSSI: Do you think it possible that your results *in vitro* might not be verified when extrapolated *in vivo*? Other factors could perhaps have an action in the human body.

Dr. PASQUIER: The results obtained *in vitro* have been verified *in vivo*; this is reported in the second part of my paper.

As to the extrapolation to man, I cannot certify anything but that our experiences have been verified on three mammal species: rat, rabbit, monkey.

E. D. DYSON: Could you please give more details of the chemical form of the lanthanum solution used in these experiments.

Dr. PASQUIER: The solution of lanthanum chloride used for the dipping *in vitro* is at pH 5·4 and its concentration $5 \cdot 10^{-4}$ M.

To make sure that lanthanum is not in a polymerized form, the aerosol used for intratracheal administration is also in acid solution.

SECTION III
BIOLOGICAL REACTIONS TO DUST

CHRONIC EXPOSURE OF CYNAMOLGUS MONKEYS TO FLY ASH

H. N. MacFarland,* C. E. Ulrich, A. Martin, A. Krumm, W. M. Busey
and Y. Alarie

*Hazleton Laboratories, Inc., a Subsidiary of TRW, Inc., Falls Church,
Virginia, U.S.A.*

Abstract — Groups of 9 cynamolgus monkeys (*M. irus*) were exposed for 18
months to 0.16 mg/m³ and 0.46 mg/m³ of fly ash while a similar group was used as
a control. The daily exposure was 24 h, except for a 20-min period twice a day to
clean the chambers and an interruption in the exposure when animals were removed
for physiological measurements. The fly ash used was collected from 4 major power
plants in the U.S. by sampling the postprecipitator effluent and was disseminated in
the exposure chambers by Wright Dust Feed generators. Measurements were made
of growth and survival prior to and during the exposure, and pulmonary function
tests were conducted to evaluate the mechanical properties of the lung, ventilation
characteristics, distribution of inspired air, diffusion, and arterial blood gas tensions. Also, haematological and clinical biochemical measurements were performed.
No significant changes in physiological parameters measured could be detected in
the groups exposed to fly ash. Microscopic examination of the lung revealed the
presence of fly ash in the alveolar macrophages, adjacent alveolar walls and peribronchial lymph nodes in both groups of exposed animals. In the groups exposed to
0.46 mg/m³, some of the macrophages had aggregated into small nodules in the
alveolar walls and a minimal fibrotic response was present in a few of these nodules.

INTRODUCTION

As concern increases about the long-term effects on human health caused by exposure
to low concentrations of atmospheric pollutants in the ambient air, it has become
evident that there is a lack of the appropriate kind of basic knowledge that can be
derived from experimental studies. Much of the data from earlier work was obtained
in short-term experiments conducted with relatively enormous concentrations of
pollutants, and small rodents have been used almost exclusively as the test organism.
As part of a larger programme concerned with the biological effects of sulphur
dioxide (Alarie *et al.*, 1970), sulphuric acid mist, fly ash and their mixtures, groups of
monkeys were exposed essentially continuously to two realistically low concentrations
of fly ash for a period of 18 months. A control group was exposed to filtered air under
similar conditions. A very comprehensive battery of pulmonary function tests was
performed at scheduled intervals prior to and throughout the exposure period. In
addition, measures of haematological and biochemical parameters, weight, growth

---

* Professor and Director, Centre of Research on Environmental Quality, York University,
Toronto, Canada.

and survival, and of blood gas tensions were obtained. At termination, gross and microscopic examination of major organs and tissues was conducted.

MATERIALS AND METHODS

Animals

Young cynamolgus monkeys (*Macaca irus*), weighing $1 \cdot 6$–$3 \cdot 0$ kg, were employed. Before assignment to control or exposed groups, the animals were tested for the presence of tuberculosis and a chest X-ray was obtained. They passed a rigorous screening procedure which consisted of evaluations of pulmonary function, electrocardiogram, haematology and clinical chemistry. Only animals having values within normal limits were accepted and about 50% of the monkeys, as received from the supplier, were rejected because of various abnormalities. Three groups of monkeys were used in the study; each group consisted of 9 animals composed of 5 males and 4 females or vice versa. Each animal was individually caged.

Pre-Exposure Control and Exposure Duration

After placing the caged animals in the exposure chambers, a period of 2 weeks was allowed for adaptation; during this time no measurements were made. This was followed by an 8 week pre-exposure control period during which time physiological parameters were measured to establish baseline values for each group and to note the week-to-week variation. Then, exposure to fly ash was started and continued for 18 months. Control animals were started in May, 1967, and the 2 groups receiving fly ash were started in September, 1967.

Exposure Conditions

Figure 1 shows a 9-monkey exposure chamber. The stainless steel cages were disposed in a 3 × 3 array in a single layer. The chambers were fabricated from stainless steel and glass, were 5 ft × 6 ft × 6 ft with pyramidal tops and bottoms and had a volume of approximately $6 \cdot 5$ m³. Air supplied to each chamber passed through a charcoal bed and an absolute filter. Temperature was maintained at 72 ± 2°F (22°C) and the relative humidity at 50 ± 5%. Air flow through each chamber was slightly over 1 m³/min.

Fly Ash

Fine fly ash was obtained by high volume sampling from 4 large coal-burning electric generating plants in the eastern United States. The samples were collected downstream from the electrostatic precipitators on the plants, just before entry into the stack. The samples were mixed to produce a homogeneous composite sample of sufficient weight to last throughout the duration of the studies. The composition, as determined spectrographically, is shown in Table I.

The fly ash was introduced into the inlet stream of the chambers by means of Wright dust feed mechanisms. Chamber concentration was determined daily by a membrane filter gravimetric technique. Particle-size distributions were obtained by the use of an automatic optical particle counter.

Biological Measurements

Pulmonary function tests included measurements of the mechanical properties of the lung and respiratory system, the distribution of inspired air, diffusing capacity of the lung, and arterial blood gas tensions. Several parameters characterizing the mechanical properties of the lung were measured utilizing a combination of methods

TABLE I. SPECTROGRAPHIC ANALYSIS OF COMPOSITE FLY ASH SAMPLE USED IN
EXPOSURE STUDIES

Element (as oxide)	Percent (by weight)
SiO_2	major
Al_2O_3	10
Fe_2O_3	6
CaO	3
MgO	2
K_2O	2
TiO_2	1
Na_2O	0·5
ZnO	0·2

The following were found in the percentage range 0·1 to 0·01: ZrO_2, MnO, BaO, SrO, V_2O_5, Cr_2O_3.

The following were found in a percentage of less than 0·01: B_2O_3, NiO, PbO, SnO, BeO, MoO_3, CuO, CoO.

The following were not detected: Cd, As, Te, Sb, W, Bi, Ge, Ag.

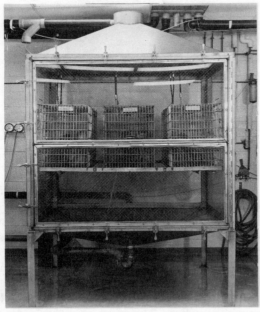

FIGURE 1. Photograph of exposure chamber housing nine cynamolgus monkeys for exposure to fly ash.

developed by Amdur & Mead (1958), Mead & Whittenberger (1953), Mead (1960), Murphy & Ulrich (1964). Swann *et al.* (1965), and King (1966). The monkeys were seated in chairs or body plethysmographs and fitted with a face mask. No anaesthetic was used; however, a period of 10 to 15 min in the chair was required in order to assure that measurements would be made when the animal was relatively quiet. Figure 2 shows a monkey seated in a plethysmograph chair, and Figure 3 shows the face mask in position. Outputs from a pneumotachograph in the face mask and pressure transducers on the plethysmograph and on an intrapleural catheter were recorded on an oscillograph and simultaneously transmitted directly to an on-line digital computer system. Test results were printed on a typewriter in the testing laboratory within a few seconds of completion of a trial. The computerized techniques of data extraction were similar in principle to those described by Stacy & Peters (1965), Peters & Stacy (1964), and Dennis *et al.* (1969). The list of basic parameters measured and the frequency of measurement are given in Table II.

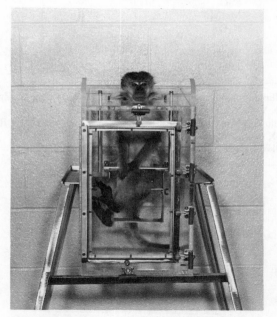

FIGURE 2. Monkey seated in body plethysmograph.

Characterization of ventilation and distribution of inspired air was based on the open circuit technique of Fowler (1948, 1949) and Fowler *et al.* (1952), in which nitrogen washout from the lung during pure oxygen breathing was measured in the unanaesthetized monkey. Table III lists the basic parameters and frequency of measurement.

The carbon monoxide uptake and diffusing capacity of the lung were measured by a rebreathing technique based on the same principles as those described by Bates (1962), Lewis *et al.* (1959), Kruhoffer (1954), and Long & Hatch (1961), after modification for use with monkeys. The parameter obtained and the frequency of measurement are shown in Table IV.

FIGURE 3. Front view of assembled face mask attached to primate chair with monkey's snout properly inserted.

TABLE II. MECHANICAL PROPERTIES OF THE LUNG AND RESPIRATORY SYSTEM MEASURED IN CYNAMOLGUS MONKEYS DURING EXPOSURE TO FLY ASH FOR A PERIOD OF 78 WEEKS.

Parameter	Abbreviation	Frequency of Measurement
Total respiratory system flow resistance during inspiration*	Rrs(i)	A
Total respiratory system flow resistance during expiration*	Rrs(e)	A
Tidal Volume	V_T	B
Respiratory rate	RR	B
Minute Volume	MV	B
Dynamic compliance of the lung†	Cdyn(1)	B
Pulmonary flow resistance†	R1	B
Pulmonary flow resistance during inspiration‡	R1(i)	B
Pulmonary flow resistance during expiration‡	R1(e)	B
Work of breathing during inspiration per ml tidal volume	$W(i)/ml\ V_T$	B
Work of breathing during expiration per ml tidal volume	$W(e)/ml\ V_T$	B

* Method similar to that of SWANN et al. (1965) and KING (1966).
† Method similar to that of MEAD (1960).
‡ Method similar to that of MURPHY & ULRICH (1964).
A Measured every week during the pre-exposure control period, every week during the first nine weeks of the exposure period, and every four weeks thereafter.
B Measured on five occasions during the pre-exposure control period, every two weeks during the first ten weeks of the exposure period, and every four weeks thereafter.

Table III. Ventilation and Distribution of Inspired Air (nitrogen washout) Measured in Cynamolgus Monkeys During Exposure to Fly Ash for a Period of 78 Weeks

Parameter	Abbreviation	Frequency of Measurement
Tidal volume	V_T	A
Respiratory rate	RR	A
Minute volume	MV	A
Number of breaths to 1% nitrogen	$N(1\% N_2)$	A
Time to 1% nitrogen	$t(1\% N_2)$	A
Cumulative tidal volume to 1% nitrogen	$CV_T(1\% N_2)$	A
Graph displaying the % and expiratory nitrogen concentration vs. number of breaths, time, or cumulative tidal volume		A

A. Measured on six occasions during the pre-exposure control period, every two weeks during the first four weeks of the exposure period, and every four weeks thereafter.

Table IV. Gas Diffusion Measurements in Cynamolgus Monkeys During Exposure to Fly Ash for a Period of 78 Weeks

Parameter	Abbreviation	Frequency of Measurement
Diffusing capacity of the lung for carbon monoxide	DL_{CO}	A

A. Measured on six occasions during the pre-exposure control period, every two weeks during the first four weeks of the exposure period, and every four weeks thereafter.

Arterial blood gas analysis was performed 10 to 20 min after intramuscular injection of phenylcyclidine (Sernylan®) for tranquillization of the animals. Blood was withdrawn from the femoral artery while the monkey was supine. The parameters measured and the frequency of measurement are shown in Table V.

Table V. Arterial Blood Gas Measurements in Cynamolgus Monkeys During Exposure to Fly Ash for a Period of 78 Weeks

Parameter	Abbreviation	Frequency of Measurement
Arterial blood oxygen tension	P_aO_2	A
Arterial blood carbon dioxide tension	P_aCO_2	A
Arterial blood acidity	pH	A

A. Measured once during the pre-exposure control period, every eight weeks for the first 24 weeks during the exposure period, and every 12 weeks thereafter.

The haematological and clinical chemistry determinations listed in Table VI were made at the frequency shown, using blood from the femoral artery. Body weights were tabulated every 2 weeks during the pre-exposure control period, and monthly thereafter.

TABLE VI. HAEMATOLOGICAL AND SERUM BIOCHEMICAL DETERMINATIONS IN CYNA-MOLGUS MONKEYS PERFORMED DURING EXPOSURE TO FLY ASH FOR A PERIOD OF 78 WEEKS

Parameter	Abbreviation	Frequency of Measurement
Haematocrit	Hct.	A
Haemoglobin	Hgb.	A
Erthyrocytes	RBC	A
Leucocytes	WBC	A
Lymphocytes	Lymph.	A
Segmented neutrophils	Seg.	A
Blood urea nitrogen	BUN	A
Total bilirubin	—	A
Serum total protein	—	A
Serum albumin	—	A
Sodium	Na	A
Potassium	K	A
Chlorides	Cl	A
Calcium	Ca	A
Serum glutamic-oxaloacetic transaminase	SGOT	A
Serum glutamic-pyruvic transaminase	SGPT	A
Serum lactic acid dehydrogenase	LDH	A
Serum alkaline phosphatase	Alk. PO_4	A

A Measured once during the pre-exposure control period and at 11, 16, 25, 49, and 77 weeks.

Data Storage and Statistical Analyses

For each pre-exposure interval, data from both male and female animals were combined and analysed to define the baseline (or normal) frequency distribution, mean value, standard deviation, and coefficient of variation. Skewed distributions were suitably transformed before computing the mean and standard deviation (OSTLE, 1956). Each of the parameters were examined by time-series analysis techniques. By means of power spectrum analysis, the appropriate polynomial regression function was determined for each parameter or was chosen on the basis of the best fit for the treatment group. Comparisons of regression coefficients between groups were made by the t-test (BROWN, 1963). For purposes of statistical comparison, $P < 0.05$ was chosen for accepting or rejecting a significant difference.

RESULTS

Fly Ash Concentrations and Size

Gravimetric determinations of fly ash concentrations revealed that the mean values with standard deviations for the 2 fly ash chambers were 0.16 ± 0.08 and 0.46

$\pm\ 0 \cdot 20\ mg/m^3$. In the case of the lower concentration, particle size distribution determinations yielded a mass median diameter of $2 \cdot 73\ \mu m$, with a standard deviation of $\pm 1 \cdot 36$; the corresponding values for the high concentration chamber were $2 \cdot 63 \pm 1 \cdot 09\ \mu m$. In general, it may be said that, while noticeable deviations occurred, the original objectives of concentrations of $0 \cdot 1$ and $0 \cdot 5\ mg/m^3$ with a mass median diameter of $<5\ \mu m$ were achieved within acceptable limits.

Biological Results

Body weight determinations prior to exposure revealed that the fly ash groups had significantly lower mean body weights than the control group. However, when growth curves were analysed, no significant differences in growth were found between the fly ash groups and the control group. Growth curve data were adequately fitted by first degree polynomials. One control monkey, a female, died 9 days prior to the termination of the 18-month exposure to clean air. Gross gastric distension following consumption of an apple used as a diet supplement was the cause of death, and the diagnosis was confirmed microscopically. No evidence of pulmonary disease was found in this animal.

In measurements of the mechanical properties of the lung and respiratory system, the total respiratory system flow resistance was obtained both during inspiration and during expiration. In both cases, a trend toward lower values as the experiment progressed and the animals grew larger was evident. However, no significant differences between control and treated groups for either parameter were detected. In the case of tidal volume estimates, it was found that the treated groups had significantly lower values than the control group at the beginning of the exposure. As the animals increased in weight during the study, a trend toward increased tidal volumes was noted. The rate of the increase in tidal volume was shown to be comparable for all groups. The respiratory rates for monkeys in all groups ranged from 32 to 33 breaths per minute, and there were no significant differences between groups nor any tendency for changes in this frequency throughout the experiment. The minute volume values showed that the exposed groups had significantly lower values than the control group at the beginning of exposure and that this parameter tended to increase as the experiment progressed. The rate of increase however, was comparable in all groups throughout the duration of the 18-month exposure. The dynamic compliance values showed an increasing trend during the study. The increase was slight in the control group, but more marked in the two exposed groups. Statistical analysis showed that the slope of the regression line for the $0 \cdot 16\ mg/m^3$ fly ash group was significantly different from that of the control group. This difference in slope was particularly influenced by the results obtained at week 64, when it was observed that all animals in the low concentration fly ash group had higher compliances. However, at termination of the 78 weeks of exposure, all groups were comparable. The pulmonary flow resistance gradually decreased during the exposure period, but no significant differences were detected between the exposed and control groups. Finally, the work of breathing was determined during both inspiration and expiration. The work of breathing during inspiration tended to increase slightly in the control group during the study, whereas the exposed groups exhibited a trend toward decreased values. A significant difference was noted in the slope of the regression line for the $0 \cdot 16\ mg/m^3$ group as compared with the control group slope. The case was the same when the work of breathing during expiration was analysed. The work tended to show a slight increase in the control group as the experiment progressed, while decreasing in the exposed groups. It was found that the slopes of both treated groups differed significantly from that of the control group.

The distribution of inspired air was studied by the nitrogen washout technique. The number of breaths taken to reduce nitrogen concentration to 1% did not differ significantly between control and exposed groups. There was a tendency for this variable to increase slightly as the experiment progressed. Similar observations were made on the time taken to attain 1% nitrogen. The values exhibited an increasing trend, but there was no significant difference between control and exposed groups. The cumulative total volume to 1% nitrogen was determined and found to show a trend to higher values. Again, however, there were no significant differences in the slopes of the regression lines.

The diffusing capacity of the lung, as determined by the carbon monoxide uptake method, did not differ significantly from the control group in those groups exposed to fly ash. The regression lines for all groups tended toward increased values as the experiment progressed.

Arterial blood gas analyses included determinations of oxygen tension, carbon dioxide tension, and acidity. Blood oxygen tensions decreased slightly in all groups during the study. This decrease was less evident in the $0 \cdot 16$ mg/m^3 fly ash group and, in fact, the slope of the regression line for this group differed significantly from that of the control. However, all values for all groups were considered to lie within normal limits. Similarly, all values of arterial carbon dioxide tension and pH were within normal limits for both control and treated groups.

The haematological determinations included the red cell and white cell counts, haemoglobin, haematocrit, lymphocyte and segmented neutrophil counts. All values were within normal limits for all groups throughout the study. The only observation of interest was that the leucocyte counts were slightly elevated in all groups during the pre-exposure period, and after 9 weeks of exposure, and then tended toward lower values up to termination.

The results of the series of biochemical determinations may now be examined. Values for blood urea nitrogen and total bilirubin exhibited some variability. No trend could be detected in the BUN values but bilirubin tended toward lower values in the control group as the experiment progressed. However, total bilirubin values in all groups were comparable at termination. Values for serum total protein and serum albumin were comparable in all groups and remained within normal limits during the 18-month exposure period. The values obtained for the serum electrolytes, sodium, potassium, calcium, and chlorides, remained within narrow limits for the entire duration of the study. The values for serum glutamic-oxaloacetic transaminase were comparable between the control group and the $0 \cdot 16$ mg/m^3 fly ash group prior to exposure, but the $0 \cdot 46$ mg/m^3 fly ash group had a 43% higher value for this enzyme. As the exposure progressed, more variation was noted in the exposed groups than in the control group. In the case of serum glutamic-pyruvic transaminase, values were considered to be within normal limits in all groups, although some variability was noted during the exposure period. Serum lactic dehydrogenase values were relatively constant for both exposed groups throughout, but the control group, which exhibited a high value in the pre-exposure period, tended to lower values as the experiment progressed. Serum alkaline phosphatase values were elevated in the fly ash groups in the pre-exposure period, but were comparable in all groups during the exposure period. A definite trend toward lower values was observed in all groups as the study progressed.

At termination of the 18 months of exposure, all animals were sacrificed and necropsies performed. Terminal body weights, organ weights and organ-to-body ratios were obtained. No differences of biological significance were found between exposed and control monkeys in these weights and weight ratios.

Pathological Findings

Samples of brain, pituitary, thyroid, trachea, lung, heart, liver, adrenal, gall bladder, spleen, kidney, stomach, small intestine, large intestine, peribronchial lymph node, urinary bladder, gonad and striated muscle were taken from each animal and fixed in neutral buffered formalin. The lungs were removed in an inflated state and were perfused intratracheally with a volume of formalin equal to the tidal volume of the animal. Haematoxylin and eosin slides were prepared from the lungs, trachea, peribronchial lymph node, heart, liver and kidney. Special whole lobe slides were prepared from each of the seven lobes of the cynamolgus lung.

In the control group, no important alterations were found in the lungs. A slight to moderate degree of perivascular and peribronchiolar pigmentation, probably resulting from lung mite infestation, was seen in some animals. The appearance of the lungs from these animals was within the limits of normal histological variation and no evidence of occult disease was present. A photomicrograph of lung tissue from a control monkey is given in Figure 4.

In the hearts from the control group, two instances of minimal to slight focal lymphocytic myocarditis were noted. The appearance of the livers was well within

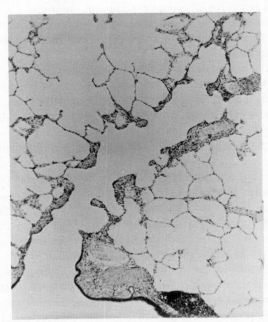

FIGURE 4. Photomicrograph of control monkey lung. Magnification 16×

limits of normal variation; a few instances of slight hepatocyte and Kupffer cell pigmentation were detected. The kidneys exhibited a few spontaneous microscopic alterations well within normal limits.

In the case of the animals exposed to $0 \cdot 16$ mg/m³ of fly ash, the low concentration, phagocytized fly ash was present in the septal macrophages of the alveoli. In many areas, these macrophages had aggregated to form small septal nodules. Fly ash was also present in the peribronchial lymph nodes. Microscopically, the trachea, kidney, heart, and liver were within normal histological limits.

In the group exposed to $0 \cdot 46$ mg/m³ of fly ash, focal areas of fly ash deposition were present, as can be seen in Figure 5. The material was also noted in the alveolar macrophages and the adjacent alveolar walls. The macrophages had aggregated into small nodules in the walls of the alveoli, as shown in Figure 6. A minimal fibrotic response was present in some of these nodules. Fly ash was also present in the peribronchial lymph nodes of these animals. Three instances of minimal interstitial nephritis were seen in this group, but the appearance of the hearts, livers and tracheas was within the limits of histological variation and compared well with that of the control animals.

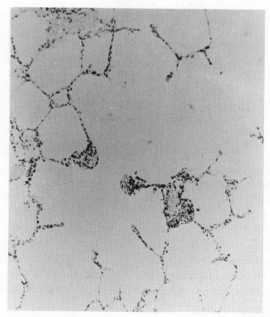

FIGURE 5. Photomicrograph of lung from monkey exposed to $0 \cdot 46$ mg/m³ of fly ash for 78 weeks. Accumulations of fly ash are present in the alveolar walls. Magnification 16 ×

SUMMARY AND CONCLUSIONS

Two groups of 9 cynamolgus monkeys were exposed for over 23 h a day, 7 days a week, for 18 months to $0 \cdot 16$ or $0 \cdot 46$ mg/m³ of fly ash, having a mass median diameter of approximately $2 \cdot 7$ μm; an additional group served as control.

No detrimental effects on growth or survival were observed. Measurements of a variety of parameters characterizing the mechanical properties of the lungs, the ventilation and the diffusing capacity revealed generally only trends to higher or lower values of a given parameter as the experiment progressed. These trends were seen equally in the control and exposed groups. Because of lower mean body weights in the exposed groups as compared with the control at the beginning of the experiment, significant differences in the absolute values of some indices were seen. A variety of haematological and biochemical parameters were examined at scheduled intervals, but no adverse effects associated with the exposures to fly ash were detected.

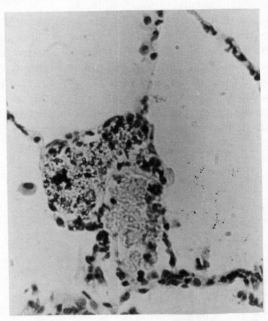

FIGURE 6. Photomicrograph of lung from monkey exposed to 0·46 mg/cu. m. of fly ash for 78 weeks. Fly ash has aggregated in alveolar macrophages and in alveolar walls. A minimal fibrotic response can be seen in some nodules. Magnification 200 ×

No detrimental effects were seen in the lungs microscopically. Focal areas of phagocytized fly ash were present in the alveolar walls. The reaction to this fly ash is similar to that seen with any "nuisance" dust and is not considered to be evidence of permanent pathological alteration. The histopathological evaluation of the lung, trachea, liver, heart, and kidney indicated that there was no deleterious effect of fly ash inhalation on these tissues.

There is little published data on the effects of fly ash on man or other mammals, as a recent review points out (NEGHERBON, 1966). Studies by TOYAMA (1964) with particulate materials bearing a close chemical similarity to fly ash have shown that these induce an increase in airway resistance in some subjects during acute exposure; a synergistic effect between sulphur dioxide and particulates is also claimed by this author. LEWIS et al. (1962), reporting on New Orleans Asthma, stated that a relationship existed between hospital admissions of asthmatic patients and the level of suspended particulates. WEILL et al. (1964) concluded that smoke plume extracts were probably allergenic. On the other hand, WRIGHT & LLOYD (1960) did not find any increase in airway resistance in a small group of normal or emphysematous men subjected to an acute exposure to fly ash, sulphur dioxide and moisture. In contrast to the work of LEWIS *et al.* (1962), Wright and Lloyd used fly ash rather than total urban suspended particulate. Experiments by AMDUR & UNDERHILL (1968) on the inhalation of fly ash by guinea pigs for short duration indicated that fly ash did not produce a bronchoconstricting effect as evaluated by measurements of pulmonary flow resistance. Also, no potentiation of the bronchoconstricting effect of sulphur dioxide occurred with fly ash. In fact, they pointed out than an attenuating effect was observed when fly ash was added to 20 ppm of sulphur dioxide. More recently, AMDUR & UNDERHILL (1970) found that redispersed open hearth dust had no effect on pulmonary flow resistance in guinea pigs up to a concentration of 7 mg/m^3 and did not potentiate the response to sulphur dioxide.

The findings reported in the present study support the conclusion that the inhalation of fly ash essentially continuously over a period of 18 months did not produce impairment in the pulmonary function of cynamolgus monkeys and did not alter the health of these animals. The fly ash concentrations employed, $0 \cdot 16$ and $0 \cdot 46$ mg/m^3, may be compared with levels of suspended particulate as reported for many urban areas. Suspended particulate, of course, contains a variety of constituents in addition to its fly ash component. Levels around $0 \cdot 1$ mg/m^3 are frequently encountered and peaks at about $0 \cdot 5$ mg/m^3 are noted under adverse conditions in dirty cities. Our studies are now being extended to the examination of mixed systems containing fly ash plus sulphur dioxide, fly ash and sulphuric acid mist, and the ternary system containing fly ash, sulphur dioxide and sulphuric acid mist.

Acknowledgement — This study was sponsored by the Air Pollution Research Programme of the Electric Research Council.

REFERENCES

ALARIE, Y., ULRICH, C. E., BUSEY, W. M., SWANN, H. E. & MACFARLAND, H. N. (1970) *Archs envir. Hlth* **21**, 769–777.

AMDUR, M. O. & MEAD, J. (1958). *Am. J. Physiol.* **192**, 364–368.

AMDUR, M. O. & UNDERHILL, D. (1968). *Archs envir. Hlth* **16**, 460–468.

AMDUR, M. O. & UNDERHILL, D. (1970). *J. Air Pollut. Control Ass.* **20**, 31–34.

BATES, D. V. (1962). *Clin. Sci.* **2**, 21–32.

BROWN, R. G. (1963). *Smoothing, forecasting and prediction of discrete time series*, New Jersey, Prentice-Hall.

DENNIS, M. W., DOUGLAS, J. S., CASBY, J. U., STOLWIJK, J. A. J. & BOUHUYS, A. (1969). *J. appl. Physiol.* **26**, 248–252.

FOWLER, W. S. (1948). *Am. J. Physiol.* **154**, 405–410.

FOWLER, W. S. (1949). *J. appl. Physiol.* **2**, 283–299.

FOWLER, W. S.; CORNISH, E. R. & KETY, S. S. (1952). *J. clin. Invest.* **31**, 40–50.

KING, T. K. (1966). *J. appl. Physiol.* **21**, 259–264.

KRUHOFFER, P. (1954). *Acta physiol. scand.* **32**, 106–111.

LEWIS, B. M., LIN, T. H., NOE, R. E. & HAYFORD-WELSING, E. J. (1959). *J. clin. Invest.* **38**, 2073–2083.

LEWIS, R., GILKESON, M. M. & McCALDIN, R. O. (1962). *U.S. Publ. Hlth Rep.* **77**, 947–954.

LONG, J. E. & HATCH, T. F. (1961). *Am. ind. Hyg. Ass. J.* **22**, 6–13.

MEAD, J. (1960). *J. appl. Physiol.* **15**, 325–336.

MEAD, J. & WHITTENBERGER, J. L. (1953). *J. appl. Physiol.* **5**, 779–796.

MURPHY, S. D. & ULRICH, C. E. (1964). *Am. ind. Hyg. Ass. J.* **25**, 28–36.

NEGHERBON, W. O. (1966). Sulfur dioxide, sulfur trioxide, sulfuric acid and fly ash: their nature and their role in air pollution. *Report for Edison Electric Institute, Research Project RP-62, EEI Publ. No. 66–900.*

Ostle, B. (1956). *Statistics in research.* Ames (Iowa), Iowa State College Press.
Peters, R. M. & Stacy, R. W. (1964). *Surgery, St. Louis* 56, 44–52.
Stacy, R. W. & Peters, R. M. (1965). In: *Computers in biomedical research*, Vol. II. *Ed.* R. W. Stacy & B. D. Waxman. New York, Academic Press. pp. 269–288.
Swann, H. E., Brunol, D. & Balchum, O. J. (1965). *Archs envir. Hlth* 10, 24–32.
Toyama, T. (1964). *Archs envir. Hlth* 8, 161–173.
Weill, H., Ziskind, M. M., Derbes, V., Lewis, R., Horton, R. J. M. & McCaldin, R. O. (1964). *Archs envir. Hlth* 8, 184–187.
Wright, G. W. & Lloyd, T. (1960). The pulmonary reaction of normal and emphysematous persons to the inhalation of sulfur dioxide, fly ash and moisture. Syllabus for the third Air Pollution Research Seminar, New Orleans.

DISCUSSION

M. CORN: You discussed the criteria for selection of fly ash exposure concentrations. What were the criteria for selection of the monkey and the associated exposure times, particularly with regard to drawing an analogy between exposure of these animals and lifetime exposures of urban dwellers to polluted air?

Dr. MACFARLAND: The investigator who wishes to learn about the health effects of urban air pollutants discovers that most of the published toxicological work has been performed in acute experiments; unfortunately, this is not the kind of information we want. We would like to know what the long-term effects of pollutants are when they are used at realistically low concentrations and not at high concentrations which do not correspond to the levels encountered in urban air. Some of our experiments have been conducted in guinea pigs exposed essentially 24 hours a day, 7 days a week for one year. This represents a third to a half of the life span of the guinea pig. However, we were more interested in working with a primate because we hope that ultimately the results could be applied to man. In our first series of experiments we exposed cynamolgus monkeys for one and a half years. For this animal, whose life span under laboratory conditions is believed to be 20 to 25 years, this represents only 6 to 7% of its life span. This is not as much as we would like to see. The problem is that experiments of this duration and magnitude are very expensive propositions. The studies on fly ash are part of a programme which costs over \$5 million and over \$500,000 worth of equipment is involved. We have 35 of the large chambers, shown in Figure 1, running 24 hours a day, 7 days a week. In later experiments, we have extended the monkey exposure duration to 2 years. This is really a compromise between what we would like to do and what we can afford to do.

S. F. McCULLAGH: Have you a TLV for occupational exposure to fly ash in the U.S.A.? If not would you care to suggest one in terms of the work you have reported here?

Dr. MACFARLAND: No, there is no TLV for fly ash and I am not aware of any plans to set one. In general, the TLV Committee does not set limits for mixtures of variable composition. The present experiments, because of the type of exposure schedule, might form a basis for estimating an air quality standard, but are not suitable for proposing a TLV.

J. FERIN: You said that there were some aggregates of macrophages and minimal fibrosis. Did that refer to each exposed animal or to the experimental group?

Dr. MACFARLAND: Some aggregates were present in all animals. In other words, we were able to demonstrate the presence of fly ash in the lungs in both groups.

S. E. DEVIR: Were the samples which you have taken examined *per se* as dispersed into the exposure chamber, or were they treated for the various gases which adhere to the fly ash, which is a substance with a very high absorption capacity?

Dr. MACFARLAND: The fly ash was collected downstream from the electrostatic precipitators, just at the base of the stack. It was collected from 4 different power plants. All samples were analysed individually and were found to have approximately the same typical composition. The samples were blended in order to provide a large enough sample for these studies and others. The material was sieved and then the large homogeneous sample was used to fill the canister of the Wright dust feed mechanism.

L. CRALLEY: Spectographic analysis is often too insensitive to determine concentrations of many trace elements at levels under a few hundred parts per million. Such levels of concentration may be biologically important for many trace elements. Other techniques such as activation analysis and atomic absorption may be much more sensitive for analysis of many trace elements at these levels. Have these procedures been used to express precise concentration of trace elements in the fly ash?

Dr. MACFARLAND: No, the fly ash samples were analysed by a consulting laboratory which specializes in this type of material. They were analysed spectrographically and I have simplified the analytical results for the purpose of presentation. I agree that the use of more precise analytical techniques might be useful since there are some elements, arsenic, cadmium, and so on, which are not detected too satisfactorily spectrographically.

FIBROGENICITY OF DUST IN DIFFERENT REGIMENS OF INTRODUCTION INTO THE ORGANISM

R. V. BORISENKOVA and T. A. KOCHETKOVA

Institute of Hygiene named after F. F. Erisman, Moscow, USSR

IN many quarries the observed dust factor is not constant during the working day. Frequently, in some operations, there is only short-term intensive production of dust. Concentrations of dust in open quarries vary greatly, depending on the season of the year, meteorological and geological conditions. To some extent this peculiarity of dust action accounts for the slow development and benign course of occupational dust diseases in quarry workers (BORISENKOVA & CHUMAK, 1966).

The fibrogenic effect of non-organic non-toxic dust of uniform composition depends primarily on the amount of dust entering the lungs (KHUKHRINA, 1956; WRIGHT, 1957). At the same time it can be assumed that the amount of dust entering the organism during inhalation will depend on its concentration and the duration of exposure. Equal amounts of dust (and, consequently, equal effect) can be observed in different ratios of the dust concentration in the air and the duration of its entering the organism. On the other hand, intermissions in exposure to dust are of positive effect as they assist in elimination of dust from the organism.

The significance of intermittent intake of dust in different concentrations was studied in terms of development of fibrosis of lungs experimentally on albino rats during inhalation by them of two kinds of dust in a special chamber: polymetallic ore (containing $36\cdot8\%$ of free silicon dioxide and $32\cdot8\%$ of bound silicon dioxide; $14\cdot7\%$ of Al_2O_3; $3\cdot26\%$ of Fe_2O_3; $2\cdot2\%$ of two-valent iron compounds; $0\cdot84\%$ of CaO; $0\cdot53\%$ of copper; $0\cdot66\%$ sulphur, etc.) and quartz dust (98% of free silicon dioxide as quartz). Concentration and duration of exposure to dust were combined in such a way that one group of animals was exposed to dust inhalation continually every day (50–100 mg/m³ during three hours — group I), another group of animals was exposed to greater concentrations (250–500 mg/m³) at regular intervals of several days (group II) and the third group of animals was exposed to high concentrations 3 hours daily for 25–40 days in two periods with an intermission of 5 months. The product of the dust concentration and the duration of inhalation was the same in all the compared groups, which enabled determination of whether equal amounts of dust produced the same effect.

The animals were sacrificed after 3, 6, 9 and 12 months of dust inhalation and 3 months (in some groups after 6 months) following the cessation of inhalation. The total number of albino rats in the experiment was 255. Only young rats were taken for experiments. During this time all the rats grew and gained weight; variations in weight between the experimental and control rats were no longer observed three months after the cessation of inhalation. The results are described below.

Histological examination of the lungs and regional lymph nodes showed that inhalation of the ore dust resulted chiefly in diffuse proliferative process of silicatosis type. At the same time catarrh of the upper respiratory tract was observed. Increase .of the duration of inhalation in all groups resulted in enhancement of the process. However, there was no massive sclerosis or typical sclerotic nodules in any group of animals even following 12 months' inhalation in spite of great amounts of free and combined silicon dioxide in the dust. The character of the process seems to be dependent on the mixed composition of dust and the presence of aluminium and iron compounds.

Electron microscopy study revealed the changes of intracellular structures during interaction of dust particles and the lung cells. Under the influence of dust particles fine fibres of connective tissue begin to form in the intercellular substance of the connective tissue, which later turn into real connective tissue. The changes were somewhat more marked in the case of constant exposure to dust; it is in this group that the greater number of dust particles was found.

Long term observation of the animals after the cessation of inhalation shows that dust is eliminated from the lungs via lymphatic and bronchial routes. After the cessation of inhalation, in all groups the proliferative process decreases and sclerotic process increases to some extent.

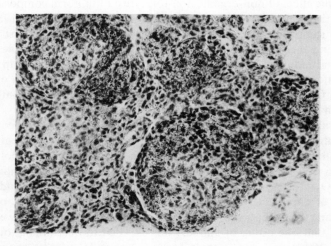

FIGURE 1. Rat's lung after 12 months of ore dust inhalation (group I). Histiocytes prevail in cellular dust nodes. Hematoxiline and eosine colouring. ×225.

Comparison of different experimental groups in which the animals were exposed to different dust concentrations and durations, but to equal amounts of dust indicates that the character of the effect is almost identical in all cases. However, there are some differences in the intensity of the process. Thus, the animals exposed to inhalation of lower dust concentration but for longer time (group I) had a somewhat more marked interalveolar process (Figure 1).

On the other hand, exposure to higher concentrations but for a shorter time resulted in a more pronounced change in the upper respiratory tract (Figure 2). Quart dust caused the development of nodular or mixed (nodular and diffuse-sclerotic) forms of silicosis. Within a short period of observation different groups varied insignificantly, but during the longer observation period the differences grew. By the end of the experiment the animals of group I appeared to have in the lungs large and partly merged silicotic nodules with hyalinization of some of them. (Figure 3). The experimental

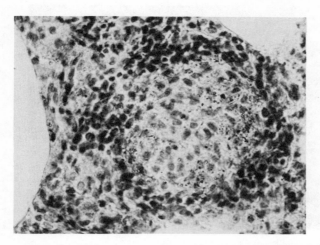

FIGURE 2. Rat's lung after 12 months of ore dust inhalation (group II). Histiocytes, lymphoid cells and dust phagocytes prevail in cellular dust nodes. ×450.

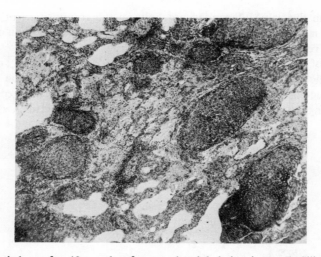

FIGURE 3. Rat's lung after 12 months of quartz dust inhalation (group I). Silicotic nodules of different size and moderately manifested thickening of interalveolar septa. Hematoxiline and eozine colouring. ×51.

animals of group II were found to have moderately manifested thickening of interalveolar septa due to proliferation of cellular elements and partial sclerosis accompanied by the nodular process (Figure 4). The animals of group III were found to have silicotic nodules of different size without marked hyalinosis. All the experimental animals exposed to dust inhalation were shown to have an increase of the lung weight and the weight of paratracheal bifurcation lymph nodes, an increase in total lipid content and oxyproline content. All these values characterize the degrees of fibrosis (RIVERS & MORRIS, 1958; SLUTSKY & SHELEKETINA, 1959; KHVAPIL, 1960; KATSNELSON *et al.*, 1964).

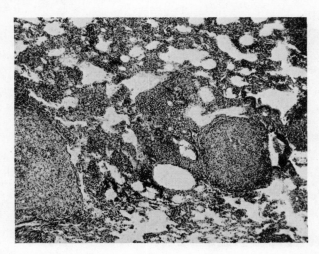

FIGURE 4. Rat's lung after 12 months of quartz (group II). Silicotic nodules and manifested thickening of interalveolar septa. Hematoxiline and eozine colouring. ×51.

An increase in the values depended not only on the composition of the effecting dust (naturally more marked in exposure to quartz dust, rather than mixed dust), but also on the regimen of inhalation.

The animals of groups I and II exposed to dust inhalation constantly or with short intermissions showed an even increase of all the values and on the cessation of inhalation an increase was less manifest. The animals of group III exposed to dust inhalation during two periods with a long intermission in between demonstrated

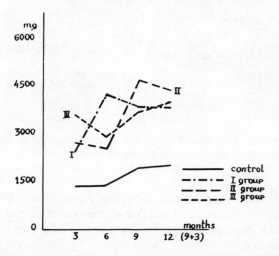

FIGURE 5. Change of the weight of the lungs of the animals exposed to inhalation of quartz dust.

uneven increases of all the values during the period of massive dust entering the organism (Figures 5, 6, 7, 8 and 9). In the intermissions all the values decrease and on subsequent inhalation increase again.

On the cessation of inhalation and by the end of the observation period, the weights of the lungs and lymph nodes, and the contents of lipids, oxyproline and dust become equalized in all the groups of experimental animals exposed to inhalation of dust of the same composition, and the differences between the groups appear to be statistically unreliable. The study has shown that in terms of the fibrogenic effect of dust, the product of its concentration and the duration of inhalation is of primary importance.

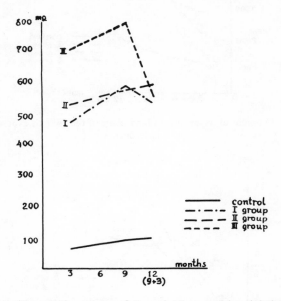

FIGURE 6. Weight of lymphatic nodules of the animals exposed to inhalation of quartz dust.

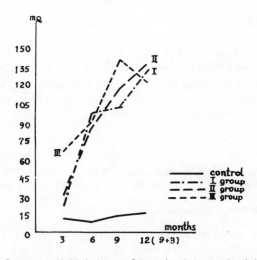

FIGURE 7. Changes of summary lipids in lungs of the animals exposed to inhalation of quartz dust.

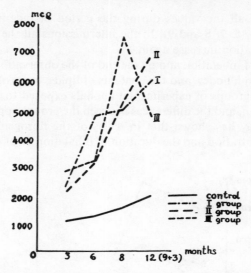

FIGURE 8. Change of content of oxyproline in lung tissue of the animals exposed to inhalation of quartz dust.

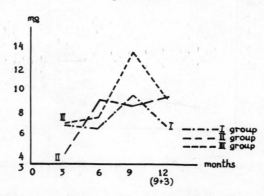

FIGURE 9. Content of dust in lungs of the animals exposed to inhalation of quartz dust.

Intermissions in inhalation are of positive effect as they assist in elimination of dust and in lessening of the process to some extent. The data obtained are of value for fixing the standards of exposure to dust in the condition of its intermittent action and for determination of the regimen of the dust exposure as one of the factors in prophylaxis of pneumoconiosis.

REFERENCES

Borisenkova, R. V. & Chumak, K. I. (1966). *Labour Hyg. prof. Dis.* **5**, 3–8.

Katsnelson, B. A., Velichkovsky, B. T. & Babushkina, L. G. (1964). *Bull. exp. Biol. Med.* **57**, 48–54.

Khukhrina, E. V. (1956). *Hyg. Sanitation* **1**, 31–38.

Khvapil, M. (1960). *Labour Hyg. prof. Dis.* **7**.

Rivers, D. & Morris, T. D. (1958). *Staublungenerkrankungen.* **3**, 181–189.

Slutsky, L. I. & Sheleketina, I. I. (1959). *Probl. Med. Chem.* **5**, 466–468.

Wright, B. M. (1957). *Br. J. ind. Med.* **14**, 219–228.

DISCUSSION

J. FERIN: Did you determine the amount of dust retained in the lungs? If so, how did you perform the analysis, particularly in the experiments with the polymetallic ore?

Madame BORISENKOVA: We determined the amount of dust retained in the organism, in the three groups; the amount at the end of the set period of observation (from three to six months after cessation of inhalation) was roughly the same in all the series. We determined the total content of dust in the lungs by ashing, after sacrifice.

W. H. WALTON: What was the aerodynamic size of the dust? Was it the same for the two kinds of dust and for the different concentrations?

MADAME BORISENKOVA: The dispersity for all series was maintained at the same level, from 85 to 90% of the particles in all groups were smaller than 5 μm. All conditions were the same, apart from the concentration and the period of inhalation.

THE RELATIONSHIP BETWEEN DURATION OF DUST INHALATION OF A COAL-QUARTZ MIXTURE AND DUST RETENTION, LUNG FUNCTION AND PATHOLOGY ON RATS

W. WELLER

*Aus der Medizinischen Abteilung des Silikose-Forschungsinstituts der
Bergbau-Berufsgenossenschaft, Bochum, W. Germany*

Summary — In a long-term inhalation test, rats were exposed to a mixture of coal-quartz dust (60% coal, 40% quartz in the original dust) at a concentration of 45 mg/m³ < 10 μm for 5 hours daily, 5 days per week, for 18 months. Some of the animals were retained for a further four months without exposure.

The coal, ash and quartz contents of the lungs and the pulmonary lymph nodes were determined after 9, 18 and 22 months. Measurements were made of the minute volume, oxygen-consumption, intrapleural pressure, lung volume, compliance, and pressures within the right ventricle. Histological preparations of the lungs and lymph nodules were also made.

The histological investigation showed that the lung changes were not very marked, despite the high quartz content of the lung dust.

Though numerous mixed dust granulomata were found in the lungs, the respiratory and circulatory functions were only slightly affected. These findings are in agreement with recent investigations on man.

The dust-content of the lungs and pulmonary lymph-nodes indicated that dust deposition within the lungs occurs linearly with exposure time. Dust elimination from the lung after exposure was not very marked. The lympho-tropism of quartz was not extensive during inhalation, but became evident 4 months after the end of dust-inhalation.

INTRODUCTION

FOR diverse reasons, animal experiments on silicosis are most often carried out with either intraperitoneal or intratracheal applications of the test dusts. However inhalation tests correspond more closely to the real conditions than these other forms of test. Furthermore, pure quartz is often used as a test dust, but for many problems it would be better to use real mine dusts or at least adequately mixed dusts. In the present investigation we report on an inhalation study with a coal-quartz mixture in rats. We were especially interested in the relations between the duration of dust-exposure, dust-retention, pathology and measurements of lung function.

METHODOLOGY

In a long-term inhalation study running for 22 months in all, 200 conventional Sprague-Dawley rats were exposed to a coal-quartz mixture, containing 60% of finely ground meagre coal and 40% of Dörentrup quartz No. 12 in the original dust, for five hours daily on five days per week for 18 months. The fine dust concentration was 45 mg/m³ < 10 μm and the particle number concentration about 14000/ml. The quartz fraction in the fine dust was 30% to 35%. Some of the animals were left for 4 more months without further dust-exposure. After experimental times of 9, 18 and 22 months respectively, the coal, ash and quartz contents of lungs and pulmonary lymph-nodes were determined. In order to study respiration and circulation, measurements were made of the respiratory minute volume, oxygen-consumption, pleural pressure, lung volume, CO-diffusion, compliance and the pressures in the right ventricle. The measurements of respiratory frequency, respiratory depth and oxygen-consumption were made by means of a low inertia spirometer, independent of frequency in this breathing range, constructed in our Institute.

Measurement of CO-diffusion was done in a closed system with air-circulation. The fall in concentration of equal amounts of CO, each time within 3 min, was registered by means of a rapid-indicating infrared absorption device. However, the results are rather a measure of alveolar ventilation than of true diffusion differences. Pleural pressure was measured by direct puncture of the anaesthetized animal, and the pressure in the right ventricle after opening the thorax, also by direct puncture. The lung volume was determined by means of Archimedes' principle. Compliance was determined in the closed thorax by slow intratracheal injection of 5 ml air, directly following the sacrifice of an animal. All pressures were recorded by Statham transducers P 23 Db. Histological preparations of lungs and pulmonary lymph-nodes were also made.

As controls, 200 rats of the same stock, breed and age were used, living under the same conditions of maintenance, etc.

RESULTS

General Data

Animal weight increased uniformly during the experimental period. There were no appreciable differences between the dust-exposed and the control groups. The spontaneous death rate increased in both groups with longer duration of the experiment. Up to the end of the dust exposure time, the average spontaneous death rate was 0·79% per month, and was about 50% higher in the dust-exposed rats than in the controls.

Pathology

Wet and dry weights of lungs and pulmonary lymph-nodes of test groups differed markedly from each other with longer experimental time. Values for the dust exposed group were much higher (Table I).

The histological examination of the lungs of the dust-exposed animals showed that, after 22 months, round dust granulomata had formed, relatively uniformly distributed throughout the whole lungs. The granulomata were often perivascularly situated. In part, a marked perifocal emphysema had formed (Figure 1). The granulomata were well organized, cells and dust particles were uniformly distributed within them. The granulomata were traversed by a not very dense network of reticular and, sporadically,

TABLE I. WET AND DRY WEIGHTS OF LUNGS AND PULMONARY LYMPH-NODES OF RATS OF THE DUST EXPOSED GROUP AND OF CONTROLS IN RELATION TO EXPERIMENTAL TIME. AVERAGE VALUE OF 20 ANIMALS PER EXAMINATION DATE AND TEST GROUP

		Lungs		Pulmonary lymph-nodes	
		Dust exposed group	Control group	Dust exposed group	Control group
Wet weight (g)	I	2·37	1·94	0·066	0·025
	II	2·95	2·32	0·220	0·060
	III	3·14	2·69	0·354	0·085
Dry weight (mg)	I	320	250	15·2	—
	II	440	340	40·0	7·1
	III	500	310	70·7	14·1

I = 9 months of dust exposure (900 h of dusting)
II = 18 months of dust exposure (1800 h of dusting)
III = 4 months after the end of dust exposure (22 months of experimental time)

also collagenous fibres (Figure 2). According to the classification of KING *et al*, (1953), the grade of fibrosis was I to II. The changes to be observed in the lymph-nodes resembled those in the lungs. The content of collagenous fibres was, in general, slightly larger (Figure 3). As was seen from examination by polarized microscope, no disintegration of coal and quartz particles occurred within the lymph-nodes.

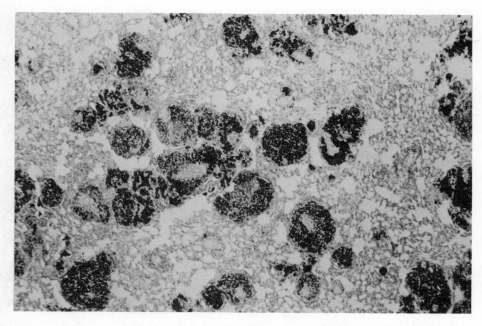

FIGURE 1. Group of mixed granulomas, some of them perivascularly arranged. In the periphery of the granulomas a perifocal emphysema is partly to be observed. Rat lung, 22 months of experimental time (1800 h of dusting), HE-coloration. Magnification ×12½.

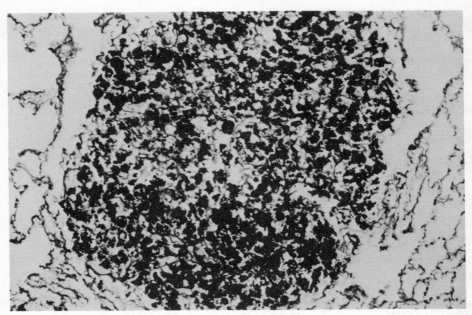

FIGURE 2. Typical mixed dust granuloma after 22 months of experimental time (1800 h of dusting). Representation of the reticular and collagenous fibres. In the whole very scarce fibre formation. Relatively uniform distribution of dust particles within the granuloma. Rat lung, Gomörri-silver impregnation. Magnification ×80.

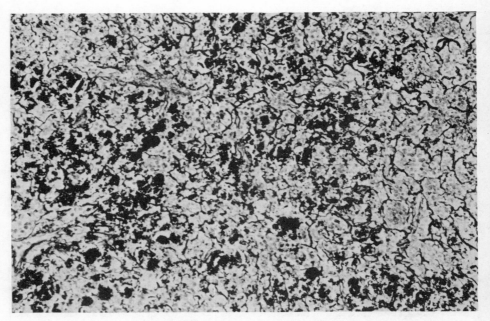

FIGURE 3. Dust incorporation and fibre formation in a pulmonary lymph-node after an experimental time of 22 months (1800 h of dusting). Representation of reticular and collagenous fibres. Only moderate fibre formation. Rat, paratracheal lymph-nodes, Gomörri-silver impregnation. Magnification ×80.

Lung Function

The results of the respiratory and circulatory function tests corresponded essentially to the values listed in Table II for all three examinations after an experimental time of 18 months. It is to be concluded from them that there were differences in the measured parameters between the dust exposed group and the controls, indicating an impairment of respiratory and circulatory functions in the dust exposed rats. The changes were in the same direction at all experimentation times. These differences were not, however, significant, except for the compliance values. These were lower by about 15% in dust exposed animals after 18 months and about 23% after 22 months, than the values found for control groups.

TABLE II. CHANGES IN THE VALUES OF RESPIRATORY AND CIRCULATORY FUNCTION IN THE DUST EXPOSED GROUPS COMPARED WITH CONTROLS. VALUES OF THE CONTROL GROUP = 100%. MEASUREMENTS AFTER 18 MONTHS OF EXPOSURE TIME. AVERAGE VALUES FOR 20 RATS

Measured value	Deviation in %
Lung volume	+12%
Respiratory frequency	+10%
Respiratory depth	+ 1%
Respiratory minute volume	+18%
Pleural pressure (Δp)	+ 6%
Compliance	−15%
CO-diffusion	−14%
O_2-consumption	+ 1%
Blood pressure, right ventricle	+ 3%

Dust Retention

Table III gives the results for dust recovery. Rats were sacrificed three days after the last dust exposure, so that the dust-elimination by bronchial clearance would not falsify the results. At first it is seen that the total dust content of the lungs increased linearly with dust exposure (Table IIIa). Percentage quartz contents did not increase with longer experimental time, i.e. no quartz enrichment took place in the lungs. In contrast to this, the percentage ash fraction showed a particularly marked increase. Elimination in the 4 months after the end of dust exposure was only 9% of the total amount of dust. The quartz content played a special part in this, decreasing about 15% during this time. 55% of it was transported into the mediastinal lymph-nodes. Total dust retention after 18 months exposure amounted to 5·5% of the inhaled dust, based on an alveolar ventilation of 6 liters per hour for the rat.

The results of dust recovery from the pulmonary lymph-nodes (Table IIIb) showed that the percentage coal and quartz fractions were similar to the values found in the lungs. With increasing time from 900 h to 1800 h of exposure, the coal content of the pulmonary lymph-nodes increased about 218% and the quartz content by about 255%. Lymphotropism of quartz was not very marked up to this time. After the end of dust exposure there was a marked aggregation of quartz within the lymph-nodes. The percentage quartz content increased from 30·5% to 40·3% while the quartz content of the lungs decreased from 25·1% to 23·4%. Up to an exposure time of

900 h, ash retention was greater, its fraction in the lymph-node at that time was 19·5%; about twice as much as that in the lungs.

With longer exposure time, the percentage deposition of the dust within the pulmonary lymph-nodes increased from 8% to 15·4% in relation to the dust in the lung (Table IIIc). The percentage quartz increase was particularly marked, from 7·5% to 26·5%.

TABLE III. LIST OF THE RESULTS OF DUST RECOVERY FROM LUNGS AND PULMONARY LYMPH-NODES RELATED TO EXPERIMENTAL TIME. AVERAGE VALUES OF 20 LUNGS AND PULMONARY LYMPH-NODES RESPECTIVELY PER EXAMINATION DATE. THE ASH CONTENT CONSISTS OF CLAY MINERALS, PARTICULARLY ILLITE

Table IIIa. Dust Content of Lungs

| | mg | | | | % | | |
	Total dust	Coal	Ash	Quartz	Coal	Ash	Quartz
I	13·5	8·6	1·3	3·6	63·7	9·6	26·7
II	26·7	15·6	4·4	6·7	58·4	16·5	25·1
III	24·3	14·2	4·5	5·7	58·2	18·4	23·4

Table IIIb. Dust Content of Pulmonary Lymph-Nodes

| | mg | | | | % | | |
	Total dust	Coal	Ash	Quartz	Coal	Ash	Quartz
I	1·08	0·60	0·21	0·27	55·6	19·5	25·0
II	3·15	1·91	0·28	0·96	60·6	9·0	30·5
III	3·75	1·86	0·38	1·51	49·6	10·1	40·3

Table IIIc. Percentage of Pulmonary Lymph-Node Dust Compared with Lung Dust

	Total dust	Coal	Ash	Quartz
I	8%	7%	16·2%	7·5%
II	12·3%	12·3%	6·4%	14·3%
III	15·0%	13·1%	8·5%	26·5%

I = 9 months of dust exposure (900 h of dusting)
II = 18 months of dust exposure (1800 h of dusting)
III = 4 months after the end of dust exposure (22 months of experimental time)

DISCUSSION

The findings of the long-term inhalation test described here are similar to those of some other long-term inhalation tests carried out previously. The recently observed findings in a long-term inhalation test with rhesus monkeys also agree with our results.

The pathological results in our experiment showed very slight silicotic changes, in spite of the very high quartz content, even after a dust exposure of 18 months and an experimental time of 22 months respectively. The quartz portion in the fine dust corresponds to a cóncentration of about 15 mg/m³. In our experiment a quartz concentration of more than 1 g of SiO_2/100 g of the dry weight of lungs was reached, even after an experimental time of 9 months. In man, exposure to this concentration causes severe silicosis within 10 years (EINBRODT & KLOSTERKÖTTER, 1965; SCHLIPKÖTER, 1969). There is no doubt that in animal experiments pure quartz inhalation with concentrations of 10–30 mg/m³ produces very clear silicotic changes in a short time (BECK, 1961; KLOSTERKÖTTER & GONO, 1969; SCHLIPKÖTER & BROCKHAUS, 1965). In the case of artificially mixed dusts as used in our test, it has been stressed again and again that even low admixtures of quartz of 3% are able to change considerably the tissue reaction to an inert dust in the sense of a silicotic reaction (KLOSTERKÖTTER, 1967; SCHLIPKÖTER, 1958, 1969). Recently, this general statement has been restricted a little on account of results of investigations carried out on pure mine dusts (HOER et al., 1969; ROBOCK & KLOSTERKÖTTER, 1969; SCHLIPKÖTER, 1969). NAGELSCHMIDT (1958) had emphasized that the etiological importance of a few percent of quartz mixed with coal, mica and kaolin had not yet been sufficiently investigated. It is assumed that decomposition processes in the artificially mixed dusts are responsible for the effect of small quartz fractions becoming effective within a few months (HOER et al, 1969; SCHLIPKÖTER, 1958, 1969). Such a decomposition has not been observed in our experiments, neither in the lungs nor in the lymph-nodes, even after an experimental time of 22 months.

Our long-term inhalation tests have shown that there are differences from the results of intraperitoneal and intratracheal tests, and that the limit value, at which the quartz portion in artificially mixed dusts will produce a clear silicotic reaction during an inhalation test, has still to be explored further.

Investigation of respiratory and circulatory function did not show any noticeable differences between the dust-exposed animals and the controls. In spite of numerous dust granulomata, and some perifocal emphysema, the functional integrity of the lungs was not significantly disturbed. This observation agrees with the results of examinations of miners suffering from silicosis as long as no PMF changes (progressive massive fibrosis) of grade (B) and (C) are present (REICHEL et al., 1969; ULMER, 1967). In contrast, an increase of the pressure in the right ventricle of more than 100% could be recorded 6 months after intratracheal injection of 30 mg of quartz. Thus, long-term inhalation tests give without doubt, a better and perhaps the only realistic insight into the functional effects of dust retention.

The values of dust recovery show a total dust retention of 5·5% assuming an alveolar ventilation of 6 l/h for the rat. This is in good agreement with the results of FRIEDBERG & POLLEY (1967), that the retention is dependent on concentration. SCHLIPKÖTER (1969) has also reported the same finding in man. There is also a good agreement with the total dust distribution between the pulmonary lymph-nodes and the lungs found in man (EINBRODT et al., 1963).

The most important finding of the dust recovery results is that a linear dust retention must be assumed. Up to now it has been assumed, based on the findings from animal experiments in short-term tests as well as from dust recovery out of human lungs, that dust retention becomes less with increasing dust exposure (EINBRODT, 1965; KLOSTERKÖTTER & EINBRODT, 1965; STÖBER et al., 1967; KLOSTERKÖTTER, 1963). But recent work suggests a linear retention (HOER, 1967). Above all, the flattened retention curve assumed for man (EINBRODT, 1965), becomes linear if the cases with longer periods of clearance are excluded.

A further important point about dust recovery was that quartz enrichment compared to the coal portion, was not so marked in pulmonary lymph-nodes during the 18 months period of exposure, but could only be observed (and then very clearly), in the relatively late follow-up 4 months. Here also there seem to be differences from the results of short term experiments (KLOSTERKÖTTER, 1963, 1967; SCHLIPKÖTER, 1969). As cytotoxicity is thought to be responsible for the "lymphotropism" of quartz (KLOSTERKÖTTER, 1963; SCHLIPKÖTER, 1969), and cytotoxicity of quartz is also the basis of silicotic changes, the question arises as to the importance of cytotoxicity and the more recent etiological-pathogenetic notions on the formation of silicotic changes in the lungs and pulmonary lymph-nodes during long-term inhalation tests. It is true that the quartz portion increases up to 40% within the pulmonary lymph-nodes after the end of inhalation but without producing a corresponding morphological change.

REFERENCES

BECK, E. G. (1961). Unters. Geb. Staub- u. Silikosebekämpfung Steinkohlenbergbau (3), 131–146.

EINBRODT, H. J. (1965). Beitr. Silikoseforsch. 87, 1–112.

EINBRODT, H. J. & KLOSTERKÖTTER, W. (1965). Ergebn. Unters. Geb. Staub- u. Silikosebekämpfung Steinkohlenbergbau 5, 97–99.

EINBRODT, H. J., METZE, H. & KELTSCH, H. J. (1963). Grundfragen Silikoseforsch. 5, 437–446.

FRIEDBERG, K. D. & POLLEY, H. (1967). Fortschr. Staublungenforsch. 2, 551–553.

HOER, P. W. (1967). Ergebn. Unters. Geb. Staub- u. Silikosebekämpfung Steinkohlenbergbau 6, 83–89.

HOER, P. W., LAUFHÜTTE, D. W. & LEITERITZ, H. (1969). Ergebn. Unters. Geb. Staub- u. Silikosebekämpfung Steinkohlenbergbau 7, 51–55.

KING, E. J., MOHANTY, G. P., HARRISON, C. V. & NAGELSCHMIDT, G. (1953). A.M.A. Archs ind. Hyg. 7, 455–477.

KLOSTERKÖTTER, W. (1958). ForschBer. Wirt. u. VerkMinist. NRhein-Westf. 490, 49–61.

KLOSTERKÖTTER, W. (1963). Grundfragen Silikoseforsch. 5, 417–463.

KLOSTERKÖTTER, W. (1967). Ergebn. Unters. Geb. Staub- u. Silikosebekämpfung Steinkohlenbergbau 6, 69–71.

KLOSTERKÖTTER, W. & GONO, F. (1969). Ergebn. Unters. Geb. Staub- u. Silikosebekämpfung Steinkohlenbergbau 7, 159–164.

KLOSTERKÖTTER, W. & EINBRODT, H. J. (1965). Ergebn. Unters. Geb. Staub- u. Silikosebekämpfung Steinkohlenbergbau 5, 87–89.

NAGELSCHMIDT, G. (1958). Staublungenerkrankungen 3, 329–336.

REICHEL, G., ULMER, W. T., BUCKUP, H., STEMPEL, G. & WERNER, U. (1969). Dt. med. Wschr. 94, 2375–2380.

ROBOCK, K. & KLOSTERKÖTTER, W. (1969). Ergebn. Unters. Geb. Staub- u. Silikosebekämpfung Steinkohlenbergbau 7, 61–62.

SCHLIPKÖTER, H. W. (1958). Staublungenerkrankungen 3, 312–326.

SCHLIPKÖTER, H. W. (1969). Arbeitsgemeinschaft Forsch. Landes NRhein-Westf., H. 197, 39–82.

SCHLIPKÖTER, H. W. & BROCKHAUS, A. (1965). Ergebn. Unters. Geb. Staub- u. Silikosebekämpfung Steinkohlenbergbau 5, 79–85.

STÖBER, W., EINBRODT, H. J. & KLOSTERKÖTTER, W. (1967). In: Inhaled particles and vapours II. Ed. C. N. Davies. Oxford, Pergamon Press, pp. 409–418.

ULMER, W. T. (1967). Fortschr. Staublungenforsch. 2, 635–653.

DISCUSSION

H.-W. SCHLIPKÖTER: What type of coal was used in your inhalation experiments? The apparently strong inhibitory effect seems to be in contrast to the work reported by Prof. Klosterkötter. Our own animal experiments have shown that bituminous coal inhibits the fibrotic reaction of quartz more strongly than does anthracite.

Dr. WELLER: We used a high rank coal with an ash content of about 5% and with a quartz content lower than 0·2%. 98% of the coal particles were <10 μm.

J. C. MARTIN: What in your opinion is the role of small quantities of quartz in the genesis of pneumoconiotic lesions? We too have noticed in animals a diminution of the toxicity of quartz while the latter is combined with coal. One can however observe the appearance of delayed lesions 15–18 months after the end of the exposure to dust.

Dr. WELLER: In spite of the high quartz fraction we only have slight reactions. Certainly time plays an important part here, though we did not see any sign of separation between coal and quartz up to an experimental time of 22 months. This is a long time for inhalation experiments. On the other hand, we heard from Dr. Klosterkötter that 1 mg/m³ of pure quartz would cause significant silicotic lesions after one year of exposure.

At the moment we do not know anything about the quartz percentage in coal-quartz mixed dusts which is necessary to produce a clear silicotic reaction.

Also we have to remember, as Dr. Nagelschmidt said 12 years ago and as found from recent investigations in man, that the etiological importance of a few percent quartz mixed with coal, mica and kaolin is unknown.

J. C. GILSON: Could you tell us more about the size distribution of the dusts and the source of the quartz. Do you know if the quartz is active when used alone?

Dr. WELLER: The mean size of our quartz was two to three μm, the same applies to the coal.

However, the distribution of quartz particles on the 10 μm side was slightly shifted. In the inhalation experiments, the dust was pre-sedimented so that only particles smaller than 10 μm were used.

We used Dörentrup quartz No. 12 for the inhalation experiment. This was also used for intraperitoneal tests, for a period of six months, and it caused severe silicosis.

P. GROSS: It seems to me that the inhibition of the histological reactions to quartz by a number of different substances has been well recognized. It occurs when quartz particles are mixed with iron. Earlier British investigators commented on the inhibitory qualities of coal on quartz. Then we had the story of aluminium dust inhibiting quartz. In experiments on the inhibitory abilities of iron on quartz, I found, about six months ago, that the inhibition was a short term one. A similar limited inhibition has been demonstrated for aluminium. I would be rather unhappy if present results were to be interpreted as showing a permanent inhibitory effect on the quartz. Perhaps, if the duration of the experiment were allowed to go on a little longer, the quartz would have escaped the inhibitory effect of the coal.

Dr. WELLER: Compared with other experiments, we have made observations for quite a long time, for a total of 22 months experimental duration. But it cannot be excluded that after several years the picture might change.

K. ROBOCK: Is it possible that the quartz used, DQ12, has different properties to the quartzes DQ12 used in other institutes, for instance by different pretreatments?

Dr. WELLER: I would agree that it is possible, but we used the same quartz here for inhalation and also for intraperitoneal injections. We used untreated Dörentrup quartz No. 12. Three months after intraperitoneal injections of this quartz there was a clear granuloma silicosis, and after six months we saw a hyaline fibrosis. This shows how damaging the quartz used in our inhalation study can be.

LUNG FUNCTION STUDIES IN EXPERIMENTAL SILICOSIS WITH A RADIOSPIROMETRIC TECHNIQUE AND SOME OBSERVATIONS ON A TECHNIQUE FOR INDUCING UNILATERAL SILICOSIS
A PRELIMINARY REPORT

Knut Dale

Work Research Institutes, Oslo, Norway

Abstract — Using an injection technique, it proved possible to deposit a known amount of quartz dust in the right lung of rabbits whilst the left lung remained free from particles.

It was shown that, using the animal's left lung as control, the wet weight of the lung provided a good quantitative measure of the fibrogenetic effect of quartz. It appeared that 50–100 mg of quartz caused no increase in the absolute collagen content of the lung after 6 months.

A radiospirometric technique for lung function studies is described. Using this, no demonstrable reduction of perfusion or ventilation in the right lung compared with the left was found 6 months after injection of 150 mg of quartz in the right lung. The silicosis in the rabbit's right lung was demonstrated radiographically on inflated lung preparations and histologically.

INTRODUCTION

IN what manner silicosis affects lung function is a problem that has not been satisfactorily solved. Not infrequently there is a disparity between the roentgenogram and the functional findings, a fact which demonstrates the complexity of the gas exchange in the silicotic-fibrotic tissue. Numerous lung function studies on humans with silicosis, aimed at solving this problem, have been reported. However, although the literature abounds in such investigations, lung function studies in experimental silicosis are scanty. To my knowledge, only VERSTRAETEN *et al.* (1966), have undertaken such experimental investigations, in the form of compliance studies on rats.*

A main reason why the problem of silicosis has not been attacked by more investigators from this angle is probably that the available methods for lung function studies on small animals have not been well suited for this purpose. Methods for determining the minute volume of ventilation, functional residual capacity, pulmonary compliance and pulmonary flow resistance in small animals have been described by, among others, DAVIDSON *et al.* (1966). These methods are based on recordings of a number of

---

* A preliminary report on function tests in experimental silicosis has been published by MOSINGER *et al.* (1961), but the results of the study are not specified.

347

separate data, and seem technically complicated. In my opinion it will be difficult to adapt these time-consuming procedures to studies on silicosis since these require a relatively large number of animals. In addition, a method permitting both ventilation and perfusion studies is preferable. For the purpose of studying the pathophysiology of silicosis experimentally, I have worked out a radiospirometric technique with which it is possible to measure the ventilation and the perfusion separately for each lung in rabbits (DALE, 1967, 1970). In order to use this method for lung function studies in induced silicosis, the silicotic changes have to be present in only one of the animal's lungs. I shall first outline the technique employed for inducing unilateral silicosis in rabbits and then describe the radiospirometric technique and the preliminary results I have obtained by applying this to animals with unilateral silicosis. It is pointed out that this is a preliminary report and that methods and results will be described in detail in *Scandinavian Journal of Respiratory Diseases*.

METHODS

Experimental Unilateral Silicosis

My starting point for inducing unilateral silicosis was to try to modify KETTLE & HILTON's (1932) method in such a manner as to permit injection of a suspension of quartz particles in one of the lungs of the experimental animals. In Nembutal-anesthetized rabbits weighing about 3 kg, a rubber catheter — Figure 1 (1) — was

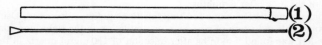

FIGURE 1. (1) Rubber catheter. (2) Nylon tube with record-fitting for syringe.

introduced, through a tracheostomy opening, to the right main bronchus. At one end the rubber catheter was thickened by a steel sphere fitting closely to the right main bronchus and preventing the dust suspension from passing from the right to the left lung. A protuberance on the steel sphere prevented the catheter from slipping too far down, maintaining it at a point where the outward opening was just above the branching off of the upper lobe bronchus. A thin nylon catheter — Figure 1 (2) — was brought down through the rubber catheter, their ends butt to butt. With the rabbit in supine position, quartz dust of the type "P9" suspended in physiological saline was injected through the nylon catheter in a period of 5–10 s. The nylon catheter was then removed and the rabbit could ventilate the right lung via the rubber catheter through the tracheostomy opening. After 2–3 min the rubber catheter was removed and the tracheostomy opening closed.

To find how much dust was retained in the right and the left lung respectively, rabbits were divided into two groups and injected with dust using the described method. The animals in the first group were injected with 50 mg quartz dust of the type "P9"* suspended in 2 ml physiological saline, whereas the animals in the other group were injected with 2 ml of a suspension containing 100 mg quartz dust of the

---

* Mean diameter of the dust particles was $1 \cdot 2\ \mu$m. A detailed description of the particle fraction "P9" has been given by GLÖMME (1967).

type "P9". Rabbits from both groups were killed and examined after 1 week and 6 months respectively, and the silica content in the various parts of the lung was determined using a method described by KING *et al.* (1955) and modified by GLÖMME (1967). Silica analyses of samples from each of the four lung lobes on the right side and from the left lung were carried out. The results are indicated in Figure 2. The quartz

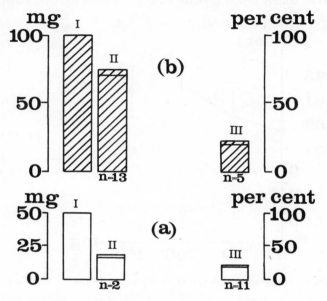

FIGURE 2. Mean silica content and percent retention of silica in the right lung 1 week (cols. II) and 6 months (cols. III) following injection of (a) 50 mg and (b) 100 mg of quartz "P9" into the right main bronchus. Below the lines in cols. II and III is indicated the amount of quartz retained in the two inferior right lung lobes.

n = number of animals.

retention after 1 week tallies well with the findings of other authors, e.g. GLÖMME (1967), in rats. In both groups only about 25% of the total amount administered was retained in the lung after 6 months. This shows that the dust elimination, within certain limits, is independent of the total amount administered. The amount of dust eliminated from the lung during the interval 1 week to 6 months, about 40% of the total amount deposited, is considerably higher than that found by, e.g. GLÖMME (1967) in rats where the elimination during the same period was no more than 10–20%. This may be due to differences in lung clearance between the two species.

Because the dust suspension was injected in caudal direction, the two inferior lobes on the right side received the bulk of the dust particles (Figure 2). The quartz content in the left lung was found to be no higher than in normal control animals.

GLÖMME (1967) found that the weight of the lung constitutes as sensitive an indicator of tissue changes in silicosis as hydroxyproline determination. GÖTHE *et al.* (1968) found the weight of the lung to be a more sensitive indicator of pulmonary tissue changes than hydroxyproline determination in rats submitted to combined treatment with quartz and BCG.

In ordinary experimental silicosis one has been dependent on control animals. This has the practical consequence that weight dissimilarities in the animals — and hence in the lungs — may complicate the interpretation of lung weight and hydroxyproline content. By comparing pneumoconiotic and healthy lungs from the same animal, this source of error is eliminated. Figure 3 shows percentage wet weight of the right lung relative to the total (right + left) lung weight. As is seen, there is very little scatter in normal animals of widely differing body weight. Figure 3 likewise shows the relative

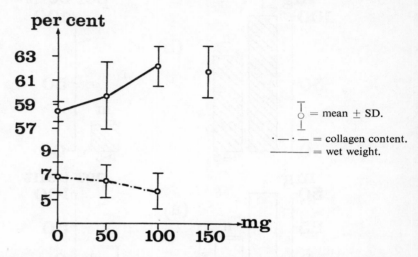

FIGURE 3. Collagen content and wet weight of the right lung 6 months after injection of different amounts of quartz.
The collagen content in the right lung is indicated in per cent of the lung's dry weight. As control material (on the ordinate) one used the normal non-treated left lung of the same animal.
The wet weight of the right lung is indicated in per cent of the total (right + left) lung wet weight. As control material (on the ordinate) one used lungs from 11 normal animals (mean right lung 58% of the total lung weight ± SD 0·70). Some of the lung preparations from the animals injected with 150 mg of quartz were not weighed until about one hour after autopsy, causing a certain inaccuracy for this group.

weight increase of the right lung 6 months after injection of 50 and 100 mg of quartz respectively. A statistically significant increase of the wet weight is found in the animals injected with 50 mg of quartz. A further considerable increase occurred in the group injected with 100 mg of quartz.

The results of collagen determinations (NEUMAN & LOGAN, 1950) are given in Figures 3 and 4. There is no rise in the relative collagen content in the right lung compared with the normal left control lung from the same experimental animal in any of the groups; on the contrary there is a slight drop in the group given 100 mg of quartz. This is because the tissue changes following administration of these relatively small doses of quartz (corresponding to 5 and 10 mg respectively in rats) are characterized by an increased cell volume which is largely responsible for the gain in weight. Figure 4 further shows the total collagen values in mg for the right lungs exposed to 100 mg quartz administration compared with an estimated normal control lung. There was no increase of the total collagen content in these lungs either. This explains the percentage decrease of collagen (the "collagen dilution").

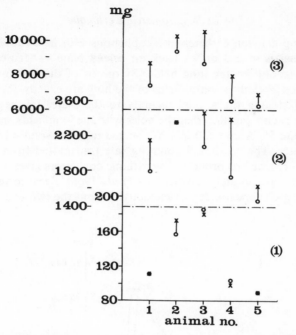

FIGURE 4. Total collagen and total lung weight. Results of determination of (1) collagen, (2) dry weight, (3) wet weight. The determinations are based on lung preparations from 5 rabbits, 6 months after injection of 100 mg of quartz in the right lung. Collagen and weight determinations for the estimated control lung are based on collagen content and weight of the animal's left lung, multiplied by the mean ratio right/left lung weight in normal animals.

X = silicotic lung, O = estimated control lung.

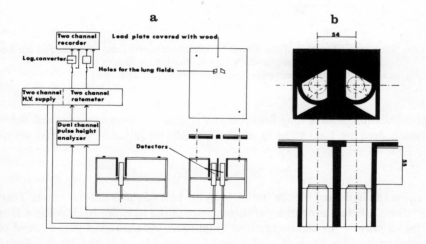

FIGURE 5. Apparatus for radiospirometry. (From *Scandinavian Journal of Respiratory Diseases*.)

The Radiospirometric Technique

After introducing a nylon catheter in a saphenous vein in a rabbit in Nembutal narcosis, the animal is placed on its back on a lead plate — Figure 5 — in which holes have been cut out for the lung fields. By means of fluoroscopy, the animal's position is corrected so that the basal fields of the lung are exactly above the holes in the plate. After fastening the animal securely to the plate, this is placed on the examining table in such a position that the holes with the lung fields are exactly above the detectors, Figure 5b. About 250 μCi Xenon 133 in saline solution is then injected through the catheter. The maximum counting rate transmitted from a two-channel ratemeter to a two-channel recorder *via* logarithmic converters gives a measure of the perfusion in each lung separately (HECKSCHER *et al.*, 1966). Because ventilation is the main factor causing disappearance of radioactivity from the two counting fields, the

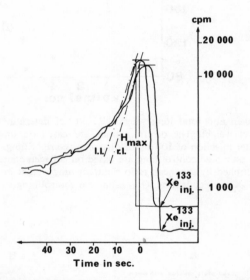

FIGURE 6. Simultaneous tracing of the Xenon 133 clearance curves from the right and left lung. Y-axis c.p.m. logarithmically scaled, X-axis time lineary scaled. (From *Scandinavian Journal of Respiratory Diseases*.)

average ventilation of each lung field per unit alveolar volume can be calculated from the formula used by Heckscher *et al.* for the relative initial slope of the wash-out curve:

$$\dot{V}/V = \ln2/t_{1/2} \text{ ml/min per ml}$$

where $t_{1/2}$ is the half-time for the initial, steepest part of the wash-out curve. This $t_{1/2}$ is found directly from the semi-logarithmic chart of the recorder by drawing a tangent to the initial part of the clearance curve (Figure 6). As the initial part is most often monoexponential, the tangent will normally coincide with the curve. Both the perfusion $\dot{Q}$ and the ventilation $\dot{V}/V$ are expressed in per cent of the total (right + left) lung perfusion and ventilation respectively.

RESULTS

Application of the Radiospirometric Technique to Normal Animals

The above radiospirometric technique was applied to normal rabbits with an average weight of about 4 kg (Table I). Mean perfusion in the left and the right basal fields was found to be approximately similar despite the fact that the right detector covered a larger lung volume than the left. It is assumed that the blood distribution in

TABLE I. RESULTS OF ^{133}XE RADIOSPIROMETRY IN 8 NORMAL ANIMALS

	Mean	SD	Range	e
Per cent $\dot{Q}$ right lung	50·2	5·0	42·2–58·9	1·2
Per cent $\dot{V}/V$ right lung	47·4	3·8	38·9–51·4	2·1

the two lungs is about equal in this species and not apportioned strictly according to lung volumes. The relative ventilation was found to be somewhat greater in the left than in the right lung. The reason for this is not clear, but it may be caused by an inhibition of the mobility of the right diaphragm due to protrusion of the liver. The scatter in regard to the distribution of perfusion and ventilation and the error of single determination are small, showing good reproducibility of the method.

Application of the Radiospirometric Technique to Animals with Induced Unilateral Silicosis

Using the technique described, rabbits injected with 150 mg quartz "P9" were investigated radiospirometrically 6 months following the injection. After radiospirometry, the rabbits were killed and examined. Lung preparations from five of the animals were immediately inflated with air to approximately *in vivo* volume and then roentgenographed (Figure 7). The right and the left lungs were weighed separately and prepared for histological examination. The lung preparations from the remaining rabbits in the group were not examined radiographically, but the right and the left lungs were weighed separately immediately after autopsy and prepared for histological examination.

Table II shows that the mean perfusion in the right lung was very similar to that in the normal control animals. The rabbits exposed to quartz administration show a slightly reduced ventilation, but the reduction is not statistically significant.

TABLE II. RESULTS OF ^{133}XE RADIOSPIROMETRY IN 8 ANIMALS 6 MONTHS FOLLOWING INJECTION OF 150 MG SiO$_2$ IN THE RIGHT MAIN BRONCHUS

	Mean	SD	Range	e
Per cent $\dot{Q}$ right lung	49·2	4·8	43·9–55·6	1·2
Per cent $\dot{V}/V$ right lung	44·6	4·9	37·9–51·9	3·8

The roentgenograms of the inflated lung preparations from the animals in this group revealed finely grained densities in the right lung, most marked basally. The infiltration is unmistakable compared with the normal left lung. Histological examination of samples from all lungs disclosed silicosis Grade 3 (GLÖMME's (1967) qualitative grading) in the two inferior lobes on the right side. The two superior lobes on the right side and the left lung showed normal conditions.

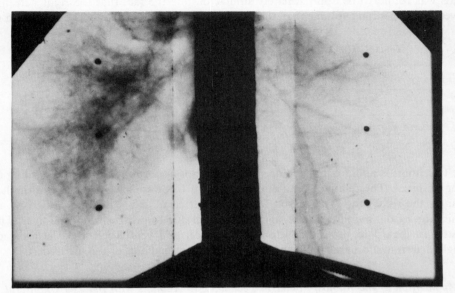

FIGURE 7. Roentgenogram of an inflated lung preparation from a rabbit 6 months following injection of 150 mg SiO_2 in the right lung. Greatly confluent nodular and linear densities in the right lung due to silicosis. Normal left lung.

DISCUSSION

KNIPPING *et al.* (1955) were the first to employ ^{133}Xe for regional lung function measurements, and since that time various ways of using Xenon 133 radiospirometry for measuring the regional perfusion and ventilation of the human lung have been reported by a number of authors. A review has been presented by MIÖRNER (1968). In the present study on experimental animals it was natural to choose, in principle, the method indicated by HECKSCHER *et al.* (1966) for measuring both perfusion and ventilation under steady-state conditions.

The principle of measuring the perfusion during maintained breathing in man has been compared with measurements during breath-holding and has proved to give approximately as reliable results (MIÖRNER, 1968) and approximately corresponding bronchospirometric measurements of the perfusion.

Regional ventilation in ml/min per ml is measured on the clearance curve of Xenon 133. This method yields information mainly on the ventilation of perfused lung alveoli, but not on the total regional ventilation, nor does it give the same information as bronchospirometry (ARBORELIUS *et al.*, 1967). In reality, $\dot{V}/V$ calculated in this manner gives a measure of ventilatory efficiency and provides information about the existence of badly ventilated parts within a counting field. It is pointed out that the measurements are of value solely in relation to the ventilation on the right side of the total (right + left) ventilation value.

The main source of error using the present technique is the influence of the overall ventilation — perfusion on the measurements. This error has been tested by means of model and *in vivo* experiments. The overlap from the normal upper lung fields on the right side has been found to be 10% whilst the overlap from the normal left lung is approximately 5%. This overlap of radioactivity will tend to reduce the difference in ventilation — perfusion between the right and the left lungs. On the other hand, with reduced function on the right side, the "normal" control lung may take over the sick lung's perfusion and ventilation, and this will go towards increasing the measured difference between the lungs.

There was no demonstrable change in perfusion or ventilation in the two right inferior lung lobes despite radiographically and histologically demonstrated silicotic changes in these parts. This indicates that a relative hyperfunction in the normal parts between the silicotic areas may counterbalance the loss of perfusion — ventilation in the affected areas, maintaining a *status quo* in the basal part of the right lung as a whole as far as possible into the pathological development.

Studies along the same lines, for further elucidation of the relation between the administered dose of quartz and functional changes, are in hand.

Acknowledgements — I am indebted to docent Åke Swensson, M.D. (Head of the Department of Occupational Medicine, Karolinska Sjukhuset, Stockholm, Sweden) for his participation in valuable discussions concerning this paper.

The skilful technical assistance of Mrs. Gunn Naevdal and Mrs. Lise Roald is gratefully acknowledged.

REFERENCES

ARBORELIUS, M. *et al.* (1967). In: *Radioaktive Isotope in Klinik und Forschung. Ed.* K. Fellinger & R. Höfer. Vol. 7, pp. 440–445.

DALE, K. (1967). *Acta physiol. scand.* **71**, 163–167.

DALE, K. (1970). *Scand. J. resp. Dis.* **51**, 125–132.

DAVIDSON, J. T., WASSERMAN, K., LILLINGTON, G. A. & SCHMIDT, R. W. (1966). *J. appl. Physiol.* **21**, 1094–1098.

GLÖMME, J. (1967). *Evaluation of the relative fibrogenetic tendency of mineral particles in animal experiments.* Oslo, Universitetsforlaget.

GÖTHE, C. J. *et al.* (1968). *Scand. J. resp. Dis.* **49**, 207–226.

HECKSCHER, TH. *et al.* (1966). *Scand. J. resp. Dis. Suppl.* **82**, 31–39.

KETTLE, E. H. & HILTON, R. (1932). *Lancet.* **222**, 1190–1192.

KING, E. J., STACY, B. D., HOLT, P. F., YATES, D. M. & PICKLES, D. (1955). *Analyst, Lond.* **80**, 441–453.

KNIPPING, H. W. *et al.* (1955). *Dt. med. Wschr.* **80**, 1146–1147.

MIÖRNER, G. (1968). *Scand. J. resp. Dis. Suppl.* **64**, 84 pp.

MOSINGER, M. *et al.* (1961). *Archs Mal. prof. Méd. trav.* **22**, 5–39.

NEUMAN, R. E. & LOGAN, M. A. (1950). *J. biol. Chem.* **184**, 299–306.

VERSTRAETEN, J. M., LACROIX, E., ROELS, H. & SPINOIT, CL. (1966). *Medna thorac.* **23**, 160–168.

DISCUSSION

W. WELLER: The measurement of perfusion is an elegant method, but I would draw your attention to the fact that measurement of pressure in the right ventricle is of particular value. During our experiments on animals dusted in the chamber, the right-hand ventricle pressure hardly increased. On the whole, this agrees with observations made on man. On the other hand, in experiments with rats where quartz was injected, we found that the pressure in the right ventricle, after three months, had increased 100 % as against the control animals. This means that a very severe state had developed very quickly. The measurement of this value is a very important aspect of the tests.

Dr. KNUT DALE: It seems that we have found much the same with different techniques. As I showed in my paper, there was no demonstrable reduction of the perfusion in the lung 6 months following injection of moderate doses of quartz. Taking into account the different lung weight in rats and rabbits, the retention in the lungs in my experimental animals corresponded to the retained doses in your animals which were exposed to quartz-coal dust in the chamber. You also were not able to demonstrate any elevated pressure in the pulmonary artery on these animals. After heavier doses of quartz which were injected in suspension, you found an elevated pressure. Corresponding to that I have — in some yet unpublished observations — found reduced perfusion in right lung in animals exposed to about the same amount of dust as your animals in relation to the lung weight, and after about the same time. Whether you use dust chamber experiments or injection, it is a question of the quantitative fibrotic changes in the lungs. An elevated pulmonary arterial pressure with your method or a reduced blood-flow with mine; both methods reflect an increased resistance in the pulmonary vascular bed.

J. FERIN: Did I understand you correctly that the collagen weight did not change in the normal lung during 6 months?

Dr. KNUT DALE: I have not investigated the collagen weight in the normal lung *during* 6 months. But when using the normal left lung (at the same time) as control, I found no increase of the collagen weight in the right lung of the same animal 6 months following injection of moderate doses of quartz.

OBSERVATIONS ON THE MECHANISM OF
SILICOTIC FIBROGENESIS

A. G. HEPPLESTON

Department of Pathology, University of Newcastle upon Tyne, England

Human and experimental evidence indicates that several basic pathological processes are involved in the silicotic reaction. Airborne particles settling on the alveolar walls are soon ingested by macrophages, which undergo necrosis when their burden is sufficiently great. Subsequently reticulin and collagen are laid down to be followed by hyalinization. The continued deposition of silica ensures that all these processes occur simultaneously though not necessarily at the same degrees of intensity. The cytotoxicity of a dust *in vitro* and its fibrogenicity *in vivo* generally correspond, and the inhibitory effect of water-soluble polymers shows a broadly similar correlation (SCHLIPKÖTER & BECK, 1965). Discrepancies between cytotoxicity and fibrogenicity nevertheless exist, as in the case of chrysotile (MACNAB & HARINGTON, 1967), while polymers may possess a negligible effect on collagen production *in vivo* although affording a high degree of protection to cells cultured in the presence of silica (SCHLIPKÖTER & BECK, 1965).

The relationship between siliceous material, macrophages and connective tissue is evidently not a simple one and studies confined to the toxic and fibrogenic actions of silica overlook an essential component of the biological response, namely the means by which a continued supply of macrophages is achieved. To understand the mechanism of silicotic fibrogenesis it is necessary to distinguish the parts played by each of the primary components. Because they operate concurrently under natural conditions, resort has been made to a combination of *in vitro* and *in vivo* techniques.

THE QUARTZ-MACROPHAGE REACTION AND HYDROXYPROLINE FORMATION

IN order to isolate the process of phagocytosis from that of fibrosis, rat peritoneal macrophages were incubated for 24 hours with quartz particles (Dörentrup, <3 μm) in a medium consisting of TROWELL's (1959) synthetic T8 supplemented by proline, ascorbic acid and horse serum and in an atmosphere of air/CO_2. Each ml of medium contained 1 million cells and 0·1 mg quartz. Repeated freeze-thawing was used to disrupt the macrophages, and the quartz particles were then deposited along with cell debris by centrifugation at 2500 g for 15 min. Cultures of chick embryo fibroblasts, explanted 3–4 days previously and maintained under the same conditions as the macrophages, were employed as the test system. Their original medium was replaced by the supernatant from the macrophage cultures and the fibroblasts incubated for further periods of 2 and 4 days. The medium was then aspirated, the cultures washed briefly in balanced salt solution, fixed with absolute alcohol and resuspended in saline to the original volume. After disintegration by freeze-thawing, aliquots were taken for estimation of DNA by CERIOTTI's (1952) method and of hydroxyproline (HOP) by WOESSNER's (1961) technique. The DNA level was used as an indicator of cell proliferation, the object being to assess whether HOP formation under the influence of macrophage extracts was related to an increased population of fibroblasts or to augmented functional activity of a static population. A variety of control procedures was adopted to gauge the specificity of the test reaction and the results were reproducible (HEPPLESTON & STYLES, 1967).

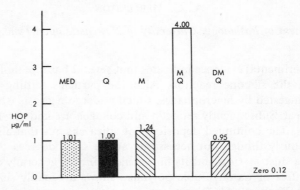

FIGURE 1. Hydroxyproline levels in fibroblast cultures after addition of extracts, etc.

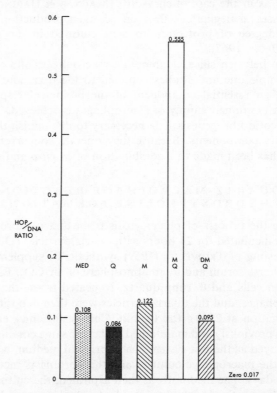

FIGURE 2. HOP/DNA ratios in the same cultures as in Figure 1.

The findings in one such experiment are shown diagrammatically in Figure 1, which expresses the absolute levels of HOP per ml of culture medium after 4 days incubation from the time when the extracts, *etc.* were added to the fibroblasts. The value M/Q was attained by the test extract obtained from macrophages exposed to quartz. DM/Q represents the effect of applying to fibroblasts the supernatant from a suspension of macrophages disrupted before the addition of quartz and maintained for the customary 24 hours. M on the other hand gives the response to extract from intact macrophages incubated on their own and then broken down. In Q fibroblasts were treated with fresh medium containing quartz in the concentration applied to macrophages, while MED represents the fibroblast control whose original medium had been replaced by medium incubated on its own for 24 hours. A further control, not represented in this particular experiment, was used to assess the effect of dissolved silica; medium containing only quartz at the usual concentration was incubated for one day, the particles removed and the supernatant transferred to fibroblasts.

Only the test extract had an effect on HOP production under the conditions of this type of experiment. The application of dissolved or particulate silica directly to fibroblasts was devoid of stimulatory effect when compared with the fibroblast control value. A similar lack of response was evident after using extracts from intact macrophages maintained alone or from disintegrated macrophages incubated with quartz. If the results are expressed as ratios between the levels of HOP and of DNA in the same cultures (Figure 2), a much higher value was obtained for the M/Q extract than for any of the control procedures which gave very similar ratios.

The same culture system was next utilized to investigate the influence of poly-vinylpyridine-N-oxide (PNO) on the production of HOP. Initially macrophages were prior exposed to a low concentration of PNO for a brief period, but no alteration of the M/Q reaction was obtained. When, however, the strength of PNO was increased to 2 mg/ml and macrophages at the usual concentration were in contact for 24 hours before the addition of quartz, a clear modification in the response ensued. This strength of PNO was shown by independent tests not to affect macrophage viability. The results after 2 days' culture of fibroblasts are depicted in Figure 3. The M/Q

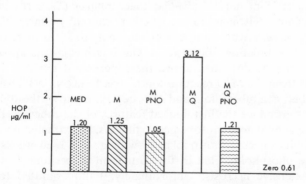

FIGURE 3. Influence of PNO on the HOP levels.

extract produced the usual elevation of HOP level, whereas the medium and macro-phage controls merely attained the same lower level as in previous experiments. Extract of viable macrophages treated only with PNO (M/PNO) was similarly devoid of stimulatory effect as also was extract of intact macrophages treated with PNO prior to the addition of quartz (M/Q/PNO). The HOP/DNA ratios corresponded to the absolute levels of HOP.

A further requirement was the comparison of quartz with a dust that possesses a negligible fibrogenic capacity *in vivo*. For this purpose anatase, a finely divided ($< 0\cdot2$ μm) form of titanium dioxide (Ti), was chosen. Since it forms a white suspension like quartz, a blind trial was possible. Comparisons were made between HOP formation by fibroblasts after the addition of extracts from M/Q and from M/Ti cultures. In addition to the medium control, disintegrated macrophages were kept with quartz and anatase, and the effects of their extracts observed. Titanium dioxide (M/Ti) failed to produce an active extract, as did DM/Ti, DM/Q and MED. The M/Q extract, however, led to the usual elevation of HOP concentration.

On this evidence it may be concluded that a factor or factors capable of stimulating the production of HOP by fibroblasts in culture is released only when living macrophages interact with quartz. The reaction appears to be specific not only in that it is inhibited by PNO but also because titanium dioxide elicited no corresponding change. That this effect does not depend on augmented growth of fibroblasts is indicated by the constancy of the DNA levels in test and control experiments. It thus appears that fibroblast function is enhanced. Moreover, in the system employed it is difficult to envisage an immunological component being involved.

MEDIATION OF THE FIBROBLAST RESPONSE

The inhibitory effect of PNO on the cytotoxicity and the fibrogenicity of silica may be interpreted as showing that the effect of the dust depends on damage to cell membranes, since NASH *et al.* (1966) considered that PNO protects such structures and so abolishes the permeability changes observed biochemically. That membrane damage may be only a partial explanation for the production of the macrophage factor(s) is suggested by the much reduced or absent effect of extract from nondusted disrupted macrophages in the culture experiments. Support for this interpretation is derived from the minimal or absent granulomatous response *in vivo* after subcutaneous injection of extracts from normal alveolar macrophages (WEBSTER *et al.*, 1967). In addition to damaging cell membranes, whether external or internal, it seems that silica reacts in some way with other cell constituents to form or release a factor or factors capable of stimulating fibrogenesis. The intermediary is apparently soluble, since in the experiments described above the supernatant but not the cellular and particulate debris from the M/Q reaction was active. FALLON (1937) was impressed by the resemblance between tuberculous and silicotic lesions and by the ability of extracted tuberculolipid to reproduce the histological features of the tubercle. Believing that a similar mechanism could account for silicotic fibrosis, he extracted phospholipid from the lungs of rabbits injected intratracheally with quartz 1–20 weeks previously. In other rabbits the phospholipid led to the formation of peritoneal nodules, some of which showed extensive necrosis. Unfortunately, Fallon omitted to test similarly extracts from the lungs of normal rabbits although they too contained phospholipid. Developing this same idea, HARINGTON (1963) proposed that, while the immediate product of the particle-cell interaction might be a lipid or lipoprotein, a subsequent step of enzymatic hydrolysis was involved with the release of degradation products, possible fatty acids, which were fibrogenic.

Evidence which suggests a different mechanism has, however, lately been adduced

(HEPPLESTON, 1967: HEPPLESTON *et al.*, 1970). Specific pathogen-free rats, exposed to the inhalation of quartz for periods up to 1200 hours extending over as long as 15 weeks, accumulated in the lungs an average of 26 mg silica in the case of males and 17 mg in the case of females. Despite prolonged post-exposure survival periods, sometimes as long as 19 months, typical silicosis failed to develop. Without exception the lungs were extensively consolidated by an amorphous granular material which filled alveoli (Figure 4) and in which micro-incineration revealed silica particles to be widely scattered. The alveolar walls for the most part remained intact on light microscopy, although in a few places small foci of intra-alveolar or interstitial fibrosis occurred.

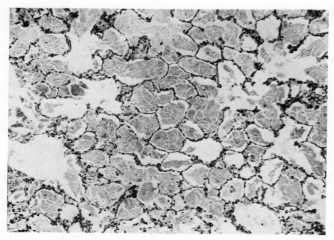

FIGURE 4. Many alveoli are filled with an amorphous granular material, which is devoid of cellular structure and which on microincineration contains silica particles. The alveolar walls show no evidence of fibrous thickening and there is no inflammatory reaction. H and E, × 90

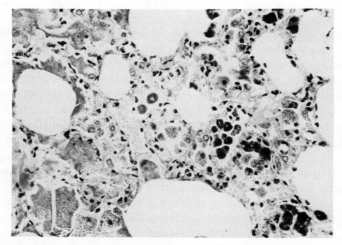

FIGURE 5. On the right, alveoli contain granular pneumocytes (darkly stained) and macrophages (lightly stained). As these cells disintegrate the granular material accumulates (left).
Diastase — PAS, × 215

In many areas granular pneumocytes projected prominently from alveolar walls, and such cells along with macrophages also collected in some alveoli where they underwent dissolution and merged with the amorphous material (Figure 5). Examination by enzymatic and other histochemical techniques showed that, although the granular material was totally devoid of enzyme activity, it had a prominent lipid component, especially phospholipid, together with mucosubstances and protein. Chemical extraction and analysis of the diseased lungs established that, while the protein content differed little from control SPF rats, the absolute quantity of lipid was raised fivefold and this increase was adequate to account for the greater dry weight of the lungs. By immunoelectrophoresis it was nevertheless possible to identify among the proteinaceous element serum derivatives especially albumin and immunoglobulin G. The experimental condition thus bore a striking resemblance to human alveolar "proteinosis" but, because lipid predominates, the disease in both species is reasonably described as alveolar lipo-proteinosis, though chemical combination is not necessarily implied.

The accumulation of lipid-containing amorphous material in the air spaces was associated with inhibition of fibrogenesis despite the continued presence of quartz. Independent collateral evidence adding force to the view that lipid is not related to fibrogenesis by quartz was provided by WEBSTER et al. (1967). Using a wash-out technique, they obtain pulmonary macrophages from guinea pigs and rabbits that had inhaled silica. Lipid was extracted from the dusted cells and its effect compared with that of the residue on subcutaneous inoculation into other animals. The non-lipid residue induced a large granuloma whereas the lipid fraction was without effect. A minimal response was sometimes detected when residues from alveolar macrophages of normal, nondusted animals were employed. In vivo procedures do not, however, permit a distinction to be drawn between a direct effect on host fibroblasts by active macrophage factors and an indirect response mediated by the host's own macrophages. Non-lipid agents thus need to be examined as possible connections between cell destruction and collagen formation. In the carrageenan granuloma MCCANDLESS (1965) considered that the active agent might be a galactan and it is reasonable to seek similar substances in the silicotic process, but proteins or their derivatives may also be concerned.

Ultrastructural observations on experimental avleolar lipo-proteinosis (HEPPLESTON & YOUNG, to be published) afford some insight into the mechanism underlying the failure of quartz to produce its customary response. In material from rats killed early in the survival period, cellular activity was a feature. Type B epithelial cells, the granular pneumocytes, were more numerous than usual, their mitochondria and the characteristic lamellar cytosomes being prominent. Although the basement membrane of alveolar walls was usually not breached, the attenuated epithelium of the type A alveolar epithelial cells appeared to be damaged in many places. Within the alveolar lumen degenerate material derived from type B cells or macrophages was evident. The alveoli also contained many extra-cellular concentric lamellar bodies (Figure 6) whose appearance left little doubt of their origin from type B cells, which histochemical techniques likewise established as being exocrine in nature. In addition an osmiophilic lattice-like structure developed within the alveoli (Figure 7). This lattice was evidently derived from phospholipid elements and, along with the lamellar bodies, became increasingly prominent in rats surviving the quartz inhalation for longer periods. Concurrently cells with some semblance of structure became scarce. In the later stages many alveoli were occupied by the lattice-work, in the spaces of which fine filaments often ran and among which lamellar bodies and quartz particles lay. Contact between quartz and cells was clearly impossible and hence the initial phase of fibrogenesis was prevented. Why alveoli come to be occupied by the mesh-work and concentric bodies in the first place remains unexplained. It does not appear to depend

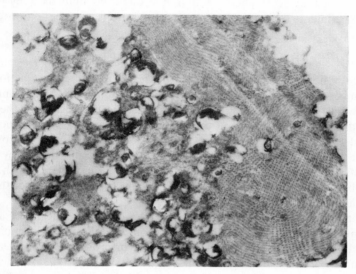

FIGURE 6. Electron micrograph showing intra-alveolar lamellar bodies, derived from type B epithelial cells, lying in amorphous debris (left) which merges with a finely-patterned meshwork (right). Araldite, × 15500

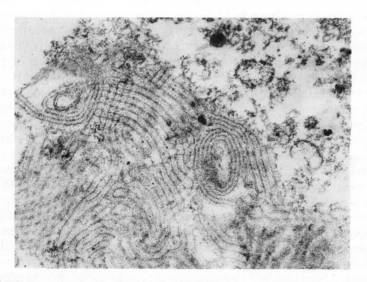

FIGURE 7. Electron micrograph. The acellular lattice component of the intra-alveolar material shows a variable pattern, partly depending on the angle of section and partly on the stage of formation. The denser framework of the mesh encloses fine filaments, both of which appear in longitudinal and in transverse section. The organized arrangement seems to develop out of the amorphous debris. Araldite, × 35000

solely on the pathogen-free status of the rats, nor upon the lipid content of the diet. Suspicion falls on the action of one or more inhalants, operating concurrently with the quartz in such a way as to render inadequate the production of lipolytic enzymes whose normal substrate is phospholipid. The problem may represent a hitherto unsuspected aspect of atmospheric pollution brought to light as a by-product of inhalation experiments designed to examine other aspects of silicotic fibrogenesis.

THE ACCESS OF MACROPHAGES

Since silicotic fibrogenesis is a prolonged process, a sustained interaction of silica with viable macrophages constitutes a fundamental requirement. A continuous supply of these cells must thus be ensured in order to replace those destroyed by their ingested silica. It is probably for this reason that the diffusion chamber technique, in which particles and a limited quantity of cells were enclosed together in the peritoneal cavity (ROWSELL et al., 1960), failed to demonstrate greater collagen formation by silica than by inert dusts. In the interpretation of the fibrogenic action of silica it is thus relevant to consider both the origin of pulmonary macrophages and the nature of the stimulus leading to their accumulation in the lungs.

Attempts to decide whether alveolar macrophages originate locally or are derived from systemic sources depend on the application of cell-marker techniques. The older procedure relies on intravenous injection of macrophages previously labelled by ingestion of particles such as carbon. UNGAR & WILSON (1935) concluded that alveolar macrophages were largely if not entirely derived from circulating blood monocytes. Although RASCHE & ULMER (1966), using ultramarine as label, were able to confirm the pulmonary excretion of circulating macrophages, they also observed that alveolar phagocytes came to contain pigment after injection on its own. In such experiments pigment-bearing cells in the alveoli are not necessarily the macrophages injected, since intravascular disintegration of donor cells could liberate their particles, which would then be taken up by the host macrophage system, conveyed by circulating host monocytes to the lung and passed into the alveoli. This process of pulmonary excretion of circulating particulate matter is evidently a physiological one (CORDINGLEY & NICOL, 1967). On the other hand, emigration of particle-labelled monocytes into the pulmonary interstitium might well be followed by inter-cellular transfer of particles (HEPPLESTON, 1963) to histiocytes of pulmonary origin and these then enter the alveoli. Cytoplasmic labelling thus fails to distinguish conclusively the local or systemic origin of alveolar macrophages.

A more recent method of cellular recognition overcomes these obstacles by dependence on nuclear characteristics. VOLKMAN & GOWANS (1965a, 1965b), SPECTOR et al. (1965) and SPECTOR & WILLOUGHBY (1968) employed nuclear labelling by tritiated thymidine, and their studies leave little doubt that macrophages which appear in inflammatory exudates are derived basically from the marrow and transported by the blood stream to the local site. It may be assumed that this conclusion also applies to the pulmonary response to irritants, but more direct evidence in regard to alveolar macrophages has been obtained by reliance on chromosomal markers in mice rendered chimaeric by irradiation. Using this technique PINKETT et al. (1966) found that approximately two-thirds of dividing cells in lung washings were of haemopoietic derivation and one-third were pulmonary in origin. According to VIROLAINEN (1968), however, only haemopoietic tissues contain precursor cells for macrophages (including alveolar) which are capable of division *in vitro*. A similar conclusion was reached by KINSKY *et al.* (1969) in regard to the origin of Kupffer cells. It thus transpires that the macrophage system as a whole is derived from the marrrow, but mature cells may develop both from stem forms of the macrophage line or from lymphocytes (HOWARD *et al.*, 1969). Population of the lung by haematogenous macrophages does not necessarily mean that these cells promptly emigrate from the capillaries into the alveoli. It now appears possible that marrow stem cells, after leaving the circulation, reside for perhaps 10 days in the pulmonary interstitium where they undergo division and assume the characteristics of lung macrophages before becoming functional in the alveoli (BOWDEN *et al.*, 1969). Hence, although the weight of evidence points to a systemic origin for alveolar macrophages, the augmentation of their production under the influence of silica needs to be considered at both systemic and local levels.

Adopting the carbon clearance technique to gauge the activity of the reticuloendothelial system, CONNING & HEPPLESTON (1966) showed that silica, introduced into the peritoneum or the lung, induced a prolonged and significant elevation of the phagocytic index (K) (Figure 8). After several weeks the index tended to fall while contempor-

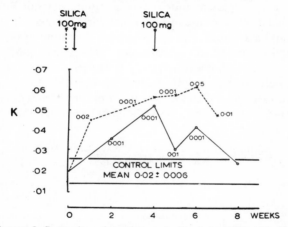

FIGURE 8. Systemic carbon clearance after intraperitoneal silica.

aneously the cellularity of the lesions diminished. Oestrogens, especially in the form of diethylstilboestrol, not only stimulated phagocytic activity as measured by carbon clearance (NICOL *et al.*, 1963) but also induced proliferation of macrophages in liver, spleen and marrow (NICOL & BILBEY, 1960; KINSKY *et al.*, 1969). Moreover, oestrogens led to the mobilization of these cells into the circulation and their elimination through the lungs (NICOL & BILBEY, 1960) as an exaggeration of the normal excretory process (CORDINGLEY & NICOL, 1967). Oestrogen acts as a membrane labilizer and as a mitogenic agent. Silica may release from macrophages an agent with a similar effect, since PNO, which stabilizes cell membranes, inhibits the stimulatory effect of silica on the phagocytic index (HEPPLESTON & CONNING, unpublished). Sustained stimulation of the reticulo-endothelial system by such a humoral mechanism may explain how production of macrophages or their immature forms is augmented. The concentration of these cells in the lungs may represent exaggerated elimination by a normal route, but, if macrophage destruction also releases locally a factor increasing vascular permeability, then emigration around local aggregations of silica would be encouraged.

If, as BOWDEN *et al.* (1969) suggest, marrow stem cells normally populate the lung interstitium and there reside to mature before entering the alveoli, the pulmonary macrophage — silica reaction might liberate a mitogenic agent that was also active locally. Investigation of this aspect depends on measurement of the rate at which alveolar wall cells enter mitosis, for which reliance must be placed on the stathmokinetic technique, that is arrest of mitosis at metaphase. Brief exposure of rats to the inhalation of very small amounts of quartz led to an increase of mitotic activity in alveolar cells, the maximum level being reached 15 days after exposure and the response subsiding after 30 days (STRECKER, 1965a; 1965b). When PNO was administered subcutaneously throughout the experiment, the mitotic response was virtually abolished, the level differing little from normal. Intraperitoneal silica granulomas similarly showed an increase of cell turnover and here too the effect was eliminated by simultaneous treatment with PNO (STRECKER, 1965a). Because PNO prevents both cell damage by silica and the mitotic response in the alveolar wall, it may well be that the two phenomena are in some way connected. Light dust burdens do not necessarily reflect the pulmonary response to greater burdens acquired over longer periods, such as usually obtains in man. Employing inbred mice to minimize strain differences together with prolonged inhalation exposures to coal or quartz, HEPPLESTON & BRIGHTWELL (to be published) applied cytokinetic techniques to the study of alveolar tissue both contiguous with and remote from intra-alveolar aggregates of particles. Each animal thus served as its own control. Because the exposures were of several weeks' duration, these experiments were concerned with the later effects of dust accumulation. Neither coal nor quartz was associated with an increase of mitotic activity in adjacent alveolar walls when compared with dust-free areas (Table 1). Although the lack of a sustained

TABLE 1. MITOTIC INCIDENCE (MI) OF ALVEOLAR WALL CELLS AFTER INHALATION OF QUARTZ FOR 400 HOURS

Survival (days)	MI per 10^5 cells per 4 hours	
	Lung without quartz	Lung with quartz
2	437 ± 165	253 ± 71† (N.S.)
20	745 ± 117*	550 ± 259 (N.S.)
41	306 ± 118	288 ± 105 (N.S.)
83	342 ± 157	315 ± 80 (N.S.)
Non-dusted Controls	437 ± 144*†	

* $p < 0.01$.   † $p < 0.05$.

and massive proliferation of pulmonary cells in relation to quartz aggregates argues against the local origin of macrophages, it is not easy to reconcile the pulmonary cytodynamics with the systemic production of macrophages. The transient augmentation of mitosis observed by Strecker in the early phase of quartz disposal may be contributed by cells belonging to the macrophage series situated in the pulmonary interstitium at the time of exposure. As more particles accumulate, the demand for phagocytes may so increase that less mature forms rapidly emigrate from the blood stream into the alveoli and fewer haematogenous cells pause interstitially than is normally the case.

The nature of the link between macrophage necrosis by silica and the production of these cells in large numbers has yet to be determined but leads nevertheless exist. A feature of silicotic nodules (VIGLIANI & PERNIS, 1958) and of silicotic lungs (MARKS & MARASAS, 1960) is the presence of excess lipid. *In vitro* studies by MUNDER *et al.*, (1966) revealed that incubation of macrophages with tridymite led to the rapid liberation of lysolecithin, but titanium dioxide had no such effect. They suggested that cell components were degraded through activation of a phospholipase A or a phospholipase B. Stimulation of reticuloendothelial activity may be accomplished by certain simple lipids as well as by mycobacteria which possess a prominent lipid component (see CONNING & HEPPLESTON, 1966). It is therefore possible to envisage a cycle of events in which lipids, released by the interaction of silica and macrophages emigrating from the pulmonary interstitium and by nonspecific stimulation of granular pneumocytes, are absorbed and so stimulate the reticuloendothelial system that an augmented supply of fresh macrophages is maintained to replace those destroyed locally. Lipids may also facilitate the maturation of macrophages lodged interstitially.

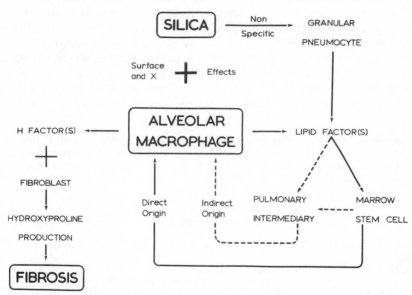

FIGURE 9. Hypothesis of the mechanism of of silicotic fibrogenesis

As a corollary it is necessary to explain why silicotic fibrosis eventually subsides. The evidence suggests that progression of the disease occurs only so long as silica can be reingested by macrophages. In older nodules, especially towards their centres, access of macrophages is evidently impaired since many though not all particles lie extracellularly between the now hyalinized collagen fibres. Reactivation is, however, possible if after an interval more dust, even a so-called inert one such as haematite, accumulates at the periphery of mature silicotic nodules (HEPPLESTON & MORRIS, 1965) and thereby initiates a further emigration of macrophages from the interstitium. The inhibition of silicotic fibrogenesis in alveolar lipo-proteinosis (HEPPLESTON, 1967; HEPPLESTON *et al.*, 1970) fits into this pattern. The accumulation of granular material in the alveoli soon followed exposure to silica and the lipid component probably had a cellular origin with macrophages and granular pneumocytes both contributing. If reticuloendothelial stimulation by lipids is a consequence, the access of macrophages will be augmented but they evidently do not survive long. Ultrastructural and histo-chemical observations showed that silica particles soon came to lie in cellular debris or products devoid of all enzymatic activity. Contact between particles and viable macrophages is thus inhibited and fibrogenic factors cannot be elaborated.

A SYNTHESIS

The macrophage-silica reaction evidently involves more than purely membrane damage. It appears that non-lipid fibrogenic factor(s) and reticuloendothelial-stimu-lating lipid factor(s) may be concerned. Whilst the latter may be derived from macro-phages, granular pneumocytes may also contribute as part of a general response to injury. The possible sequence of events may be summarized diagrammatically (Figure 9), although clearly this hypothesis poses many questions. Sustained collagen production probably requires fresh generations of fibroblasts and, if they are derived from macrophages, the lipid factor(s) could serve a dual role in providing the cellular elements both for the development of the fibrogenic factor(s) and for their target. Furthermore, this hypothesis could embrace in outline mechanisms of fibrogenesis by other agents which like silica evoke a macrophage response and are cytotoxic. Among such agents microorganisms, for instance mycobacteria, and chemical compounds, like paraquat which leads to pulmonary fibrosis, might well figure.

Acknowledgments — These studies were supported by grants from the Medical Research Council and the National Coal Board. Figures 1, 2 and 3 are reproduced from HEPPLESTON & STYLES (1967) Fortschr. Staublungenforsch., **2**, 123, and Figure 8 from CONNING & HEPPLESTON (1966) by courtesy of the respective Editors.

REFERENCES

BOWDEN, D. H., ADAMSON, I. Y. R., GRANTHAM, W. G. & WYATT, J. P. (1969). *Archs. Path.* **88,** 540–546.
CERIOTTI, G. (1952). *J. biol. Chem.* **198,** 297–303.
CONNING, D. M. & HEPPLESTON, A. G. (1966). *Br. J. exp. Path.* **47,** 388–400.
CORDINGLEY, J. L. & NICOL, T. (1967). *J. Physiol., Lond.* **190,** 7P.
FALLON, J. T. (1937). *Can. med. Ass. J.* **36,** 223–228.
HARINGTON, J. S. (1963). *S. Afr. med. J.* **37,** 451–456.
HEPPLESTON, A. G. (1963). *Am. J. Path.* **42,** 119–135.
HEPPLESTON, A. G. (1967). *Nature, Lond.* **213,** 199.
HEPPLESTON, A. G. & MORRIS, T. G. (1965). *Am. J. Path.* **46,** 945–958.
HEPPLESTON, A. G. & STYLES, J. S. (1967). *Nature, Lond.* **214,** 521–522.
HEPPLESTON, A. G., WRIGHT, N. A. & STEWART, J. S. (1970). *J. Path.* (In Press).
HOWARD, J. G., CHRISTIE, G. H., BOAK, J. L. & KINSKY, R. G. (1969). *Br. J. exp. Path.* **50,** 448–455.
KINSKY, R. G., CHRISTIE, G. H., ELSON, J. & HOWARD, J. G. (1969). *Br. J. exp. Path.* **50,** 438–447.
MCCANDLESS, E. L. (1965). *Ann. N.Y. Acad. Sci.* **118,** 867–882.
MACNAB, G. & HARINGTON, J. S. (1967). *Nature, Lond.* **214,** 522–523.
MARKS, G. S. & MARASAS, L. W. (1960). *Br. J. ind. Med.* **17,** 31–35.
MUNDER, P. G., MODOLELL, M., FERBER, E. & FISCHER, H. (1966). *Biochem. Z.* **344,** 310–313.
NASH, T., ALLISON, A. C. & HARINGTON, J. S. (1966). *Nature, Lond.* **210,** 259–261.
NICOL, T. & BILBEY, D. L. J. (1960). In: *Reticuloendothelial structure and function.* Ed. J. H. Heller. New York, Ronald Press. pp. 301–320.

NICOL, T., CORDINGLEY, J., CHARLES, L., MCKELVIE, P. & BILBEY, D. (1963). In: *Role du système réticuloendothélial dans l'immunité antibactérienne et antitumorale*. Paris, Colloques Internationaux du Centre Nationale de la Recherche Scientifique, No. 115. pp. 165–183.
PINKETT, M. O., COWDREY, C. R. & NOWELL, P. C. (1966). *Am. J. Path.* **48,** 859–867.
RASCHE, B. & ULMER, W. T. (1966). *Klin. Wschr.* **44,** 841–844.
ROWSELL, E. V., NAGELSCHMIDT, G. & CURRAN, R: C. (1960). *J. Path. Bact.* **80,** 337–344.
SCHLIPKÖTER, H. -W. & BECK, E. G. (1965). *Medna Lav.* **56,** 485–493.
SPECTOR, W. G., WALTERS, M. N-I., & WILLOUGHBY, D. A. (1965). *J. Path. Bact.* **90,** 181–192.
SPECTOR, W. G. & WILLOUGHBY, D. A. (1968). *J. Path. Bact.* **96,** 389–399.
STRECKER, F. J. (1965a). *Beitr. Silikoseforsch.* **Sb 6,** 259–272.
STRECKER, F. J. (1965b). *Beitr. Silikoseforsch.* **Sb 6,** 437–464.
TROWELL, O. A. (1959). *Expl Cell Res.* **16,** 118–147.
UNGAR, J. & WILSON, G. R. (1935). *Am. J. Path.* **11,** 681–691.
VIGLIANI, E. C. & PERNIS, B. (1958). *Br. J. ind. Med.* **15,** 8–14.
VIROLAINEN, M. (1968). *J. exp. Med.* **127,** 943–951.
VOLKMAN, A. & GOWANS, J. L. (1965a). *Br. J. exp. Path.* **46,** 50–61.
VOLKMAN, A. & GOWANS, J. L. (1965b). *Br. J. exp. Path.* **46,** 62–70.
WEBSTER, I., HENDERSON, C. I., MARASAS, L. W. & KEEGAN, D. J. (1967). In: *Inhaled particles and vapours II. Ed.* C. N. Davies. Oxford, Pergamon Press. pp. 111–120.
WOESSNER, J. F. (1961). *Archs Biochem. Biophys.* **93,** 440–447.

DISCUSSION

E. SCHILLER: The production of lattice structures (tubular myelin) is an unspecific reaction to a variety of stimuli such as powdered aluminium, thyroxine, pilocarpine, dibenzheptropine and oxygen deficiency (cf. Schiller, *Verhandlungen der Anatomischen Gesellschaft*, Wversburg, 1970; in the press).

Do I understand, from your Figure 9, that the scheme of the silicotic fibrogenesis mechanism means that you end with fibrosis?

You mentioned the lipid content. What types of lipids were there?

Prof. HEPPLESTON: This was a tissue-culture not an *in vivo* system, and the silica used was crystalline. We employed titanium dioxide as a control among other procedures.

Analysis of the lipids was confined to histochemistry, which showed accumulation of neutral lipid and phospho-lipid. We did not define further the precise kinds.

I agree with your view on the lattice structure. It can be seen, though in far less quantity, in a variety of situations, including the foetal lung. It seems to be a physio-chemical form of deposition, and I agree that it is not necessarily a specific feature.

A. L. REEVES: I believe that there has been at one time a school of thought which claimed that the pulmonary fibroblast, the granular alveolar cell, and the macrophage are evolutionary stages in the development of a single cell line. From your remarks, I gather that you do not subscribe to that opinion. Is that correct?

Prof. HEPPLESTON: I would not care to be dogmatic. I think it unlikely that the granular pneumocyte develops into a fibroblast, but it is possible that the macrophage might become a fibroblast.

A. L. REEVES: A detached macrophage could migrate back into the alveolar wall?

Prof. HEPPLESTON: The macrophage is not detached from the alveolar wall normally, it is lying on it. The macrophage might be transformed into a fibroblast which lays down fibres *in situ*. Fibrogenesis might thus proceed from one cell type which was macrophagic in the early stage and fibrogenic later.

H. SAKABE: Quartz particles which you used in inhalation experiments seem not to be sharp in the illustration. I would like to know the cell toxicity of these quartz particles.

Prof. HEPPLESTON: We used the same type of quartz for the inhalation experiments as for the tissue-culture ones. In the tissue-culture experiments the macrophages were to a large extent killed by the quartz after 24 hours.

J. D. BRAIN: Your suggestion that lipid factors can increase alveolar macrophage production is an interesting one. Could you please tell me what evidence you have for this hypothesis? You did mention that lipid injection stimulates the activity of the reticuloendothelial system. But this experiment is inconclusive in relation to increased alveolar macrophage production because: (i) it may represent a change in the phagocytic activity of the RES rather than a change in the number of cells in the RES and (ii) it may be completely accounted for by non-pulmonary fractions of the RES.

Prof. HEPPLESTON: I did not have time to mention the evidence suggesting proliferative activity of the RES, but the paper includes the experimental evidence and references on which this part of my hypothesis is based. As I indicated, alveolar macrophages are now considered to be marrow derived, and our cytodynamic observations in dusted mice hardly suggest a pulmonary origin. I agree that more direct evidence is needed on lipid stimulation of macrophage production by the RES. In the exposure of this and other problems lies the essential virtue of the hypothesis.

H.-W. SCHLIPKÖTER: You drew particular attention to the lattice structures which were observable on the electron microscope slides you showed. This is a matter of the myelin structures which I first described some time ago in accounts of experimental silicosis and which originate in my opinion from necrotic macrophages. These myelin structures occur also in the normal lung. I would therefore like to ask you whether these lattice structures are more profuse in association with the quartz effect and whether in your opinion they have any significance in the pathogenesis of silicosis.

Prof. HEPPLESTON: I have studied the ultra-structural appearance of the lung after inhalation of inert dust, and in recent experiments with coal dust there was a much lesser degree of lattice formation as compared with silica. This agrees with Dr. Schiller's view that the lattice is probably not a specific feature associated with quartz.

M. GRUNSPAN: The lung can synthesize fatty acid from acetate, and also retain this. In 1965 it was found in alveolar cells in lungs which had been newly labelled, and this might explain why the macrophage participates in the increase of lipid and why we find so many lipids in the lung with the quartz effect.

G. DARLEA: Our researches using guinea-pigs exposed to coal dust inhalations (with free SiO_2 at 4·5%) showed important serum changes after 2 years of exposure. The most important of these changes was the increase of the groups –S–S– from 0·35 mm to 0·93 mm (by polarography). This increase shows disturbance of protein synthesis and contributes to the appearance of insoluble proteins which precede the appearance of the X-ray changes. Histologically there is absence of collagen.

It will be necessary to continue biochemical studies on normal lung and in early pneumoconiosis.

BIOCHEMICAL AND BIOPHYSICAL REACTIONS OF RAT LUNG TISSUE TO QUARTZ AND CORUNDUM WITH AND WITHOUT PVN-OXIDE TREATMENT

M. Grünspan and H. Antweiler

Medizinisches Institut für Lufthygiene und Silikoseforschung an der Universität Düsseldorf, W. Germany

Abstract — Rats have been treated by intratracheal injection of 20 mg quartz or corundum in saline suspension and 2 hours later by intravenous injection of 2 mg Polyvinylpyridine-N-oxide (PVNO). Lung weight, quartz and PVNO content and phospholipid substances of the lungs have been estimated at various intervals after the injections.

Up to 30 days after application, quartz-lungs contained much more PVNO than lungs of quartz-free animals. The amount of PVNO in quart-lungs surpassed the theoretically possible maximum of PVNO adsorption on the quartz found in these rats. Corundum did not show the same effect. From these findings it may be supposed that quartz in lungs induces the development of special adsorbent receptors for PVNO, possibly in macrophages.

Furthermore, the amount of phospholipids in quartz-lungs was markedly increased, whereas in quartz + PVNO-treated lungs the phospholipids increased only moderately. Thus, the phospholipids may be a good indicator of the extent of necrosis of quartz-macrophages.

So eindeutig der inhibitorische Effekt des Polyvinylpyridin-N-oxids (PVNO) gegen über der experimentellen Quarzwirkung ist (SCHLIPKÖTER, 1967), so schwierig ist es, den Wirkungsmechanismus dieser Substanz zu erklären. Wir hoffen, mit dieser Arbeit, die sich mit der Verweildauer des Polymeren im Organismus befasst, hierzu einen Beitrag zu liefern.

Während das Schicksal des injizierten PVNO bei der normalen Ratte durch die Arbeit von LIEFLÄNDER & STRECKER (1966) bekannt ist, ist das Schicksal des PVNO nach vorausgehender i.tr. Quarzinjektion noch nicht untersucht worden. Das erscheint aber besonders interessant, wenn man bedenkt, dass schon eine einmalige i.v. Injektion von 2 mg PVNO pro Ratte die Entwicklung einer Silikose nach i.tr. Injektion von 20 mg Quarz während mehrerer Wochen hemmt.

Wir hatten in eigenen Untersuchungen festgestellt, dass 2 Wochen nach der Injektion von 2 mg PVNO in einer normalen Lunge nur noch wenige μg PVNO gefunden werden. Da aber die Fibrosehemmung an die Anwesenheit von PVNO in der Lunge gebunden ist, dürfen wir vermuten, dass das Polymere bei Anwesenheit von Quarz in der Lunge in einer noch nicht genauer bekannten Weise in der Lunge festgehalten wird.

Wenn eine adsorptive Bindung des PVNO an die Quarzoberfläche die Ursache für eine langdauernde Speicherung des Polymeren sein sollte, müsste der PVNO-Gehalt der Lunge der Adsorptionsfähigkeit des Quarzes entsprechen. Wenn aber der PVNO-Gehalt grösser ist, muss ausser der Quarzadsorption zusätzlich eine noch unbekannte Bindungspotenz in quarzhaltigen Lungen existieren, die in quarzfreien Lungen nicht vorhanden ist. Diese Überlegungen scheinen insofern wichtig, als es andere Polymersubstanzen wie z.B. Polyvinylpyrrolidon gibt, die ebenfalls an Quarz adsorbiert werden, die aber keine nennenswerte Hemmwirkung bei der experimentellen Silikose haben.

Um die Frage der Verweildauer von PVNO in der Lunge zu klären, haben wir im ersten Teil unserer Arbeit den Gehalt der Lunge an Quarz und PVNO zu verschiedenen Zeitpunkten nach deren Injektion (20 mg Quarz i.tr., 2 mg PVNO i.v.) bestimmt und berechnet, ob die gefundene PVNO-Menge der Adsorptionsfähigkeit des vorhandenen Quarzes entspricht. Dabei gingen wir von der Feststellung aus, dass 1 mg des benutzten Quarzes maximal 8 μg PVNO adsorbiert (Antweiler & Djie, 1971). Im zweiten Teil unserer Arbeit untersuchten wir den Einfluss von PVNO auf den Phospholipidgehalt der Lunge unter den gleichen Versuchsbedingungen.

METHODIK

Als Versuchstiere dienten 400 weibliche Ratten eines Wistar-Stammes im Gewicht von 180–200 g (Fa. Ivanovas, Kisslegg-Allgäu). Die Tiere wurden in Gemeinschaftskäfigen gehalten und mit Standardfutter (Fa. Höveler, Langenfeld/Rhld.) ernährt. Trinkwasser stand ad libitum zur Verfügung. Quarzstaub einer Teilchengrösse von maximal 3 μm (9,1 m²/g) wurde mit 20 mg in 0,5 ml physiologischer Kochsalzlösung i.tr. injiziert. 2 mg PVNO in 0,1 ml physiologischer Salzlösung wurden einmal 2 Std. nach der Quarzinjektion i.v. appliziert.

Die Tiere waren in folgende Gruppen unterteilt:

Gruppe 1: Kontrollen ohne Behandlung
Gruppe 2: 2 mg PVNO i.v.
Gruppe 3: 20 mg Quarz i.tr.
Gruppe 4: 20 mg Quarz i.tr. + 2 mg PVNO i.v.

Um vergleichsweise die Wirkung eines Inertstaubs zu prüfen, erhielten weitere 80 Ratten in gleichartiger Weise statt Quarz Korund (5,34 m²/g):

Gruppe 1: Kontrollen ohne Behandlung
Gruppe 2: 2 mg PVNO i.v.
Gruppe 3: 20 mg Korund i.tr.
Gruppe 4: 20 mg Korund i.tr. + 2 mg PVNO i.v.

Die Ratten wurden zu verschiedenen Intervallzeiten nach den Injektionen mit Äther getötet. Die Lungen wurden ohne Trachea, Lymphknoten und Fettgewebe gewogen und anschliessend homogenisiert.

Die Homogenate wurden für folgende Bestimmungen benutzt:

a) PVNO-Gehalt mit einer von uns entwickelten Methode (Grünspan & Antweiler, 1969)

b) Quarzgehalt nach dem Verfahren von BAUMANN (1960)*
c) Phospholipidgehalt nach BROCKMANN & GERCKEN (1969)*
   1) Sphingomyelin
   2) Phosphatidylcholin (= Lecithin)
   3) Phosphatidylserin
   4) Phosphatidyläthanolamin

ERGEBNISSE UND DISKUSSION

Es gelang in unseren Versuchen, den Verlauf der Gewebsreaktion auf Quarz bei der Ratte mit einer einmaligen Dosis von 2 mg PVNO pro Ratte zu hemmen, denn das Lungengewicht der mit PVNO behandelten Ratten ist am 30. Tag nach der Quarz-injektion bedeutend geringer als das Gewicht der nicht behandelten Tiere (Tabelle I).

Wie man aus der Tabelle ersehen kann, ist während der gesamten Versuchszeit von 30 Tagen der PVNO-Gehalt der Quarzlungen immer grösser als derjenige normaler Tiere, die mit PVNO behandelt wurden. Bei den Quarztieren wurde PVNO während der ganzen Versuchszeit nachgewiesen. Mit PVNO behandelte quarzfreie Ratten hatten dagegen in den ersten Versuchstagen nur etwa ein Drittel des bei Quarztieren gefundenen PVNO retiniert (Tabelle I).

So finden sich in den ersten 7 Tagen nach Versuchsbeginn in quarzfreien Lungen 25–64 μg PVNO pro Lunge, während zur gleichen Zeit in Quarzlungen 122–207 μg PVNO nachgewiesen wurden.

Zwischen dem 15. und 30. Tag nach den Injektionen enthalten die quarzfreien Lungen meist nur noch wenige μg PVNO (maximal 41 μg), die Quarzlungen dagegen noch 129–300 μg.

TABELLE I. QUARZ UND PVNO IN RATTENLUNGEN

Tage post inj.	Lung.-Gew. (g)		PVNO/Lunge (μg)		Quarz/Lunge (mg) (PVNO) Gp. 4	Max. Adsorpt. (μg PVNO) (Theoret.)
	Quarz Gp. 3	Quarz +PVNO Gp. 4	Norm Gp.2	Quarz Gp. 4		
2	1,7	1,1	44	122	9,8	78,4
3	1,9	1,0	64	180	6,0	48,0
4	1,9	1,2	38	207	8,5	68,2
7	1,9	1,1	25	170	11.0	88,3
12	2,6	2,0	0	208	12,7	101,6
15	2,8	1,9	32	129	11,3	90,4
20	3,3	1,9	0	258	11,6	92,8
21	3,6	2.1	41	218	14,0	112,5
22	3,6	1,9	0	280	10,6	84,8
30	3,8	2,2	0	300	11,8	94,4

Als Ursache für die langdauernde und starke Fixierung des Polymeren in der quarzhaltigen Lunge ist zunächst an die Möglichkeit zu denken, dass PVNO an die Oberfläche der Quarzteilchen adsorbiert wird und deshalb eine Anreicherung zustande kommt. Bei Berechnung der maximalen PVNO-Adsorption an die vorhandenen

* Wir danken Herrn Dipl. Chem. Dr. A. Brockhaus für die Quarzbestimmungen und Herrn Dr. Dehnen für die Phospholipidbestimmungen.

Quarzmengen ergibt sich aber, dass diese wesentlich geringer ist als das wirklich gefundene PVNO (Tabelle I). Die gefundenen PVNO-Mengen liegen um 50–200% höher als die zur maximalen Quarzbedeckung notwendigen.

Quarz kann also nicht die einzige Ursache für die PVNO-Retention in diesen Lungen sein. Die quarzhaltige Lunge muss zusätzlich noch andere Eigenschaften haben, die in der quarzfreien Lunge nicht vorhanden sind.

Mit der Feststellung einer PVNO-Menge, die das maximal adsorbierbare PVNO übertrifft, ist jedoch noch keine Aussage darüber möglich, ob nicht schon allein die Menge von adsorbiertem PVNO zur Hemmung einer Silikoseentwicklung genügt.

Wenn wir gleichartige Versuche mit Korund durchführen, kommt es nicht zu einer langdauernden Bindung des PVNO in der Lunge wie beim Quarz (Tabelle II); die erhaltenen Werte zwischen 10 und 43 μg übertreffen nur gering die PVNO-Mengen, die bei quarzfreien Lungen gefunden werden.

TABELLE II. Korund, PVNO und Phospholipide in Rattenlungen

Tage post inj.	Lung.-Gew. (g)		PVNO/Lunge (μg)		Phospholipide/Lunge (μg)							
	Korund	Korund +Quarz	Norm.	Korund	Korund				Korund + PVNO			
					1	2	3	4	1	2	3	4
7	1,2	0,9	10	43								
10	1,3	1,2	—	—								
14	1,3	1,3	0	30	1,3	25,5	2,3	5,1	3,9	32,7	3,8	12, 5
21	1,2	1,1	0	22								
30	1,3	1,2	0	10	2,5	16,8	1,25	5,0	1,5	16,8	2,0	5,3

Unsere Befunde lassen vermuten, dass unter der Einwirkung des Quarzes in der Lunge selbst neue Bindungsmöglichkeiten für PVNO entwickelt werden, die sich möglicherweise in den Makrophagen befinden, deren Zahl unter der Quarzwirkung bedeutend vermehrt ist. Vielleicht spielen diese Bindungskapazitäten eine wesentliche Rolle für den Wirkungsmechanismus des PVNO (siehe Antweiler, 1970).

Unsere Untersuchungen haben schliesslich noch eine bisher unbekannte Wirkung des PVNO gezeigt, die aus den Daten der Tabelle III ersichtlich ist. Der Phospholipid-

TABELLE III. Phospholipide/Lunge
(μg)

Tage post Inj.	Norm. Lunge				Lunge: Quarz				Lunge: Quarz + PVNO			
	1	2	3	4	1	2	3	4	1	2	3	4
3	1,5	11,5	1,2	5,2	2,37	33,2	4,8	10,5				
4	2,5	12,5	1,5	5,5	3,32	43,7	4,5	13,7	2,4	10,9	2,9	5,5
7	2,5	14,2	2,4	5,2	3,8	61,0	9,2	16,0	2,7	9,2	2,8	5,2
15					8,7	147,0	6,4	20,1	3,0	38,4	3,0	11,2
20	2,3	13,5	2,2	5,4	5,0	220,5	3,9	23,8				
60	2,2	9,4	1,5	3,8	6,0	300,5	15,2	19,6	3,4	130,5	7,4	12,5

gehalt in den Lungen der unbehandelten Tiere ist sehr gross. Alle untersuchten 4 Fraktionen zeigen schon am 3., 4. und 7. Tag nach Versuchsbeginn hohe Werte. Auch im weiteren Verlauf des Versuchs liegen die Phospholipidwerte bei diesen Tieren besonders in der Phosphatidylcholinfraktion (Lecithin) sehr hoch. Die Lecithin- werte sind fast 3 mal höher als diejenigen, die bei mit PVNO behandelten Quarztieren gefunden wurden. Bei Anwendung von Korund statt Quarz war keine Zunahme der Phospholipide festzustellen.

PVNO hat also nicht nur eine inhibitorische Wirkung auf die Kollagen- (Oxyprolin-) -entwicklung, sondern auch auf die Bildung der Phospholipide. Die Menge der Phospholipide in der Lunge scheint einen Index für das Ausmass der Nekrose der Quarzmakrophagen darzustellen.

REFERENCES

ANTWEILER, H. (1970) *Beitr. Silikoseforsch.* **22,** 93–172.
ANTWEILER, H. & DJIE, T. T. (1971). *Beitr. Silikoseforsch.* **23,** 59–90.
BAUMANN, H. (1960). *Hoppe Seyler's Z. physiol. Chem.* **319,** 38–51.
BROCKMANN, U. & GERCKEN, G. (1969). *Clinica chim. Acta* **23,** 489–494.
GRÜNSPAN, M. & ANTWEILER, H. (1969). *Int. Arch. Gewerbepath. Gewerbehyg.* **25,** 338–346.
LIEFLÄNDER, M. & STRECKER, F. J. (1966). *Hoppe Seyler's Z. physiol. Chem.* **347,** 268–271.
SCHLIPKÖTER, H.-W. (1967). *Fortschr. Staublungenforsch.* **2,** 189–203.

DISCUSSION

B. Rasche: I feel that there must be PVNO in other organs at the effective time of this substance. We gave PVNO intravenously and found an increase of macrophages with PVNO in the lung after a short time, so the substance must be stored, perhaps in the liver etc.

Dr. Grunspan: In our investigation, during the time when the lung contained little PVNO, there was a great deal in the liver and the spleen. These organs store PVNO over a long time. We do not know, but it is possible that they pass it to the lungs later. I am almost certain that PVNO is transported back to the lungs by cells. I know that you consider the lung as a way of elimination for the macrophages from the whole body.

A. L. Reeves: How were the so-called "theoretical maximum values" of PVNO adsorption to quartz calculated? I have the impression that such a calculation must have been very difficult, as it is not known whether the adsorption layer is monomolecular or not, whether the quartz particles have inner surfaces and, in addition, size of particles and geometry play their well-known part.

Dr. Antweiler: We studied the maximum adsorption capability of the quartz used in these animal tests with respect to PVNO *in vitro* under quasi-physiological conditions in the serum of pigs (37°C, by difference, using ultraviolet spectrometric determination of the not-absorbed PVNO.

A. L. Reeves: Was the layer monomolecular?

Dr. Antweiler: I do not know. Even with increasing amounts of polymer the maximum absorption limit was not affected, however much the excess or however long we waited.

J. Ferin: During the determination of the adsorption value of PVNO to quartz *in vitro*, the particle size of the dust did not change. In tests with rats, however, one can suppose the size distribution did change during the 30 days after dusting.

Dr. Antweiler: If the assumptions which you mention are true, then the theoretical value of absorption would be even smaller, and the value we found would have an even greater distance from this level.

J. M. Barnes: Have you any view on the suggestion that the macrophage may come mainly from the bone marrow? Is there any evidence about the deposition of PVNO in the bone marrow compared with other organs? The amount in the liver and spleen is comparatively small and decreases fairly quickly; the amount of polymer stored in the bone marrow after a few days might be very small.

Dr. Antweiler: I am not sure about the origin of the lung macrophages, perhaps they come from the blood and, lastly, from the bone marrow.

After 3 weeks, the deposition of PVNO in the bone marrow is, autoradiographically, as strong as the deposition in the liver. It remains, according to the experiments of Grundmann, up to one year at least.

W. Weller: We are able to confirm from our own studies with intravenous application of PVNO to mice, that the deposition of PVNO in the bone marrow is smaller than, for instance, in the liver and spleen.

H.-W. Schlipköter: Polyvinylpyridin-N-oxide is absorbed by quartz with a surface deposition of 700–900 $\mu g/m^2$ (Reference: Schlipköter and Brockhaus, also Stober). This value is obtained even with a very low concentration in the solution and this leads to particularly strong bonding between the partners. According to Frisch and Simha one may consider the adsorption spatially as a statistical accumulation of segments of molecular fibres on the particle surface. If the adsorption layer is thus definitely thicker than a monomolecular covering through the monomer vinylpyridine-N-oxide, one can hardly regard this as a multi-molecular covering.

INVESTIGATIONS ON THE AETIOLOGY OF COAL WORKERS' PNEUMOCONIOSIS WITH THE USE OF PVN-OXIDE

H.-W. Schlipköter, W. Hilscher, F. Pott and E. G. Beck

Medizinisches Institut für Lufthygiene und Silikoseforschung an der Universität Düsseldorf, W. Germany

Abstract — Animal experiments were carried out using mixed dusts, natural mine dust and dust isolated from human lungs.

It was shown that the inhibition of the action of quartz by other admixed dusts is only a short-term effect. This inhibition depends upon a close contact of the accompanying dusts with the quartz. The activity reappears, after a time, probably due to separation of the dusts. These reactions are particularly noticeable in lymph nodes examined histologically. Dusts isolated from human lungs and used in animal experiments showed typical quartz reactions significantly earlier than mine dusts. These reactions could be prevented by injecting the animals with polyvinyl-pyridine-N-oxide (PVNO), which indicated that they were due to quartz.

Mine dust shows an acute toxicity *in vivo* and *in vitro*, which probably has no relation to any eventual fibrogenic action.

INTRODUCTION

ALTHOUGH it has been accepted for a long time that quartz and other forms of SiO_2 cause a progressive fibrosis in various animal species with the formation of fibrous granulomata and eventual hyalinization, the aetiology of coal workers' pneumoconiosis requires further investigation. According to most measurements, the amount of quartz in the respirable dust of mines in the Ruhr-area is only $0\cdot5$–5%.

Hence, when planning new experiments on the aetiology of coal miners' pneumoconiosis, we had to keep in mind that the quartz content of mine dust is low, that other dust components might inhibit the silicogenic quartz action in man, and furthermore that other factors, independent of quartz, might be important in initiating coal workers' pneumoconiosis.

EFECTS OF INERT DUST MIXED WITH 4% QUARTZ

In animal experiments we first of all tested a dust mixture consisting of 48 mg titanium dioxide and 2 mg quartz ($\leqslant 5$ μm). This low-quartz dust mixture was administered intratracheally to 60 rats, of which 30 served as controls. The other animals were treated every 8 weeks with 2 ml of a 2% PVNO-solution injected subcutaneously. The rats were sacrificed 12 months later. The control animals showed an advanced fibrosis and the fibrotic changes were generally more severe in the lymph nodes than in the lungs. The PVNO-treated rats on the other hand showed

379

only an inert deposition of dust in the lungs and lymph nodes without any fibrotic reaction.

This experiment showed that even small quantities of quartz as found in mine dusts can cause significant fibrosis, and that PVNO, because of its SiO_2-specific inhibition, can be used as an indicator of quartz activity (Figure 1). In our experiments the

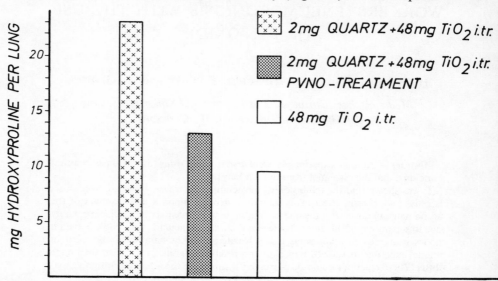

FIGURE 1. Hydroxyproline-content of rat lungs 12 months after intratracheal injection of TiO_2 with 4% quartz.

bacterial flora of conventionally kept rats did not appear to influence the development of experimental silicosis in rats. It is not possible to relate these experimental results to dusts which occur in mines, because the non-quartz components of mine dust are not inert but contain materials which show a significant inhibitory action upon quartz.

INHIBITORY INFLUENCE OF OTHER DUST-COMPONENTS ON QUARTZ ACTIVITY

It has been known for a long time that clay minerals have a lasting inhibitory effect on the fibroblastic activity of quartz dust. Several clay minerals when mixed with 3% of crystalline silica ($\leqslant 5$ μm), cause a marked inhibition of the fibroblastic reaction, lasting for 6–9 months. This inhibition decreases after long retention in the body (12–18 months), and then an excessive proliferation in the lungs and particularly in the lymph nodes becomes visible. Apart from considerable deposits of inert clay dust in dust cells which are situated at the periphery, the lymph nodes show increased nests of quartz specific cells in which an increase of reticulin and collagen fibres can be observed (KLOSTERKÖTTER et al., 1960).

The appearance of separate inert dust cell foci and reticulohistiocytic cell nests, typical of quartz, could be interpreted as evidence of separation of the dust components.

Even the predominating coal fraction of mine dust shows an inhibitory action. In two experimental series, titanium dioxide, anthracite and long flame coal were mixed with 40% quartz and these mixtures were applied intratracheally. An inhibition of fibrosis could be demonstrated, by histological examination and by determination of hydroxyproline, particularly in the case of long flame coal. This effect decreased after 6 months (Figure 2). However, with this high quartz concentration, the lymph

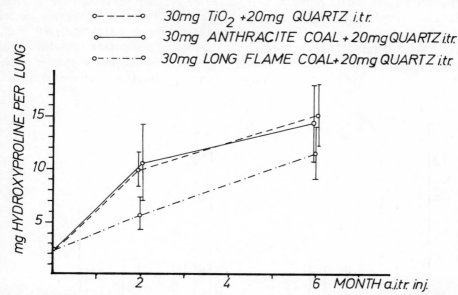

FIGURE 2. Hydroxyproline content in the lungs of rats, after intratracheal injection of suspensions of dust.

nodes, where deposits of the separated dust components were most marked, did not show a delay of the fibroblastic reaction caused by SiO_2 (fibrosis grade II–III, after Belt and King). The control of quartz activity by PVNO was also studied in this experiment. The results showed that the fibrosis from the coal-quartz mixtures could be inhibited by weekly subcutaneous injections of $1 \cdot 25 - 5$ mg PVNO (Figure 3).

The inhibiting influence of coal becomes even clearer if much smaller quantities of quartz are added to the mixture. After intratracheal injection of anthracite or long flame coal containing 3% quartz, it could be demonstrated by hydroxyproline-determination in the lung as well as by histological examination, that quartz is less active in combination with coal than in a corresponding TiO_2-quartz mixture. The fibroblastic reaction typical of quartz only occurred in a reduced and delayed fashion after 12 months, which was most marked in the lymph nodes. These findings con-firmed results of earlier long term experiments (18 months) in rats, in which con-version of the inert reaction of four different coal dusts into a fibroblastic reaction (II⁰) could be demonstrated by an addition of 3% quartz (KLOSTERKÖTTER et al., 1958).

SIGNIFICANCE OF CLOSE CONTACT OF DUST COMPONENTS FOR INHIBITION OF THE QUARTZ ACTION

It can be assumed that inhibition of the silicogenic action of quartz by other accompanying dusts depends on their close contact with quartz. In earlier investigations using mixed dusts containing 70 mg anthracite and 30 mg rock dust with a natural quartz content of 10–13% (quartz content in the total dust 3–4%), the inhibitory action of the clay minerals was more marked than in the case of artificial mixtures of the same quantity of quartz and clay minerals. In this experiment lasting 18 months, typical quartz cell nests with increased reticulin fibres and few collagen fibres were found in the central areas of lymph· nodes, whereas the heavily loaded dust cells (inert reaction) were usually situated peripherally (Klosterkötter et al., 1961). Also moderate changes in the lungs, in the form of a nodular reticulohistiocytic proliferation, occurred. Again this finding points to a dissociation of storage mechanisms *in vivo* which lasts longer with dust containing natural quantities of quartz.

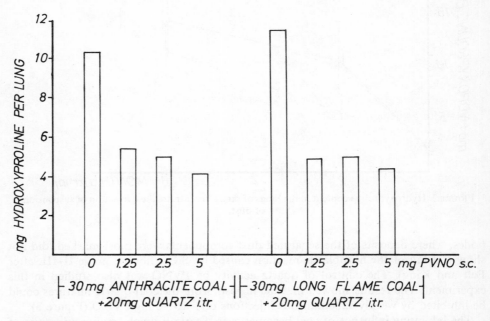

Figure 3. Hydroxyproline content in the lungs, 30 weeks after intratracheal injection of a dust mixture containing 30 mg of anthracite or long flame coal and 20 mg of quartz. Effect of subcutaneous application of PVNO.

Recently we were able to demonstrate the great significance of a close contact between clay minerals and quartz by an animal experiment (Dolgner et al., 1969). A mixture of 10% quartz and 90% kaolin was applied intratracheally to 30 rats; another group was given the same mixture after both components had been ground together. In the group treated with the simple dust mixture, the inhibitory action of the clay minerals was exhausted after 12 months; fibrosis I^0 was found in the lungs and a more marked fibroblastic reaction (II^0) in the lymph nodes. The dusts that had been ground together, however, led to a markedly longer-lasting inhibition of the quartz effect, since the liberation or separation of the quartz takes longer in such mixtures.

Thus the inhibition of the silocogenic action of quartz by accompanying dusts appears to depend on the close contact of these dusts with quartz. This effect only persists for a limited time; after which a liberation of the silicogenic quartz activity is observed. This probably is due to a separation of the dusts. This phenomenon can be demonstrated in lymph nodes 18 months post application, but is hardly seen in the lung. The techniques of biochemical estimation of collagen and histological diagnosis of fibrosis (according to Belt and King) are not very accurate for the diagnosis of these low-grade alterations during the lifetime of rats kept under conventional conditions. For this reason HÖER et al. (1969) have successfully used the different sites of dust foci in relation to the interstitial tissues of the lung as a criterion for the classification of mine dusts according to their quartz content. However, after some experience with mixed dusts, we consider that the histological observation of the cellular reaction in lymph nodes is a suitable method for the evaluation of early reactions.

INVESTIGATIONS OF THE BIOLOGICAL EFFECTS OF MINE DUSTS

Clarification of the aetiology of coal workers' pneumoconiosis is only possible by investigations on respirable mine dusts, conducted in light of the results of experiments with artificial dust mixtures. Therefore, we tested 8 different mine dusts *in vivo* and *in vitro* using alveolar and peritoneal macrophages. These dusts were obtained from different collieries with the aid of the fine dust filter apparatus BAT II. These natural mine dusts had previously been defined according to their grain size distribution and mineral content by the Hauptstelle fur Staub- und Silikosebekämpfung des Steinkohlenbergbauvereins, Essen.

(a) *Acute Toxicity of Mine Dusts* in vivo *and* in vitro

Experiments with these samples showed at first a marked acute toxicity *in vivo* and *in vitro*. For a quantitative study of this effect, the mortality rate of rats (Wistar) was examined in two experiments started at different times. The mine dusts were administered intratracheally to 60 rats in the form of a suspension (40 mg and 35 mg of dust in $0 \cdot 7$ and $0 \cdot 6$ ml of normal saline). After 16 h the mortality rate in both experiments was 56%, and after 24 h it was 61%. No immediate deaths due to an obstruction of the upper respiratory tract by the dust were noted.

In order to examine if this acute toxicity could be influenced by PVNO, a control group of 34 rats was injected with 5 ml PVNO subcutaneously 4 days before the injection of dust. This pre-treatment did not significantly influence the death-rate of the rats. The acute toxic action was certainly not dependent on the amount of quartz in the mine dust since no such action was observed with the application of equally large amounts of pure quartz dust.

To test the significance of the acute toxicity for the aetiology of pneumoconiosis, similar dust samples were suspended in rat serum and administered to 51 albino-rats. No animal died after the intratracheal injection of this suspension; the addition of serum, therefore, had completely neutralized the acute toxicity of the mine dusts.

A similar effect was observed in cell-culture of macrophages of the lung or peritoneum of guinea pigs. $3 - 4 \times 10^6$ cells were seeded in Leighton-tubes containing cover glasses. The medium (NCTC 109 and 5% homologous serum) was discarded 1 h after expansion of the cells on the glass surface, and the mine dust suspensions with and without serum were added in concentrations of 75–100 μg dust per 10^6 cells. The dust in these suspensions had been well-dispersed by ultrasonics. Cytotoxicity was assessed by determining, among other parameters, the affinity of cells for an acid stain (Erythrosin) and the liberation of enzymes from the cell into the overlying medium, as measured by the activity of lactic dehydrogenase (LDH).

The results demonstrated a toxic effect of mine dusts *in vitro*, independent of the quartz concentration. This effect is less pronounced and is observed later than that caused by a pure quartz specimen. Quartz dust showed a marked cellular toxicity after 50 to 60 min which increased after 24 h to such a degree that 98% of cells took up the dye and an LDH activity of 540 mU/ml was measured in the overlying medium. The values found 6 h after incubation with mine dust were within the variations of the controls. Here, after an exposure of 24 h, only approximately 40% of cells took up the acid dye (control 9%); and at this time liberation of LDH reached a level of 280 to 340 mU/ml. This cytotoxicity of mine dust could be neutralized by the addition of 5% homologous serum, as was found in the animal experiment. The percentage of stained cells as well as the LDH activity determined in the overlying medium were within the variation of the "inert dust" controls. On the other hand quartz dust with the addition of guinea-pig serum caused a delayed but fully developed cytotoxicity after 24 h, in which 98% of cells could be stained and an LDH activity of 550 mU/ml was found. The toxicity of quartz could be depressed significantly by pre-treatment of the cells (30 min) with PVNO (400 μg/ml), an effect not observed with mine dust.

The results of these *in vitro* and *in vivo* investigations show that mine dusts possess a high acute toxicity. Since this toxic action can be inhibited by homologous serum *in vitro* as well as *in vivo*, it can be assumed that the acute effect is independent of the potential fibrosis. Presumably it has no connection with the observed pneumoconiotic alterations in man which usually occur only after an exposure of 8 to 13 years.

(b) Investigations of the Fibrogenic Action of Mine Dusts

We carried out 9 series of experiments in order to investigate the chronic fibrogenic action of mine dusts. If quartz is a causative agent in the development of coal miners' pneumoconiosis, and only comes into action after a long time, then the mechanisms discussed above should also be true for the natural mine dust. We tried to procure evidence for this from animal experiments, using intratracheal or intra-peritoneal injection of mine dusts with a quartz content of 1 to 6%, and the histological criteria described earlier. The animals used were female Wistar and Sprague-Dawley rats weighing 160 to 200 g at the beginning of the experiment. The injected natural mine dusts were suspended in saline with the aid of Tween 80 and ultrasonics. Up to 50 mg of dust in 0·7 ml of saline were injected intratracheally under a short ether anaesthesia, and up to 100 mg in 1 ml saline intraperitoneally. One group of rats was treated at intervals of 4 to 8 weeks by subcutaneous injection of a 2% PVNO solution after administration of the mine dusts. The animals were then killed at different intervals up to 18 months after the application of the dust. Lung, omentum and lymph nodes were fixed, cut and stained. We have not yet been able to evaluate all animals.

From the results so far available neither the PVNO-treated rats nor the untreated controls showed any fibrosis in the lung or in the omentum up to the 11th month, nor did they show any cell proliferation typical for quartz. The lymph nodes, too, showed only considerable inert deposition of dust in dust cells. Apart from these dust cell foci, only after 12 and 18 months could areas with typical quartz reaction and proliferation of reticulin fibres, situated mainly in the central parts, be demonstrated in the regional lymph nodes (bronchial, intestinal and hepatic lymph nodes) (Figure 4). These areas with typical quartz reaction are similar to those seen after application of $96 \cdot 3\%$ titanium dioxide and $3 \cdot 7\%$ quartz (Figure 5). The dust cells were massively loaded with black dust. Cells in the areas with typical quartz reaction contained only a few black dust particles but many birefringent particles. From this we could presume a dissociation of the storage mechanisms for the separate dust components *in vivo*, parallel to that observed in experiments using artificial dust mixtures. Retention of the BAT dust for 18 months is apparently insufficient for the necessary separation of the dust and hence for the induction of connective tissue proliferation in the lung or omentum.

The cell proliferations observed in the lymph nodes are caused by quartz, as was shown by the negligible amount of typical quartz reaction in the PVNO treated rats (Figure 6). By analogy, rats treated with PVNO after application of $96 \cdot 3\%$ titanium dioxide and $3 \cdot 7\%$ quartz contained no areas of typical quartz reaction (Figure 7).

ANIMAL EXPERIMENTS WITH DUST ISOLATED FROM LUNGS (LUNG DUSTS)

In the human lung, retention of quartz-containing mine dust for 8 to 13 years is necessary for the development of coal miners' pneumoconiosis. If one assumes that this time is necessary for the separation or for the decrease of the inhibitory action of the accompanying dust components, then dust isolated from lungs of deceased miners should produce tissue reactions in the experimental animal after a shorter period than was possible with the genuine mine dust. For this reason we used two specimens of dust, isolated by Brockhaus from the lungs of deceased miners, for animal experiments.

The first specimen of dust came from the lung of a 57-year old miner with severe silicosis who had died of a pulmonary embolism. The dust content of the lung tissue, kindly sent to us by Könn, Bochum, consisted of $0 \cdot 2963$ g/g dry weight of lung. The ash residue was $11 \cdot 7\%$ and the quartz only 1% $(+0 \cdot 2\%)$. A group of 50 rats was taken for intraperitoneal and intratracheal injections. Each animal received 50 mg of the dust. From each group 25 animals were treated subcutaneously after the administration of dust with 2 ml of a 2% solution of PVNO at intervals of 2 months. The first animals were killed after 8 months and specimens of lung and omentum as well as regional lymph nodes were examined histologically. Even after this short period it was clearly seen macroscopically at autopsy that the regional lymph nodes in those animals which were not treated with PVNO were markedly larger than normal. On the other hand in those animals which had received PVNO subcutaneously every 8 weeks the corresponding lymph nodes were markedly smaller than those of the control animals.

The suspicion that this enlargement of the lymph nodes had been caused by quartz could be verified by histological examination. The lymph nodes of the animals treated with PVNO only contained inert deposits of dust in foci of dust cells (Figures 8 and 9). The corresponding lymph nodes of the untreated controls, on the other hand, showed marked reactions typical of quartz, even with signs of fibrosis, in the imme-

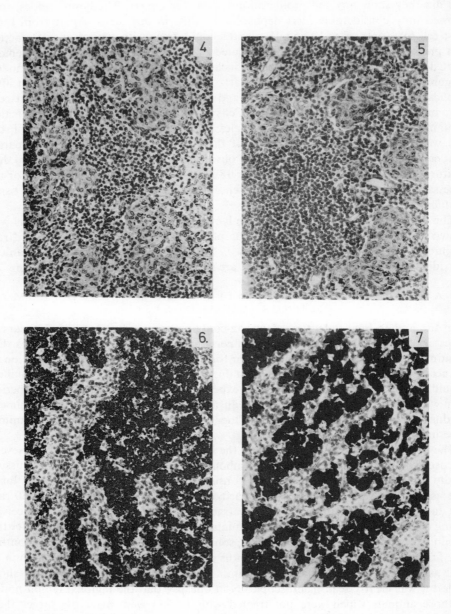

Figure 4. Liver lymph node 18 months after application of mine dust. No treatment with PVNO. Reaction typical for quartz. Obj. 25. Azane.

Figure 5. Liver lymph node 8 months after application of titanium dioxide (96·3%) and quartz (3·7%). No treatment with PVNO. Reaction typical for quartz. Obj. 25. Azane.

Figure 6. Liver lymph node 18 months after application of mine dust. Treatment with PVNO. No reaction typical for quartz. Obj. 25. Azane.

Figure 7. Liver lymph node 8 months after application of titanium dioxide and quartz. Treatment with PVNO. No reaction typical for quartz. Obj. 25. Azane.

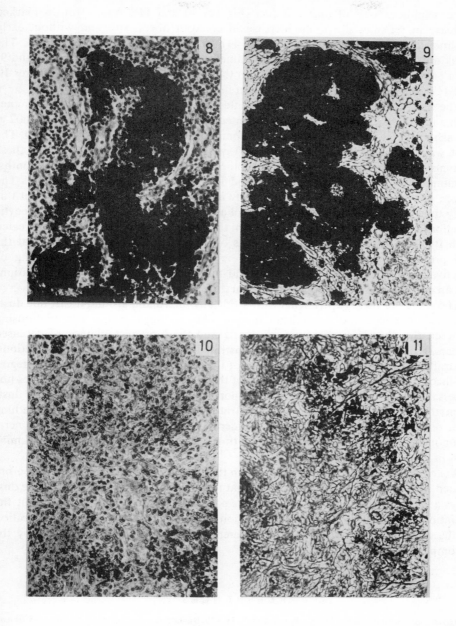

FIGURE 8. Liver lymph node 8 months after application of lung dust. Treatment with **PVNO**.
No reaction typical for quartz. Obj. 25. Azane.

FIGURE 9. Liver lymph node 8 months after application of lung dust. Treatment with **PVNO**.
No reaction typical for quartz. Obj. 25. Silver stain.

FIGURE 10. Liver lymph node 8 months after application of lung dust. No treatment with **PVNO**.
Reaction typical for quartz. Obj. 25. Azane.

FIGURE 11. Liver lymph node 8 months after application of lung dust. No treatment with **PVNO**.
Reaction typical for quartz. Obj. 25. Silver stain.

diate neighbourhood of dust cell foci (Figures 10 and 11). Apart from a marked increase in reticulin fibers, an increase in collagen fibers with and without early hyalinization was seen (Figures 10 and 11). Also the density of dust varied. The black dust particles in the dust cells of animals treated with PVNO (Figures 8 and 9) were packed much closer together than in those of the untreated control (Figures 10 and 11). This experiment has not yet been finished.

The second dust sample had been isolated from the lung of a 60-year-old miner with a low degree of silicosis. The dust content per g dry weight of lung was $0 \cdot 0602$ g, the ash residue was 24% and the quartz component in the dust $2 \cdot 3\%$ ($+0 \cdot 2\%$). The dust was injected into the tail-vein of 60 rats each receiving 30 mg. Half of these animals were treated with PVNO, the others serving as control. After 3 months, 4 animals were killed and the spleen and liver were examined histologically. The spleen of all animals showed only a largely inert deposition of dust, but even at this early time the liver of the untreated control animals showed small nodular histiocytic reactions around the collections of dust. On the other hand the liver of animals treated with PVNO showed largely inert deposits of dust. This finding points out that the cell proliferation caused by mine dusts is only initiated after the de-mixing or reactivation of the quartz component, and that the demonstrated tissue alterations are an effect of the low proportion of quartz in the dust.

The results of these experiments with artificially mixed and ground dusts, fine dusts collected in mines and dusts from human silicotic lungs, clarify the relationship between the fibrosis caused by pure quartz and the lung-dust analysis of deceased miners, RIVERS et al. (1960) having demonstrated, in spite of the observed variations, a parallelism between the quartz content of the lungs or the lung dust and the degree of silicosis. However, the quartz content of the lung at the end of a life span does not necessarily have to correspond to the proportion of quartz in the inhaled mine dust. WORTH et al. (1967) were able to demonstrate that elimination of dust from the lung after removal from dust exposure is considerably higher for coal than for its mineral component. This finding is in keeping with the mechanisms of dissociation of mine dust in vivo.

Apart from special circumstances, e.g. in the case of certain infections, the demonstrated results of our experiments show that the presence of free SiO_2 in the mine dust plays a significant role in the development of coal miners' pneumoconiosis. But the initiation of a connective tissue proliferation depends significantly on the separation of the dust components and on the differential inhibition of quartz action by the accompanying dusts.

REFERENCES

DOLGNER, R., SCHLIPKOTER, H.-W. & LEITERITZ, H. (1969). Ergebn. Unters. Geb. Staub- u. Silikose-bek. Steinkohlenbergbau 7, 45–49.
EINBRODT, H. J. (1965). Beitr. Silikoseforsch. 87, 1–105.
HÖER, P.-W., EINBRODT, H. J. & LEITERITZ, H. (1967). Fortschr. Staublungenforsch. 2, 607–612.
HÖER, P.-W., LAUFHÜTTE, D. W. & LEITERITZ, H. (1969). Ergebn. Unters. Geb. Staub- u. Silikosebek. Steinkohlenbergbau 7, 51–55.
KLOSTERKÖTTER, W., MACKOWSKI, M. T., SCHILLER, E., SCHLIPKÖTER, H.-W. & THAER, A. (1958). Staublungenerkrankungen 3, 312–329.
KLOSTERKÖTTER, W., SCHLIPKÖTER, H.-W., SCHILLER, E. & THAER, A. (1960). Forschs.-Arb. Geb. Staub- u. Silikosebek. Steinkohlenbergbau (2), 15–36.

KLOSTERKÖTTER, W., SCHLIPKÖTER, H.-W., SCHILLER, E., THAER, A. & LEITERITZ, H. (1961). *Unters. Geb. Staub- u. Silikosebek.* (3), 23–49.
NAGELSCHMIDT, G. (1960). *Br. J. ind. Med.* **17**, 247–259.
NAGELSCHMIDT, G., RIVERS, D., KING, E. J. & TREVELLA, W. (1963). *Br. J. ind. Med.* **20**, 181–191.
RIVERS, D., WISE, M. E., KING, E. J. & NAGELSCHMIDT, G. (1960). *Br. J. ind. Med.* **17**, 87–108.
ROSSITER, C. E., RIVERS, D., BERGMANN, I., CASSWELL, C. & NAGELSCHMIDT, G. (1967). In: *Inhaled particles and vapours II. Ed.* C. N. Davies. Oxford, Pergamon Press, pp. 419–437.
WORTH, G., MUYSERS, K. & EINBRODT, H. J. (1967). *Fortschr. Staublungenforsch.* **2**, 443–448.

DISCUSSION

K. Robock: It is surprising that you found one sample, of only 1% quartz, that produced a distinctive silicotic reaction. Do you think that in this case you may have encountered a synergistic effect of the mineral or coal components?

Prof. Schlipköter: Apart from inhibiting effects, such additional components in the mine dust could have a fibroblastic effect, or might increase it. However, the acute toxicity of mine dust in general, which can be cancelled by homologous serum, means that this is of no great importance *re* the aetiology of pneumoconiosis.

J. Ferin: Do you believe that the acute toxicity is a general reaction to mine dusts? Were there differences between the mine dusts (used in your tests), and what was the chemical composition and the size of these dusts? Have these dusts all been sampled from one colliery?

Prof. Schlipköter: I believe that the dust samples which we examined, which came from various coal mines and which had been used in intratracheal tests and also *in vivo*, have an acute toxicity independent of quartz. I cannot say what the position is in regard to other mines and plants. I only feel that this cytotoxicity should be further examined, and we should try to find its cause.

N. Kavoussi: During a visit (in 1969) to the Institute of Industrial Medicine in Tiflis, U.S.S.R., I learned about some studies then in progress on the use of adrenaline in the treatment of dust disease in miners. Radiographs of the lungs of affected miners showed significant improvements after a few months.

Prof. Schlipköter: These tests with adrenaline are not known to me. I would like to say that it is very difficult, on an X-ray, to see changes after a comparatively short time, and I would be particularly interested to know more of these findings. PVNO is being given to a considerable number of patients. It is very difficult to see if they have improved or deteriorated. If there is such a big — and quick — improvement, it merits special attention.

W. Klosterkötter: In the pictures of lymph nodules, the rats treated by PVNO appeared to have deposited more coal dust. Do you feel that in the case of treatment with PVNO, more coal dust gets into the lymph nodes? If so, this would be in contrast to the results we obtained in our tests with TiO_2 and PVNO.

Prof. Schlipköter: The dust content of the lymph nodes in animals treated with PVNO appears higher only because of the absence of all proliferation: the dust is packed closer than in the control animals.

H. Daniel: What technique have you used to separate dust from the lungs of coal mine workers?

Prof. Schlipköter: We used the formic acid technique according to Bergmann, which was modified by Dr. Brockhaus from my Institute. You can get the details from me.

K. Robock: We are beginning a comprehensive joint work, in Germany, between Steinkohlenbergbauverein and the Silikoseforschungsinstitut, taking samples from four mines. These are very different with regard to silicosis frequency. We shall carry out animal experiments, and hope afterwards to have further results.

W. H. Walton: Would not the dust from human lungs be re-mixed during the extraction process, so that it would be expected to show only the original activity?

Prof. Schlipköter: Experiments just carried out with pit dust subjected to the extraction technique of Bergmann will elucidate this problem.

REACTIONS OF ALVEOLAR MACROPHAGES DURING SHORT-TERM DUST EXPOSURE WITH AND WITHOUT VARIOUS PHARMACOLOGICAL SUBSTANCES (*GLUCOCORTICOIDS AND PVN-OXIDE*)

B. RASCHE

Aus der Medizinischen Abteilung des Silikose-Forschungsinstituts der Bergbau-Berufsgenossenschaft, Bochum, W. Germany

Abstract — It is possible to define cellular performance in lung clearance after dust infiltration.

We investigated how far the phagocytic capacity in the alveolar space may be affected by the age of the experimental animals.

The cellular cleaning mechanism may be influenced also by pharmacological substances, e.g. by glucocorticoids, which may be of great importance in the therapy of chronic bronchitis.

The substance PVNO acts by protecting the cell-membranes during dust uptake, particularly by protecting the lysosome matrix. We found that the substance is also actively engaged in the cellular alveolar clearance, following intravenous injection of animals with PVNO and also after inhalation of this substance.

FOUR factors may be defined as responsible for the cellular lung clearance capacity after dust infiltration.

(1) Migration of monocytic cells into the alveolar space,
(2) Number of macrophages engaged in phagocytosis,
(3) Number of dust particles taken up by phagocytes,
(4) Elimination of dust-laden phagocytes.

Monocytic cells are encountered after massive dust irritation of the lungs just as in any inflammatory reaction. They migrate from the bloodstream into the alveolar space where they become active as macrophages (PINKETT *et al.*, 1966; RASCHE & ULMER, 1965; FERIN *et al.*, 1965).

In order to investigate cellular alveolar clearance, we made experimental animals inhale coloured dust (ultramarine) (*ca.* 40 mg/m³ during 5 h) which is easily seen in the rinsed out phagocytes. The criterion for the macrophage migration is the number of macrophages rinsed out from the alveolar space. We determined the phagocytic activity of the macrophages of the alveolar space by the indices: phagocytic rate (in per cent of the rinsed out cells) and mean particle index; phagocytic capacity is judged by the factor: phagocytic rate × particle index. The elimination of the dust-laden phagocytes from the alveolar space results from following-up the phagocytic rate and phagocytic index after dust irritation for a longer period of time. We observed that even 6 months after a single dust exposure of 5 h (40 mg/m³), marked phagocytes remain in the alveolar space or pass through it (RASCHE & ULMER, 1967; RASCHE, 1967).

AGE DEPENDENCE

We conclude from numerous investigations that dust retention in the lungs is dependent on age (EINBRODT, 1956; KLOSTERKÖTTER & EINBRODT, 1967; REISNER, 1968). Using our method, we investigated on rats for more than 20 months whether cellular elimination by alveolar macrophages is also dependent on the age of the animals, and whether the number of macropyages available for phagocytosis and their phagocytosic capacity are changed with increasing age.

The number of rinsed out macrophages increased with increasing weight of the lungs. The mean curve of the total number of cells was slightly higher in the non-dusted controls than in the dust exposed animals. It decreased after dust exposure on account of the elimination of dust-laden phagocytes from the alveolar space. The strongly increasing total number of cells at the end of the experiment from the 18th to the 21st month is explained by the increase of acute inflammatory processes (Figure 1).

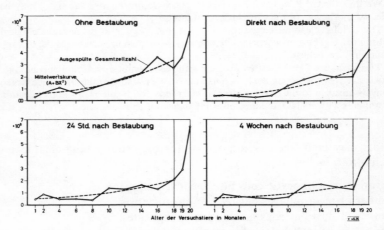

FIGURE 1. Average total number of cells of the macrophages rinsed out from the alveolar space without dust exposure and after dust exposure for 5 h. Number of experimental animals per measuring point = 10.

The phagocytic rate reached a maximum between the 4th and the 8th month of life of the animals. Subsequently the phagocytic percentage value in the alveolar space decreased again to roughly the initial value of the 2nd month. The maximum could still be verified 4 weeks after the dusting, although only slightly. After the 18th month, the phagocytic percentage value decreased (Figure 2).

The mean phagocytic index did not increase proportionally to the phagocytic rate. It increased greatly in 10 months old animals 24 h after dust exposure. The high mean values resulted from cells having phagocytized up to 40 particles of ultra-marine. The factor formed from the phagocytic percentage value and mean phagocytic index showed that, the amount of dust offered being the same, the largest number of particles was taken up from the alveolar space during the 4th to the 8th month of life.

Though the number of phagocytes increased with the lung weight and age of the animals — favoured by inflammatory processes — the phagocytic capacity of these cells was less, measured in terms of the number of dust particles taken up. The problem arises as to whether inflammatory phagocytes have less phagocytic capacity than lung macrophages. Our findings permit the conclusion that phagocytic activity is age dependent with a maximum between the 4th and the 10th month and a lower level persisting from the 12th to the 18th month of age of the rats. Comparison of the

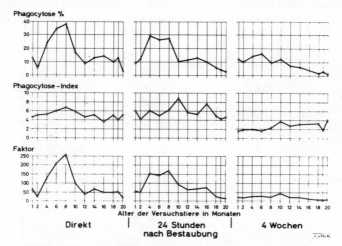

FIGURE 2. Phagocytosis rate, mean phagocytic index and phagocytic factor (rate × index) of rinsed out alveolar macrophages related to the age of the rats. Number of animals per measuring point = 10. (Age date at 4 weeks after exposure refers to the dust exposure day).

absolute number of dust-laden macrophages obtained by rinsing out the lungs after dust exposures of 24 h and 4 weeks showed that, up to the 4th week, a uniform elimination of the ultramarine dust took place independently of the total number of washed out cells. Evacuation of the dust-laden cells seems also not to be affected by older age.

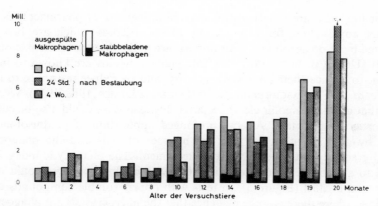

FIGURE 3. Number of rinsed out alveolar macrophages, including those phagocytes loaded with ultramarine, after the end of the dusting till 4 weeks after exposure related to the age of the experimental animals. (Age date at 4 weeks after exposure refers to the dust exposure day). Number of experimental animals per measuring point = 10.

This would mean that the macrophages present in the older lungs are less active with regard to phagocytosis but are eliminated just as quickly (Figure 3).

Beginning with the 4th month of life, there was, in contrast to the two earlier measurements, more free ultramarine dust present in the alveolar volume and in the alveolar septa so that more dust could apparently reach the interstice free from cells. As the phagocytic rate was especially high in these months, but larger concentrations of particles within single phagocytes could not be detected, the cells are probably eliminated without having used their phagocytosis capacities to the full. This is, perhaps, the reason for a stronger dust reaction within the tissue (Figure 4).

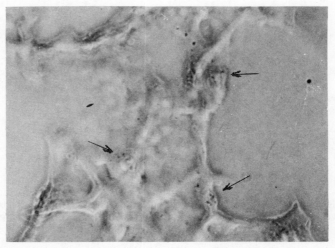

FIGURE 4. Frozen slide of rat lung after dusting with ultramarine (Phase-contrast — 1 : 312) → Ultramarine particles.

INFLUENCES OF GLUCOCORTICOIDS

Cellular lung clearance mechanisms may be influenced by pharmacological agents in various ways. Thus, for example, by glucocorticoids which are being closely investigated by us on account of their importance in the therapy of chronic obstructive bronchitis (ULMER & NICOLAS, 1966). The glucocorticoids are known to inhibit cell migration, to reduce their phagocytic activity, and to reduce resistance to infections (RASCHE et al., 1967; RASCHE et al., 1965; RASCHE & ULMER, 1968, 1970). We were able to show that cellular alveolar clearance after dust exposure could also be changed by a glucocorticoid treatment. After a prolonged application of prednisolone in rats, followed by dust irritation for 5 h, the number of cells and the phagocytic rate decreased gradually with the duration of treatment. The phagocytic index, however, increased to about the same extent, i.e. the available macrophages could digest the larger amount of dust (Figure 5). In tests with poorly soluble compounds of fluoro-prednisolone where there is some evidence that the microcrystals are phagocytosed in the blood stream — the supply of macrophages into the lungs was more efficiently inhibited (RASCHE & ULMER, 1969). The phagocytic activity of the phagocytes present in the lungs, however, has not been inhibited (Figure 6).

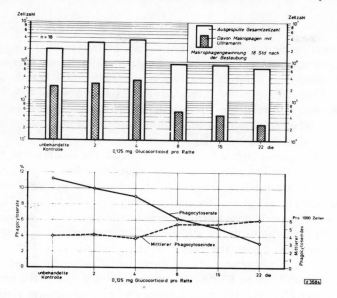

FIGURE 5. Number of cells, phagocytic rate and mean phagocytic index after ultramarine dusting in relation to the time of prednisolone treatment.

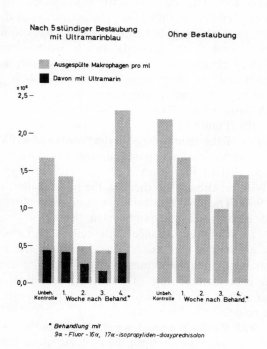

FIGURE 6. Number of rinsed out macrophages of the alveolar space over 4 weeks after single injection of 0·1 mg FIDP/rat I.M.: without dusting (to the right) and after ultramarine dusting for 5 h (to the left). Medium values from 12 experimental animals per measuring point. Treatment with 9 α flourine-16 α, 17 α isopropyliden-dioxy-prednisolone.

INFLUENCE OF PVPNO (P 204)

At the last meeting here in Great Britain, I reported that cellular lung clearance is also influenced by substances that reduce or hinder the silicogenous action of quartz, above all, by aluminium chloride (Rasche *et al.*, 1965). Our results showed that aluminium chloride considerably increased the haematogenous cell supply. The phagocytic rate increased relatively to the number of rinsed out cells, and the percent value also increased after prolonged inhalation. Lung clearance was thus intensified and prolonged by aluminium chloride.

Cellular lung clearance is also influenced by PVPNO, the substance not only works by membrane protection but also by actively influencing the cellular lung clearance (Brockhaus, 1968). We used two series of rats for these experiments: (1) Administration by intravenous injection of the tail vein with 1 ml of 2 % PVPNO dissolved in sodium chloride, respectively once and at four consecutive weeks, (2) Administration by inhalation of PVPNO aerosols of different concentrations dissolved in sodium chloride. In the first test group, the haematogenous irritation by the polymeric substance was investigated, in the second, the direct irritation on the alveolar space.

Our results with intravenous PVPNO show that, on account of the probably non-specific stimulation by the relatively high doses of PVPNO, an increase of the migration of monocytic cells and of their phagocytic activity is caused. But the irritation of the RES seems to be so strong in this case that a steep decline of the macrophage migration could be measured after 24 h. The stimulus to the macrophage migration was higher after a single dose than after four applications. The activation of the monocytic cells, caused by the irritation through the polymer for the first time, did not remain equally strong to its full extent over 4 weeks. A steady state between subsequent production and migration of cells, actively engaged in phagocytosis, probably occurred during the longer test time. In each case, the effect came to an end after 48 h. A control *in vitro*, where ultramarine dust was subsequently given to washed out alveolar macrophages of animals treated with intravenous PVPNO, also showed an elevated phagocytic activity within these cells (Figure 7).

Marked vacuolization of the macrophages after intravenous PVPNO application was conspicuous. This vacuolization intensified with the duration of the test and continued for 48 h, parallel to the elevated phagocytic activity. It was no longer observed after 96 h. Without subsequent dusting, the peak of the vacuolization in the phagocytes was after 96 h. This result confirms the monocytic supply of macrophages. The cells which had pinocytosed the polymer in the blood — and vacuolization indicates strongly an uptake of the substance by the cells — had speedily migrated into the alveolar space on account of the massive dust irritation. But in no case was the appearance of the strongly vacuolized macrophages after intravenous application associated within the experimental time of 96 h, with an inhibition of phagocytic activity in the alveolar space as compared to the untreated animals and those treated with sodium chloride respectively (Figure 8).

In our experiments with PVPNO aerosol, we started from the results of Pott *et al.* (1968) who found a greater elimination from the alveolar space after quartz exposure when very low PVPNO concentrations were applied. We thus pretreated the rats with PVPNO in three different ways:

(1) by inhalation of 100 μg–400 μg PVPNO aerosol, dissolved in sodium chloride, for 1 h and subsequent dusting for 5 h, 1 to 4 times on consecutive days,

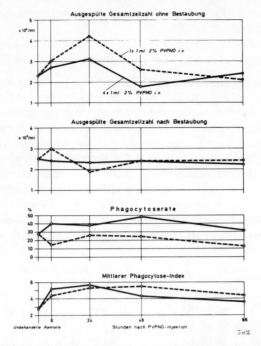

Ausgespülte Gesamtzellzahl ohne Bestaubung

x 10⁴/ml

1x 1ml 2% PVPNO i.v.

4x 1ml 2% PVPNO i.v.

Ausgespülte Gesamtzellzahl nach Bestaubung

x 10⁴/ml

Phagocytoserate

%

Mittlerer Phagocytose-Index

Unbehandelte Kontrolle   Stunden nach PVPNO-Injektion

FIGURE 7. Comparative representation of the rinsed out alveolar macrophages without dust exposure (at the top) and after dust exposure (2nd part from above) followed by single PVPNO treatment (dotted curves) and 4 times PVPNO treatment (drawn curves) of the experimental animals in relation to the time after the last treatment with PVPNO (average values from 12 experimental animals per measuring point) as well as phagocytic rate and phagocytic index of both experimental groups.

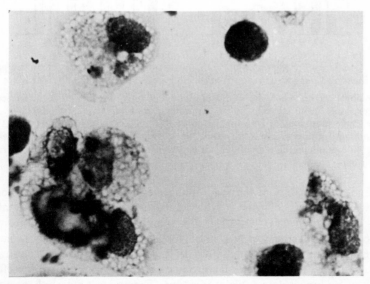

FIGURE 8. Alveolar macrophages from rat lung after intravenous application of PVPNO and dusting with ultramarin (1 : 1250).

(2) after treatment with 100 μg PVPNO aerosol and subsequent dusting immediately thereafter for 4 times, and

(3) after application with a higher PVPNO concentration, namely 7 mg/m³ on average for 3 h and dusting for 5 h, 24 to 96 h after inhalation of PVPNO.

The stimulus to cell migration from the RES seems to be stronger with high PVPNO concentrations than with low dosages, particulary 24 h after inhalation. After intra-venous application of PVPNO with correspondingly high concentrations, the stimulus on the RES was so massive that a subsequent deep decline of the number of cells rinsed out was observed. During the experiment we also observed an inhibition, though much smaller, after the inhalation of high concentrations of PVPNO. After the application of low PVPNO concentrations, we also observed cell reproduction in the alveolar space. When administering the PVPNO dose all at once before the dust exposure, no accentuated stimulating effect on the RES or one lasting throughout the experimental time evidently occurs. This dose seems to be too small to exercise an activating effect on the cells of the RES for longer experimental periods (Figure 9).

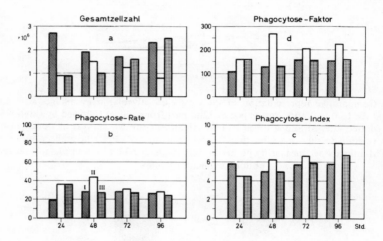

FIGURE 9. Comparison of the rinsed out total number of cells, phagocytic rate, mean phagocytic index and phagocytic factor (phagocytic rate × index) in the alveolar space.

  I. After single pretreatment with inhalation for 3 h of 7 mg/m³ of PVPNO and subsequent single dust exposure to 40 mg/m³ of ultramarine for 5 h.
 II. After single pretreatment with inhalation of 100, 200, 300 and 400 μg/m³ of PVPNO for 1 h and subsequent dust exposure to 1 up to 4 × 40 mg/m³ of ultramarine on consecutive days.
III. After 4 times inhalation of 100μg/m³ of PVPNO for 1 h and of 40 mg/m³ of ultramarine for 5 h in daily change.

The phagocytic capacity of the macrophages expressed as the product of the cells actively engaged in phagocytosis and the number of ultramarine particles taken up by them, was higher in all PVPNO test groups than that of the sodium chloride control group, except for one measuring point. No decline of the phagocytic activity was observed even 96 h after the inhalation of high concentrations in contrast to the intravenous administration of about the same concentrations, where the effect of the substance was no longer detectable at this time. The greatest macrophage activity was measured when a lower dosage of the polymeric substance (1 h, 100–400 μg PVPNO/

m³) was given before dust exposure. At the highest dosage of PVPNO (3 h, 7 mg/m³), the high initial phagocytic activity did not remain on the same level. Nevertheless, the phagocytic activity under the effect of PVPNO at this dosage was considerably higher than that of the controls up to 96 h after application. If the uptake of dust by macrophages is increased by PVPNO, and our intravenous experiments pointed in this direction, it could be concluded that, in case of a very strong stimulus on the RES, the supply of such macrophages, disposed by PVPNO, is exhausted, while a feebler irritation maintains the cell supply, activated by PVPNO, at a uniform level. With regard to the balance of dust uptake, the single administration of the substance before dust exposure was the most effective. With regard to a silicosis prophylaxis, it would also be advantageous if a weekly application were as effective or even more effective than a repeated application of the polymeric substance (Figure 10).

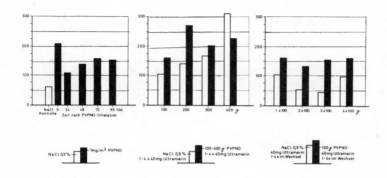

FIGURE 10. Phagocytic factor in the alveolar space after inhalation of PVPNO:

  I. After single pretreatment with inhalation for 3 h of 7 mg/m³ of PVPNO and subsequent single dust exposure to 40 mg/m³ of ultramarine for 5 h.

 II. After single pretreatment with inhalation of 100, 200, 300 and 400 µg/m³ of PVPNO for 1 h and subsequent dust exposure to 1 up to 4 × 40 mg/m³ of ultramarine on consecutive days.

III. After 4 times inhalation of 100 µg/m³ of PVPNO for 1 h and of 40 mg/m³ of ultramarine for 5 h in daily change.

Our experimental results show that PVPNO inhaled in small dosages increases the phagocytic activity of the alveolar macrophages *in vivo* as well as *in vitro*, probably by exercising a stimulating effect on the phagocytes, the cause of which could not be elucidated by the investigations carried out so far (GRUNDMANN, 1967). We also observed in these experiments that vacuolization of the phagocytes under the effect of PVPNO also increased during inhalation in relation to time. But the particle uptake of these cells was not different in these experimental groups from those of the non-vacuolized cells which did not contain PVPNO.

REFERENCES

BROCKHAUS, A. (1968). Symposium "Grundlagenforschung über die Pneumokoniosen", Florenz/ Italien. In Press.

EINBRODT, H. J. (1956). *Beitr. Silikoseforsch.* (87).

FERIN, J., URBANKOVA, G. & VLCKOVA, A. (1965). *Archs. envir. Hlth* 10, 790–795.

GRUNDMANN, E. (1967). *Fortschr. Staublungenforsch.* 2, 223.

KLOSTERKÖTTER, W. & EINBRODT, H. J. (1967). *Ergebn. Unters. Geb. Staub- u. Silikosebekämpf. Steinkohlenbergbau* 6, 73.

PINKETT, M. O., COWDRY, C. R. & NOWELL, P. C. (1966). *Am. J. Path.* 48, 859–867.

POTT, F., SCHLIPKÖTER, H. W. & BROCKHAUS, A. (1968). *Dt. med. Wschr.* 51, 2479.

RASCHE, B. (1967). *Fortschr. Staublungenforsch.* 2, 563.

RASCHE, B. & ULMER, W. T. (1965). *Medna. thorac.* 22, 516–529.

RASCHE, B. & ULMER, W. T. (1967). *Medna. thorac.* 24, 227–236.

RASCHE, B. & ULMER, W. T. (1968). *Z. Zellforsch. mikrosk. Anat.* 84, 506.

RASCHE, B. & ULMER, W. T. (1969). *Z. ges. exp. Med.* 149, 316.

RASCHE, B. & ULMER, W. T. (1970). *Z. ges. exp. Med.* 152, 42.

RASCHE, B., MAY, G. & ULMER, W. T. (1967). *Z. ges. exp. Med.* 144, 335.

RASCHE, B., ULMER, W. T. & LEDER, L.-D. (1965). *Int. Arch. Gewerbepath. Gewerbehyg.* 21, 193.

REISNER, M. (1968). *Beitr. Silikoseforsch.* 95, 1.

ULMER, W. T. & NICOLAS, R. (1966). *Dt. med. Wschr.* 91, 1861.

DISCUSSION

J. M. BARNES: Are the cells you wash out of the lungs of the older rats the same type as those you wash out of the lungs of the younger ones?

Dr. RASCHE: In young rats most of the macrophages were smaller than in the older ones. Nevertheless I am not of opinion that we have to do with young and old macrophages but with two different types of various functions. In the first type, the plasma is more densely packed while in the second it is more widely dispersed. According to recent investigations, above all by Policard, both these types, which also have different life expectations (Weibel and Gil), are present in the alveolar space. It seems possible that in the very young animals the smaller type with densely packed plasma is preponderant.

J. D. BRAIN: I found Dr. Rasche's paper very interesting but I am afraid I must disagree with some of the interpretations of her observations. I do not believe that macrophage migration is measured by looking at the number of macrophages rinsed out of the lungs. The technique of repeated lung washings gives only the pool size of macrophages at one point in time. The pool size is in turn determined by the relative rates at which macrophages migrate on to the alveolar surface and are eliminated from the lungs. Thus if the pool size increases it may represent decreased elimination rather than increased migration. Therefore, washing the lungs does *not* measure macrophage migration. It measures the combined effects of migration and elimination.

I also would suggest that the elimination of macrophages was not in fact measured. Elimination of macrophages can only be judged accurately by actually collecting and counting macrophages removed from the lungs via the airways and lymphatic and vascular channels. Probably more than 90% of macrophages in normal animals are eliminated *via* the airways and thus the assessment of aolveolar macrophages in respiratory tract fluid extruded from the trachea is a good indicator of macrophage elimination. Could you please clarify, Dr. Rasche, how your measurements reflect macrophage elimination?

Finally, I would request that Dr. Rasche include some of the details of her lung washing technique such as wash volume, number of washes, electrolyte composition of the washing fluid, and so on.

Dr. RASCHE: Dr. Brain is right in saying that we are measuring a combination effect between migration and elimination of macrophages in the lung in our measurement of the number of washed-out macrophages.

But finding under the same experimental test conditions an increase or decrease of macrophages when using certain therapeutics, and assuming that in sound rats of a large uniform population the elimination rate remains about the same, we may interpret these alterations as effect of the administered substances on the RES. Besides, we counted the rinsed-out macrophages washed out of lungs of treated animals not exposed to dust. The difference between the number of macrophages gained from non-dusted and dusted lungs is an additional indicator for the elimination rate after dust exposure.

To determine only the elimination rate of dust-exposed macrophages from the alveolar space, it is best to do the measurements for a longer period after stopping the dust exposure. In a long-term experiment running for 6 months, we counted daily the number of the washed-out dust-marked macrophages. In this way we obtained the elimination curve after dust exposure within the alveolar space.

Using this technique by us each lung was washed five times with 4 ml of Hanks solution. My observations are that this technique is only to be recommended when working with large numbers of animals, that suffice for statistic calculation, as in our case.

EXPERIMENTAL PATHOLOGY AND PHARMACOLOGY OF DUST EXPOSURE: AN ELECTRON MICROSCOPIC STUDY

ERICH SCHILLER

*Department of Experimental Pathology, Cassella Farbwerke Mainkur Ltd.,
D-6 Frankfurt am Main, W. Germany*

Summary — The alveolar macrophages of the rat are originally situated beneath the epithelium which is often only 20 nm (200Å) thick. The great alveolar cells are rich in organelles, especially in concentrically lamellated spheres and mitochondria. Under the influence of thyroxine, vacuoles containing osmiophilic lamellae are protruded at their free surfaces. Orciprenaline activates the GOLGI apparatus and the ergastoplasmic reticulum. Pilocarpine induces large autophagous vacuoles. Alveolar macrophages of rats dusted with powdered aluminium contain numerous cytoplasmic inclusions with a moderately dense matrix bounded by a unit membrane. Very electron-dense bizarre structures are formed; they increase by consuming their matrix and finally occupy the entire space limited by the membrane. Poly-2-vinylpyridine-N-oxide inhaled in a micronized solid state is stored within lysosomes. Bronchiolar studies show a vesicular component in the outer zone of the axonema, the transformation of ciliated cells into club cells, and the formation of a branched system of membranous tubes after phenylephrine inhalation.

INTRODUCTION

ELECTRON microscopy of ultra-thin sections has proven that many views on the histology of the lung, the primary reactions to particulate matter deposited intraalveolarly, and the influence of pharmacological agents on alveolar and bronchiolar epithelia are wrong.

This paper deals with the re-examination of our own results gained by light microscopy during the last 15 years. It answers the following questions:

1. Origin of the alveolar macrophages (*cf*. SCHILLER, 1956*a*, *b*).
2. Secretory processes in the alveolar region with special regard to the pulmonary surfactant.
3. Changes in the ultrastructure of alveolar macrophages after ingestion of powdered aluminium (*cf*. SCHILLER, 1961*a*).
4. Changes in the ultrastructure of alveolar macrophages after ingestion of iron oxide dust (*cf*. SCHILLER, 1961*b*).
5. Storage of poly-2-vinylpyridine-N-oxide (P 204) inhaled in a solid state.
6. Transformation of bronchiolar ciliated cells into club cells (*cf*. SCHILLER, 1967).

MATERIAL AND METHODS

Female rats weighing about 250 g were dusted with powdered aluminium (*cf.* Schiller, 1954; Figures 38, 41 and 47) and magnetite from Grängesberg in Sweden respectively. N-isopropylnoradrenaline, phenylephrine, metaproterenol, dibenzheptropine, and poly-2-vinylpyridine-N-oxide were micronized (particle sizes below 3 μm) and given with halogenated methanes[1] and aethanes[2] as propellents[3] using a Medihaler®.

Over a period of 5 min, a puff was blown every 5 s into a closed experimental chamber of 183·5 l volume, in which the rats remained for 15 min. Retinol palmitate (82 mg/kg) was given by stomach tube, d,1-α-tocopherol acetate (150 mg/kg), thyroxine (12·5 μg/kg), and pilocarpine-HCl (1 mg/kg) were injected. Lung tissue was taken after narcotizing the rats by sodium 5-(β-methylthioethyl)-5-(2'-pentyl)-thiobarbiturate (Thiogenal®). 2·5% glutaraldehyde in phosphate buffer (pH 7·4) was injected intratracheally before opening the chest box. Thus the lungs were fixed under intact blood circulation in an inflated state. Tissue specimens of 0·5 mm edge length were kept in the fixative for 2 h at 4°C, washed with phosphate buffer (pH 7·4) and post-fixed in 1% OsO_4 in phosphate buffer (pH 7·4) for 2 h. After another washing with phosphate buffer they were dehydrated by ethanol of increasing concentrations, contrasted for 12 h in 0·5% uranyl acetate in 70% C_2H_5OH and run through the alcohols up to (100%) ethanol. They were embedded into a 2:8 mixture of methyl methacrylate and butyl methacrylate. 50 nm (500 Å) sections were cut with a glass knife on the LKB ultrotome III, contrasted with lead citrate after Reynolds (1963) and examined under the Philips EM 200 at 80 kV. The photographs were taken on AGFA-GEVAERT "scientia" plates.

RESULTS

The Alveolar Cells

The alveolar epithelium covers the alveolar wall as a continuous layer, which in its nuclear-free parts is often only 20 nm thick. It also covers the parietal macrophages, which strictly speaking are hypoepithelial. On stress, alveolar macrophages migrate through the alveolar epithelium. In contrast to the type I epithelial cells the type II (great) cells (Figure 1) are rich in organelles as relative electron-dense, concentrically-lamellated spheres of about 1·2 μm diameter, mitochondria of the crista type, ribosomes both free and bound to the ergastoplasmic reticulum and GOLGI vesicles. Their free surface is studded with microvilli 0·5 to 1 μm long, while the type I epithelial cells show but a few stout microvilli.

Secretory Activity of the Great Alveolar Cells

Under the influence of thyroxine applied subcutaneously from April 12 to June 20, 1967, in daily doses of 12·5 μg/kg body weight vacuoles containing osmiophilic lamellae protrude on the free surfaces of the great alveolar cells (Figure 2). The distances

[1] Trichlorofluoromethane (Propellent 11, B.P.C.), dichlorodifluoromethane (Propellent 12, B.P.C.).

[2] 1, 1, 2-Trichloro-1, 2, 2-trifluoroethane (Propellent 113), dichlorotetrafluoroethane (Propellant 114, B.P.C.).

[3] According to Taylor & Harris (1970) the fluoroalkane gases used to propel aerosols are toxic to the hearts of mice, sensitizing them to asphyxia-induced sinus bradycardia, atrioventricular block, and T-wave depression.

between the lamellae are about 18 nm. The numerous mitochondria are oblong and strongly enlarged.

One hour after an inhalation of orciprenaline the GOLGI apparatus and the ergastoplasmic reticulum will be activated. Polysomes will be found in the inter-membranous spaces.

Thirty minutes after a subcutaneous injection of pilocarpine large autophagous vacuoles may also contain some mitochondria.

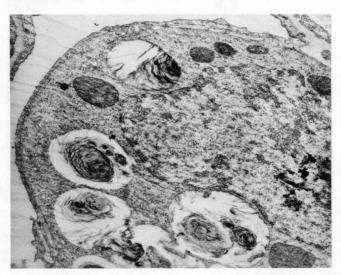

FIGURE 1. Alveolar wall of a female rat killed by Thiogenal® 1 h after an inhalation of micro-crystals passable to the alveoli of a 2 to 3 mixture of isoprenaline hydrochloride + phenylephrine bitartrate. Fixation: $2 \cdot 5\%$ glutaraldehyde in phosphate buffer (pH $7 \cdot 4$). After washing in phosphate buffer the tissue was post-fixed in 1 % osmium tetroxide in phosphate buffer for 2 h. Then it was dehydrated in ethanol, embedded in a mixture of methyl and butyl methacrylates 2 : 8, sectioned at 500 Å (50 nm) on a LKB Ultrotome III and stained with lead citrate. ($\times$ 14 200.) Beneath the ultramicroscopically thin alveolar epithelium one recognises a great alveolar cell containing numerous relatively electron dense myelin figures and some mitochondria. (from SCHILLER, 1969).

Ultrastructure of the Alveolar Macrophages After the Ingestion of Powdered Aluminium

The alveolar macrophages of rats dusted with powdered aluminium for long periods contain both the usual concentrically-laminated myelin figures and many cytoplasmic inclusions with a moderate electron dense matrix bounded by a unit membrane (Figure 3). Very electron-dense bizarre structures are formed; they increase in size by consuming their matrix and finally occupy the entire space limited by the membrane. In the alveolar lumina, tubular myelin lattices with about 30 nm spacing are found in the direct vicinity of free alveolar macrophages.

Ultrastructure of the Alveolar Macrophages After the Ingestion of Powdered Magnetite

Autophagous vacuoles signify the alveolar macrophages after the inhalation of magnetite dust (Figure 4).

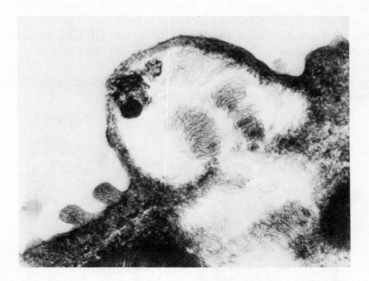

FIGURE 2. Great alveolar cell of a female rat. Daily subcutaneous injections of 12·5 μg thyroxine per kg body weight were given from April 12 to June 20, 1967. Sacrificed by Thiogenal ®. Fixation: 2·5% glutaraldehyde in phosphate buffer (pH 7·4). After washing in phosphate buffer the tissue was post-fixed in 1% osmium tetroxide in phosphate buffer for 2 h. Then it was dehydrated in ethanol, embedded in a mixture of methyl and butyl methacrylates 2: 8, sectioned at 500 Å (50 nm) on a LKB Ultrotome III and stained with lead citrate. (× 46 600). A vacuole containing osmiophilic lamellae is protruded at the free surface. The distance of the lamellae is 180 Å (18 nm). The numerous mitochondria are oblong and increased in size.

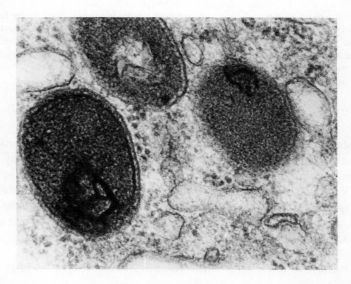

FIGURE 3. Alveolar macrophage of a female rat that inhaled 10 mg powdered aluminium per m³ air for 4 hours each on 51 days from August 16 to October 27, 1967 and was killed by Thiogenal® on January 15, 1968. Preparation as Figure 1. (× 80 000).

Storage of Poly-2-Vinylpyridine-N-Oxide

Poly-2-vinylpyridine-N-oxide (Bayer 3504) inhaled in a solid state is stored in lysosomes that may increase in size beyond 1 μm (Figure 5). Near these phagolysosomes there are some membranes studded with ribosomes. Some pneumocytes demonstrate lamellar transformation of mitochondria.

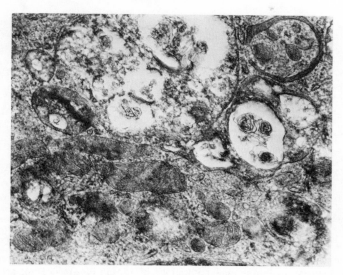

FIGURE 4. Alveolar macrophage of a female rat (final weight 286 g) that inhaled 10 mg powdered magnetite from Grängesberg, Sweden, per m³ air for 4 hours each on 40 days from August 24 to October 19, 1967, and was killed by Thiogenal® on October 30, 1967. Preparation as Figure 1. (× 35 300).

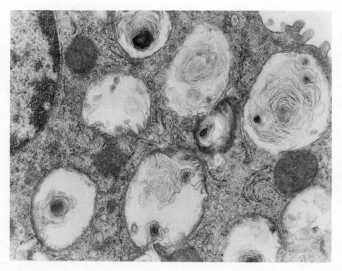

FIGURE 5. Alveolar macrophage of a female rat that inhaled micronized solid poly-2-vinylpyridine-N-oxide passable to the alveoli from July 25, 1967, to January 15, 1968, for 15 min. each five times a week. Sacrificed by Thiogenal®. Preparation as Figure 1. (× 20 500).

Transformation of Ciliated Cells into Club Cells

The bronchioli of the rat are lined by a bathyprismatic epithelium with typical cinocilia on its surface (Figures 6–8). Figure 6 shows a vesicular component in the outer zone of the axonema of bronchiolar cilia.

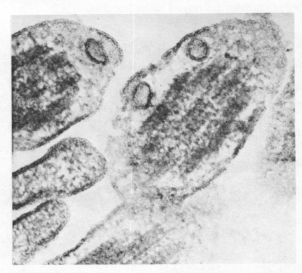

FIGURE 6. Bronchiolar epithelial cells with a vesicular component in the outer zone alongside the axonema. Female rat. Intramuscular injections of 150 mg dl-α-tocopherol acetate per kg body weight using a colloidal aqueous solution (Ephynal®) were given from April 12 to June 20, 1967, five times a week, i.e. 45 times at all. Sacrificed by Thiogenal®. Preparation as Figure 1. (× 102 500).

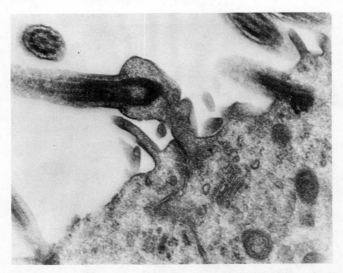

FIGURE 7. Protrusion of a cilium. Bronchiolar epithelium of a female rat. Intramuscular injections of 150 mg dl-α-tocopherol acetate per kg body weight using a colloidal aqueous solution (Ephynal®) were given from April 12 to June 20, 1967, five times a week, i.e. 45 times in all. Sacrificed by Thiogenal®. Preparation as Figure 1. (× 35 300).

Between the ciliated cells one finds individual non-ciliated cells that protrude into the lumen like a club or a flap (Figure 8). Their number has often increased remarkably in animals dusted or treated by pharmaca.

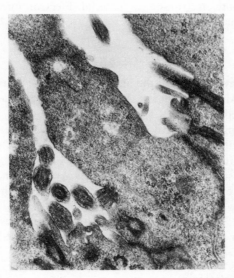

FIGURE 8. Transformation of ciliated cells into club cells. Bronchiolar epithelium of female rat. 82 mg retinol palmitate per kg body weight was given by stomach tube from April 17 to June 20, 1967, five times a week, i.e. 42 times in all. Sacrificed by Thiogenal®. Preparation as Figure 1. ($\times$ 22 100).

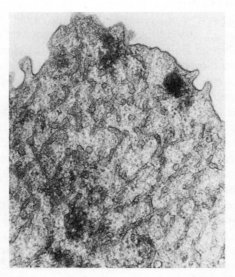

FIGURE 9. Apicol pole of a club cell. Bronchiolus of a female rat killed by Thiogenal® 30 min after a single inhalation of phenylephrine crystals passable to the alveoli. Preparation as Figure 1. ($\times$ 36 300).

Transitions from ciliated cells are found in the form of club cells demonstrating several cilia (Figure 8) or having a cinocilium in the protruded area (Figure 7).

Figure 9 shows the apical pole of a bronchiolar epithelial cell half an hour after inhalation of phenylephrine. A branched system of membranous tubes is filled with a finely granular, moderate electron-dense material. Electron microscopy does not give any idea of the secretory mechanism.

DISCUSSION

While there is not any doubt as to the lining of the alveoli by a continuous epithelium (*cf.* GIESE, 1961, pp. 541–542; SCHILLER, 1963, p. 89) the discussion on alveolar macrophages is not yet closed.

Phagocytes appearing in the alveolar lumina after the intratracheal application of corpuscular foreign materials were identified by their ultrastructure to be desquamated alveolar lining cells (GIESEKING, 1958).

From tissue culture studies, we (SCHILLER, 1956*a, b*) argued in favour of an epithelial and thus entodermal origin, which we (SCHILLER, 1961*c*, with H. SCHULZ) believed could be confirmed by electron microscopy.

We ascertained that, after 3 days, cells that contained no dust particles had significantly greater nuclear projected areas than phagocytes that had engulfed quartz, chromite or coke dusts.

HAPKE & PEDERSON (1968) differentiate between two types of alveolar epithelial cells. At least 90% of the alveolar surface is covered by type I cells (LOW, 1953) that have attenuated cytoplasmic processes containing few mitochondria and sparse endoplasmic reticulum. Type II cells, wedged between type I cells, are cuboidal and their cytoplasm is rich in mitochondria, endoplasmic reticulum, and also electron-dense lamellar inclusion bodies (SCHLIPKÖTER, 1954, 1956; KISCH, 1955, 1957; GIESEKING, 1956; KARRER, 1956*a*; VON HAYEK, 1958; KIKUTH, 1958; KLOSTERKÖTTER & THEMANN, 1958; BENSCH *et al.*, 1964; DE GASPERIS, 1968; DE GASPERIS & DONATELLI, 1968; CORRIN *et al.*, 1969; SCHILLER, 1969). According to HAPKE & PEDERSON (1968, 1969), type I alveolar lining cells participate in the clearing mechanism of the lung tissue, as they were most active in the aggregation of radioactive macroaggregated albumin injected intravenously. KLAUS *et al.* (1962); SUN & MENDENHALL (1965) and GRONIOWSKI & BICZYSKOWA (1966) associate lamellar transformation of type II cells mitochondria with the formation of the pulmonary surfactant. FREEMAN *et al.* (1968) described a conversion of these concentric membranes into lattice structures in the bronchiolar area of normal rats and rats exposed to NO_2.

The bizarre, ravelled, very electron-dense structures observed in rats dusted with aluminium powder resemble the lesions observed by SWIFT & HRUBAN (1964) in the rat's pancreas after the application of β-3-thienyl alanine.

Poly-2-vinylpyridine-N-oxide after FETZER (1967) is concentrated within lysosomes *via* the smooth endoplasmic reticulum. Besides the influences of poly-vinylpyridine-N-oxide on enzymatic reactions and membranes (DEHNEN & FETZER, 1967) the storage of the polymer in the lysosomes and the covering of their surface supposes that this may prevent the destruction of rat's liver lysosomes incubated with quartz.

A vesicular component in the outer zone of the axonema was found by PORTER (1957) in paramecium, by AFZELIUS (1962) in a myzostomoid helminth, by Humphreys & Swift (quoted from SATIR, 1965) in rotifer, by SATIR (1962, 1965) in elliptio and by

Porter (quoted from SATIR, 1965) in petromyzon. We can confirm this structure for the rat treated with tocopherol acetate (SCHILLER, 1969).

Ciliated and club cells are different functional stages of one type of cell (Figures 7 and 8). According to STOCKINGER (1966), in prenatal development non-differentiated cells turn first to secretory and afterwards to ciliated cells. For the goblet cells in the septum nasi of the rat STOCKINGER (1963) describes the characteristic structure (9 + 2 filaments) of the transverse section of a cinocilium in the apical cytoplasm of a goblet cell. In 1964 he demonstrated the transformation of a goblet cell producing mucus into a ciliated cell. In the ciliated cells of rats that had received N-cyclohexyl-N-methyl-(2-amino-3, 5-dibrombenzyl) ammonium chloride, MERKER (1966) showed changes in favour of a transformation into secretory cells.

REFERENCES

AFZELIUS, B. A. (1962). In: Proc. Fifth Int. Cong. Electron Microscopy, Philadelphia, Pennsylvania, August 29–September 5, 1962. Ed. S. S. Breese. Vol. 2. Biology. New York, Academic Press.
BENSCH, K., SCHAEFER, K. & AVERY, M. E. (1964). Science, N.Y. 145, 1318–1319.
CORRIN, B., CLARK, A E. & SPENCER, H. (1969). J. Anat. 104, 65–70.
DE GASPERIS, C. (1968). Quad. anat. prat., Napoli 24, 1–14.
DE GASPERIS, C. & DONATELLI, R. (1968). Bull. Ass. anat. 53, (141), 797–803.
DEHNEN, W. & FETZER, J. (1967). Naturwissenschaften 54, 23.
FETZER, J. (1967). Naturwissenschaften 54, 518–519.
FREEMAN, G., CRANE, S. C., STEPHENS, R. J. & FURIOSI, N. J. (1968). Yale J. Biol. Med. 40, 566–575.
GIESE, W. (1961). Die allgemeine Pathologie der äußeren Atmung. In: Handbuch der allgemeinen Pathologie, Ed. F. Büchner, E. Letterer & F. Roulet. Vol. 5, Hilfsmechanismen des Stoffwechsels. Part 1. Berlin, Springer. pp. 402–638.
GIESEKING, R. (1956). Beitr. path. Anat. 116, 177–199.
GIESEKING, R. (1958). Ergebn. allg. Path., Berlin 38, 92–126.
GRONIOWSKI, J. & BICZYSKOWA, W. (1966). 6th Int. Cong. Electron Microscopy, Kyoto 1966. Tokyo, Maruzen. pp. 597–598.
HAPKE, E. J. & PEDERSON, H. J. (1968). Science, N.Y. 161, 580–582.
HAPKE, E. J. & PEDERSON, H. J. (1969). Am. Rev. resp. Dis. 100, 194–205.
HAYEK, H. VON (1958). Verh. anat. Ges., Jena 55, 211.
KARRER, H. E. (1956a). Bull. Johns Hopkins Hosp. 98, 65–83.
KARRER, H. E. (1956b). Expl Cell Res. 10, 237–241.
KARRER, H. E. (1956c). J. biophys. biochem. Cytol. 2, Suppl. 287–292.
KARRER, H. E. (1956d). Expl Cell Res. 11, 542–547.
KIKUTH, W. (1958). In: Die Staublungenerkrankungen. Ed. K. W. Jotten and W. Klosterkötter, Vol. 3, pp. 353–368.
KISCH, B. (1955). Expl Med. Surg. 13, 101–117.
KISCH, B. (1957). Expl Med. Surg. 15, 101–118.
KLAUS, M., REISS, O. K., TOOLEY, W. H., PIEL, C. & CLEMENTS, J. A. (1962). Science, N.Y. 137, 750–751.
KLOSTERKÖTTER, W. & THEMANN, H. (1958). In: Die Staublungenerkrankungen. Ed. K. W. Jötten & W. Klosterkötter, Vol. 3, pp. 373–384.
LOW, F. N. (1953). Anat. Rec. 117, 241–263.
MERKER, H. J. (1966). Drug Res., Aulendorf 16, 509–516.
PORTER, K. R. (1957). Harvey Lect. 51, 175–228.
REYNOLDS, E. S. (1963). J. Cell Biol. 17, 208–212.
SATIR, P. (1962). Abstracts, 2nd Annual Meeting, Am. Soc. Cell Biol. San Francisco, p. 163.
SATIR, P. (1965). Structure and function in cilia and flagella. In: Protoplasmatologia. Handbuch der Protoplasmaforschung. Vol. 3 E. Ed. M. Alfert, H. Bauer, C. V. Harding & P. Sitte. Wien, Springer.

412   ERICH SCHILLER

SCHILLER, E. (1954). Geschichte, Pathogenese und Morphologie. In: *Die Pneumokoniosen. Ed.* G. Worth & E. Schiller. Köln, Staufen-Verlag. pp. 1–233.

SCHILLER, E. (1956a). *Anat. Anz.* **102,** 389–395.

SCHILLER, E. (1956b). *Z. Aerosol-Forsch. u. Ther.* **5,** 13–30.

SCHILLER, E. (1961a). Aluminiumlunge. In: *Handbuch der gesamten Arbeitsmedizin. Ed.* E. W. Baader, Berlin. Vol. 2. Berufskrankheiten, Teil 2, Berlin, Urban & Schwarzenberg. pp. 256–265.

SCHILLER, E. (1961b). Eisenlunge. In: *Handbuch der gesamten Arbeitsmedizin. Ed.* E. W. Baader. Vol. 2. Berufskrankheiten, Teil 2. Berlin, Urban & Schwarzenberg. pp. 266–270.

SCHILLER, E. (1961c). *Beitr. Silikose-Forsch.* (72), 47–53.

SCHILLER, E. (1963). In: *Untersuchungen auf dem Gebiet der Staub- und Silikosebekämpfungen.* 4 Tiel. Detmold: Bösmann. pp. 79–94.

SCHILLER, E. (1967) *Fortschr. Staublungenforsch.* **2,** 575–582.

SCHILLER, E. (1969). *Verh. anat. Ges., Jena* **64,** 597–598.

SCHILLER, E. (1970). *Verh. anat. Ges., Jena* **65.** In Press.

SCHLIPKÖTER, H.-W. (1954). *Dt. med. Wschr.* **79,** 1658–1659, 1675.

SCHLIPKÖTER, H.-W. (1956). In: *Neue Ergebnisse der Aerosol-Forschung.* Bericht über den 2. Aerosol-Kongress des Deutschen Kuratoriums für Aerosol-Forschung in Münster/Westf. *Ed.* H. Nückel & G. Pfefferkorn. Stuttgart, Schattauer. pp. 238–252.

STOCKINGER, L. (1963). *Z. Zellforsch. mikrosk. Anat.* **59,** 443–466.

STOCKINGER, L. (1964). *Verh. anat. Ges., Jena* **60,** 523.

STOCKINGER, L. (1966). *Wien. klin. Wschr.* **78,** 523–525, fig. pp. 518–519.

SUN, C. N. & MENDENHALL, R. M. (1965). *Cytologia* **30,** 465–469.

SWIFT, H. & HRUBAN, Z. (1964). *Fed. Proc. Fedn Am. Socs exp. Biol.* **23,** 1026–1037.

TAYLOR, IV, G. J. & HARRIS, W. S. (1970). *J. Am. med. Ass.* **214,** 81–85.

DISCUSSION

B. RASCHE: Do you think that phagocytes containing dust are able to return into the interstitium?

Dr. SCHILLER: The way of dust-laden cells into the pulmonary interstice and its lymphatics was discussed by Policard in 1955, but he was unable to demonstrate it. Our own experiments, reported in 1955, 1956, 1959 and 1961, showed free particles entering the rat's interstice and being engulfed by interstitial phagocytes accumulating there. According to Policard and Collet (1963), these histocytes markedly differ from alveolar phagocytes. As to man and cat Policard, Collet and Martin (1964) write: "Dans ces voies lymphatiques peuvent être entraînées les cellules à poussières venues des alvéoles d'amont". In a recent note (3rd trimester, 1970) of the "Institut National de Recherche et de Sécurité" (note no. 697–60–70) there is the comment: "Les particules ainsi phagocytées peuvent alors être entraînées, soit vers l'extérieur comme dans le cas des poussières déposées sur les bronches, soit vers l'intérieur du tissu pulmonaire en passant à travers les cloisons des alvéoles".

J. BRUCH: At the beginning you demonstrated two corner cells. The corner cells lie immediately beside the basal membrane and show characteristics of lamellate bodies and features typical of the mitochrondria and reticular membranes. A septal migration of macrophages would loosen and broaden the basal membrane. Such a change in the basal membrane was, however, not discernible.

My second point concerns the myelin figures demonstrated by Schlipköter in lungs exposed to quartz dust. Are they produced by macrophages or by corner cells?

H.-W. SCHLIPKÖTER: In electronmicroscopic slides of macrophages we are concerned in many cases with so-called corner cells and these must be clearly distinguished from alveolar epithelial cells and alveolar macrophages. Alveolar macrophages are quite accurately defined using electron-microscopy. Also the appearance of bulb-scale, onion-peel formations included in these corner cells is not attributable to PVNO action.

Dr. SCHILLER: Electron micrographs reveal three types of cells coating the alveolar wall: type I pneumonocytes cover the major part of the alveolar surface. Type II pneumonocytes are the great alveolar cells or specific cells as called by Kisch (1955). A third type has been identified in the rat's lung by Meyrick and Reid (1968). Only a small part of the membrane of the type III pneumonocyte contributes to the free alveolar surface as most of the surface is covered with a thin cytoplasmic process from a type I pneumonocyte or abuts against a type II cell. The relatively small free area is covered with microvilli of the same dimensions as the microvilli found in the epithelium of the small intestine. Glycogen granules are found in abundance through the cell.

The alveolar macrophages according to Collet, Normand-Reuet and Policard (1967) may be derived from a small cell analogous to a lymphocyte: little bright cytoplasm with a sparse smooth ergastoplasmic reticulum, a few Golgi saccules and some voluminous mitochondria. While the cytoplasm increases the size of the nucleus decreases. At the end of the development lysosomes appear and the Golgi apparatus gets prominent. After Caulet, Adnet and Hopfner (1968) the alveolar macrophages lying in the alveolar space do not contain any complex lipid inclusions but only neutral fat; alkaline phosphatase, cytochrome, oxidase, several dehydrogenases and unspecific esterase are not demonstrable or show but little activity. Alveolar macrophages contain large quantities of aryl sulfatase while type II pneumonocytes show only traces of this enzyme (Corrin and Clark, 1968; Goldfischer, Kikkawa and Hoffman, 1968).

By labelling desoxyribonucleic acid with tritium Bowden, Davies and Wyatt (1968) identified two cell populations in the pulmonary alveoli of the mouse: the generation time of the macrophages is about 7 days, while that of the alveolar epithelial cells ranges between 28 and 35 days.

As to the origin of the pulmonary surfactant, Goldenberg, Buckingham and Sommers (1969) found osmiophilic inclusions of type II pneumonocytes to be discharged into the alveolar lumina by a merocrine process. The secretory activity could be increased by pilocarpine. Between 4 and 7 hours after pilocarpine administration free alveolar macrophages increase massively and appear to ingest excess alveolar contents (see also Kistler, Caldwell and Weibel, 1967).

J. D. BRAIN: I would point out that the lungs Dr. Schiller showed us were fixed by intracheal injection of a glutaraldehyde solution. Unfortunately, this technique is inappropriate for studying the alveolar surface although it is adequate for examination of the fixed cells of the lung. During the intratracheal injection of the fixative, airway mucus, debris and cells are carried down to the alveoli by the fixative solution. Similarly, alveolar macrophages on the epithelium may be lost or at least rounded up. The surfactant lining layer is inevitably lost and artifact myelin figures are sometimes produced.

Thus, I am forced to be sceptical about the configuration and location of alveolar macrophages as described by Dr. Schiller. I am also uncertain as to the identity of the myelin figures Dr. Schiller described. As Weibel and Gil have pointed out, if one is to look at the surfactant layer, alveolar macrophages, and alveolar surface in its undistorted, natural state, unusual care must be taken to fix the lung without distorting these highly labile structures. The preferred technique seems to be intravascular perfusion of fixative (at a controlled perfusion pressure and at a controlled lung volume). Using this technique Gil and Weibel have demonstrated the surfactant lining layer and alveolar macrophages spread out and adhering to the alveolar epithelium.

Dr. SCHILLER: My experiments were done in 1967, and the latest animals were sacrificed on January 15, 1968. Weibel, Kistler and Töndury (1966) introduced 1 % OsO_4 (phosphate buffered at pH 7·4) into the airways. Two years later Gil and Weibel used prefixation with glutar aldehyde, washing in isotonic buffer, and osmium postfixation. In order to avoid a destruction of the hydrophobic surface film at the moment of changing the intra-alveolar air for water Weibel and Gil (1968) perfused their rats from the inferior vena cava at a vascular pressure of 40 mm H_2O. This resulted in a slight overdistension and consequently in a side-to-side approximation of capillaries in the relaxed alveolar septum. As my primary aim was not to study the surface layer but the intracellular structures in relation to the experimental prophylaxis of pneumoconioses I decided to continue my electron microscopic technique as started in 1967.

As I pointed out at the 65th Meeting of the "Anatomische Gesellschaft" held at Würzburg (April 6–9, 1970) phospholipids are fixed neither by glutar aldehyde nor by OsO_4 (Dermer, 1969). According to Elbers, Ververgaert and Demel (1965) these ampholytes must form a triple complex with a cation and an anion to persist as a layer of electron dense polymorphous material. Dermer (*loc. cit.*) does not identify the structures observed by Weibel and Gil (1968) with the pulmonary surfactant. As Petrik (1969), I leave unanswered the question whether a local change of the surfactant by irritation might produce tubular myelin.

ACTION DE COMPOSES DE L'ALUMINIUM SUR LA FORMATION ET L'EVOLUTION DE LESIONS SILICOTIQUES EXPERIMENTALES

H. Daniel, J. C. Martin et L. Le Bouffant

Centre d'Etudes et Recherches des Charbonnages de France, Groupe Pneumoconiose, B.P. 27 F-60—Creil, France

Abstract — The use of aerosols containing aluminium chlorhydroxyallantoïnate or aluminium hydroxide shows a possibility of preventing the formation of silicotic lesions produced in the rat by quartz inhalation. The efficiency of this treatment is shown by long-lasting experiments over 14 months. Prevention is quite complete for an amount of 5 mg of aluminium compound (calculated as Al_2O_3)/m³ in the case of on average dusting of about 6 mg of quartz per lung. For very high concentrations — for instance 12 mg of quartz per lung — complete protection would be achieved by using amounts of aerosols greater than 5 mg/m³ or longer lasting treatments.

Evolution of already formed lesions is stopped by the use of the same treatment.

The aerosols used showed no toxicity for the lung.

INTRODUCTION

Les essais de prevention des lésions pulmonaires provoquées par l'inhalation des poussières de quartz ont fait l'objet de nombreux travaux dans deux directions principales:

— la plus ancienne concerne l'utilisation d'aluminium métallique et de divers composés aluminiques. Ce sont les auteurs canadiens Denny *et al.* (1937) qui, les premiers, mettaient en évidence l'action inhibitrice de l'aluminium métallique sur la formation de lésions silicotiques expérimentales. De nombreux autres travaux effectués principalement avec des hydroxydes d'aluminium et divers sels de ce métal ont donné des résultats variables suivant la nature des produits employés et suivant les conditions expérimentales.

— la deuxième voie de recherche concerne une substance polymère: le polyvinylpyridine-N-oxyde (P 204) utilisé pour la première fois par Schlipköter *et al.* (1961). Le P 204 est capable de supprimer les réactions tissulaires dues au quartz, qu'il soit administré par voie générale ou par aérosols.

Nos travaux se rapportent à la première catégorie de produits. Après avoir mis en évidence la propriété que possèdent certaines alumines hydratées naturelles d'inhiber les effets tissulaires du quartz, nous avons recherché des composés plus solubles qui ne s'accumulent pas dans les poumons et ne risquent pas d'en augmenter la charge coniotique. Nos essais ont porté principalement sur deux substances: le chlorhydroxyallantoïnate d'aluminium (CHA-Al) et un sol d'hydroxyde d'aluminium très dispersé (Policard *et al.*, 1966, Le Bouffant *et al.*, 1969). Ces substances sont utilisées sous forme d'aérosols.

Leur efficacité pour prévenir la formation de lésions silicotiques a été nettement démontrée à la suite de plusieurs expériences d'une durée relativement courte comprenant deux mois d'empoussiérage suivis de trois mois d'évolution. On pouvait alors se demander si l'action de ce traitement était vraiment durable pour des durées d'évolution plus longues et si la cytotoxicité du quartz ne risquait pas de réapparaître progressivement. Des expériences d'un an ont alors été entreprises. Elles comportent deux parties: étude de l'action préventive des aérosols, le traitement étant commencé en même temps que l'empoussiérage et recherche d'un effect curatif éventuel sur des lésions silicotiques déjà établies.

METHODE EXPERIMENTALE

Ces essais sont réalisés sur des rats qui sont empoussiérés par inhalation de quartz. La concentration en quartz dans la cage est de 300 mg/m^3 et les séances quotidiennes d'empoussiérage durent $2 \cdot 5$ à 4 h, pendant 2 ou 3 mois suivant les expériences.

Les rats traités inhalent des aérosols de CHA-A1 ou d'hydroxyde 30 min par jour pendant le temps de l'empoussiérage et ensuit 2 fois par semaine pour le traitement préventif et 3 fois par semaine pour le traitement curatif.

La concentration en aérosols dans les cages, exprimée en mg d'Al$_2$O$_3$ par m^3 pour les deux produits examinés est de l'ordre de 5 à 6 mg.

Divers groupes de rats servent de témoins: rats exposés uniquement au quartz, rats non empoussiérés mais traités par les aérosols et rats témoins normaux.

L'efficacité du traitement est appréciée par détermination du poids des poumons, de la quantité de collagène formé et de la silice retenue dans les poumons, De plus, l'examen des coupes histologiques indique l'aspect des lésions obtenues.

ACTION PREVENTIVE DES AEROSOLS

Elle comprend deux expériences réalisées avec des empoussiérages d'une durée différente.

Dans le premier cas, la charge des poumons en quartz est de l'ordre de 4 à 6 mg, ce qui représente un empoussiérage moyen. Les analyses effectuées après différents délais d'évolution montrent que l'augmentation du poids des poumons est assez lente mais régulière dans la série quartz seul (Figure 1); après 14 mois, le poids des poumons atteint 4 à 5 fois celui de poumons normaux. Au contraire, chez les animaux traités, les poumons subissent une très légère augmentation de poids pendant les premiers mois mais pas de modification ensuite.

La synthèse de collagène sous l'action des poussières subit sensiblement la même évolution. Relativement faible dans les premiers stades de formation des lésions, elle est après 14 mois de 50 mg par rat. Au contraire, sous l'influence du traitement et quel que soit l'aérosol employé, la quantité de collagène formé n'est que de 6 à 11 mg et elle n'augmente pratiquement pas en fonction du temps.

La réduction importante de la formation des lésions ne peut pas être attribuée à une diminution de la quantité de poussière retenue dans les poumons, mais bien à une inhibition de la toxicité du quartz. En effet, les quantités de quartz dosées dans les poumons sont, pour le délai le plus long, de 4,3 mg pour les rats non traités et de 3,5 et 4,6 mg pour les rats soumis aux aérosols.

Ces résultats sont confirmés par l'examen des coupes histologiques. Avec le quartz, on observe la présence de lésions silicotiques d'intensité moyenne dont la fibrose atteint les grades II et III de King. Par contre, il n'y a aucune tendance à la formation de lésions fibreuses et la structure pulmonaire demeure normale chez les rats traités par les aérosols. Dans les ganglions trachéo-bronchiques, la concentration très élevée en particules de quartz fait que la protection exercée par lees aérosols est nettement moins efficace que dans les poumons.

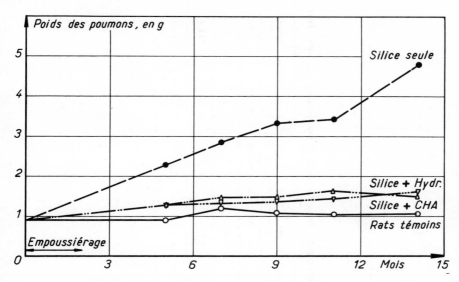

FIGURE 1. Traitement préventif. Evolution du poids des poumons en fonction du temps (dose moyenne de quartz).

Dans la deuxième expérience qui comporte un empoussiérage de 3 mois au lieu de 2, avec des séances quotidiennes de 4 h, la charge des poumons en quartz est beaucoup plus élevée: environ 12 mg à la fin de l'empoussiérage. La comparaison des poumons ne porte que sur le point 12 mois (Tableau 1). A ce stade les rats témoins silice présentent des lésions très importantes et massives avec un poids moyen des poumons de 7 g, au lieu de 1,2 g pour des rats normaux. Les poumons des rats traités au contraire ont seulement doublé de poids et les lésions observées sont très réduites.

Parallèlement, la synthèse de collagène est très élevée et l'importance des lésions est telle dans ce cas que le traitement par aérosols n'a pas assuré une protection complète des poumons. Il y a néanmoins une différence très grande entre animaux témoins et traités. La réduction de la quantité de collagène formé sous l'action des poussières est de 76% avec les aérosols de CHA-A1 et 82% avec les aérosols d'hydroxyde.

Dans cette expérience, nous avons volontairement réalisé un empoussiérage au quartz très massif, de façon à déterminer la limite d'action des aérosols dans les conditions étudiées. Il est probable qu'une adaptation de ces conditions, par exemple, des séances d'aérolosation plus longues ou plus fréquentes auraient permis d'obtenir à nouveau un effet protecteur complet.

TABLEAU 1. ÉTUDE DE L'ACTION PRÉVENTIVE POUR DEUX CHARGES PULMONAIRES EN QUARTZ DIFFÉRENTES

	Série I: 6 mg par poumon				Série II: 12 mg par poumon			
	Témoins normaux	Quartz seul	Quartz + CHA-A1	Quartz + hydroxyde	Témoins normaux	Quartz seul	Quartz + CHA-A1	Quartz + hydroxyde
Poids des poumons (g)	1,04	4,77	1,51	1,57	1,22	6,97	2,63	2,38
Quantité de collagène formée (mg)	—	49,4	5,7	11,4	—	144,2	34,3	26,2
Collagène/quartz	—	11,5	1,6	2,5	—	13,0	4,5	4,2

ACTION CURATIVE

Une seule expérience a été réalisée avec un empoussiérage intense d'une durée de 3 mois. Le traitement a été commencé pour une partie des rats à la fin de l'empoussiérage (traitement curatif précoce) et pour les autres, 3 mois plus tard (traitement curatif tardif). Les résultats connus ne portent actuellement que sur le poids des poumons (Figure 2). Il apparaît très clairement d'après les courbes d'évolution du poids des

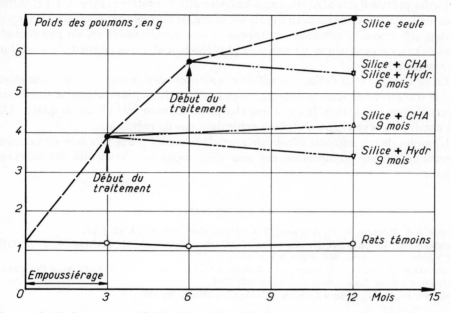

FIGURE 2. Traitement curatif. Evolution du poids des poumons en fonction du temps (dose forte de quartz).

poumons que les aérosols ont empêché l'évolution des lésions. On constate également qu'il n'y a pas eu de régression de ces lésions. Il faut cependant préciser qu'une charge pulmonaire en quartz aussi élevée provoque des lésions très rapidement évolutives et constitue de ce fait une condition nettement défavorable pour apprécier l'efficacité d'un traitement curatif.

D'autres expériences doivent être faites avec des empoussiérages qui se rapprochent davantage des conditions observées dans la pratique.

De même que dans tous les essais précédents, l'efficacité du chlorhydroxyallantoïnate et du sol colloïdal d'hydroxyde est du même ordre.

EFFET DES AEROSOLS EMPLOYES SEULS

Deux groupes de rats ont été traités uniquement par les aérosols afin de mettre en évidence la nocivité pulmonaire éventuelle des substances utilisées. Les conditions d'exposition sont les mêmes que pour les essais précédents soit 5 séances de 30 min par semaine pendant les 3 premiers mois et 3 séances par semaine jusqu'à un an. A ce stade, les poumons ont aspect normal. Leur poids ainsi que leur teneur en collagène sont identiques à ceux de poumons de rats témoins de même âge. Les quantités d'aluminium dosées dans les poumons des rats traités sont à peine supérieures à celles de poumons normaux: 70 à 90 μg par poumon (exprimés en Al_2O_3) après un an de traitement et 10 à 15 μg chez les témoins. Ceci montre que les deux composés expérimentés ne s'accumulent pas dans les poumons.

CONCLUSION

L'effet préventif des aérosols employés peut être considéré comme total et durable pour une charge pulmonaire en quartz moyenne. Si les rats sont soumis à un empoussiérage très massif, l'efficacité du traitement aux mêmes doses est un peu moindre; dans ce cas, on peut penser qu'une dose plus élevée d'aérosols permettrait d'améliorer les résultats.

En ce qui concerne l'effect curatif de ces aérosols une première expérience montre que le traitement de lésions silicotiques en cours de formation permet la stabilisation de ces lésions même dans le cas d'une charge pulmonaire très élevée en quartz. Dans ces conditions sévères, on n'observe cependant pas de régression.

L'emploi de ces aérosols administrés pendant un an à des rats non empoussiérés n'entraine aucune modification des poumons, montrant l'innocuité des substances utilisées.

REFERENCES

Denny, J. J., Robson, W. D. & Irwin, D. A. (1937). *Can. med. Ass. J.* **37**, 1–11.
Policard, A., Letort, M., Charbonnier, J., Daniel-Moussard, H. & Martin, J. C. (1966). *C.r.hebd. Séanc. Acad. Sci., Paris* **263**, 1789.
Le Bouffant, L., Daniel-Moussard, H., Martin, J. C., Charbonnier, J., Letort, M. & Policard, A. (1969). *C.r.hebd. Séanc. Acad.Sci., Paris* **268**, 3001.
Schlipköter, H.-W. & Brockaus, A. (1961). *Klin. Wschr.* **39**, 1182.

DISCUSSION

C. L. SANDERS: Were your treatments with the aluminium compounds toxic to areas outside the lung?

Mme DANIEL: We only considered the long-term pulmonary toxicity of the aerosols used; it was absolutely zero under our experimental conditions. Elsewhere, tests of acute and chronic toxicity have shown that aluminium allantoinates have a very low toxicity which only manifests itself at larger doses than actually used in certain pharmaceutical products.

H. ANTWEILER: What ideas have you on the mechanism of the impressive inhibitive action that you have shown?

Mme DANIEL: It is probably a surface action. We were able to show by experiments *in vitro* that quartz suspended in a solution of CHA-Al then washed in water underwent surface modifications resulting in a marked diminution in solubility, a disappearance of surface crystalline structure as shown by electron diffraction, and an almost complete inhibition of its harmful effects on tissue during three months in the lungs.

O. G. RAABE: Anti-perspirant body deodorants sold in the U.S.A. and presumably elsewhere contain aluminium chlorhydroxyallantoinate. Accidental inhalation of these sprays has been considered as a problem. Do your results not suggest that inhalation of these sprays might in fact be of therapeutic value?

Mme DANIEL: We have no information on this question.

ON THE CELL TOXICITY OF MINERAL DUSTS

H. Sakabe, K. Koshi and H. Hayashi

National Institute of Industrial Health, Kawasaki, Japan

Abstract — Cytotoxicity and hemolysis were studied in 22 silicate dusts and in quartz dust. The effects of different silicate dusts on acid phosphatase activation, lactic acid production and hemolysis were similar but quartz had a different effect on the macrophages and red blood cells. The biological activity of the surface seemed to be different between silicate and quartz. Changes of cytotoxicity and hemolytic action of 12 silicate dusts and quartz dust after heat treatment were studied. Many minerals lost their cytotoxicity and hemolytic action by heat treatment, but serpentine minerals heated around 650°C showed a high biological activity.

Quartz lost its cytotoxicity by heating over about 500°C, and these particles absorbed methylene blue though quartz treated under about 500°C did not.

The role of serum in cytotoxicity of mineral dusts was also studied.

INTRODUCTION

We have studied the cytotoxicity of mineral dusts to clarify the pathogenesis of pneumoconiosis. In this paper, we intend to review our recent work carried out by Koshi *et al.* (1968; 1969) and Hayashi *et al.* (1969) with several new data added.

MATERIALS

Silicate Dust Samples

Dust samples used in our studies are shown in Table 1. Particle sizes of silicate minerals were prepared to be under about 10 μm in length.

Ground Quartz and Alkali-Treated Quartz

Ground quartz: Finely crushed quartz particles were ground for 6 h in the dry state with a mechanical grinding apparatus and sized to be 0·5–2 μm.

Alkali-treated quartz: Ground quartz particles were boiled in a platinum vessel three times, first for 20 min and then twice for 10 min, with 10% NaOH solution renewed each time. After this treatment, the particles were washed with water 20 times.

Heat-treatment of mineral dusts: Dusts were heated in air in an electric furnace at the rate of 5°C/min and kept at various temperatures for 1 h. After cooling they were used for the experiment.

DETERMINATION OF CYTOTOXICITY OF MINERAL DUSTS

Macrophages

Macrophages were collected from the intraperitoneal cavities of rats 72 h after the injection of sterile Tyrode's solution containing 0·001 % glycogen, and washed with Tyrode's solution. The cells were suspended in Tyrode's solution in a concentration of 1×10^7 cells/ml and used for the determination of cytotoxicity of mineral dusts.

TABLE 1. SPECIES, LOCALITY AND DESCRIPTION OF THE SILICATE DUSTS USED IN THE EXPERIMENTS

No.	Species	Locality	Description and Reference
Serpentine			
1	Chrysotile	Rhodesia	U.I.C.C. Standard Reference Sample*
2	Chrysotile	Yamabe, Japan	Oinuma & Hayashi (1968)
3	Chrysotile	Wagasennin, Japan	
4	Clino-chrysotile	Canada	
5	2-layer clino-chrysotile	Sambagawa, Japan	Shimoda (1967)
6	1-layer ortho-serpentine	Ogose, Japan	
7	6-layer ortho-serpentine	Ogose, Japan	Shimoda (1967)
8	Antigorite	Komori, Japan	Shimoda (1967)
9	Antigorite	Kamuikotan, Japan	Oinuma & Hayashi (1968)
Amphibole			
10	Anthophyllite	Unknown	Koshi et al. (1968)
11	Amosite	South Africa	U.I.C.C. Standard Reference Sample*
12	Actinolite	Ohgushi, Japan	Koshi et al. (1968)
13	Richterite	Nagatoro, Japan	
14	Crocidolite	South Africa	U.I.C.C. Standard Reference Sample*
Sepiolite			
15	α-sepiolite	Canada	Shimoda (1964)
16	α-sepiolite	Akatani, Japan	Imai et al. (1967)
17	α-sepiolite	Kuzu, Japan	Imai et al. (1966)
18	Aluminian sepiolite	Spain	Otsuka et al. (1968)
19	β-sepiolite	Oheyama, Japan	Otsuka et al. (1968)
Palygorskite			
20	Palygorskite	Kuzu, Japan	Minato et al. (1969)
21	Attapulgite	Kawahage, Japan	Otsuka et al. (1968)
22	Attapulgite	Attapulgas, U.S.A.	
Kaolin			
23	Halloysite	Kusatsu, Japan	Hayashi & Oinuma (1963)
24	Kaolinate	Kampaku, Japan	Hayashi & Oinuma (1963)
Mica			
25	Illite	Sanshi, Japan	

* U.I.C.C. Standard Reference Samples were presented by Dr. J. S. Harington.

Lactic Acid Production

5×10^6 macrophages in $0·5$ ml of Tyrode's solution were mixed with 2 mg of each sample of dust suspended in 1 ml of Tyrode's solution. After 3 h incubation at 37°C, 1 ml of 10% TCA solution was added. The amount of lactic acid in the supernatant was measured by BAKER & SUMMERSON's method (1941).

Acid Phosphatase Activity

To 5×10^6 cells in $0·5$ ml of Tyrode's solution of 1 mg of sample dust ($0·4$ mg in the case of heat-treated quartz) in 1 ml of Tyrode's solution was added, and promptly after mixing the supernatant was removed. Substrate-buffer solution composed of $0·01$ M disodium phenylphosphate and $0·2$ M citrate buffer (pH $4·9$) was added to the precipitated cells. After incubation at 37°C for 20 min the reaction was stopped by $0·5$ N NaOH solution. Yielded phenol was determined by the method of KIND & KING (1954).

TTC Reducing Capacity

To 5×10^6 cells suspended in Tyrode's solution containing 20% rat serum various amounts of each dust sample ($0·4$ mg in the case of heat-treated quartz) were added and, after incubation for 1 h at 37°C, 2, 3, 5-triphenyl tetrazolium chloride and cystein solution was added. After reincubation for 1 h at 37°C the formazan produced was determined by the method of MARKS & JAMES (1959). Toxicity was expressed as the amount of dust necessary to depress the TTC reducing capacity of the cells by 50%.

Hemolytic Action

Blood was taken from the hearts of rats with a syringe containing $3·8$% sodium citrate solution. Blood cells were washed three times with saline solution and the white cell layer was removed from the sediment. To 1 ml of 3% red blood cell saline suspension 1 ml of saline solution containing 2 mg of sample dust was added and the mixture was incubated for 1 h at 37°C shaking at the rate of 40 times per min. After incubation the mixture was centrifuged and the amount of hemoglobin in the supernatant was determined spectrophotometrically at 530 nm. Hemolytic activity of the dust was expressed as a percentage of the total hemoglobin which was liberated from total cells by freezing and thawing.

CYTOTOXICITY OF MINERAL DUSTS

Correlation Between Tests of Cytotoxicity

The effects of dusts on lactic acid production, acid phosphatase activity of the macrophages and red blood cells were examined on 22 silicate dust samples (No. 1 to No. 22 in Table 1). We found a high correlation between the effects of dusts on acid phosphatase activity and on lactic acid production, between their effect on lactic acid production and hemolysis by them, and between hemolysis by them and their effect on acid phosphatase activity. Figure 1 shows the close correlation between acid phosphatase activation and hemolysis by silicate dusts. As far as these silicate minerals are concerned it may be said that a dust which produces hemolysis to a larger extent has a greater cytotoxic effect on the macrophages. However, this relation cannot be extended to all mineral dusts. Alkali-treated quartz increased the acid phosphatase activity, inhibited the lactic acid production, decreased the TTC reducing capacity, but it did not cause greater hemolysis. Ground quartz, on the contrary, had no adverse effects on the macrophages but it did produce hemolysis. Figure 2 shows this relation.

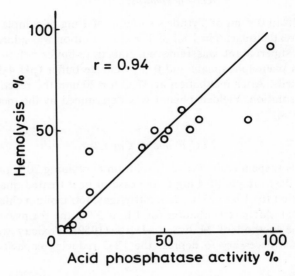

FIGURE 1. Correlation between the effect of various silicate dusts on acid phosphatase activity and hemolysis.

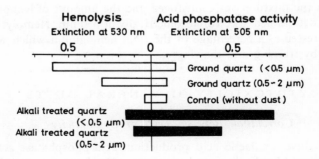

FIGURE 2. Hemolysis and acid phosphatase activation by quartz particles.

Mineralogical Group and Cytotoxicity

If the 22 silicate dust samples used in this experiment are classified into the following six mineral groups, (i) antigorite and ortho-serpentine group, (ii) chrysotile group, (iii) clino-chrysotile group, (iv) amphibole group, (v) sepiolite group and (vi) palygorskite group. It may be said that mineral dusts which belong to the same group show a similar cytotoxicity even if they vary in locality and minute chemical composition. Figure 3 shows this effect of dusts on lactic acid production and TTC reducing capacity.

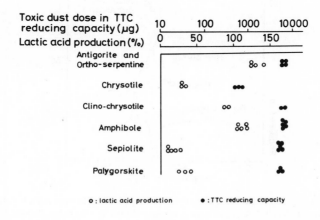

FIGURE 3. Effects of silicates dusts on lactic acid production and TTC reducing capacity.

CYTOTOXICITY OF HEAT-TREATED MINERAL DUSTS

Heat-Treatment of Silicate Minerals, Especially Serpentines

Dust samples No. 1, 2, 5, 8, 10, 11, 13, 14, 17, 20, 23, 24 and 25 were heated at various temperatures for 1 h, and the effects of these treated dusts on lactic acid production and hemolysis were determined. Sepiolite and kaolinite showed a gradual drop of cytotoxicity and hemolysis with the increase of treating temperature, though there were some fluctuations. The cytotoxicity of palygorskite showed a gradual decrease with an increase of temperature but it rose at 1250°C. Four amphibole minerals showed a similar weak toxicity in both the original and heat-treated samples, and no noticeble change of hemolysis by heat-treatment. Only serpentine minerals showed a marked change. When three chrysotile minerals were heated, inhibition of lactic acid production decreased gradually till 400–500°C, but beyond this temperature it increased rapidly and then decreased again after showing the highest inhibition at 500–700°C. Three chrysotile dusts showed a similar hemolytic pattern, that is, a remarkable increase in hemolysis in the temperature range of about 500° to 800°C.

Cytotoxicity and hemolytic effects of heat-treated antigorite did not differ much from chrysotile. Figure 4 shows the results on chrysotile (U.I.C.C.). Concerning the mineralogical study, chrysotile showed the endothermic peak followed by an exothermic one in the range of 600°–900°C, and x-ray and infrared analysis proved that chrysotile was transformed into forsterite in the temperature range of 550°–700°C. Since chrysotile and forsterite coexist in the chrysotile sample heated for 1 h around 650°C, rapid changes in the biological activity of chrysotile may be due to the highly

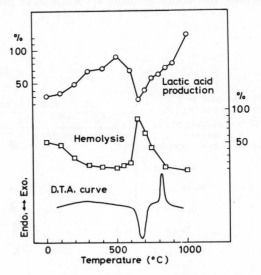

FIGURE 4. Cytotoxicity of Chrysotile (U.I.C.C.) heated to various temperatures.
(It should be noted that DTA curve does not correspond to the other curves, since chyrostile samples are heated for one hour at each temperature but in DTA temperature increases at rate of 5°C/min.)

disordered state during the transformation. However, mineralogical changes were also observed in other silicate minerals when they were heated but corresponding changes in their toxicity were not evident. Electron microscopic study of these heated chrysotile fibers showed that the characteristic uniform and regular appearance of the original fiber was lost gradually with the increase of temperature.

Heat Treatment of Alkali-Treated Quartz Particles

As seen in Figure 5, the cytotoxic effect of quartz was lost when alkali-treated quartz was heated over about 500°C. Alkali-treatment could not recover the cytotoxicity of quartz which became inert after heat treatment. It is not clear whether this may have some relation to the inversion point of 573°C between low and high quartz or to some other factors such as cracks. X-ray diffraction, infra-red analysis, and ESR absorption did not show any difference between the original alkali-treated quartz and quartz treated with heat over 500°C. Only methylene blue adsorption differentiated these two sorts of quartz. When methylene blue was added to the particle suspension in water, precipitated dusts took a blue colour in the case of non-toxic, heat-treated quartz which was not seen in original alkali-treated quartz.

THE ROLE OF SERUM IN CYTOTOXICITY OF MINERAL DUST

On Silicate

Figure 3 shows the effect of mineral dusts on TTC reducing capacity. Dust samples used in this experiment were the same as in the experiment for determination of the effect of dusts on lactic acid production. This figure shows that minerals belonging to chrysotile, sepiolite and palygorskite groups which inhibited lactic acid production

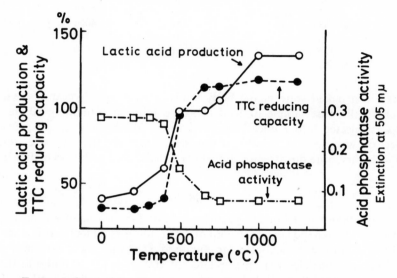

FIGURE 5. Cytotoxicity of quartz particles heated to various temperatures.

had no inhibitory effect on TTC reducing capacity. This discrepancy was assumed to be due to the serum added to the medium for determining TTC reducing capacity. In other words, it is assumed that silicate minerals absorbed the added serum and became inert in the TTC reducing test. Detailed studies were carried out on the effect of heat-treated chrysotile (U.I.C.C.) on lactic acid production and hemolysis in connection with protein.

As seen in Table 2, among the chrysotile samples, the original sample and the sample treated at 650°C had the highest suppressing effect on the lactic acid production. However, when 0·2 ml of 10% bovine albumin was added to the cell-dust system the two samples behaved differently. The inhibitory effect of the original sample was reduced remarkably by albumin, but that of a sample treated at 650°C was not reduced. A similar phenomenon was also observed in hemolysis, that is, hemolysis by the original chrysotile sample was reduced by 50% with the addition of 11 mg albumin, but 4000 mg albumin was needed for the same reducing effect in the sample treated at 750°C which showed a hemolytic action similar to that of the original sample without albumin. This means that the former sample easily adsorbed protein and became inert but the latter sample absorbed it with difficulty. If so, chrysotile heated at 650°C or 750°C may be very harmful to the body when introduced into it, since it

TABLE 2. EFFECTS OF HEAT TREATED CHRYSOTILE (U.I.C.C.) ON MACROPHAGES,
ERYTHROCYTES AND MICE

Heat Treatment	Lactic acid Production without albumin (% of control)	Lactic acid production with albumin (% of control)	Hemolysis (% of control)	Amount of albumin for reducing hemolysis by 50% (mg)	Gain of body weight 8 days after injection (g)
Original	30	112	52	11	8·0
200°C	48		28	36	
300°C	68		17	38	7·2
500°C	90		12	21	7·7
650°C	25	36	87	9000	died
750°C	58		44	4000	died
850°C	73		15	540	6·4
1000°C	125		8	10	5·1

might stay in a naked state in the body fluids. To test this hypothesis, each heat-treated chrysotile dust sample (0·5 ml of saline solution containing 10 mg of each sample) was injected into 3 mice intraperitoneally. Mean body weight gains 8 days after injection were seen in Table 2. It was very significant that all mice which were injected with chrysotile dust treated at 650°C or 750°C died within 48 h after injection.

On Quartz

To 6 mg of alkali-treated quartz particles 3 ml of Tyrode's solution was added and stirred well by a magnetic stirrer; 0·6 ml of rat serum was added to this dust suspension and the mixture was incubated for 20 min at 37°C shaking at 40 times per min. After incubation, particles were precipitated at 2000 rpm for 10 min and the supernatant was decanted. Precipitated particles were resuspended in 3 ml of Tyrode's solution. These particles were assumed to be coated with serum. Naked quartz particle suspensions were prepared by suspending 6 mg alkali-treated quartz in 3 ml of Tyrode's solution. The effects of these two sorts of quartz particles on the lactic acid production, acid phosphatase activity and TTC reducing capacity were examined. To 5×10^6 cells in 0·5 ml of Tyrode's solution 1 ml of dust suspension was added to see the effect of lactic acid production and 0·2 ml of it was added for the acid phosphatase and TTC reducing capacity survey. Results are shown in Table 3.

The cytotoxic activity of alkali-treated quartz covered with serum was remarkably

TABLE 3. EFFECTS OF QUARTZ COVERED WITH SERUM ON CELL ACTIVITIES

Dust	Lactic acid production: 3 h. (μg)	Acid phosphatase activity; phenol production: 20 min. (μg)	TTC reducing capacity; formazan production: 2 h. (μg)
Control (without quartz)	61·0	4·0	38·0
Alkali-treated quartz	22·5	15·2	4·0
Alkali-treated quartz covered with serum	53·6	5·5	14·5

reduced in comparison with naked quartz. This suppression of cytotoxicity of quartz by serum coating was not seen when the incubation time was prolonged as seen in Table IV. The experiment shown in Table 4 was designed to study the change of effect of serum coated quartz on lactic acid production in course of time, and 2 ml of

TABLE 4. CHANGE OF INHIBITION OF LACTIC ACID PRODUCTION BY SERUM-COATED QUARTZ IN COURSE OF TIME (IN MEDIUM CONTAINING 20% SERUM)

Dust	Lactic acid production			
	3 h incubation		22 h incubation	
	(Tg)	(%)	(Tg)	(%)
Control (without quartz)	182	100	622·5	100
Alkali-treated quartz	145	80·1	207·5	32·8
Alkali-treated quartz covered with serum	149	82·1	242·2	38·3

Tyrode's solution containing serum (20%), quartz (2 mg) and macrophages (3·52 × 10^6 cells) was incubated at 37°C for 3 h and 22 h respectively. Alkali-treated quartz showed a similar reducing effect on lactic acid production regardless of the pretreatment of serum coating. This was assumed to be due to the coating of quartz surface by serum in the medium.

THE EFFECT OF SERUM-COATED QUARTZ AND CHRYSOTILE(U.I.C.C.) ON THE INCORPORATION OF DL-LEUCINE-1-^{14}C INTO THE MACROPHAGES

To 5 × 10^6 cells in Tyrode's solution, 400 μg of quartz (naked or serum coated) or 2 mg of chrysotile (naked or serum coated) were added, and then 0·4 μCi of DL-Leucine-1-^{14}C were added. After the various times of incubation at 37°C, incorporation was determined with the liquid scintillation counter by the method described in the paper of KOSHI (1967). The results are shown in Figures 6 and 7. Chrysotile became inert by serum coating though quartz lost the effect of serum coating with time.

DISCUSSION

Biologically Active Properties of Dust Surface in Naked State

Our studies on silicate minerals, especially on the fibrous silicates, showed a high correlation between their activation of acid phosphatase, inhibition of lactic acid production and hemolytic activity. This may suggest that these silicate minerals cannot differentiate the membrane of the macrophages or phagosomes and the red blood cells. For this we can assume two hypotheses; the one is that the particle surface has two different biologically active factors, one of which attacks macrophages and the other the red blood cells, and the other is that one biologically active factor attacks both the macrophages and red blood cells. In silicate dusts, the latter hypothesis seems to be more probable.

Quartz particles, on the other hand, differentiate between these two sorts of membrane; alkali-treated quartz affects the macrophage activity remarkably and produces slight hemolysis, but ground quartz has a reverse effect. It seems that there are two sorts of biologically active factors or parts in the surface of the same quartz particle, one of which attacks the macrophages and the other the red blood cells.

The physico-chemical property of quartz which is responsible for its cytotoxic activity seems to be very sensitive, because cytotoxicity is lost when quartz particles are ground for a long time as shown by Sakabe et al. (1960), or treated with NaCl, KCl, KBr or NaF solution as reported by Sakabe et al. (1966) or when heated over about 500°C as in this report. We often encountered cases in which the particles of pure silica such as quartz, tridymite and cristobalite did not show cytotoxicity though

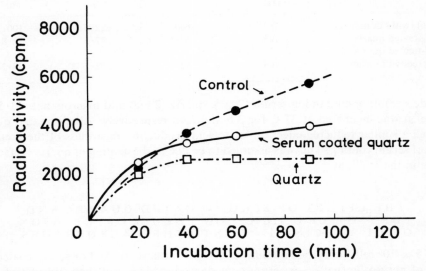

Figure 6. Effect of serum-coated quartz on incorporation of DL-leucine-1-^{14}C into the macrophage.

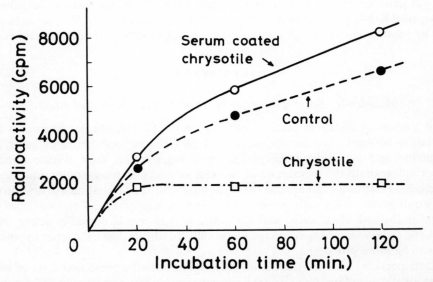

Figure 7. Effect of serum-coated chrysotile (U.I.C.C.) on incorporation of DL-leucine-1-^{14}C.

they gave the high grade of crystallinity and purity by X-ray and other analysis. Cell toxicity of silica particles seems to be dependent on the method of preparation. The most important point is that the physico-chemical property of quartz responsible for its cytotoxic activity exists in the thin surface layer of the particle.

Chrysotile (U.I.C.C.) treated around 650°C is very interesting because of its peculiar biological activity. This sample is difficult to coat with protein, though it inhibits the lactic acid production and produces hemolysis. We have at present no data to explain this new specific property.

Protein Adsorption of Mineral Dusts

Cytotoxic effects of mineral dusts which belong to some mineralogical groups are lost by the addition of serum or albumin. A dust which is cell-toxic and which has hemolytic activity but which cannot be covered with protein, is expected to have a high animal toxicity. Chrysotile heated around 650°C seems to be of this type. When quartz particles coexist with serum or are treated with protein, their cytotoxic effects are remarkably reduced. However, when quartz dusts which show different grades of cytotoxicity are introduced into the lungs of rats intratracheally, grades of lung fibrosis produced by these dusts correspond very well to the grades of cytotoxicity *in vitro* as reported by SAKABE *et al.* (1961). For the mediation between the cytotoxicity of quartz *in vitro* and lung fibrosis Table 4 seems to be interesting. Experimental data shown in Table 4 may be explained by two assumptions, one of which is that protein covering the quartz surface will be removed in the phagosome after ingestion into the cells and naked particles attack the phagosome membrane. The other is that the covering of quartz surface by protein is not sufficient to eliminate the cytotoxic action of quartz completely. The former assumption may be assumed to be reasonable.

PARAZZI *et al.* (1968) also suggested that the digestion of the protein coating by lysosomal enzymes is a prerequisite for the damage of the lysosomal membrane. But, in the TTC reducing capacity test in which serum is added, the amount of dust necessary to depress the TTC reducing capacity by 50% is much less with quartz than with silicate minerals. In many experiments, the cytotoxic action of quartz could not be prevented completely even if serum was added or the quartz pretreated with serum. Further studies must be made to see if the cytotoxicity of quartz is lost completely if the medium contains proteins similar to those in the body fluids and whether it reappears after the protein coating is removed in phagosomes.

Damage to the membrane of the macrophage or of its phagosome by naked quartz surface seems to be the first step for the development of silicosis. On the pathogenesis of asbestosis, our study shows that, in the original non-treated state, crocidolite and amosite are not cytotoxic, though chrysotile is toxic. Chrysotile also is not toxic if the medium contains protein. These facts may suggest that fibrosis by asbestos dusts is produced without damaging the macrophages. This problem should be studied further.

REFERENCES

BAKER, S. B. & SUMMERSON, W. H. (1941). *J. biol. Chem.* **138**, 535–554.
HAYASHI, H. & OINUMA, K. (1963). *Clay Sci.* **1**, 134–154.
HAYASHI, H., KOSHI, K. & SAKABE, H. (1969). *Proc. Int. Clay Conf., Tokyo* 1969, Vol. I. Jerusalem, Israel Universities Press. pp. 903–913.

IMAI, N., OTSYKA, R., NAKAMURA, T. & INOUE, H. (1966). *J. Clay Sci., Japan* **6**, 30–40. (In Japanese with English abstract).

IMAI, N., OTSUKA, R. & NAKAMURA, T. (1967). *J. Jap. Ass. Miner. Petrol. econ. Geol.* **57**, 39–56.

KIND, P. R. N. & KING, E. J. (1954). *J. clin. Path.* **7**, 322–326.

KOSHI, K. & SAKABE, H. (1967). *Ind. Hlth, Japan* **5**, 9–11.

KOSHI, K., HAYASHI, H. & SAKABE, H. (1968). *Ind. Hlth, Japan* **6**, 69–79.

KOSHI, K., HAYASHI, H. & SAKABE, H. (1969). *Ind. Hlth, Japan* **7**, 66–85.

MARKS, J. & JAMES, D. M. (1954). *J. Path. Bact.* **77**, 401–406.

MINATO, H., IMAI, N. & OTSUKA, R. (1969). *J. Jap. Ass. Miner. Petrol. econ. Geol.* **61**, 125–139.

OINUMA, K. & HAYASHI, H. (1968). *J. Tokyo Univ. Gen. Educ. (Nat. Sci.)* (9), 57–98.

OTSUKA, R., HAYASHI, H. & SHIMODA, S. (1968). *Mem. Sch. Sci. Eng. Waseda Univ.* (32), 13–24.

PARAZZI, E., SECCHI, G. C., PERNIS, B. & VIGLIANI, E. (1968). *Archs envir. Hlth* **17**, 850–859.

SAKABE, H., KAWAI, K., KOSHI, K., SODA, R., HAMADA, A., SHIMAZU, H. & HAYASHI, H. (1960); *Bull. Nat. Inst. Ind. Health.* (4), 1–28.

SAKABE, H., KAJITA, A. & KOSHI, K. (1961). *Bull. natn. Inst. ind. Hlth* (6), 28–34.

SAKABE, H., KOSHI, K. & HAMADA, A. (1966). Proceedings of the 15th International Congress on Occupational Health, Vienna, Vol. II–2, Vienna, Verlag der Winer Medizinischen Akademie. pp. 659–660.

SATO, M. (1962). *Mineral. J.* **3**, 296–305.

SHIMODA, S. (1964). *Clay Sci.* **2**, 8–21.

SHIMODA, S. (1967). *Sci. Rep. Tokyo Univ. Educ., Section C No.* 92, 263–278.

DISCUSSION

G. W. GIBBS: I suggest that the high hemolytic activity of what you described as 650° — chrysotile, might be due to silica released in the reaction

$$Mg_3Si_2O_5(OH)_4 \rightarrow Mg_2SiO_4 + SiO_2 + MgO + 2H_2O.$$
Heat   Forsterite   Silica
650°

The decrease in hemolytic activity after treatment at higher temperatures might be related to the removal of this silica by reaction of the forsterite with silica to form enstatite $Mg_2Si_2O_6$.

Prof. SAKABE: Chrysotile heated to 650° C may contain silica as you suggest, but silica has no such severe toxicity as to kill animals. Silica adsorbs protein, but this 650° C chrysotile is difficult to cover. So, the biological effect of 650° C chrysotile seems to be due to chrysotile itself.

M. NAVRATIL: We observed in persons exposed to chrysotile and with findings of pleural calcifications, as well as in patients suffering from the same pleural process without chrysotile exposure, that the serum level of acid phosphatase is significantly higher. Is this in some relationship to your experimental results?

Prof. SAKABE: Pathogenesis of asbestosis is still obscure. Our data were obtained only in the cellular level. I cannot say further at present.

I. BERGMAN: The work you have described confirms my long held impression that groups representing a relatively small proportion of the silica surface are responsible for the various cytotoxic effects. It is interesting that different groups must be responsible for haemolysis and macrophage death. You have used high temperatures to modify the silica surfaces. We found that the effect of hydrochloric acid on the electrophoretic inability of silica powders could be reversed by boiling water, but not by cold water. If, however, the powders were first dried at 105° C, the effect could not be reversed in this way.

Prof. SAKABE: We have already reported that quartz surface is very sensitive and its cytotoxicity can be easily modified by grinding or chemical treatment. Alkali-treated quartz has a high cytotoxicity. Treatment of this quartz by boiling in NaCl, KCl, KBr and NaBr solutions reduces the cytotoxicity but treatment by HNO_3, $CaCl_2$, HCl, and KNO_3 does not.

Preparation of dust for experimental use should be very careful.

H.-W. SCHLIPKÖTER: In the examination of cell toxicity it is necessary to pay particular attention to the presence of silicon dioxide. We have conducted experiments with hydrochloric acid treated asbestos. The HCl pre-treated asbestos led to unequivocal membrane damage which was measurable in erythrocytes both in the cell plantation and particularly in the haemolytic test. PVNO inhibited this cell toxicity arising from HCl pre-treated asbestos. This is attributable to the action of the SiO_2 component which is released in the HCl pre-treatment.

E. G. BECK: An acid treatment of chrysotile produces, in the case of macrophages, a considerable disturbance of permeability with a depressed formation of lactate (Beck, Holt and Nasrallah (1970)). The morphology of the fibre is maintained by the treatment by HCl, but the chemical structure of the mineral is changed. This causes a toxicity which is due to the exposed surface of SiO_2. This is also supported by the fact that PVNO suppresses the toxic effect. The effect of the long fibre dust on the permeability of the cell membrane, reported in our paper, is maintained however and corresponds to that of natural chrysotile. By a combined treatment by HCl and heat, chrysotile is changed chemically as well as structurally in such a way that the effect on macrophages corresponds wellnigh to that of quartz. Also in a morphological aspect, the changed chrysotile behaves like a crystalline SiO_2. A pre-treatment of the cells with PVNO also suppresses this cytotoxic effect, as with quartz.

Prof. SAKABE: Generally, an acid treatment of clay minerals liberates a silica. But this silica does not mean a crystalline silica.

We have not examined the cell toxicity of acid-treated asbestos.

EFFECTS OF SILICA AND ASBESTOS ON CELLS IN CULTURE

A. C. ALLISON

Clinical Research Centre, Harrow, Middlesex, England

Abstract — Evidence is summarized that silica particles do not damage macrophages by interaction with plasma membranes but are ingested into secondary
lysosomes. A hydrogen-bonding interaction with membrane phospholipids makes
the lysosomal membrane permeable, and this on a large scale is damaging. Protection against silica toxicity can be achieved by polymers which are stored in
lysosomes and have hydrogen-accepting groups, such as polyvinylpyridinio-acetic
acid. Asbestos varieties, especially chrysotile, added to macrophages or mesothelial cells in the absence of serum, rapidly lyse the cells by interaction with the
plasma membrane. In the presence of serum the particles are much less damaging
than silica, irrespective of whether they are ingested into the lysosomal system,
which happens if they are short enough.

THE interpretation of silica toxicity which was presented at the last International
Symposium on Inhaled Particles and Vapours in 1965 (ALLISON *et al.*, 1966, 1967) has
been widely accepted. According to this view, the main target for inhaled silica is the
alveolar macrophage, and damage to macrophages stimulates fibrogenesis by cells of
a different lineage, the fibroblasts. The capacity of different forms of silica to stimulate
collagen synthesis parallels their toxic effects on cultures of macrophages, as found by
MARKS (1957). Although high concentrations of silica added to macrophages in a
saline medium can kill the cells quickly by lysis of plasma membranes, this is an
artificial situation. Silica particles coated with serum proteins or bronchial washings
are ingested by macrophages and then lie in vacuoles containing lysosomal enzymes
(secondary lysosomes). The cells remain viable for several hours, as shown by
motility and other criteria. Then the protein coat around the silica particles is digested
away and the surface of the silica particles can interact with the membrane surrounding
the secondary lysosome and make it permeable. As a result silica particles and hydrolytic enzymes escape into the cytoplasm, mitochondria and other cytoplasmic constituents are damaged and the cell is killed.

The capacity of various mineral dusts to react with membranes, as shown by
haemolysis, is related to their fibrogenic capacity. The one crystalline form of silica
which is not fibrogenic, stishovite, and non-toxic dusts show little membrane reactivity.
We have attributed the reactivity of silica particles to the presence on the surface of
numerous, rigid hydroxyl groups of silicic acid, which can act as hydrogen donors in
hydrogen-bonding interactions with membrane constituents, especially phosphate
ester groups. The protection against silica toxicity *in vitro* and fibrogenesis *in vivo*
afforded by poly-2-vinylpyridine-N-oxide, discovered by Schlipköter and his colleagues (SCHLIPKÖTER, 1967), supports this interpretation. This compound, like

other polymers, is taken up into lysosomes, and being resistant to hydrolytic enzymes, remains there indefinitely. It is found in the same secondary lysosomes as silica, and the N-oxide groups can form strong hydrogen bonds with hydroxyl groups of silicic acid, preventing the latter from attacking the lysosomal membrane.

Our observations have been confirmed repeatedly. Silica particles taken up in culture (BECK et al., 1967; BECK, 1970), or following inhalation exposure (BRUCH, 1967; BRUCH & OTTO, 1967) are initially in membrane-bound vacuoles or secondary lysosomes but are later observed free in the cytoplasm; the latter coincides with morphological signs of damage to mitochondria and other cell organelles. Ingested coal (COLLET et al., 1967) or kaolin (RUTTNER et al., 1967) produced only minimal cytological changes. The effects of inhaled silica on macrophages progress more slowly than in culture, in which the number of particles or aggregates per cell is higher, but the sequence of events is essentially the same (BRUCH & OTTO, 1967). Release of acid phosphatase and other lysosomal enzymes from macrophages exposed to silica into the medium, and its prevention by PVPNO, has been confirmed by COMOLLI (1967), SAKABE & KOSHI (1967) and BECK (1970).

Histochemical studies showing release of peroxidase taken up into lysosomes of macrophages after treatment with silica, confirming our observations with acid phosphatase, have been published by NADLER & GOLDFISCHER (1970).

The uptake of PVPNO into lysosomes of macrophages and other cells has been confirmed by GRUNDMAN (1967), BRUCH (1967), BECK & BOJE (1967), BAIRATIE & CASTANO (1968) and others; these observations have been made by histochemistry, electron microscopy, and cell fractionation and autoradiography using labelled polymer. DEHNEN & FETZER (1967) and others have reported that quartz particles release hydrolases from the lysosomes of rat liver and that this is prevented by PVPNO.

In 1966 NASH et al. synthesized another compound, polyvinylpyridinioacetic acid, which has even greater hydrogen bonding capacity than PVPNO and very efficiently protects macrophages from silica toxicity. This protection was confirmed by SAKABE & KOSHI (1967), who also showed that it prevents the increase in acid phosphatase in macrophages following exposure to silica. HOLT et al. (1970) also reported that some poly-2-vinylpyridinium salts prevented quartz toxicity in cultures. Thus the presence of hydrogen accepting groups (either N-oxides or pyridinium groups) is frequently associated with protection, although other factors may also be involved. Thus HOLT et al. (1970) found a difference between the protective effect of syndiotactic and isotactic PVPNO, polymers that differ only in the spatial arrangement of the structural units.

These two facts are sufficient to explain why silica is so toxic to macrophages: the particles are taken up into lysosomes and readily damage lysosomal membranes through hydrogen bonding interactions. Various secondary reactions may occur. Thus, MUNDER et al. (1966) have found a considerable increase in the concentration of lysolecithin, as compared with lecithin, in macrophages damaged by quartz. This could follow activation of the enzyme phospholipase A, which catalyses the reaction lecithin → lysolecithin and which is known to be lysosomal. However, the fact that silica lyses erythrocytes (membranes of which do not contain demonstrable amounts of phospholipase A) suggests that this process is unnecessary for interaction of silica with membrane systems, although the formation of surface-active lysolecithin could well accelerate damage induced by silica in macrophages.

Suspensions of silica particles readily release enzymes from isolated liver lysosomes *in vitro*, as DEHNEN & FETZER's (1967) experiments and our own have shown; the relatively low temperature coefficient for this release suggests that physico-chemical rather than enzymic reactions are involved.

Although the presence of many mineral forms of asbestos, variety of sizes and variability of results depending on experimental conditions makes it difficult to draw general conclusions about effects of asbestos on cells, some overall points are beginning to emerge. The first is that certain types of asbestos can certainly interact with cell membranes. This is shown by the hemolytic effects of asbestos described by MACNAB & HARINGTON (1967) and SECCHI & REZZONICO (1968). Both groups of authors found chrysotile is at least as hemolytic as silica but Macnab and Harington reported that PVPNO and aluminium oxide, which markedly reduced hemolysis by silica, had less effect on chrysotile hemolysis. Ethylenediaminetetra-acetate or simple phosphates markedly reduced chrysotile hemolysis, which is not surprising since the crystal structure of chrysotile is such that the surface consists of magnesium hydroxide. Chrysotile was found by Secchi and Rezzonico to adsorb the erythrocyte membrane enzyme acetylcholinesterase strongly but the cytoplasmic enzyme lactate dehydrogenase only weakly. They suggested that the highly hemolytic activity of chrysotile is related to the adsorptive capacity of the dust for erythrocyte membrane components. Crocidolite, amosite and anthophyllite were only weakly lytic.

There are apparent discrepancies between descriptions by various authors of effects of asbestos on macrophages and other cells in culture. On the one hand, there is a report by PARAZZI et al. (1968) that crocidolite and chrysotile are very toxic to guinea pig macrophages, crocidolite being more toxic than chrysotile or tridymite dust used for comparison; fibers were more damaging than particles. On the other hand, the cellular changes found by BECK et al. (1967) and DAVIS (1967) on exposure of organ cultures to chrysotile were relatively slight.

I have examined the effects of various asbestos dusts (International Union Against Cancer Standard Samples) on cultures of mouse peritoneal macrophages, prepared as previously described (ALLISON et al., 1966) and on organ cultures of mouse peritoneum in the same medium. The peritoneum is lined by mesothelial cells which are involved in asbestos malignancies, so that their reaction to asbestos was worth studying. This preparation was of interest for several reasons—fibroblasts quickly grew out and were found to take up and be affected by asbestos particles much less than mesothelial cells. The first experiment concerned the capacity of cells to take up asbestos fibers of different lengths. Fractions containing high and low percentages of long fibers were added to cells in medium 199 containing 10% fetal calf serum. Independently of the asbestos type, short fibers ($<5 \mu$m) were readily and completely taken up by phagocytosis, whereas long fibers ($>30 \mu$m) were not. The cells were closely attached to or enveloped the ends of the latter, as shown by ordinary and stereoscan electron micrographs, but part of the asbestos fibers remained outside the cell. This was confirmed by phase-contrast ciné-photomicrographs. With very long fibers, two or more cells could be seen closely attached to a single fiber, sometimes with apparent continuity of cytoplasm; such attachment may favour syncytium formation. Cells attached to long fibers in the presence of serum in the medium remained healthy for at least a week in culture.

In contrast, when asbestos fibers were added to macrophages in buffered saline medium lacking serum, marked cytotoxic effects rapidly occurred. Thus, when mouse macrophages were exposed to 100 μg/ml medium of I.U.C.C. standard chrysotile, 90% of cells had lost the capacity to split fluorescein diacetate within 2 h. Release from cells of protein, including the cytoplasmic enzyme lactate dehydrogenase, was marked within 1 h of exposure to asbestos, whereas release of acid phosphatase and β-glucuronidase was delayed until later. Ciné-photomicrography showed sudden cessation of movement and sometimes blebbing of the cell membrane. Hence it seems highly probable that this type of rapid cytotoxicity is due to a direct interaction of asbestos fibers with cell membranes, analogous to hemolysis. The analogy is strengthened by the observation in my experiments that chrysotile is the most effective of all the I.U.C.C. samples in early cytotoxicity, followed by crocidolite, amosite and anthophyllite in that order. This is in contrast to the rather surprising report of PARAZZI et al. (1968) that the rapid early cytotoxicity of crocidolite is greater than that of chrysotile.

In any case, it is doubtful whether the rapid cytotoxicity produced by asbestos fibers in media lacking serum or bronchial washings has much physiological relevance. I have therefore examined the long-term effects on macrophages and mesothelial cells of exposure to fibers that are mostly of ingestible size in medium containing 10% fetal calf serum. Such fibers are taken up into vacuoles that become secondary lysosomes, as shown by acid phosphatase and other marker enzymes. It is already clear that all types of asbestos dusts are much less toxic to macrophages and other cells than are silica dusts. However, it would be wrong to conclude that asbestos dusts are entirely devoid of cytotoxic potential. Macrophages exposed to chrysotile (20–50 μg/ml I.U.C.C. standard) often show after two or three days in culture very large lightly-staining vacuoles in their cytoplasm. Some cells show pyknotic cytoplasm and nuclei and about 20% are no longer viable. Hence there is certainly some cytotoxicity, as well as other abnormalities. One of the most striking was the development in meso-thelial cells and to a lesser extent in macrophages, of brown pigmented autofluorescent granules in the cytoplasm; this was greatly accentuated after ingestion of asbestos, especially crocidolite. Perhaps the iron favours lipid peroxidation.

Apart from formation of iron-containing pigment, already mentioned, the most striking ultrastructural change in asbestos-treated cells is the development of an electron-dense matrix surrounding the asbestos particles in secondary lysosomes. This is not seen in silica-treated cells and could provide a protective layer between the asbestos particles and the vulnerable membrane surrounding the secondary lysosome. This may, in fact, explain why asbestos is less toxic than would be expected from its capacity to react with membranes, as shown by hemolysis.

Although much remains to be learned about the effects of asbestos on cells, certain important differences from effects of silica are already apparent. One is the failure of ingestion of many asbestos fibers because they are too long. Another is the obviously weaker cytotoxicity of asbestos than silica, although some forms of asbestos, especially chrysotile, are certainly more toxic than inert dusts such as anatase or diamond dust. The slowly progressive damage to macrophages so produced may be an important factor in the fibrotic reaction to asbestos. The third change observed in asbestos-treated cells is lipid peroxidation and accumulation in vacuoles of iron-containing pigment; this contributes to the formation of asbestos bodies in vivo.

REFERENCES

ALLISON, A. C., HARINGTON, J. S. & BIRBECK, M. (1966). *J. exp. Med.* **124**, 141–154.
ALLISON, A. C., HARINGTON, J. S., BIRBECK, M. & NASH, T. (1967). In: *Inhaled particles and vapours II. Ed.* C. N. Davies. Oxford, Pergamon Press. pp. 121–131.
BAIRATI, A. & CASTANO, P. (1968). *Medna. Lav.* **59**, 81.
BECK, E. G. (1970). *ForschBer. Landes NRhein-Westf.* (2083), 125.
BECK, E. G. & BOJE, H. (1967). *Fortschr. Staublungenforsch.*, **2**, 231.
BECK, E. G., BRUCH, J. & SACK, J. (1967). *Ergebn. Unters. Geb. Staub-u. Silikosebekämpf. Steinkohlenbergbau* **6**, 131.
BRUCH, J. (1967). *Fortschr. Staublungenforsch.* **2**, 249.
BRUCH, J. & OTTO, H. (1967). *Ergebn. Unters. Geb. Staub-u. Silikosebekämpf. Steinkohlenbergbau* **6**, 141.
COLLET, A., MARTIN, J. C., NORMAND-REUET, C. & POLICARD, A. (1967). In: *Inhaled particles and vapours II. Ed.* C. N. Davies. Oxford, Pergamon Press. pp. 155–165.
COMOLLI, R. (1967). *J. Path. Bact.* **93**, 241–253.
DAVIS, J. M. G. (1967). *Br. J. exp. Path.* **48**, 379–385.
DEHNEN, W. & FETZER, J. (1967). *Ergebn. Unters. Geb. Staub-u. Silikosebekämpf. Steinkohlenbergbau* **6**, 161.
GRUNDMANN, E. (1967). *Fortschr. Staublungenforsch.* **2**, 223.
HOLT, P. F., LINDSAY, H. & BECK, E. G. (1970). *Br. J. Pharmac.* **38**, 192–201.
MACNAB, G. & HARINGTON, J. S. (1967). *Nature, Lond.* **214**, 522–523.
MARKS, J. (1957). *Br. J. ind. Med.* **14**, 81–84.
MUNDER, P. G., MODOLELL, M., FERBER, E. & FISCHER, H. (1966). *Biochem. Z.* **344**, 310–313.
NADLER, S. & GOLDFISCHER, S. (1970). *J. Histochem. Cytochem.* **18**, 368–371.
NASH, T., ALLISON, A. C. & HARINGTON, J. S. (1966). *Nature, Lond.* **210**, 259–261.
PARAZZI, E., PERNIS, B., SECCHI, G. C. & VIGLIANI, E. C. (1968). *Medna Lav.* **59**, 561–576.
RUTTNER, J. R., GRIESHABER, E., VOGEL, A. & LEU, H. J. (1967). *Fortschr. Staublungenforsch.* **2**, 89.
SAKABE, H. & KOSHI, K. (1967). *Ind. Hlth, Japan* **5**, 181.
SCHLIPKÖTER, H. W. (1967). *Arbeitshyg.* **4**, 133.
SECCHI, G. C. & REZZONICO, A. (1968). *Medna Lav.* **59**, 1.

ADDENDUM

Lysosomal hydrolases and emphysema

Lysosomal hydrolases can effectively digest many connective tissue components (DINGLE & FELL, 1969). The possibility arises that enzymic breakdown of the connective tissue fibres and matrix may be an important factor in the development of emphysema. The finding that papain inhalation can cause emphysema is highly suggestive of a role of proteolysis in the aetiology of this condition. It is reasonable to conclude that when macrophages are damaged by some agent such as silica, the ensuing fibrogenic reaction strengthens rather than weakens the lung. If, however, hydrolases are released under circumstances when there is no fibrogenic reaction, the structure of the lung can be weakened and this leads to emphysema. The hydrolases may well arise from alveolar macrophages, but other possible sources should not be overlooked. The supposed relationship of emphysema with sites of deposition of non-silicotic dusts—if correct—may be an example of this. The other relevant point is the increased susceptibility to emphysema shown by individuals with an inherited deficiency of serum α-antitrypsin (FAGERHOL, 1968). If this factor can inhibit the action of a protease, release of which is aetiologically important in emphysema, the findings are readily explained. My colleagues and I have found that organ cultures of lung show many points of resemblance to the organ cultures of bone rudiments extensively studied in relation to connective tissue breakdown by lysosomal hydro-lases (DINGLE & FELL, 1969), and this strengthens the possibility that these enzymes may be involved in pathological reactions, including emphysema.

ADDENDA TO REFERENCES

DINGLE, J. T. & FELL, H. B. (1969). *Lysosomes in Biology and pathology*. Amsterdam, North Holland Press.
FAGERHOL, M. K. (1968). *Series Haematologica*, **1,** 153.

DISCUSSION

(ALSO OF PAPER BY J. BRUCH, p. 447)

H. ANTWEILER: Mr. Allison spoke just now mainly about the interaction between quartz and PVNO. It may be interesting in this connection that PVNO has also an effect on cellular membranes. We were able to show in our institute that rats were protected by a pre-treatment with PVNO (this pre-treatment being dependent on the dosage) from an intoxication by sub-lethal dosages of CCl_4. According to our knowledge of the mechanism of CCl_4, one may conclude that there is a protective effect of PVNO to intracellular membrane structures.

K. ROBOCK: Your experiments and your theory of lysosomal interaction are very interesting. However, I would like you to consider the possibility that the reaction with the lysosome membranes occurs rather late in the process. In agreement with Dr. Bruch, I would suggest that this reaction is of a subsequent nature. In our tests of the chemi-luminescence indicating the interaction between SiO_2 particles and cells we were able to detect primary reactions of electron transfer within 40 seconds after contact.

In agreement with the experiments by Dr. Antweiler, our studies with PVNO (P204) support primarily the assumption of an interaction of PVNO with biological material of the cells rather than an adsorption on the SiO_2 surface. This is indicated by the long incubation period necessary for a full and permanent protection of the cells.

Dr. ALLISON: If you look at a simple system, such as haemolysis by silica particles, you find that treatment of cells beforehand with PVNO and washing them does not protect them at all. On the other hand treatment of the silica particles with PVNO and washing them greatly inhibits the haemolysis. So there is no evidence that PVNO reacts with or stabilizes membranes while there is clear evidence that the polymer interacts with silica and diminishes its capacity to damage membranes. These observations are accepted by everyone who has worked in the field, and no long incubation is required. The second point of agreement between the German workers and ourselves is that PVNO administered *in vivo* or *in vitro* is — like other polymers — stored in lysosomes. Prolonged incubation increases this storage. The polymer may affect other intracellular membrane systems as well, causing, for example, proliferation of smooth membranes of the endoplasmic reticulum of liver which, along with lysosomes, are involved in chloroform toxicity. However, I should be surprised if that reaction is specific or relevant to prevention of silica toxicity. Have you tried experiments on chloroform toxicity with polymers that do not protect against silica? Many other compounds, such as cationic surface-active agents, reduce chloroform hepatotoxicity.

With regard to the cell membrane and lysosomal membrane, these are effective barriers preventing movement of all materials except some small molecules and ions selectively through them. I cannot accept that under anything like normal conditions silica can gain access to the cytoplasm within 40 seconds of exposure.

Dr. BRUCH: We have used a number of fixatives and observed the quartz particles not always attached to the membranes but free in the cytoplasm. Problems associated with fixation of membranes are well known, particularly in regard to the Unit Membrane and Subunit Concept of membranes. We are of the opinion that the structures that we have observed in our electron-micrographs are not artefacts.

Most of the known results *in vitro* have been obtained using comparatively higher doses of silica in order to prove its cytotoxic effect. It is probable that such doses may have caused rapid lysis of the lysosomes and overshadowed the appearance of primary effects. *In vivo* the cells take up lesser amounts of silica. With such small doses necrosis of the cells may not ensue, but such changes which have been discussed by us in our paper. It may further be concluded that in the study of the effect of dust more reliance must be placed on the *in vivo* than *in vitro* studies.

H.-W. SCHLIPKÖTER: Several years ago I showed that quartz may freely exist in cytoplasma. This finding, which demonstrates the real discrepancy between the experiences of Dr. Allison and Dr. Bruch, is explainable in my opinion in terms of the membrane damaging activity of quartz. It is probable that when quartz is incorporated in cells, the phagocytosed quartz disturbs the phago-somal membrane and subsequently occurs temporarily as a free agent in the cytoplasma before it is taken up by secondary lysosomes.

I agree that the results obtained from *in vitro* experiments cannot always be translated to *in vivo* studies. As discussed in my paper, we tested the behavior of original mine dust *in vivo* and *in vitro*.

Despite these dust samples having a high toxic potential *in vitro*, they were only slightly fibrogenic *in vivo*.

Dr. ALLISON: We agree that silica is ingested in relation to invaginated cell membranes and that after a time interval the silica particles are found in secondary lysosomes. Dr. Bruch and Professor Schlipköter suggest that in between these stages silica may be free in the cytoplasm. I think that this may happen occasionally without seriously damaging cells but that release of silica from the lysosomal vacuolar system on any scale produces damage to alveolar macrophages. Several possible sources of artifacts have to be borne in mind. One is that fixation, preservation and demonstration of membranes in electron micrographs can be difficult. There are secondary effects of exposure of macrophages to amounts of quartz that they can tolerate, including increased formation of lysosomes and release of lysosomal enzymes into the medium.

H. ANTWEILER: You did not reply to my observation that there is a secured protecting effect of PVNO to cellular membranes; you took only the quartz particles into consideration. However, I hope you will be interested to hear that PVNO *in vitro* is capable of replacing by competitive adsorption serumprotein previously adsorbed to quartz as we were recently able to demonstrate in our Institute.

Dr. ALLISON: I am interested in your observation which emphasizes the strength of the interaction between PVNO and quartz.

P. GROSS: Dr. Allison asks what do pathologists think of his idea that proteolytic enzymes derived from leucocytes and macrophages may play a role in the digestion of alveolar tissue which then results in emphysema. My response to his question is that this concept has become my working hypothesis since I found that emphysema could be produced by intratracheal injection of papain. But we are not alone in this view, there are at least two other groups of experimentalists in the United States putting this hypothesis to the test.

Dr. ALLISON: I have not seen any published information on leucocytes, but you can produce emphysema beautifully with papain aerosols.

I. BERGMAN: Do you have any evidence or speculations about the "messenger substance" which allows a silica-affected macrophage to trigger off the production of fibrotic material by fibroblasts? The work of Curran and Rowsell with diffusion chambers would suggest that an intimate association of the two types of cell is necessary; no "messenger substance" diffused through their silica containing chamber walls to lead to fibrosis outside.

Dr. ALLISON: I think the evidence does suggest that a fairly close spatial relationship is necessary for the macrophage to "activate" synthesis by fibroblasts. The only evidence we have is that the macrophage does not become a fibroblast. At the electron-microscopic level, you never see such a thing and this is confirmed by labelling with tritiated DNA. Fibrogenesis is a two-stage operation. There is damage to the macrophage — not necessarily death, but minor damage which is enough to produce the derepression of the fibroblast. It would be fascinating to know the nature of this stimulus. It has been very difficult to get extracts of macrophage to stimulate fibrogenesis: in two laboratories the preliminary report of Heppleston and Styles that macrophage extracts stimulate incorporation of label into hydroxyproline by fibroblasts has not yet been confirmed. Fibrogenesis is a problem which is important in general pathology, but almost nothing has been done about the basic underlying mechanism.

H.-W. SCHLIPKÖTER: The inhibitory mechanism of polymer has not been clarified to date. Dr. Allison's important contribution to the study of chemical bonding of polyvinl-pyridine with SiOH groups opens the way to the formulation of a significant hypothesis. In our own efforts to find effective high polymeric substances other than PVNO, we have up to now been unable to show any association between the efficacy of a protective substance and the adsorption on the quartz surface. Among the high polymers which we have tested so far, we have found, like Mr. Grundmann, only one substance, apart from PVNO, which has an inhibitory effect. In this case the protective effect is approximately ten times as strong as that of PVNO.

Regarding the high polymeric substance synthesized by yourself and Nash which has an impressive inhibitory action on the cytotoxicity of quartz in cell structure, I would like to ask whether these polyvinl-pyridine acetates have been tested also in animal experiments and what your findings have been to date. We ourselves have often found that with compounds which *in vitro* show distinct restrictions in the cytotoxic activity of quartz, *in vivo* show only marginal or no inhibitory effect on experimental silicosis.

Dr. ALLISON: Experiments in progress show that polyvinyl-pyridinioacetic acid confers marked protection against silica fibrogenesis in rats. All the protective compounds described by your colleagues have hydrogen-accepting groups such as the N-oxide or pyridinium groups. This supports our hypothesis. Strict parallelism between *in vitro* and *in vivo* effects cannot be expected. To confer efficient protection in animals the compounds must gain access to the sites where silica accumulates and must persist in an active form. Many possible protective compounds might be metabolized rapidly or be ineffective for some such reason.

ELEKTRONENMIKROSKOPISCHE BEOBACHTUNGEN ZUR QUARZSTAUBPHAGOZYTOSE

J. Bruch

Institut für Lufthygiene und Silikoseforschung an der Universität Düsseldorf, Düsseldorf W. Germany

Abstract — In quartz phagocytizing alveolar macrophages and histiocytes membrane organelles are involved in the phagocytic process. These organelles with a diameter of 41 nm, consist of an 11 nm thick inner membrane and two triple-layered limiting membranes. Depending upon the orientation in the section plane, the inner membrane gives a pentalaminar, a cross-striated or a globular appearance with a centre-to-centre distance of 4·7 nm. It is likely that the underlying substructure is a double layer of hexagonally arranged subunits with a diameter of 5·5 nm.

Quartz, entering the cell in a phagosome, leaves the vacuole and lies free in the groundplasma. Subsequently, the particle is trapped by the cupshaped organelle. Morphological findings indicate that the inner membrane of the membrane organelle participates in the formation of the secondary lysosome.

The question, whether a lysosomal damage is causally related to a direct quartz action or whether it is a secondary event, is discussed in the light of these and other findings.

IN früheren Untersuchungen zur Phagozytose von Staub durch Makrophagen konnten wir zeigen, dass die Partikeln nach Inkorporation das Phagosom verlassen und vor der Einlagerung in sekundäre Lysosomen zunächst frei im Grundplasma lokalisiert sind. Nachdem sie von einem Paar glatter Membranen umlagert sind, tritt innerhalb der Membranen feingranuläre Matrix auf, in der der Staub eingelagert ist. Dieser Prozess war bisher nicht völlig geklärt. Vor allem fiel auf, dass innerhalb des den Quarz umlagernden Membranpaares häufig eine dritte, etwas dickere Membran erkennbar war. Da diese Membransysteme bei der Formierung sekundärer Lysosomen eine wichtige Rolle zu spielen scheinen, wurden sie eingehend elektronenmikroskopisch untersucht. Wir untersuchten freie Alveolarmakrophagen und Histiozyten aus Granulomen der experimentellen Silikose von Ratten, die 20 mg Doerentroper Quarz Nr. 12 intratracheal erhalten hatten. Übersichtsaufnahmen lassen erkennen, dass die Zellen zahlreiche Quarzpartikeln phagozytiert hatten. Der Staub wurde in verschiedenen Lokalisationsformen gefunden. In den Alveolarmakrophagen und Histiozyten lagen die Partikeln entweder frei im Grundplasma oder in sekundären Lysosomen. In der Histiozyten konnte noch zusätzlich der Quarz in Phagosomen beobachtet werden. Die Partikeln penetrieren die Vakuolenmembran und liegen anschliessend frei im Grundplasma. An der Stelle des Durchtritts ist die Vakuolenmembran verwaschen oder myelinartig verändert. (Abb. 1 u. 2.)

In den Quarzphagozyten, besonders in den Histiozyten, fielen zahlreiche multilamelläre Strukturen auf. Sie bestehen aus zwei dreischichtigen begrenzenden Mem-

448 J. BRUCH

branen, die eine innere 11 nm dicke Membran einschliessen und einen Durchmesser von ca. 41 nm haben. Bei höherer Vergrösserung zeigt die innere Membran je nach der Lage in der Schnittebene ein fünfschichtiges oder quergestreiftes Aussehen mit einer Periode von 4·7 nm. In selteneren Fällen wird bei der Membran eine Doppelreihe von sich gegenüberliegenden Globula beobachtet. Der Zentrum-zu-Zentrum-Abstand der Globula beträgt ebenso wie der Periodenabstand 4·7 nm. Eine eingehende Analyse, über die an anderer Stelle berichtet wurde, ergab, dass die innere Membran einen micellären Bauplan besitzt (BRUCH, 1970). Als eigentliche Substruktur wurde eine Doppelschicht hexagonal angeordneter Untereinheiten mit einem Durchmesser von 5·5 nm angenommen. (Abb. 3, 4, 5 u. 6.)

Die äussere Form der multilamellären Struktur ist sehr unterschiedlich. Obwohl

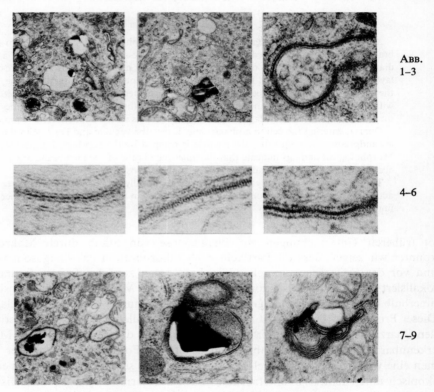

ABB. 1-3

4-6

7-9

ABB. 1. Quarzpartikel, ein Phagosom verlassend. Vergr. 14 000 ×

ABB. 2. Quarz liegt frei im Grundplasma der Zelle. Vergr. 14 000 ×

ABB. 3. Zwei dreischichtige Membranen begleiten die 10 nm dicke innere Membran. Das Grundplasma erscheint auf der konkaven Seite der Membranorganelle gegenüber der Umgebung aufgehellt. Vergr. 40 000 ×

ABB. 4. Fünfschichtiges Aussehen der inneren Membran. Vergr. 200 000 ×

ABB. 5. Bei der inneren Membran stellt sich eine Doppelreihe von Globula dar. Vergr. 160 000 ×

ABB. 6. Querstreifung bei der inneren Membran. Vergr. 95 000 ×

ABB. 7. Quarz wird von einer Membranorganelle umschlossen. Vergr. 12 000 ×

ABB. 8. Quarz in einem sekundären Lysosom liegend. Unterhalb der begrenzenden dreischichtigen Membran wird die 11 nm dicke innere Membran erkennbar. Vergr. 35 000 ×

ABB. 9. Die inneren Membranen liegen in mehrfachen Lagen übereinander. Vergr. 23 000 ×

es schwierig ist, anhand von elecktronenmikroskopischen Bildern fixierter Zellen auf dynamische Veränderungen von Zellorganellen zu schliessen, wurde versucht, das Verhalten der multilamellären Struktur in Beziehung zu dem phagozytierten Quarz zu setzen: Ausgehend von einer langgestreckten Gestalt biegen sie sich tassenförmig um und umschliessen dabei einen Plasmabezirk. Mikrodensitometrische Messungen ergaben, dass das Grundplasma auf der konkaven Seite des Membransystems gegenüber der Umgebung aufgehellt ist. Auffallend ist weiterhin eine Fusion von 0,02 μm grossen Vakuolen mit der begrenzenden Membran. Der inkorporierte Quarz gelangt in die Bucht der multilamellären Struktur und wird im weiteren Verlauf mit etwas Plasma, in dem Ribosomen und Mebranen liegen können, vollständig umschlossen. (Abb. 7.)

Nach dem Einschluss des Quarzes kommt es zu einer Auflösung der auf der konkaven Seite gelegenen derischichtigen Membran, so dass der Quarz nunmehr der inneren 10 nm dicken Membran unmittelbar gegenüber liegt. Häufig werden Organellen beobachtet, in denen die 11 nm dicke Membran in bis zu 6 oder 7 Lagen in einem Abstand von 6 nm übereinanderliegen. Wir nehmen an, dass die Proliferation der inneren Membran durch den Quarz induziert wird. Feingranuläre Matrix tritt immer zuerst an der innersten, also auf der dem Quarz zugewandten Seite der übereinanderliegenden Membranen auf. Am Ende der Entwicklung stehen bis zu 0,5 grosse, quarztragende Zytosomen, die innerhalb einer dreischichtigen begrenzenden Membran in der feingranulären Matrix regellos gelagerte, fünfschichtig oder quergestreift erscheinende Membran enthalten. (Abb. 8 u. 9.) In der schematischen Zeichnung sind die hier beschriebenen Vorgänge zusammengefasst dargestellt. (Abb. 10.)

Aufgrund der regelmässigen Struktur und der definierten Funktion bei der Umschliessung von Quarz halten wir die Benennung der multilamellären Struktur als Membranorganelle für gerechtfertigt.

Die Befunde zeigen, dass die Einlagerung des frei im Plasma liegenden Quarzes in Zytosomen sich in verschiedenen Stufen vollzieht. Die Lokalisation des Partikels in der Bucht der tassenförmigen Membranorganelle kann nicht nur als ein zufälliges Nebeneinanderliegen von Membranorganelle und Staub angesehen werden. Die Aufhellung deutet darauf hin, dass der Plasmabezirk, auch wenn er noch in breiter Verbindung mit dem allgemeinen Plasma steht, bereits von der Membranorganelle kontrolliert wird. Die vollständige Absonderung des Quarzes vom übrigen Plasma ist durch die komplette Umschliessung durch die Membranorganelle, die Vorgänge nach der Einlagerung in die Membranorganelle durch die Auflösung der inneren begrenzenden Membran morphologisch definiert.

Die 11 nm dicken Membran scheint nach unseren Befunden beim Aufbau der zytosomalen Matrix eine wichtige Rolle zu spielen. Hierfür spricht, dass die zytosomale Matrix erst nach der Einschliessung des Staubes durch die Membranorganelle in unmittelbarer Nähe der speziellen Membran auf der konkaven Seite auftritt und nicht an der äusseren dreischichtigen Membran. Der micelläre Bauplan der inneren Membran erleichtert die Vorstellung, dass Enzyme, die für die Synthese der zytosomalen Matrix notwendig wären, unmittelbar in die Membran integriert sind (GLAUERT & LUCY, 1968).

Welche Bedeutung in diesem Prozess die Fusion der 0,02 μm grossen Vesikeln mit der Membranorganelle hat, ist noch unklar.

Nach den elektronenmikroskopischen Befunden von ALLISON et al. (1967) gelangt der Staub in Phagosomen in das Zellinnere. Durch Fusion von primären Lysosomen mit den Phagosomen sollen sekundäre Lysosomen entstehen. Die unterschiedlichen Befunde sind möglicherweise darauf zurückzuführen, dass Allison und Mitarbeiter die Phagozytoseuntersuchungen in der Zellkultur durchgeführt hat, bei der mit der Applikation des Staubes gleichzeitig eine Makropinozytose stimuliert wird, die den Phagozytoseablauf verändern kann (Beck, 1970). Ausserdem wurde von den Autoren eine extrem feinkörnige SiO_2-Modifikation (Fransil) verwandt, bei der sich zahlreiche zelluläre Prozesse auf einen sehr engen Bereich zeitlich übereinanderschieben.

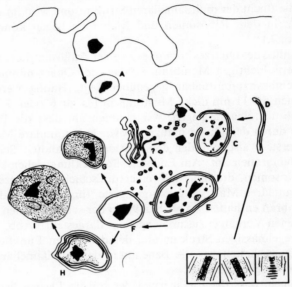

Abb. 10. Schematische Darstellung zum Ablauf der Phagozytose von Quarz. Quarz im Phagosom liegend (A); die Partikel verlässt die Vakuole und liegt frei im Grundplasma (B), um anschliessend in die Bucht einer tassenförmigen Membranorganelle zu gelangen (C). Nach vollständigem Einschluss (E) verliert die Membranorganelle die auf der konkaven Seit gelegene dreischichtige Membran, so dass der Quarz von der inneren 11 nm dicken Membran direkt umgeben wird (F). Innherhalb der 11 nm dicken Membran tritt feingranuläre Matrix auf (G). Häufig proliferiert diese Membran; sie liegt dann in bis zu 7 Schichten übereinander (H). Mit dem Auftreten feingranulärer Matrix vergrössert sich das Zytosom, die inneren Membranen sind jetzt regellos gelagert (I). Die 11 nm dicke Membran zeigt je nach der Lage in der Schnittebene ein fünfschichtiges, globuläres oder quergestreiftes Aussehen (D). Ob die mit der Membranorganelle fusionierenden Bläschen aus dem Golgia-Apparat stammen, ist noch nicht völlig geklärt.

Aufgrund der bisherigen Vorstellungen zum Ablauf der Quarzphagozytose wurde die zytotoxische Wirkung von Quarz nur auf einen Einfluss der Staubes auf die beim Phagozytoseprozess primär beteiligten Strukturen (Phagosomen und Phagolysosomen) zurückgeführt.

Auch die bisher vorgelegten Theorien zum zytotoxischen Effekt von Quarz weisen alle in diese Richtung (Allison et al., 1967; Munder et al., 1967; Bruch, 1967). Es ist jedoch schwierig zu bestimmen, ob eine beobachtete Freisetzung von lysosomalen Enzymen kausal durch eine quarzbedingte Lysosomenschädigung verursacht wird oder ob der Lysosomenzerfall ein sekundäres Ereignis ist.

Da nach unseren Untersuchungen eine freie Lokalisation des Staubes im Grundplasma vor der Einlagerung in sekundäre Lysosomen wahrscheinlich gemacht werden konnte, wäre ein Einfluss von Quarz auch auf andere Zellstrukturen als Phagosomen oder Lysosomen denkbar. Bei der Diskussion über die Frage, inwieweit die Labilisierung der Lysosomen und die nachfolgende Zellnekrose als eigentliches pathogenetisches Prinzip des Quarzes im Hinblick auf die Silikose anzusehen ist, müssen die drei folgenden Beobachtungen berücksichtigt werden:

1. Quarzhaltige Lysosomen von Retikulumzellen aus dem silikotischen Granulom werden durch den SiO_2-Staub nicht geschädigt. Die Zellen erscheinen intakt und sind teilungsfähig. Einige dieser Quarz tragenden Zellen enthalten rauhes endoplasmatisches Retikulum mit allen morphologischen Merkmalen einer hohen Aktivität (BRUCH, 1971).

2. Quarzstaub liegt zumindestens temporär frei, also ohne umgebende Membran, im Zytoplasma von Phagozyten.

3. Nach Phagozytose von Quarz durch Alveolarmakrophagen in vivo zerfallen nach unseren Beobachtungen alle — auch die nicht quartztragenden — sekundären Lysosomen nahezu simultan. Auffallend war gleichzeitig eine starke Vermehrung der freien Ribosomen (BRUCH, 1967).

Aufgrund der obenerwähnten Befunde nehmen wir an, dass der Quarz nicht in jedem Fall eine lysosomenschädigende Wirkung ausübt. Es muss erwogen werden, ob der gleichzeitige Zerfall aller sekundären Lysosomen in den freien Alveolarmakrophagen nicht möglicherweise sekundär durch ein Ereignis herbeigeführt wird, dass zeitlich früher an anderen Zellstrukturen vor der Einlagerung des Staubes in die Phagolysosomen stattgefunden hat. Unter Umständen sind solche Prozesse in quarzphagozytierenden Zellen auch für die Produktion eines die Kollagenbildung stimulierenden Faktors verantwortlich zu machen (HEPPLESTON & STYLES, 1967). Die deutliche Vermehrung der Ribosomen während der Phagozytose im Quarz liesse sich in diesem Sinne deuten.

REFERENCES

ALLISON, A. C., HARINGTON, J. S., BIRBECK, M. & NASH T. (1967). In: *Inhaled particles and vapours II*. Ed. C. N. Davies. Oxford, Pergamon Press. pp. 121–131.
BECK, E. G. (1970) In: *Die Reaktion in vitro gezuchteter Zellen auf partikelformige Luftverunreinigungen und hoch palymere Stofie*. Koln, Westdt. Verl. (Forschungsber. Landes NRhein-Westf. Nr 2083).
BECK, E. G., BRUCH, J. & SACK, J. (1967). *Ergebn. Unters. Geb. Staub-u. Silikosebek. Steinkohlenbergbau*, **6**, 131.
BRUCH, J. (1967). *Fortschr. Staublungenforsch.* **2**, 249.
BRUCH, J. (1969). *Zentbl. Bakt. Parasitkde*, I, **215**, 507.
BRUCH, J. (1971). In Press.
GLAUERT, A. M. & LUCY, J. A. (1968). In: *The membranes*. Ed. A. J. Dalton & Fr. Haguenau. New York, Academic Press. p. 28.
HARINGTON, J. S. & ALLISON, A. C. (1965). *Medna Lav.* **56**, 471.
HEPPLESTON, A. G. & STYLES, J. A. (1967). *Fortschr. Staublungenforsch.* **2**, 123.
MUNDER, P. G., FERBER, E., MODOLELL, M. & FISCHER, H. (1967). *Fortschr. Staublungenforsch.* **2**, 129.

For DISCUSSION see p. 443.

THE CYTOTOXIC ACTION AND THE SEMICONDUCTOR PROPERTIES OF MINE DUSTS*

K. Robock and W. Klosterkötter

Steinkohlenbergbauverein, Essen, und Institut für Hygiene und Arbeitsmedizin des Klinikum Essen der Ruhruniversität Bochum, W. Germany

Summary — The paper describes the results of studies on the cytotoxic action and the semiconductor properties of mine dusts and a quartz-free clayey shale. The mine dusts were collected with a BAT I Fine Dust Filter Device. No clear relationship was found between the cytotoxic behaviour of the samples and their quartz and ash contents. Mine dusts with only $0 \cdot 2\%$ quartz and also the quartz-free clayey shale have a strong cytotoxic effect. Measurements of the semiconductor properties by means of luminescence indicate that the quartzes in the samples have very different electron structures, that the association with accompanying minerals and types of coals also has a certain influence, and that the cytotoxic effect of the clayey shale showing a strong lymphatic transport in the animal experiment can be explained by its electron structure.

INTRODUCTION

As a fundamental contribution to the pathogenesis of the pneumoconioses and to the occupational-hygienic assessment of dusts, numerous tests *in vivo* and *in vitro* have been carried out in the past two decades using mainly dusts prepared from various minerals, especially different SiO_2 modifications, rocks and coals as well as artificial mixtures of these components. Mine dusts were also used in recent years, after suitable dust samplers became available.

The results of the animal experiments (inhalation, intratracheal and intraperitoneal tests), using chemical and histological methods to indicate the extent of the tissue and lymph-node reaction, can be summarized as follows. Crystalline and amorphous SiO_2 modifications showed strong tissue and lymph-node reactions after longer periods of action, but only small differences in the intratracheal test (Klosterkötter *et al.*, 1965; Klosterkötter, 1966, 1967; Swensson, 1967). Samples of the adjacent rock of the Ruhr Carboniferous series showed a tissue reaction after 18 months only with quartz contents $\geqslant 10\%$ (Klosterkötter *et al.*, 1963; Schlipköter & Pott, 1969). Samples of pure coal and clay minerals showed, up to test periods of 18 months, only depositions of inert dust, and, for an anthracite coal, a weak tissue reaction (Grade 1) in the intratracheal test (Klosterkötter *et al.*, 1965, 1963; Dolgner *et al.*,

* Report No. 140 of the Centre for Dust and Silicosis Suppression of Steinkohlenbergbauverein in Essen.

Research project with the financial aid of the European Community for Coal and Steel and the Land Nordrhein-Westfalen.

1969). When 3% Dörentrup quartz sand DQ 12 was added to samples of open-burning and anthracite coals, a fibrosis developed in all cases with increasing duration of tests which, after 12 months, corresponded to the Grade 2 according to Belt and King (KLOSTERKÖTTER et al., 1965; SCHLIPKÖTER & POTT, 1969; DOLGNER et al., 1969). The open-burning coal sample indicated a certain inhibitory effect. Mine dusts from collieries of the Ruhr and the Saar District with a known pneumoconiosis risk, how-ever, caused no tissue reaction during test periods of 18 months independent of their quartz contents which ranged up to 6% for the test samples used (DOLGNER et al., 1967, 1969; HÖER et al., 1969). However, 95% of all mine dust samples studied so far by routine measurements have quartz contents only between 0·3 and 6% (BREUER & STUKE, 1965).

The opinion (DOLGNER et al., 1969) that dusts from clay minerals and different types of coal are inert appears doubtful in view of these results from mine dusts. Besides, it requires to be examined whether quartz plays a predominant part in hard coal mining, whether the quartzes in the different mine dusts have different properties when compared with the Dörentrup quartz sand, and what is the influence of the other mineral components and types of coal on the cytotoxic effects. Only when these questions have been answered can a clear occupational hygienic assessment of the dusts be made. Above all is the question whether animal experiments are suitable means, with the present test conditions, to find proper answers to these problems.

Tests with isolated cells, macrophages from the lung or the peritoneal cavity of rats and guinea pigs, however, gave more clear-cut results. Samples of various crystalline and amorphous SiO_2 modifications of different origin showed considerable differences in the development time and extent of their cytotoxic effect (ROBOCK, 1968; KLOSTER-KÖTTER & ROBOCK, 1967; PARAZZI et al., 1968; BECK & STÜTTGEN, 1969). These and other results of chemi-luminescence measurements indicate that, during the inter-action of SiO_2 particles with the cells, electron transfer reactions occur according to the electron theory of catalysis which lead to cytotoxic reactions at the cell membrane (ROBOCK, 1967, 1968; ROBOCK & KLOSTERKÖTTER 1967). As the electron structure of the samples assumes a decisive importance during this process, a very different action of real mixed dusts, i.e. of genuine mine dusts, can be expected with respect to their toxic effects.

Results of investigations with mine dusts from the Ruhr and the Saar District and with a quartz-free clayey shale are presented and described in this paper.

DUST AND CELL MATERIAL

Thirty-nine samples of mine dust were collected in 16 collieries of the Ruhr District and 5 samples of mine dust in 3 collieries of the Saar District by the BAT I Fine Dust Filter Device (BREUER, 1964). The fine dust samples collected on the membrane filter in the BAT I device showed an upper particle size of 7 μm, corresponding to the size selection curve of the device. In addition the separated fine dust together with the coarse dust in the cylone, was screened on a 7 μm micro-sieve, thus producing a fine dust which we call "micro-sieved fine dust".

The weight distribution curves (as a function of particle size) of the fine dust filter samples, as measured by the Coulter Counter, showed a maximum at 1 μm or between 1 and 2·5 μm, depending on the sample. The higher the ash contents of the fine dust filter samples, the more pronounced the maximum at 1 μm. The weight distribution curves of the micro-sieved samples as a function of particle size, however, showed a plateau in the range from $0 \cdot 78$ μm to $6 \cdot 2$ μm.

The quartz contents, found by X-ray diffraction and infrared spectroscopy, of the fine dust filter samples varied between $0 \cdot 2$ and $18 \cdot 6\%$. The ash contents of the fine dust filter samples fluctuated between 5 and $81 \cdot 2\%$ and that of the micro-sieved samples between $10 \cdot 3$ and $84 \cdot 6\%$.

A quartz-free dust sample from adjacent rock, with an upper particle size of 5 μm, was prepared by crushing, grinding and pneumatic-sizing a clayey-shale FLE obtained from Seam Erda. This clayey shale contained a well-crystallized kaolinite as the main constituent. The Dörentrup quartz sand DQ 12 with quartz contents of 87% and an upper particle size of 5 μm served as comparison material during all tests. The weight distribution curves against the particle sizes for both samples were identical.

For the cell tests, peritoneal macrophages from guinea pigs were used, the preparation of which was fully described elsewhere (KLOSTERKÖTTER & ROBOCK, 1967). During all tests, a dust concentration of $0 \cdot 6$ mg per 4×10^6 cells was used. For this purpose, the dust samples were dispersed by means of ultra-sound (3 min) in a tyrode solution to which a wetting agent (RBS 25), in a non-cytotoxic concentration, had been added.

METHOD OF TESTS

TTC-Method

Four cell preparations each of 8×10^6 cells per ml of tyrode solution were mixed with $1 \cdot 2$ mg dust samples per ml tyrode solution. Cell preparations without dust were used as controls. After an incubation time of 120 min at 37°C in a shaking water bath, the TTC-reduction activities of the cells were determined by the TTC-method (KLOSTERKÖTTER & ROBOCK, 1967) which gives a measure of the cytotoxicity, S_{120}, caused by the dust samples, in per cent of the values of the controls. Ten dusts were investigated simultaneously per day, and these tests were repeated on three days. Thus, a minimum of 12 individual measured values were available for each dust. The mean values of these measurements were used for the results described below, with a standard deviation of about $\pm 5\%$.

Luminescence Method

The luminescence of the dust samples after X-ray excitation ($2 \cdot 8 \times 10^4$r) was measured, as a function of the wavelength in the range 200 to 550 nm and as a function of the temperature in the range 20°C to 50°C, with a photomultiplier in the testing arrangement mentioned above (ROBOCK, 1967). For this purpose, the samples were suspended in tyrode solution ($\rho_H = 7 \cdot 2$).

The chemiluminescence which develops by interaction between samples not excited by X-ray and cells was measured in the same manner.

RESULTS OF TESTS

In Figure 1, the cytotoxicities S_{120} (after an incubation time of 120 min) are plotted in per cent of the cell control for 39 fine dust filter samples against the quartz contents of the samples.

It can be seen that dust samples with quartz contents of only 0.2% have strong cytotoxic effects. A clear relationship between the cytotoxic action and the quartz content of the samples could not be found. Figure 2 shows furthermore that there is also no relationship between cytotoxic action and ash content for samples containing up to 50% ash.

Whether and to what extent there is a relationship for higher ash contents will have to be examined by further testing. For the sake of comparison, it must still be mentioned that the Dörentrup Quartz Sand DQ 12, with a quartz content of 87%, caused a cytotoxic action of 95% under the same test conditions.

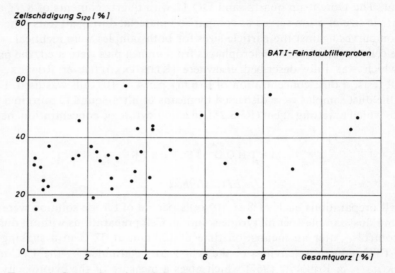

FIGURE 1. Cytotoxic action of the fine dust filter samples *vs.* the quartz content.

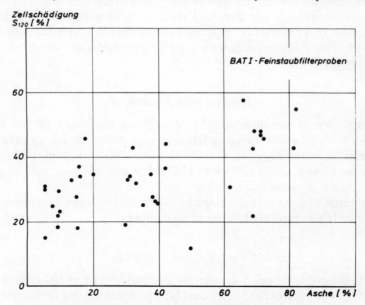

FIGURE 2. Cytotoxic action of the fine dust filter samples *vs.* the ash content.

For fine dust filter samples with quartz contents of $1 \cdot 7\%$, ash contents of $17 \cdot 3\%$ and cytotoxicities of 46%, the chemiluminescence developing by interaction with cells is shown in Figure 3 together with the effect caused by using the Dörentrup Quartz Sand DQ 12, as functions of the incubation times of the samples.

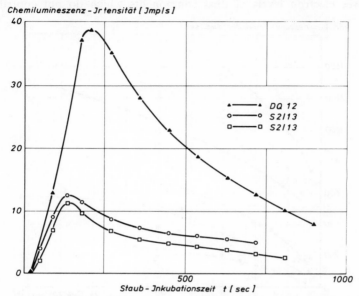

FIGURE 3. Chemiluminescence-intensity as a function of the dust incubation time.

The chemiluminescence determinable for the fine dust filter sample indicates that an electron transfer reaction occurs when this mine dust interacts with cells. In case of SiO_2 samples, the different cytotoxic actions can be correlated with the intensity of chemiluminescence (ROBOCK, 1968).

As insufficient material from fine dust filter samples was available, the microsieved fine dust samples had to be used for studying the semiconductor properties. These samples showed no clear relationship between their cytotoxic effects, varying from 0 to 50%, and their quartz and ash contents.

The intensity of luminescence (corrected for the spectral response of the photomultiplier), in the wavelength range from 200 to 550 nm, of the micro-sieved samples after X-ray excitation, is plotted in Figure 4 as a function of quartz content.

It can be seen that very different intensities of luminescence were obtained with the same quartz contents, but that the samples split into different groups and that there is within these groups a relationship between the intensity of luminescence and the quartz content. Which parameter ought to be attached to the various groups, i.e. whether we have to do here with quartzes of a different electron structure or whether the association with other minerals or coal types has any effect, is the subject of current investigations. It appears that, with the same quartz contents, samples may have a very different electron structure, since the luminescence phenomen is based on this structure.

The determination of the activation energies of the electron traps (ROBOCK, 1967, 1968) of the samples by means of luminescence measurements and their dependence on temperature showed no relation with the cytotoxic action of the samples. Such a connection, however, was found for samples of unmixed SiO_2 modifications. The probable reasons for this difference are, on the one hand, the existence of luminescence-absorbing constituents of the fine dust samples and, on the other, that the procedure also involves electron levels of dust components which do not contribute to the

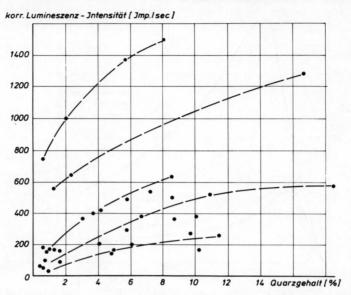

FIGURE 4. Radioluminescence-intensity as a function of the quartz content.

cytotoxic effect. Thus, we attempt at present to determine the cytotoxic action by measuring the electron emission of the mine dust samples and not by measuring the luminescence, in the meaning of the electron theory of catalysis.

Table I shows, for five fine dust filter samples from the Saar District, the values of their cytotoxic action, their quartz contents, their ash contents and the frequency of mineworkers underground with definite pulmonary changes (B_2-frequency) within the collieries where these samples were taken.

It will be seen that the ash and the quartz contents of the samples have no decisive influence on their cytotoxic actions. The results, which still have to be confirmed by further measurements, indicate that the cytotoxic actions found can be correlated to

TABLE I. RESULTS FOR FIVE FINE DUST FILTER SAMPLES FROM SAAR COLLIERIES WITH A KNOWN FREQUENCY OF PNEUMOCONIOSIS (B_2-FREQUENCY)

Sample	Cytotoxic action S_{120} (%)	Quartz-Content (%)	Ash-Content (%)	B_2-Frequency (%)
465	50	8·3	71·4	12
466	26	5·5	43·9	1·2
467	32	4·1	38·0	1·2
478	43	3·5	35·0	20
481	41	5·7	41·2	17

the frequency of pneumonconiosis cases. The samples Nos. 466 and 467 with a signifi-cantly lower cytotoxic effect come from the collieries with the lowest B_2-frequency.

To conclude, results will be given for a quartz-free clayey shale from the Ruhr Carboniferous which was distinguished by a very high lymphatic transport during animal experiments on the retention and elimination of dusts. Chemical and histologi-cal findings from the lungs of the animals are not yet complete. Figure 5 shows the high cytotoxic action of this material as a function of the incubation time of the cells, in comparison with the behaviour of the Dörentrup Quartz Sand DQ 12. After an incubation time of 120 min, this clayey shale caused 75% cytotoxic action to the cells.

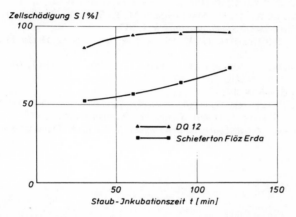

FIGURE 5. Cytotoxic action of a quartz-free clayey-shale FLE and of the Dörentrup quartz sand DQ 12 as a function of incubation time.

The determination of the activation energy of the electron traps by two different methods, E_H^{iso} and E_H^{lin}, gave, in conformity with the cytotoxic effect, somewhat lower values (0·50 eV and 0·41 eV) for the clayey shale than for the Dörentrup Quartz Sand (0·57 eV and 0·43 eV). The values for the clayey shales, however, are still within the range of the activation energies of the unmixed, strongly cytotoxic SiO_2 modifications studied so far. This could be taken as an indication that SiO_4 tetrahedra of the same structure as in the SiO_2 modifications, could be present in silicates without quartz determinable by X-ray or infra-red spectroscopy. According to the surface theory extended by us to an "electron theory" about the specific proper-ties of the SiO_2 particles responsible for the cytotoxic actions, the internal structure of the individual SiO_4-tetrahedra is of decisive importance, not their structural arrangements with each other.

The results presented here and summarized at the beginning of this paper indicate that we cannot attribute uniform cytotoxic activity to quartz, but that quartzes may have very different cytotoxic actions depending upon their petrogenesis, and also that other associated minerals and types of coal must be taken into consideration.

For this reason, future animal experiments and cell tests concerning the occupa-tional-hygienic assessment of dusts should be carried out only with real airborne dust and not with dusts from non-mining minerals or artificially made from rocks or coal.

REFERENCES

Beck, E. G. & Stüttgen, N. (1969). *Silikoseber. NRhein-Westf.* **7**, 189.

Breuer, H. (1964). *Staub* **24**, 324.

Breuer, H. & Stuke, J. (1965). *Z. Arbeitsmedizin* **2**, 35.

Dolgner, R., Einbrodt, H. J., Höer, P. W., Klosterkötter, W., Leiteritz, H. & Schlipköter, W. (1967). *Fortchr. Staublungenforsch.* **2**, 361.

Dolgner, R., Schlipköter, H. W. & Leiteritz, H. (1969). *Silikoseber. NRhein-Westf.* **7**, 45.

Höer, P. W., Laufhütte, D. W. & Leiteritz, H. (1969). *Silikoseber. NRhein-Westf.* **7**, 51.

Klosterkötter, W. (1966). *Arch. Hyg. Bakt.* **150**, 542.

Klosterkötter, W. (1967). *Silikoseber. NRhein-Westf.* **6**, 65.

Klosterkötter, W. & Robock, K. (1967). *Silikoseber. NRhein-Westf.* **6**, 51.

Klosterkötter, W., Leiteritz, H., Mackowsky, M. T., Schiller, E., Schlipköter, H. W. & Thaer, A. (1963). *Fortschr. Staublungenforsch.* **1**, 517.

Klosterkötter, W., Schlipköter, H. W., Höer, P. W. & Leiteritz, H. (1965). *Silikoseber. NRhein-Westf.* **5**, 31.

Parazzi, E., Secchi, G. C., Pernis, B. & Vigliani, E. (1968). *Archs envir. Hlth* **17**, 850–859.

Robock, K. (1967). *Beitr. Silikoseforsch.* **92**, 1.

Robock, K. (1968). *Staub* **28**, 148.

Robock, K. & Klosterkötter, W. (1967). *Fortschr. Staublungenforsch.* **2**, 115.

Schlipköter, H. W. & Pott, F. (1969). *Silikoseber. NRhein-Westf.* **7**, 57.

Swensson, A. (1967). In: *Inhaled particles and vapours II. Ed.* C. N. Davies. Oxford, Pergamon Press. pp. 95–104.

DISCUSSION

E. G. BECK: Have your investigations shown that different quartz dusts can have different cytotoxic and fibrogenic effects and have you found a correlation between the results of the cell culture and animal experiments?

Dr. ROBOCK: Two SiO_2 dusts received from the Institute for Occupational Hygiene and Industrial Diseases in Ostrava, CSSR, were analysed both by infrared spectroscopy and by X-ray and found to be 100% α-quartzes. In intratracheal tests (50 mg) with rats at the Ostrava Institute, these two quartz dusts caused very different tissue reactions two months after exposure, as shown in Figure 1. The quartz SiO_2 I showed much less effect than the quartz SiO_2 II, for which there was no explanation.

We were asked to investigate whether the two quartz dusts were different also with regard to their semiconductor properties and their cytotoxicity. Figure 2 shows the dependence, with time, of the cytotoxicity of these samples and of our standard quartz DQ 12, as determined by the TTC test.

In the cell test, the quartzes behaved in different ways, as in the intratracheal test. In further biochemical and morphological methods Dr. Beck of the Medical Institute for Air Hygiene and Silicosis Research at the University of Düsseldorf also found a correspondingly different behaviour of these quartz samples. This is another indication that there is a correlation between the cytotoxic effect of the SiO_2 samples and their fibrogenic effect.

Figure 3 shows the values of the activation energies of the electron traps and the trace element content of aluminium in the samples. In the SiO_2 lattice, aluminium can occupy preferentially, in the form of Al^{3+}, the lattice sites of Si^{4+} atoms and can thus, according to the electron theory of catalysis, influence essentially the electron and the internal structure of the SiO_4 tetrahedron. It can be seen from the Table that the No. 1 quartz with the lower cytotoxic effects has an Al-content higher by one order, as determined by the X-ray fluorescence analysis, and that also the activation energies of its electron traps differ essentially from those of the two other quartzes and are outside of the range found for the cytotoxic SiO_2 samples. Thus, a relationship between cytotoxic effect and electron structure is shown for these SiO_2 samples.

A. M. LANGER: Did you check the quartz for trace element content? Was all the quartz low-temperature quartz? Was the relative degree of crystallinity checked by X-ray analysis? The property of electron transfer is influenced by each of these.

Dr. ROBOCK: We made trace element determinations by X-ray fluorescence analysis in the ppm range. We determined the components of these samples by infra-red spectroscopy and X-ray spectroscopy; for the two samples, SiO_2 I and SiO_2 II, we had low-temperature quartz.

		SiO_2 I	SiO_2 II	Kontrolle
Lungenfeuchtgewicht	[mg]	2800	6100	1210
Hydroxyprolin	[mg]	5,34	17,22	3,33
Gesamtlipide	[mg]	209	488	65,7
Phospholipide	[mg]	121	225	26,8

FIGURE 1. Comparison of the lung findings of test rats and of control rats.

M. T. R. Reisner: The findings by Robock and Klosterkötter that no uniform biologically toxic effect can be allocated to the mineral quartz and that, obviously, other minerals, too, influence the development of pulmonary changes, is confirmed by comparing the dust conditions in the Ruhr coal field with the prevalence of simple pneumoconiosis. In order to obtain more information on the quartz content of the dust, we analysed more than 3000 gravimetric dust measurements taken between 1963–65.

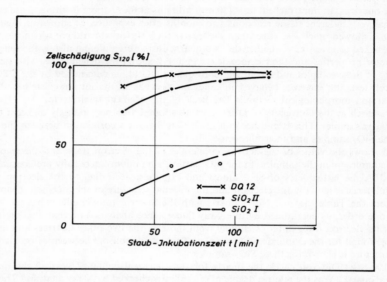

FIGURE 2. Cytotoxicity as a function of the incubation period, related to the control values, for DQ 12, SiO₂ I and SiO₂ II

		SiO_2 I	SiO_2 II	DQ 12
Al-Gehalt	[ppm]	3100	100	120
E_H^{iso}	[eV]	0.81	0.67	0.57
E_H^{lin}	[eV]	0.70	0.54	0.43

FIGURE 3. Activation energies of the electron traps and of the trace element content of aluminium of the three SiO₂ samples.

It was found that the quartz content is significantly different in the various seam horizons. Figure 1 shows the respective cumulative frequency distribution of the samples taken in coal faces according to the quartz content of the respirable dust. The lowest quartz content was found in the seams of the Sprockhövel and Witten Strata (median = $1 \cdot 7\%$) and, very similar, in the Bochum Strata ($1 \cdot 4\%$). A much higher quartz content was found in the Essen Strata ($2 \cdot 5\%$) and, still more, in the Horst and the Dorsten Strata ($3 \cdot 5\%$).

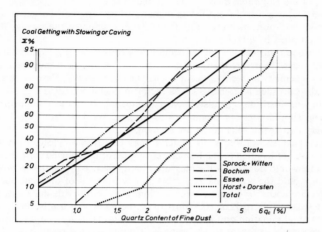

FIGURE 4. Cumulative frequency distributions of BAT I fine dust samples taken in coal faces of different seam horizons in the Ruhr coal field against the quartz content.

When comparing the mean values of the quartz content Q in the respirable dust from all measurements in seams (Table I), we find a ratio of about 1 : 2 between the mean quartz content in the Sprockhövel to Bochum Strata on the one hand and that in the Essen to Dorsten Strata, on the other. This ratio also applies to the ash contents (A) of the respirable dust.

In the Ruhr coal mines, however, the frequency of simple pneumoconiosis is generally greater in collieries producing medium-rank bituminous coal from the Bochum Strata and higher-rank coal from the Sprockhövel and Witten Strata than in those producing low-rank coal from the Essen to Dorsten Strata. Table I shows that the percentage of miners with simple pneumoconiosis is also the highest ($22 \cdot 1\%$) in the mines working high-rank seams. This percentage is a little lower ($17 \cdot 7\%$) in the mines working seams in the Bochum Strata. The percentage drops to only about one-third of that ($8 \cdot 5\%$) for miners employed in collieries extracting low-rank coal.

As against the relationship to quartz content, we found that the percentage of miners with simple pneumoconiosis is lower where the quartz content is generally higher. As the quartz concentration (C_q) rather than the quartz percentage content is likely to be responsible for the development of pneumoconiosis, these values have to be compared, too. As Table I shows, the quartz concentration, too, was higher in the seams of the Essen to Dorsten Strata ($0 \cdot 036$ mg/m³ as against $0 \cdot 026$ and $0 \cdot 028$ mg/m³), although fewer miners working in these seams had simple pneumoconiosis.

TABLE I. DUST CONDITIONS AND PREVALENCE OF PNEUMOCONIOSIS IN DIFFERENT SEAM HORIZONS OF THE RUHR COAL FIELD

Seam horizon strata	Rank of coal	BAT-sampling in coalfaces					Percentage of miners with simple pneumoc. (1965)
		No.	C mg/m³	A %	Q %	C_q mg/m³	
Sprockhövel and Witten	High	298	$2 \cdot 63$	$14 \cdot 3$	$1 \cdot 36$	$0 \cdot 026$	$22 \cdot 1$
Bochum	Medium	1859	$2 \cdot 26$	$16 \cdot 8$	$1 \cdot 58$	$0 \cdot 028$	$17 \cdot 7$
Essen to Dorsten	Low	872	$1 \cdot 25$	$29 \cdot 7$	$2 \cdot 96$	$0 \cdot 036$	$8 \cdot 5$

Thus, an influence of quartz on the development of pneumoconiosis cannot be proved by these rough statistics from the conditions in the Ruhr. This indicates that, with the generally low quartz content in the fine dust ($<5\%$) and its small variation, the influence of quartz is either not uniform or is overruled by other factors which have still to be found.

The total fine dust in coal mines can be correlated, however, with the frequency of pneumoconiosis. Where the percentage of miners with pulmonary changes is higher, we measured also higher mass concentrations (C) of the respirable dust on average (see Table I).

The samples were taken with the BAT I gravimetric dust sampler. To get a rough idea for a comparison with concentrations measured with the MRE-dust sampler, the average BAT I concentration C has to be multiplied by a factor of 4 to 5.

S. E. DEVIR: The question whether pneumoconiosis is caused by silica quartz has been debated over the last fifteen years. There are many approaches, and the problem must be attacked by teamwork; with organic chemists as well as occupational health workers. Carbon can be replaced by silica in amino acids. Can such interchanges be a factor in pneumoconiosis?

Dr. ROBOCK: In our Institute, chemists have participated. It is most important that research workers in this field should consider themselves as a team. Workers from the United States and Germany meet every two years, when ideas are exchanged.

J. DODGSON: You have shown that shale material may be strongly cytotoxic; is it not likely that such minerals will have contributed to the luminescence intensities reported for the mixed dusts from coalmines? If so, one would not expect the measured luminescence intensities to be solely related to quartz content, nor would the scatter be explicable simply in terms of different quartz "activities".

Dr. ROBOCK: We are about to examine this question. This result with shale was unexpected. We were looking for a quartz-free rock or rock dust from the Ruhr, for use by Prof. Klosterkötter in animal experiments on elimination and deposition. He found that this material showed a very good lymph transport, especially in regard to fibrogenesis. The unexpected result has led us to start new animal experiments, to examine the tissue, as over the last two years the lungs had been incinerated and these measurements have not been made.

As to whether it is due to different quartzes, that is what we are now trying to check.

J. G. GILSON: Dr. Robock's and Dr. Sakabe's papers emphasize the need to establish standard reference samples of quartz for use in biological testing. We have heard about ten papers at this Conference where quartz has been used. Some of the results reported conflict. Is this due to differences in the physical or chemical properties of the quartz used, or the biological test system?

We probably have a quorum of the world's experts on this type of work here in this hall. I suggest we need international co-operation in establishing reference samples of quartz for the future work. These would be available to all and would be well characterized physically and chemically including, of course, trace elements.

This is just what has been done by the UICC Committee on Asbestos Cancers for asbestos samples. A great deal of information about the nature of these samples has been established in a short time, as they have been a source of investigation and use in more than 20 countries, some of it reported at this Conference. Perhaps Dr. Robock and his colleagues would like to give a lead. For the future this might be one of the more useful practical results of this International Symposium.

Dr. K. ROBOCK: We would be in a position to supply sufficient quantities of quartz. We have one ton of the standard material which is used by all German Institutes concerned with silicosis research. If you would like to receive quantities of this, please let me know. I agree that use of standard samples could overcome many difficulties. Our material is fine, <5 μm, with maximum weight distribution at $1\cdot5$ μm.

H.-W. SCHLIPKÖTER: I understand that we have a quartz which is silicogenic, and we also find that it is cytotoxic, so we assume some major relationship between cytotoxicity and silicogenicity. But is it legitimate to conclude that if you find cytotoxicity of a certain degree, you can assume from this that the material is also silicogenic?

Dr. ROBOCK: At the moment I cannot comment. We hope to get evidence from the animal experiments.

BIOLOGICAL ACTION OF DIFFERENT ASBESTOS DUSTS WITH SPECIAL RESPECT TO FIBRE LENGTH AND SEMICONDUCTOR PROPERTIES

K. Robock* and W. Klosterkötter**

Steinkohlenbergbauverein, Essen und Institut für Hygiene und
Arbeitsmedizin des Klinikum Essen der Ruhruniversität, Bochum,**
W. Germany*

Summary — The paper describes studies on the cytotoxic effect of five U.I.C.C. standard reference asbestos samples by the TTC method, the nigrosin method and by polarographic determination of the oxygen-consumption of cells. The influence of dry grinding on the structure of the samples was analysed by infrared spectroscopy and the influence on the cytotoxic effect was studied. Measurements of luminescence were made to determine the activation energies of the electron traps of the samples. Indications were found on the cytotoxicity of the asbestos dusts and on a considerable structural influence by grinding.

INTRODUCTION

A NUMBER of papers are available on the effect of asbestos dusts *in vitro* on alveolar and peritoneal macrophages. It was the aim of the investigations here described to determine whether asbestos dusts have cytotoxic effects, whether different effects between asbestos of the amphibole group and the serpentine group can be found and the influence of the fibre length of the asbestos dusts.

KLOSTERKÖTTER *et al.* (1965) found, by the lactate test with incubation times of up to 20 h, a different depression of the formation of lactic acid of peritoneal macrophages under the influence of amosite, crocidolite and chrysotile. These asbestos dusts were used as original samples with a high fibre length as well as after dry grinding to fibre lengths <3 μm. A clear relationship between the depression of lactic acid and fibre length, however, could not be found. Morphologically, no certain signs of cell damage could be proved. BECK *et al.* (1967) and BECK (1970) also could not observe any acute cell damage by asbestos dusts by the optical or the electron microscope, also up to incubation times of 20 h, using morphological and histochemical criteria. Yet there was a retardation of the propagation rate of L-cells after an addition of asbestos dusts as well as a loss of vitality of macrophages when checked with eosin Y

Report No. 144 of the Centre for Dust and Silicosis Suppression of Steinkohlenbergbauverein in Essen.

Research project with the financial aid of the European Community for Coal and Steel and the Land Nordrhein-Westfalen.

465

and, finally, a higher activity of lactate dehydrogenase in the culture medium. These findings indicate an increased permeability of the membrane of the macrophages. An acute toxic effect cannot be presumed, however, because of the continued formation of lactate by the cells and their unchanged consumption of oxygen. In L-cells, the oxygen consumption remained unaffected. However, PARAZZI et al. (1968) found, after the action of a chrysotile from Balangero and a South African crocidolite on macrophages, a depression of the production of lactic acid, a rapid loss of the fluorochromatic colouring and a considerable release of enzymes into the culture medium. An increased toxicity of the fibre fraction as against the particle fraction was observed. Pre-treatment of the asbestos dusts with polyvinyl-pyridin-N-oxide (PVNO) remained without effect. In the haemolysis tests, carried out by SECCHI & REZZONICO (1968) with five U.I.C.C. standard reference asbestos samples, only the serpentine asbestos chrysotile proved to be strongly haemolytic, but the asbestos of the amphibole group: amosite, crocidolite and anthophyllite, only slightly haemolytic. KOSHI et al. (1968) and SCHNITZER & PUNDSAK (1970) found a strong haemolytic activity in serpentine asbestos. KOSHI et al. (1968) found, by measuring the acid phosphatase and the production of lactic acid in macrophages, very different and partly significant cytotoxic effects of a high number of Amphibol and Serpentine asbestos samples of different origin. The TTC method also used by KOSHI et al. (1968), however, showed no cytotoxic effect of these asbestos samples, which will be discussed later. The authors also published papers on the cytotoxic effect of U.I.C.C. samples as well as of other asbestos dusts with the use of the TTC method (KLOSTERKÖTTER & ROBOCK, 1970) but have to admit certain restrictive statements with regard to this method when using asbestos dusts. KOSHI et al. (1969) found that the different cytotoxicity of various serpentines is much influenced by annealing the samples. After a heat treatment in the range between 500°C to 700°C, all samples investigated showed a strong cytotoxic effect which decreased again with higher annealing temperatures. The authors assume an interrelationship between the cytotoxic effect and the disordered structure (in the range between 500°C and 700°C) of the asbestos samples, as the transformation of serpentine asbestos into forsterite, which ends at about 800°C, takes place in this temperature range.

The findings show that there is no agreement yet about the cytotoxic effect of asbestos dusts. This could be due, on the one hand, to the testing method applied in each case, e.g. whether sera were used or not, or to differences between the asbestos dust samples themselves as not only the five U.I.C.C. standard reference asbestos samples were used. As for the studies on the influence of the fibre length, the method of comminution of the asbestos dusts could play an important part. This fact is indicated, above all, by the results with the annealed asbestos dusts of KOSHI et al. (1969). As for dry grinding and the testing conditions used therefore, the structure of the samples could be influenced in the same way as proved by KOSHI et al. (1963). HOLT et al. (1963) found, for a chrysotile which they crushed in a hammer mill at high speed, severe fibrosis in animal experiments even for fibre lengths <3 μm.

Our programme was aimed at an investigation of the effect of the five U.I.C.C. standard reference asbestos samples on peritoneal macrophages by three different biochemical methods. The samples were analysed by infrared spectroscopy before and after dry grinding, and their semiconductor properties, too, were determined by measurements of luminescence.

DUST AND CELL MATERIAL

The U.I.C.C. standard reference asbestos samples used by us were made available by Dr. V. Timbrell of the Pneumoconiosis Research Unit, Llandough Hospital, Penarth, and had already been fully described with respect to their mineralogical, physical and chemical properties (TIMBRELL et al., 1968; TIMBRELL, 1970; TIMBRELL et al., 1970). The following samples were concerned:

> banded silicates: an amosite, a crocidolite and an anthophyllite of the amphibole group,
> stratified silicates: two chrysotiles, chrysotile A and chrysotile B of the serpentine group.

The same samples were ground for 100 h in an agate ball mill and were provided with a label "100 h" or "short".

The infrared spectroscopical analyses* showed that the crystalline contents in all asbestos samples were essentially reduced by grinding. For the amosite-100 h the cation layer linked octahedrally was changed, while the SiO_4 tetrahedra of the chains remained mostly without influence. In addition, quartz and chloride were found. For the crocidolite, a longer distance of the oxygen atoms to the cation layer is given than for the amosite. The cation layer was changed also for the crocidolite-100 h, as well as the silicate chains. The crocidolite was more changed by grinding than the amosite. Quartz was also found in crocidolite-100 h. Anthophyllite has the largest distance between the oxygen atoms and the cations. With the anthophyllite-100 h, the silicate bands remain largely intact, but noticeable dislocation were caused in the metal layer with the result that the distances between the oxygen and the metal atoms were much distorted. Chrysotile A has smaller distances between Si-O-Me than chrysotile B. Thus, its absorption bands are situated at higher wave numbers. In addition contamination of the carbonates were found. The chrysotiles A-100 h and B-100 h were much more changed by grinding than amphibole asbestos and the absorption spectrum no longer showed the typical Si-O vibration of individual layers. Only with the chrysotile B-100 h, was a negligible portion of the SiO_4-tetrahedra preserved such as to be measurable.

The Dörentrup quartz sand DQ 12 served as material for comparison (ROBOCK, 1967). After grinding, the quartz sand DQ12-100 h showed in its spectral distribution no principal difference from the starting material, except a strong reduction of the intensities of all absorption bands. At the same time, a modified distance of the individual tetrahedra must be assumed.

Peritoneal macrophages of guinea pigs were used for the cell tests. The method by which they were obtained and prepared, has been fully described elsewhere (KLOSTER-KÖTTER & ROBOCK, 1967).

The samples of asbestos dusts were dispersed for all measurements, by means of ultra-sound (3 min), in tyrode solution to which a surface wetting agent (RBS 25) had been added in a non cytotoxic concentration.

---

* The authors wish to thank cordially Frau Dr. M. Gade, Bergbau-Forschung GmbH in Essen-Kray, for these infrared spectroscopic analyses and their interpretation.

METHOD OF TESTS

TTC-Method

Four cell preparations each of $8 \cdot 10^6$ cells per ml of tyrode solution were mixed with $1 \cdot 2$ mg of sample material per ml tyrode solution. Cells without dust material were used as controls and reference values. After an incubation time of 120 min at 37°C in the shaking water bath, the TTC-reduction activities of the cells were measured by the TTC-method (KLOSTERKÖTTER & ROBOCK, 1967) which provides a measure of the cytotoxicity S, caused by the dust samples, as a percentage of the values of the cell control. All samples were tested simultaneously on the same day, and the tests were repeated at least three times.

Nigrosine-Method

In 35 mm diameter tissue culture dishes (Falcon Plastics) $8 \cdot 10^6$ cells were incubated for 90 min in a tyrode solution at 37°C in an incubator until pseudopodia were formed. Then, the covering liquid was poured off and 1 ml of dust-nigrosine-suspension or 1 ml of nigrosine solution for the control values was pipetted. This process is the time $t = 0$ for the incubation period of 120 min of the test concentrations in the incubator at 37°C in an CO_2-atmosphere. For each test concentration, the coloured (damaged) and the non-coloured (undamaged) cells were counted microscopically, after termination of the incubation time, always in 4 squares of an eyepiece graticule. Then, the percentage of the coloured cells was calculated from the mean values, and this percentage was given as factor of cytotoxicity, after subtraction of the damaged portion of cells in the cell control concentrations.

Polarographic Oxygen Determination

In order to measure the oxygen consumption of the cells after the influence of dust, apparatus developed by MUNDER & FISCHER (1963) and MUNDER & MODOLELL (1965), for the polarographic O_2-determination, and modified by the authors, was used.

The cells were placed on a Teflon membrane in a vessel of V2-A steel and filled with tyrode solution. This vessel was connected air-tight to a gas chamber of a volume of about 2 ml. The cells inhaled oxygen through the Teflon membrane which is permeable to gas. The decrease of the oxygen partial pressure in the gas chamber was continuously and automatically recorded by a Clark platinum electrode. The temperature was held constantly at 37°C. During the tests, a concentration of 24 million cells and a concentration of $4 \cdot 8$ mg dust were used.

Luminescence-Method

The luminescence of the samples after X-ray excitation ($2 \cdot 8 \times 10^4$r) was measured, as a function of the temperature in the range 20°C to 50°C and as a function of time, with the photomultiplier in the testing setup and arrangement mentioned before (ROBOCK, 1967). For this purpose, the samples were suspended in tyrode solution.

RESULTS OF TESTS

TTC-Method

Table I shows, for all dust samples, in the first column the TTC reduction activities (TTC-RA) of the macrophages after a dust incubation time of 120 min.

TABLE I. TTC REDUCTION ACTIVITIES (TTC-RA) OF THE DUST SAMPLES WITH AND WITHOUT CELLS

Sample	TTC-RA$_{120}$ (%) with cells	TTC-RA (Extinction Units) without cells
DQ 12	5	0·022
DQ 12 100 h	40	0·018
Amosite	(60)	0·208
Amosite 100 h	(0)	>3·000
Anthophyllite	44	0·025
Anthophyllite 100 h	(0)	>3·000
Chrysotile A	41	0.092
Chrysotile 100 h	(0)	>3·000
Chrysotile B	(70)	0·462
Chrysotile 100 h	(0)	>3·000
Crocidolite	(68)	0·517
Crocidolite 100 h	(0)	>3·000
Cell Control	100	1·000

Relative to the 100% value of the cell control, the quartz sand DQ 12 caused a 95% depression of the TTC-RA, and the DQ 12 — 100 h a depression of 60%. Thus, dry grinding this quartz sand caused a 35% reduction of its cytotoxic effect.

It looked at first as if the unground asbestos dust samples had a different, but definite cytotoxic effect, and as if the asbestos samples ground for 100 h had no cytotoxic effect. It was found later on, however, that — contrary to all SiO_2 and mine dust samples studied so far — the asbestos samples are themselves capable of reducing the TTC (2, 3, 5-triphenyl tetrazol chloride) and not only the active cells. These TTC-RA-values of all samples without cells are shown, in extinction units, in Col. 2 of Table I, and also the value of the cell control (8 · 10^6 cells). Among the unground asbestos dust samples, only the anthophyllite and the chrysotile A had a weakly reducing effect with the result that their cytotoxic effect S with 56% and 59% can be considered proven. The cytotoxicity of the other asbestos dust samples, especially of the 100 h samples, however, cannot be determined by the TTC-method. Therefore, the TTC-RA$_{120}$ values with cells were put into brackets.

In the paper by KOSHI et al. (1968), no cytotoxic effects of asbestos dusts could be measured by the TTC-method, as mentioned before, but this is presumably due also to the TTC reducing properties of the samples used for their work.

For this reason, different methods of investigating the effect of asbestos dusts were used.

Nigrosine-Method

Figure 1 shows the cytotoxic effect of quartz sand DQ 12 as found by the Nigrosine-method, plotted against the time of dust incubation.

If the time is increased with this test, the cytotoxic effect of the quartz sand DQ 12 does not increase as, the cell controls also absorb more dyestuff.

Figure 2 shows, for an incubation period of 120 min, the absorption of dyestuff in consequence of the permeability disturbance of the membrane of the macrophages, also called cytotoxicity, for the asbestos dust samples.

Of the "long" samples, the two chrysotiles had the strongest effects. A definite influence due to the dry grinding can be observed for the crocidolite and the amosite. The influence on the other samples remains small. Likewise, a pre-treatment of the

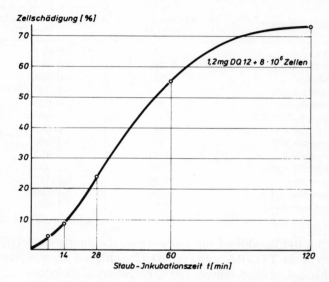

FIGURE 1. Cytotoxic effect by quartz sand DQ 12, according to the nigrosine-method.

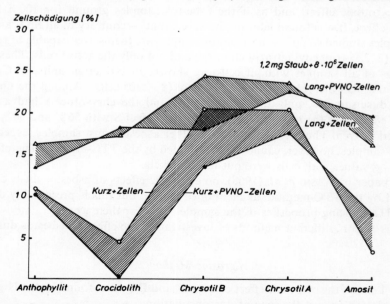

FIGURE 2. Cytotoxicity, according to the nigrosine-method, by "long" and "short" asbestos.

macrophages with 2% polyvinylpyridine-N-oxide (PVNO), injected intraperitoneally 48 h before the withdrawal of cells, remained without much influence.

Polarographic O_2 Determination

Unfortunately, we can give only preliminary results, as the apparatus used for our tests was ready for measurements only a short time before the writing up of this paper due to technical defects.

Figure 3 shows the O_2-reading in % in the gas chamber against the dust incubation time for a cell control, the amosite and the quartz sand DQ 12.

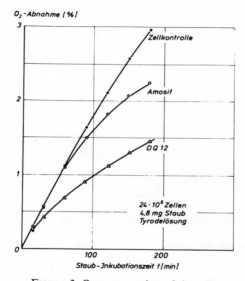

FIGURE 3. O_2-consumption of the cells.

It can be seen that this method enables a depression of cellular respiration to be demonstrated after 30 min for the quartz sand DQ 12 and that this depression amounts to 50% after 180 min. Amosite caused a clear depression of cellular respiration after an incubation period of 90 min, although to a smaller extent thant the DQ 12.

Figure 4 shows that, in another test, the cell control had an O_2-consumption of the same level and that the chrysotile B-100 caused a strong depression of cellular respiration.

These results must still be confirmed by further measurements with these asbestos dust samples as well as with the other samples. Above all, the influence of the addition of sera on the tyrode solution will have to be studied. It could be imagined that the adsorption of sera (KOSHI et al., 1969) checks the cytotoxic effects either temporarily or permanently. Thus, this polarographic determination of the O_2-consumption of the cells, under the influence of asbestos dusts samples and the use of different sera, will be extended in future to test periods up to 24 h. However, we can state already at this time that the findings presented at this Symposium indicate a cytotoxic effect of the U.I.C.C. samples.

Luminescence-Method

The temperature dependence of luminescence in the wavelength range from 200 to 550 nm, after X-ray excitation, was measured in order to obtain the electron structure of the samples. As for the asbestos samples, there is a considerable dependence of the luminescence intensity on temperature in the range from 20 to 50°C, similar to the SiO_2 samples (ROBOCK, 1967) as Figure 5 shows for the chrysotile B.

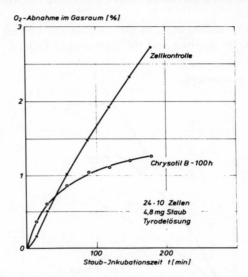

FIGURE 4. O_2-consumption of the cells as a function of the incubation period.

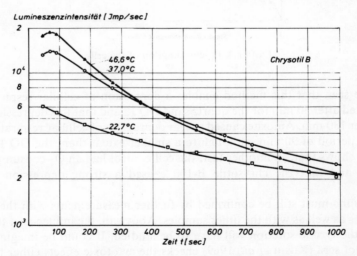

FIGURE 5. Intensity of radioluminescence as a function of time for three different temperatures.

Table II shows, for all samples, these luminescence intensities at a measuring temperature of 39·5°C. It will be seen that very different luminescence intensities (100 Imp/s for crocidolite and 1600 imp/s for chrysotile A) were found for the samples, due to a different structure and, therefore, also to a different electron structure (ROBOCK, 1967; ROBOCK, 1968).

It is especially striking that these luminescence intensities are very much reduced by dry grinding. This fact, too, appears to indicate a considerable structural effect of the grinding process on the samples.

TABLE II. ACTIVATION ENERGIES OF THE ELECTRON TRAPS AND
INTENSITIES OF THERMOLUMINESCENCE

Sample	E_H^{lin} (eV)	E_H^{iso} (eV)	$L_{39.5°C}^{iso}$ (imp/s)
DQ 12	0·43	0·58	580
DQ 12 100 h	0·38	0·57	330
Amosite	0·27	0·48	210
Amosite 100 h	0·05	0·29	32
Anthophyllite	0·40	0·61	1150
Anthophyllite 100 h	0·27	0·60	500
Chrysotile A	0·30	0·50	1600
Chrysotile 100 h	0·20	0·41	430
Chrysotile B	0·42	0·60	1000
Chrysotile 100 h	0·30	0·54	175
Crocidolite	0·31	0·52	110
Crocidolite 100 h	0·22	0·35	31

In the first column of Table II, the activation energies of the electron traps are shown as determined by linear heating of the samples after X-ray treatment by luminescence measurements. The second column gives the values found by isothermal measurements. These values show a shifting of the energies position of the electron traps by dry grinding.

For the samples of different SiO_2 modifications investigated so far, a relationship was found between the activation energies of the electron traps of the samples and their cytotoxic effect (ROBOCK, 1967, 1968). How far such a relationship applies also for asbestos dusts, in the event that their cytotoxic effects can be confirmed, will be the subject of further studies.

CONCLUSIONS

The results of the cell tests show that chrysotile has the highest cytotoxic effect and that crocidolite has a very much weaker one. Epidemiological studies, however, show that the health hazard is probably lower with the chrysotile than with the crocidolite. This was explained to us by the work of Dr. TIMBRELL and his colleagues of the Pneumoconiosis Research Unit, Cardiff. This research team, which was not surprised by our results, had found that the shape of the fibres must be taken into account as an important factor for the inhalation of asbestos dusts, as described in another paper in a contribution to this symposium (TIMBRELL & SKIDMORE, 1971). According to these authors, the thin and straight crocidolite fibres can penetrate into the pleura in a certain quantity during inhalation but not the chrysotile with its curved fibres. This curved fibre shape of the chrysotile has the effect that it is nearly completely arrested and deposited high in the respiratory tract and does not penetrate to the pleura. This explains the observed relation between an exposure to crocidolite and tumors of the pleura.

When applying asbestos dusts by pleural injection *in vivo*, the influence of the shape of the fibres is eliminated. A preliminary comparison of the results thus obtained by the research team in Cardiff with our findings *in vitro* led to a satisfactory agreement. The chrysotile had the highest cytotoxic effects. In our opinion, the findings about the noxious effects of these asbestos dusts do thus no longer contradict each other.

REFERENCES

BECK, E. G. (1970). *ForschsBer. Land NRhein-Westf.* (2083).
BECK, E. G., SACK, J. & BRUCH, J. (1967). *Fortschr. Staublungenforsch.* **2**, 481.
HOLT, P. F., MILLS, J. & YOUNG, D. K. (1963). *Fortschr. Staublungenforsch.* **1**, 201.
KLOSTERKÖTTER, W. & ROBOCK, K. (1967). *Silikoseber. NRhein-Westf.* **6**, 51.
KLOSTERKÖTTER, W. & ROBOCK, K. (1970). *Arbeitsmedizin, Sozialmedizin, Arbeitshyg.* **36**, 111.
KLOSTERKÖTTER, W., EINBRODT, H. J., RITZERFELD, W. & ZEITLER, S. (1965). *Silikoseber. NRhein-Westf.* **5**, 65.
KOSHI, K., HAYASHI, H. & SAKABE, H. (1968). *Ind. Hlth, Japan* **6**, 69.
KOSHI, K., HAYASHI, H. & SAKABE, H. (1969). *Ind. Hlth, Japan* **7**, 66.
MODOLELL, M., MUNDER, P. G. & FISCHER, H. (1967). *Fortschr. Staublungenforsch.* **2**, 179.
MUNDER, P. G. & FISCHER, H. (1963). *Beitr. Silikoseforsch. S.-Bd. Grundfragen Silikoseforsch.* **5**, 21.
MUNDER, P. G. & MODOLELL, M. (1965). *Z. analyt. Chem.* **212**, 177–187.
PARAZZI, E., PERNIS, B., SECCHI, G. C. & VIGLIANI, E. (1968). *Medna Lav.* **59**, 561.
ROBOCK, K. (1967). *Beitr. Silikoseforsch.* **92**, 1.
ROBOCK, K. (1968). *Staub* **28**, 148.
SECCHI, G. C. & REZZONICO, A. (1968). *Medna. Lav.* **59**, 1.
TIMBRELL, V. (1970). In: Proc. int. Conf. Pneumoconiosis, Johannesburg, 1969. *Ed.* H. A. Shapiro. Cape Town, Oxford University Press. pp. 28–36.
TIMBRELL, V. & SKIDMORE, J. W. (1971). This Symposium. pp 49–56.
TIMBRELL, V., GIBSON, J. C. & WEBSTER, J. (1968). *Int. J. Cancer* **3**, 406.
TIMBRELL, V., POOLEY, F. & WAGNER, J. C. (1970). In: Proc. int. Conf. Pneumoconiosis, Johannesburg, 1969. *Ed.* H. A. Shapiro. Cape Town, Oxford University Press. pp. 120–125.

DISCUSSION

M. NAVRATIL: You conclude that the toxicity of crocidolite is higher than that of chrysotile although chrysotile with its long fibres penetrates only into the airways. We find in persons exposed to chrysotile fibrosis as well as pleural hyalinosis. How can this be explained from the point of view of the low penetration of serpentine into the lung parenchyma.

Dr. ROBOCK: You are interested in the effects on man? Please, can Dr. Timbrell answer the question?

V. TIMBRELL: The falling speed of a fibre depends primarily on its diameter, not its length or shape. In the larger airways, where deposition is mainly by sedimentation, it is of little importance that amphibole fibres are straight and chrysotile fibres curly. Both types of asbestos are consequently associated with fibrosis and carcinoma of these regions of the lung. On the other hand, in the narrow airways deposition by interception is very important and depends on the length and shape of fibres. Penetration by amphibole fibres is favoured by the tendency of the aerodynamic forces to orientate straight fibres parallel to the axis of an airway. Crocidolite fibres penetrate more efficiently than amosite since they are thinner and consequently less readily deposited by sedimentation; also because normally they are shorter. Chrysotile fibres are readily deposited by interception. Crocidolite can thus reach the pleura and is associated with mesothelial tumours. Amosite reaches the pleura less readily, and chrysotile only in minute amounts.

A. L. REEVES: I would like to give you a preliminary report on a long, large-scale animal experiment, with three different kinds of asbestos, started five years ago. We are using different species of animals — rabbits, rats, guinea pigs and hamsters. We have found that out of about 300 rats we got six cancers in the group exposed to chrysotile; four cancers out of about 200 rats exposed to crocidolite, and in the animals exposed to amosite we found nothing.

A. C. ALLISON: One reason why some people are doubtful about the semiconductor theory of cell damage is that so many features of samples, such as metal contamination, can produce semiconductor effects. The most striking discrepancy is with asbestos samples, when crocidolite, the blue colour of which is due to charge transfer, has little cytotoxicity (as your own experiment shows).

Dr. ROBOCK: Unfortunately we are not yet in a position to explain this; it is something we are still working on. There are also other factors to be considered, e.g. the effect of the fibre length, and a possible structure effect.

FIBROUS SILICATES IN ANIMAL EXPERIMENTS AND CELL-CULTURE—MORPHOLOGICAL CELL AND TISSUE REACTIONS ACCORDING TO DIFFERENT PHYSICAL CHEMICAL INFLUENCES

E. G. Beck, J. Bruch, K.-H. Friedrichs, W. Hilscher and F. Pott

*Medizinisches Institut für Lufthygiene und Silikoseforschung,
University of Düsseldorf, Düsseldorf, W. Germany*

Abstract — Animal experiments in which different types of asbestos having various fibre lengths were administered intraperitoneally, indicate that asbestosis is produced mainly by long fibres.

In another experiment, rats were given U.I.C.C. amphiboles (amosite, crocidolite, anthophyllite) intraperitoneally. On measuring the fibre lengths in the ashed sections of the granulomata, it could be demonstrated that the percentage of long fibres is relatively higher than in the original dust. On the other hand, in the lymph nodes mainly the short fibres are deposited. These results suggest that the short fibre fraction is readily transported by the lymphatic channels.

Long asbestos and glass fibres produced a rise in the permeability of cells from monolayer or suspension cultures of line-L.

This could be attributed to slower and incomplete phagocytosis of the longer fibres.

Die Pathogenese der Asbestose ist bis heute weitgehend ungeklärt. In neuester Zeit wird die Bedeutung der Faserlänge erneut hervorgehoben (Klosterkötter & Robock, 1969; Hilscher *et al.*, 1970). In Tierexperimenten und Untersuchungen an in vitro gezüchteten Zellen sollte daher die Wirkung des Asbestes unter besonderer Berücksichtigung der Faserlänge geprüft werden.

(1) UNTERSUCHUNGEN MIT DEFINIERTEN FASERFRAKTIONEN UNTERSCHIEDLICHER LÄNGE VON CHRYSOTIL UND KROKYDOLITH

In einem Tierexperiment wurden nach intraperitonealer Applikation die Gewebsreaktionen auf jeweils 3 verschiedene Chrysotil- und Krokydolith-Fraktionen mit weitgehend begrenztem Faserlängen-Spektrum geprüft. Als Ausgangsmaterial dienten Handstücke, bei denen die Faserlänge 40 mm betrug. Nach Vorzerkleinerung mit einer Schere auf eine Länge von 6 mm wurde ein Teil des Staubes in einer Achat-Kugelmühle 48 Stunden lang nass gemahlen. Es wurde so ein sehr feinkörniges Kollektiv von Teilchen gewonnen, die bei elektronenmikroskopischer Untersuchung

478   E. G. Beck, J. Bruch, K.-H. Friedrichs, W. Hilscher and F. Pott

erkennen ließen, daß die kurzsäulige Textur durch den Mahlvorgang nicht verloren
gegangen war. Zur Gewinnung zweier Fraktionen mit längerem Faserspektrum wurde
ein Teil des Ausgangsmaterials mit einem normalen Mikrotom geschnitten. Durch
entsprechende Wahl der Schnittbreite konnten geeignete Faserfraktionen hergestellt
werden. Einen Überblick über die mittleren erzielten Faserlängen (entsprechend
dem 50-%-Wert der Summenhäufigkeitskurve), sowie die obere Abgrenzung
(=95-%-Wert) liefert Tabelle 1.

TABELLE 1.

Tier-Gruppe		Länge der Fasern	
		50%	95%
1. Chrysotil	gemahlen	$\leqslant$ 0,2 μm	$\leqslant$ 0,7 μm
2.	geschnitten kurz	1,7	6,0
3.	geschnitten lang	8,5	38,0
4. Krokydolith	gemahlen	0,1	0,4
5.	geschnitten kurz	2,1	7,5
6.	geschnitten lang	6,5	39,0

Die 54 Versuchstiere — männliche Wistarratten von 180–200 g Gewicht — zusammengefasst in 6 Versuchsgruppen mit je 9 Tieren — wurden 2, 4, 8 und 16 Wochen
nach einmaliger i.p. Gabe von Chrysotil und Krokydolith getötet. Makroskopisch
konnte festgestellt werden, dass nach Gabe von gemahlenem Asbest viel geringere
Veränderungen auftraten als nach Gabe von geschnittenem kurz- oder langfaserigem
Asbest:
Tiere, die kurz- oder langfaserigen geschnittenen Asbest erhalten hatten, zeigten
meist zahlreiche, z.T. miteinander konfluierende Knötchen im Bereich der Leber-
und Milzkapsel sowie des Omentums und Verwachsungen zwischen unterem Leber-
rand, Omentum, Magen, Milz und Darmschlingen. Allerdings waren nach Appli-
kation von längerfaserigem Asbest die Veränderungen in der Regel ausgeprägter.
Ein Vergleich der Veränderungen nach Gabe der beiden Asbestsorten ergab, dass
geschnittener Krokydolith etwas kleinere Knötchen, dafür aber ausgedehntere
Verwachsungen verursachte als geschnittener Chrysotil.
Nach Gabe von gemahlenem Chrysotil oder Krokydolith entstanden nur geringe
Veränderungen in Form kleiner umschriebener Knötchen. Die Grösse der Knötchen
nahm mit zunehmender Versuchsdauer ab.
Die mikroskopischen Untersuchungen ergaben, dass die Zelldichte in den verschiedenen Granulomen nicht wesentlich differierte, einerlei, ob sie durch gemahlenen
oder geschnittenen Asbest hervorgerufen worden waren. Das gleiche gilt für die
Anzahl der Rundzellen und Riesenzellen. Unterschiede fanden sich aber im Gehalt
an Fibrocyten und Makrophagen. In sämtlichen, durch geschnittennen kurzfaserigen
und längerfaserigen Asbest hervorgerufenen Granulomen überwogen von Anfang
an die Fibrocyten, deren prozentualer Anteil an der Gesamtzellzahl von der 2. bis
zur 16. Woche zwischen 60% und 80% lag. Weiterhin wird mit zunehmender
Versuchsdauer eine deutliche Vermehrung der kollagenen Fasern beobachtet. In den
durch gemahlenen Asbest hervorgerufenen kleinen Knötchen herrschen bis zur 4.

Woche die Makrophagen vor; von der 8. bis zur 16. Woche nahm ihre Zahl ab und die der Fibrocyten zu.

Zusammengefasst zeigen diese Tierversuche, dass der Grad einer experimentellen Asbestose mit der Faserlänge der verabfolgten Fraktion korreliert. Die fibrotischen Veränderungen sind umso ausgeprägter, je grösser der Anteil an längeren Fasern in den verabfolgten Fraktionen war. Diese Befunde stehen in Einklang mit den Angaben von Klosterkötter & Robock (1969).

Die wesentlich geringere Fibrose im Bereich der Bauchhöhle nach Injektion von kurzfaserigem Asbest kann auf 2 Ursachen beruhen:

1. auf einer schwachen fibrogenen Wirkung der kurzen Asbestfasern,
2. auf einen durch den Abtransport der kurzen Fasern bedingten kleineren Asbestdosis am Ort der primären Deposition.

Vermutlich spielen beide Effekte eine Rolle.

(2) UNTERSUCHUNGEN MIT U.I.C.C.-STANDARDSTÄUBEN

15 weibliche Wistarratten von 160–180 g Gewicht erhielten jeweils 5 mal 20 mg Amosit, Anthophyllit und Krokydolith im Abstand von jeweils 1 Woche in 2 ml 0,9% NaCl-Lösung i.p. injiziert.

Orientierende histologische Untersuchungen ergaben, dass die entstandenen intra-abdominellen Granulome sowohl längere als auch kürzere Fasern enthielten (Abb. 1). In den entsprechenden Lymphknoten überwogen dagegen die Ablagerungen kürzerer Fasern. Längere Fasern waren nicht zu erkennen. Ausserdem war hier die dichte

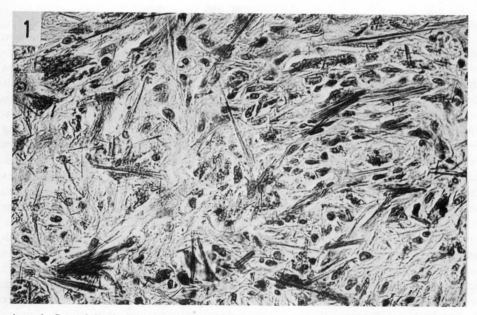

ABB. 1. Intraabdominelles Asbestgranulon, 4 Monate nach i.p. Gabe von Krokydolith, Ablagerung langer und kurzer Fasern.
H.E.-Farbung, Obj. 40.

Lagerung der Asbestfasern noch ausgeprägter als in den intraabdominellen Granulomen (Abb. 2). Diese Befunde zeigten, dass ein Teil der kürzeren Fasern in die
Lymphknoten abtransportiert worden war.

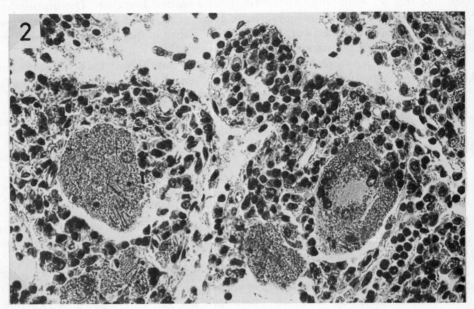

ABB. 2. Zugehöriger Lymphknoten mit Marksträngen und Marksinus. Ablagerung überwiegend
kurzer Fasern.
H.E.-Färbung, Obj. 40.

Um zu einer quantitativen Aussage zu gelangen, wurden zunächst die Faserlängen
der Amosit- und Krokydolith-Fraktionen vor der i.p. Gabe licht- und elektronenmikroskopisch bestimmt und ihre Häufigkeitsverteilung ermittelt. Die gewonnenen
Daten dieser "Ausgangsfraktionen" stimmen mit den von der Pneumoconiosis
Research Unit angegebenen Werten überein. Um die Faserlängen in den intraabdominellen Granulomen zu messen, wurden die histologischen Schnitte auf dem Objekt-
träger nach Ablösen des Deckglases bei einer Temperatur von 600° C 3 Stunden lang
verascht und nach dem Erkalten in Aroclor 1254 (Monsanto) eingebettet. Beim
Vergleich von Mikrofotografien aus eindeutig festgelegten Bezirken von Gewebs-
schnitten vor und nach der Veraschung konnte eine Veränderung der Lage und des
Zustandes der Fasern nicht beobachtet werden. Selbst Asbestosekörperchen zeigten
nach Veraschung lichtmikroskopisch keine Veränderungen. An den Rändern der
intraabdominellen Granulome verliefen die Fasern vorwiegend parallel zur Abgrenzung, im Innern waren sie ohne erkennbare Orientierung angeordnet. Für die quantitative Bestimmung der Faserlängen wurden insgesamt 1000 Teilchen pro Staubart in
den erfassten Längenbereichen von 2–40 μm gemessen. Für beide Staubarten ergaben
sich nahezu identische Faserverteilungskurven. Diese Kurven zeigten im Vergleich
zur jeweiligen "Ausgangsfraktion" eine Abnahme der kürzeren und eine — scheinbare
— Zunahme der längeren Fasern. Unter der Voraussetzung, dass durch die i.p.
Injektion eine Veränderung der Faserverteilung der jeweiligen "Ausgangsfraktion"
nicht eingetreten war, lassen sich die Kurven so deuten, dass mit abnehmender

Faserlänge der Abtransport der Fasern vom Ort ihrer primären Deposition zunimmt. In den Lymphknoten konnten nur bis höchstens 10 μm lange Fasern nachgewiesen werden. Häufig wurde eine eindeutig parallele Lagerung der Fasern beobachtet, wobei mehrere Fasern, zu Bündeln zusammengeschlossen, in den Staubnestern gefunden wurden.

Eingehende histologische Untersuchungen über die Reaktion des Gewebes auf die Fasern ergaben dass sich nur im Bereich der Bauchhöhle eine Fibrose entwickelt hatte (Abb. 1). In den entstandenen intraabdominellen Granulomen fanden sich die Fasern sowohl intra- als auch extrazellulär. Bei den intrazellulär abgelagerten Fasern handelte es sich überwiegend um kurze Fasern, die langen Fasern wurden vielfach nur zum Teil oder gar nicht intrazellulär deponiert. In der Regel lagen die kurzen Fasern in Makrophagen oder Riesenzellen vom Langhanstyp, während die langen Fasern — häufig nur partiell — von einzelnen oder mehreren Fibrocyten und Riesenzellen vom Fremdkörpertyp umgeben bzw. inkorporiert waren. Ein Teil der Riesenzellen konnte weder dem einen noch dem anderen Typ zugeordnet werden. Die meisten Riesenzellen pro Volumeneinheit fanden sich bei der Krokydolith-Gruppe; es folgten die Anthophyllit- und die Amosit-Gruppe. Mit Hilfe der Turnbullreaktion liessen sich besonders bei der Amosit-Gruppe am Rande der Herde reichlich Hämosiderin-Ablagerungen nachweisen. Doppelbrechende Beimengungen waren vor allem in der Anthophyllit-Gruppe zu erkennen. Die meisten Asbestosekörperchen pro Volumeneinheit wurden bei der Amosit-Gruppe beobachtet.

In den zugehörigen Lymphknoten konnte keine Fibrose nachgewiesen werden (Abb. 2). Hier fanden sich im wesentlichen nur kurze Asbestfasern, die in den Marksträngen fast ausschliesslich intrazellulär deponiert waren. Sie lagen hier dicht gedrängt in einzelnen oder zu Gruppen formierter Makrophagen und Riesenzellen von z.T. beträchtlicher Grösse. Die Riesenzellen erinnerten vielfach an solche vom Touton-Typ, die Kerne lagen kreisförmig um die faserfreie Zellmitte und waren von Cytoplasma umgeben, das vollgepfropft mit Fasern war. Bei der Anthophyllit-Gruppe fielen einzelne Nester quarztypischer Zellen auf, die wahrscheinlich auf Begleitmineralien zurückgeführt werden können. In den Sinus und in den Marksträngen waren häufig eisenpositive Makrophagen zu sehen. Asbestosekörperchen hingegen waren im Vergleich zu den intraabdominellen Granulomen ausgesprochen selten.

Zusammengefasst zeigen diese Versuche, dass ein grosser Teil des kurzfaserigen Asbestes in die Lymphknoten transportiert wird. Das Fehlen einer Fibrose in den Lymphknoten könnte einerseits darauf beruhen, dass hier nur sehr wenige lange Fasern deponiert werden. Andererseits ist ungeklärt, ob Asbest überhaupt im Lymphknoten einen gleich starken fibrogenen Effekt auslöst wie in der Bauchhöhle.

Die Beobachtungen an den intraabdominellen Granulomen legen den Verdacht nahe, dass eventuell die unvollständige Phagocytierbarkeit besonders der langen Asbestfasern Voraussetzung dafür ist, ob eine Fibrose entsteht.

Inwieweit verschiedene Faserlängen einen unterschiedlichen Effekt auf Zellen ausüben, soll in den folgenden Versuchen beschrieben werden.

(3) DIE WIRKUNG FASERIGER STÄUBE MIT UNTERSCHIEDLICHER LÄNGE AUF ZELLEN IN VITRO

Über eine toxische Wirkung von Asbest auf in vitro gezüchtete Zellen herrscht keine einheitliche Auffassung. Im Gegensatz zur italienischen Arbeitsgruppe, die zuerst eine zytotoxische Wirkung von Asbest *in vitro* nicht nachweisen konnte (Pernis *et al.*, 1966), später aber einen hochtoxischen Effekt an Meerschweinchen-Peritonealmakrophagen nach Inkubation mit Krokydolith und Chrysotil in Abwesenheit von Serum beobachtete (Parazzi *et al.*, 1968), konnten wir eine akut zellschädigende Wirkung verschiedener Asbestarten weder an Meerschweinchenmakrophagen noch an Zellen der Linie L in Monolayerkulturen nachweisen (Beck *et al.*, 1967). Allerdings wird unter Einwirkung von Asbest in Abhängigkeit von der Staubkonzentration die Vermehrung von L-Fibroblasten beeinträchtigt. Wie kürzlich mitgeteilt (Beck, 1970; Beck *et al.*, 1970), wurde bei Prüfung der Permeabilität von Alveolar- und Peritonealmakrophagen vom Meerschweinchen nach Inkubation mit Chrysotil ein gegenüber der Kontrolle erhöhter Prozentsatz mit Erythrosin B angefärbter Zellen festgestellt. Damit korrelierte eine gesteigerte Enzymfreisetzung, gemessen an der LDH-Aktivität im überstehenden Nährmedium, bei unverminderter Lactatbildung. Die durch Koshi *et al.* (1968) nachgewiesene vermehrt freigesetzte saure Phosphatase aus Peritonealmakrophagen von Ratten weist ebenfalls auf eine durch Asbestfasern bedingte Permeabilitätsstörung hin.

Es sollte nunmehr geprüft werden, ob lange Asbestfasern oder auch lange Glasfasern gegenüber kürzeren oder gemahlenen einen unterschiedlichen Effekt auf Zellen in vitro haben. Für die Versuche wurden die bereits angeführten Chrysotilfraktionen herangezogen (Tab. 1). Die ungemahlenen oder gemahlenen Glasfasern wurden uns freundlicherweise von Herrn Dr. Holt, University of Reading, zur Verfügung gestellt. Der faserige Staub wurde in einem synthetischen Nährmedium mit einem Zusatz von 10 % Serum in Konzentrationen von 200–1000 μg/10^6 Zellen suspendiert.

TABELLE 2. LA-Zellen (statische Suspensionskultur)
Staubkonzentration 200 μg/10^6 Zellen.

Proben	25 h	48 h	72 h
KO	311*	499	757
Chrysotil 2 μm	362	605	810
Chrysotil 40 μm	678	696	1030
Glasfaser	413	569	822
Glasfaser gemahlen	312	423	490

* mE LDH/ml Nährmedium.

Nach Zugabe der Staubsuspension zu den Zellkulturen fiel auf, dass nur Fasern unter einer bestimmten Länge sedimentierten und mit dem Zellrasen in Kontakt kamen, lange Fasern dagegen im Überstand ein freischwimmendes Netzwerk bildeten. Wir entschlossen uns daher einen Klon der Zellinie L, der sich in Suspension hält und vermehrt, für die Versuche heranzuziehen. Wenn Sedimente dieser Zellen in faserstaubhaltigem Nährmedium resuspendiert werden, kommt es zu einem sofortigen Kontakt zwischen Zellen und Fasern. Diese Affinität manifestiert sich in einer traubenförmigen Anordnung der Zellen im Fasernetzwerk. Durch Verwendung der statischen Suspensionskultur wurde es möglich, eine von der Faserlänge abhängige Wirkung auf die Zellen nachzuweisen. Besonders Chrysotil aus der langen Faserfraktion aber auch Glasfasern bewirkten gegenüber den Fraktionen kürzerer und gemahlener Chrysotilfasern oder gemahlener Glasfasern eine deutlich gesteigerte Enzym-LDH-Ausschüttung 48 und 72 Stunden nach Inkubation (Tab. 2). Gleichsinnig verhielten sich Zellen von Monolayerkulturen der Linie L, wenn sie nach Trypsinierung im faserhaltigen Nährmedium resuspendiert wurden (Tab. 3).

TABELLE 3. L-ZELLEN (MONOLAYER IN SUSPENSION)
STAUBKONZENTRATION 1000 μg/10^6 ZELLEN.

Proben	24 h	48 h	72 h
KO	482	570	687
Chrysotil gemahlen	753	791	1067
Chrysotil 2 μm	715	1120	1210
Chrysotil 40 μm	753	1280	2384
Glasfaser	678	1120	1863
Glasfaser gemahlen	791	810	829

* mE LDH/ml Nährmedium (E-MEM + 10% FKS).

Die morphologische Beurteilung dieser Kulturen ergab, dass bei Exposition mit Chrysotil der langen Faserfraktion die Zellen im freischwimmenden Netzwerk der langen Fasern verflochten sind, mit diesen in Kontakt stehen oder sie teilweise einverleibt haben (Abb. 3 and 4). Darüber hinaus sind Zellen sichtbar geschädigt. Nach Inkubation mit gemahlenen Asbest- oder Glasfasern sind alle Zellen auf dem Boden des Züchtungsgefässes ausgebreitet. Die Inkorporation von Partikeln der

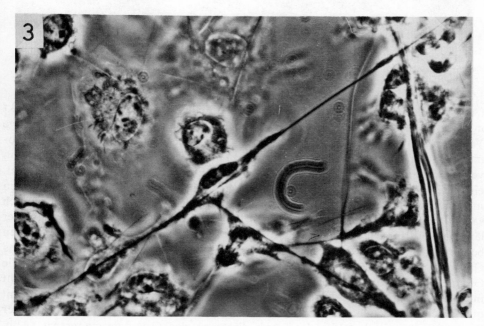

ABB. 3. Alveolarmakrophagen von Meerschweinchen *in vitro* gezüchtet (Monolayerkultur), 3 Stunden nach Inkubation mit geschnittenem Chrysotil (40 μm). Spindelförmige Verformung eines Makrophagen entlang der inkorporierten Fasern.

gemahlenen Fraktionen entspricht hinsichtlich Modus und Geschwindigkeit der Phagozytose von nichtfaserigem Staub.

Zusätzlich wurde die Phagozytose faserigen Staubes durch Zellen aus Monolayer- oder Suspensionskulturen der Linie L elektronenmikroskopisch untersucht. In Übersichtsaufnahmen lassen sich morphologisch intakte und nekrotische Zellen erkennen. Die Phagozytose der Fasern erfolgt durch Invaginationen der Zellmembran

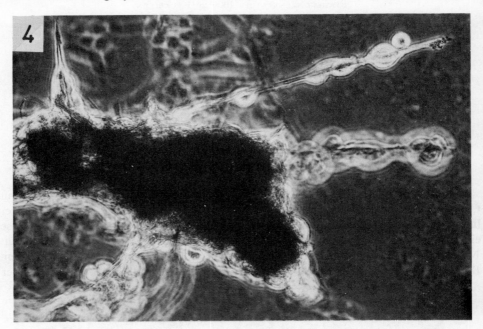

Abb. 4. Zellen der Linie L 48 Stunden nach Resuspension in faserstaubhaltigem Medium (Chrysotil 40 μm). Traubenförmige Anhäufung von Zellen im freischwimmenden Fasernetz- werk. Perlenschnurartige Anordnung von Zellen entlang herausragender Fasern.

(Abb. 5). Die den Staub unmittelbar umgebende Zellmembran ist zu diesem Zeitpunkt in ihrer dreischichtigen Struktur unverändert. Auffallend ist eine feine netzartige Verdichtung des Ektoplasmas in der Nähe der die Faser umschliessenden Phagoso- menmembran. Im Zellinnern werden sowohl kürzere Chrysotil-als auch Glasfasern in verschiedenartigsten Lokalisationen beobachtet. Ein Teil ist eng membranumgrenzt, ein anderer Teil befindet sich in bis zu 1 μm grossen Vakuolen oder in 0,5 μm grossen membranbegrenzten Organellen mit feingranulärer Matrix, in denen histochemisch saure Phosphatase nachgewiesen werden kann. Allerdings fällt bei tangential oder längsgeschnittenen längeren Fasern auf, dass sie selten vollständig in eine der oben beschriebenen Strukturen eingeschlossen sind, sondern mit einem Ende frei ins Grundplasma ragen (Abb. 6, 7 and 8). An der Stelle des Faserdurchtrittes ist die Organellenmembran zipfelförmig ausgezogen und ihre regelrechte Feinstruktur nicht mehr erkennbar. Bei elektronenmikroskopischen Aufnahmen von Phagosomen mit quergeschnittenen Asbest- oder Glasfasern ist die Membran häufig an einem Ende der Faser aufgelöst, so dass hier der Staub direkt an das Grundplasma grenzt (Abb. 6 and 7).

Nach elektronenmikroskopischen Untersuchungen längs geschnittener Fasern liegt ein Teil der Faser extrazellulär, ein anderer Teil von einer Phagosomenmembran umschlossen und ein letzter Teil frei im Grundplasma lokalisiert (Abb. 8). Da hier ein kontinuierlicher, nicht durch eine Membran begrenzter Übergang von Intra- zum Extra-zellulärraum besteht, nehmen wir an, dass an dieser Stelle Enzyme die Zelle verlassen bzw. saurer Farbstoff in das Zellinnere eindringt. Über die Bedeutung der unvollständigen Einschliessung der Fasern durch Phagolysosomen können nur Vermutungen angestellt werden. Doch weist der Befund auf einen Eingriff des faserigen Staubes in das Kompartmentsystem der Zelle hin, wodurch zwangsläufig das vor allem durch Membranen kontrollierte Milieu der Zelle gestört wird.

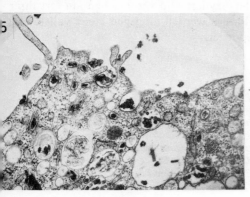
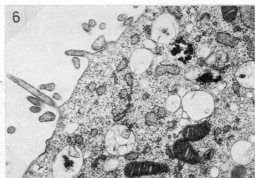

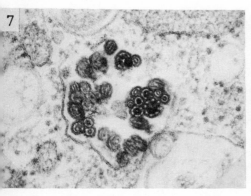
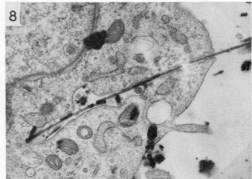

ABB. 5. Phagozytose von Asbeststaub. Anlagerung an der äußeren Zellmembran (1), Invagination (2) und Lage in einem Phagosom.

ABB. 6. Asbestfasern in einer LA-Zelle.

ABB. 7. Vergrößerung aus Abb. 2 Partielle Auflösung der Phagosomenmembran.

ABB. 8. Asbestfaser längsgetroffen. Der Staub liegt am linken Bildrand frei im Grundplasma der Zelle.

Aus den vorliegenden Ergebnissen bieten sich folgende Schlussfolgerungen an:

Die durch faserigen Staub verursachte Permeabilitätsstörung an der *in vitro* gezüchteten Zelle wird massgeblich durch die Länge der Faser bestimmt. Die Ursache der Permeabilitätsstörung sehen wir in der verzögerten oder unvollständigen Phagozytose langer Fasern. Die elektronenmikroskopischen Befunde zeigen, dass die Abdichtung durch die Zellmembran in der Nähe der Faser aufgehoben ist. Es wird angenommen, dass die im Nährmedium nachgewiesenen zellulären Enzyme an dieser Stelle austreten. Ein ständig anhaltender, aber kompensierter Enzymverlust bedingt einen veränderten Stoffwechsel der Zelle. Unter Umständen spielt dabei ein Eingriff der Faser in das Kompartmentsystem der Zelle eine zusätzliche Rolle. Dieses durch die Länge der Faser verursachte zelluläre Geschehen stellt letztlich einen chronischen Reiz und damit möglicherweise den Ausgangspunkt für die Bindegewebsentwicklung bei der Asbestose dar. Auch die histologischen Befunde weisen daraufhin: Lange Fasern werden häufig nur unvollständig phagozytiert und verursachen am Ort ihrer primären Deposition eine Fibrose. Kurze Fasern werden hingegen meist vollständig phagozytiert und zum grossen Teil abtransportiert.

REFERENCES

Beck, E. G. (1970). *Forsch. Ber. Landes NRhein-Westf.* (2083), 125.

Beck, E. G., Holt, P. F. & Nasrallah, E. T. (1971). *Br. J. ind. Med.* **28**, 179–185.

Beck, E. G., Sack, J. & Bruch, J. (1967). *Fortschr. Staublungenforsch.* **2**, 481–487.

Hilscher, W., Sethi, S., Friedrichs, K.-H. & Pott, F. (1970). *Naturwissenschaften.* **57**, 356–357.

Klosterkötter, W. & Robock, K. (1969). *Arbeitsmedizin, Sozialmedizin, Arbeitshyg.* **36**, 111–130.

Koshi, K., Hayashi, H. & Sakabe, H. (1968). *Ind. Hlth, Japan* **6**, 69–79.

Parazzi, E., Pernis, B., Secchi, C. & Vigliani, E. C. (1968). *Medna Lav.* **59**, 561–576.

Pernis, B., Vigliani, E. C., Marchisio, M. A. & Zanardi, S. (1966). *Medna Lav.* **57**, 721–729.

DISCUSSION

W. KLOSTERKÖTTER: Do you believe glass fibres may have fibrogenic effects?

Prof. HILSCHER: I have to refer to the work of Gross, Kaschak and Tolkner, published recently. These authors found a clear fibrosis in the satellite lymph nodes of the lung of rats, 2 years after inhalation of fibrous glass dust.

Dr. BECK: I was personally informed by Dr. Davies of Cambridge that glass fibres injected intra-pleurally can cause a fibrosis. The non-existence of a lung fibrosis is considered to be due to the fact that in the case of an intratracheal injection the glass fibres get broken and consequently only short fibres penetrate into the alveoli. Results from Mrs. Szentei of our Institute may be of interest in this connection, that in order to develop a 40% haemolysis, only 0·25 mg of chrysotile but 5·2 mg of glass powder and 11 mg of glass fibres are required. Thus, haemolysis is not caused by the fibre morphology as is the case with the proved change of permeability of the cell membrane, but by the chemical structure.

PULMONARY DISTRIBUTION OF ALPHA DOSE FROM ^{239}PuO$_2$ AND INDUCTION OF NEOPLASIA IN RATS AND DOGS*

C. L. SANDERS and J. F. PARK

Battelle Memorial Institute, Richland, Washington, U.S.A.

THE carcinogenicity of ^{239}PuO$_2$ in the lung has been demonstrated in mice, rats and dogs by TEMPLE *et al.* (1960), LISCO (1959) and CLARKE *et al.* (1964). The alpha radiation dose from inhaled ^{239}PuO$_2$ is non-uniformly distributed within the lung because the range of the alpha emissions from Pu is 48–100 μm in lung tissue; because inhaled ^{239}PuO$_2$ is initially localized in alveolar macrophages and epithelium (SANDERS, 1969; SANDERS & ADEE, 1970), and, finally, because Pu accumulates at later times in the peripheral areas of the lung and pulmonary lymphatics. These are critical factors in the establishment of radiation protection guidelines, since the extreme variation in the spatial distribution of absorbed dose is the basis for much of the uncertainty about the carcinogenicity of PuO$_2$ in the lung.

The ICRP Task Group, in *Spatial Distribution of Radiation Dose* (1969), "were of the opinion that, for late effects, the same radiation energy absorption might well be less effective when distributed as a series of "hot spots" than when uniformly distributed". On the other hand, DEAN & LANGHAM (1969) and GEESAMAN (1968) proposed that a high incidence of pulmonary neoplasia may be expected from deposition of larger sized PuO$_2$ particles than from smaller particles spread evenly throughout the lung. Induction of pulmonary neoplasms from areas of high PuO$_2$ concentration is described, implicating "hot spots" as sites for tumor formation.

MATERIALS AND METHODS

Transthoracic Injection of PuO$_2$ into the Lungs of Rats — Sixty-nine three-month old, Charles River albino, female rats were used in this study. Rats, lightly anesthetized with ether, were injected through the thoracic wall on the right lateral side at the level of the xiphoid process, into the lung parenchyma. The injected material was either 0·2 ml saline (controls) or 1·0 μCi ^{239}PuO$_2$ in 0·2 ml saline (treated), of which 0·74 $\pm$ 0·03 μCi (standard deviation) was actually deposited in the animal with the remaining 0·26 μCi being retained within the tuberculin syringe. A new syringe and 22 gauge needle were used for each rat. The PuO$_2$ was prepared for all studies reported in this paper by calcination of plutonium oxalate. The particles had a count median diameter of 0·18 μm and a mass median diameter of 0·96 μm. Particles of up to 4 μm

* This paper is based on work performed under the United States Atomic Energy Commission Contract AT(45–1)–1830.

diameter were seen in the particle suspension. Twenty-one rats received only saline and 48 received PuO_2 in saline. Two of the control and one of the PuO_2-injected rats died within one hour of injection from bleeding in the thoracic cavity. Of the PuO_2-injected rats, 18 were killed at intervals up to 81 days and the amount of Pu present in their lungs and remaining in the body were determined by the method of Keough & Powers (1970). The remaining 29 PuO_2 rats were killed at 27 to 400 days and the controls at 360 to 400 days after injection. The lungs were fixed in 10% neutral buffered formalin and approximately 40 serial, paraffin sections, 7 μm thick, were prepared from each lung. To prepare autoradiograms, every other section was covered with a Kodak NTB nuclear emulsion plate and exposed for three days. Of the 29 rats so examined, 13 exhibited either marked localization of PuO_2 on the pleural surface due to injection into the pleural cavity of diffuse dispersal of PuO_2 throughout one or more lobes of the lung due to injection into a major airway. These 13 rats were eliminated from the study; no metaplasia or tumors were observed in these rats. The remaining 16 rats exhibited focal localization of nearly all the injected PuO_2 in pockets of the lung parenchyma with less than about 10% of the lung mass containing the PuO_2 particles. These 16 rats are the subject of this report on the pathogenesis of induced lung tumors.

Pathological Response of Dogs to Inhaled PuO_2 — A lifetime study of the deposition, retention, translocation and pathological responses of the dog to inhaled $^{239}PuO_2$ particles has been described in numerous publications by Park *et al.* (1962; 1964; 1970), Clarke & Bair (1964) and Clarke *et al.* (1966). The most recent data from this study is reviewed to illustrate the relationship between dose and lung tumor induction.

RESULTS

Transthoracic Injection of PuO_2 — From $0\cdot2$ μCi to $0\cdot3$ μCi of injected PuO_2 was retained in the lung during the sampling period of up to 81 days (Table I). No significant loss of lung PuO_2 was observed from 3 days to 81 days after injection; about 25% of the injected Pu was cleared from the animal in the first few days. The remaining non-lung PuO_2 was found mostly in the liver, chest wall, spleen and thymus.

TABLE I. Pulmonary Retention of Transthoracically Injected PuO_2 Particles. (Means of Pu Assays from Three Rats per Group)

Time after Injection	^{239}Pu Content (μCi)	
	Lung	All other Tissues
3 hours	0·58	0·13
3 days	0·31	0·36
25 days	0·20	0·24
41 days	0·21	0·23
61 days	0·30	0·22
81 days	0·30	0·26

Estimates were made of the radiation dose delivered to small volumes of lung containing PuO_2 particles. Assuming a mass of irradiated tissue of 50 or 100 mg, it was calculated that $0 \cdot 2$ μCi and $0 \cdot 3$ μCi PuO_2 in these lung masses would deliver 4×10^5 rads and 6×10^5 rads, respectively, in 50 mg of tissue and 2×10^5 rads and 3×10^5 rads, respectively, in 100 mg tissue, over a 400-day retention period.

No difference was found between controls and PuO_2-injected lungs in the incidence or severity of pulmonary infections. The only evidence of injection in the control rats was a narrow tract of scarring where the needle had pentrated the lung parenchyma. All subsequent pulmonary pathology, other than that associated with pulmonary infections indigenous to the rat, was related exclusively to the site of PuO_2 deposition. The degree of fibrosis and metaplasia associated with sites of PuO_2 deposition were classified as: * minimal, but easily discernible with a 10X objective under the light microscope; † intermediate; and ‡ marked response.

Minimal translocation or movement of PuO_2 from the site of injection was observed in the 16 rats exhibiting focal deposition, with only rarely PuO_2 particles being found in lung tissue distant from the injection site or in tracheobroncial lymph nodes.

In areas of PuO_2 deposition, there was observed first an inflammatory exudative response characterized by a large nomonuclear cell accumulation. This phase was then followed by a rapid and marked fibrosis of the area, replacing all normal lung alveolar areas within the alpha irradiation zone. Squamous cell metaplasia was observed as early as 185 days, with 9/11 lungs examined at 314–400 days exhibiting squamous cell metaplasia. Metaplastic areas were found within fibrotic zones, containing few PuO_2 particles at the time of sampling, but immediately adjacent to the main deposit of PuO_2 particles (Figures 1 and 2). One large endothelioma was found at 283 days,

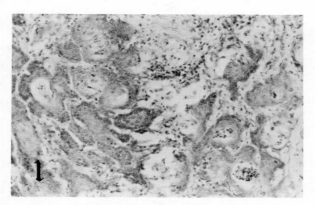

FIGURE 1. Metaplastic area in rat lung 380 days following transthoracic injection of $^{239}PuO_2$ particles. × 267

originating from the lung parenchyma. Its large size precluded determination of its site of origin, although the tumor was found originating from the same lobe containing the PuO_2 deposit. Four of the eleven rats killed at 314–400 days exhibited pulmonary tumors which were classified as either adenocarcinomas or squamous cell carcinomas. One rat had a mixed squamous cell carcinoma and adenocarcinoma. Metastases of one squamous cell carcinoma to an adjacent lobe not containing PuO_2 were observed. All the carcinomas were found immediately adjacent to fibrotic areas containing PuO_2 particles (Figures 2, 3 and 4). The development of fibrosis, metaplasia and neoplasia as associated with the site of PuO_2 deposition is listed in Table II.

Pulmonary Response of Dogs to Inhaled $^{239}PuO_2$ — Thirty-five beagle dogs, approximately 1 year of age, were given 10 to 30 min exposures to $^{239}PuO_2$ aerosols with count median diameters of $0\cdot1$ to $0\cdot5$ μm and were held for life-span observations. Initial alveolar deposition ranged from $0\cdot5$ to $3\cdot5$ μCi of ^{239}Pu. Twenty-two of the 35 dogs had primary pulmonary neoplasia 38 to 110 months postexposure. Five of the dogs are still alive of which two show radiographic evidence of pulmonary neoplasia.

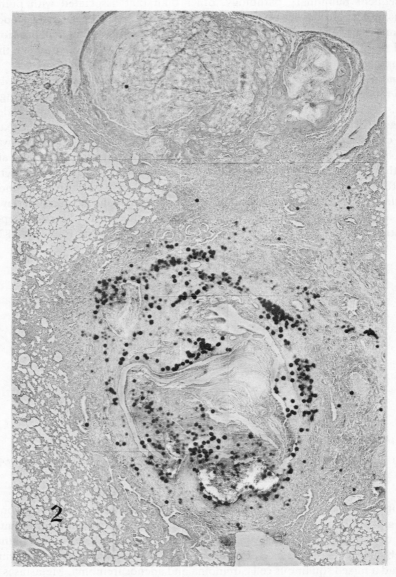

FIGURE 2. Composite photomicrograph demonstrating the localization of $^{239}PuO_2$ particles and associated pathologic changes, 400 days after injection into rat lung. Note the severe fibrosis in areas containing PuO_2 particles, the metaplastic area immediately surrounding the pocket of particles and a squamous cell carcinoma, with abundant keratin formation, apparently originating from these areas. Autoradiogram, 3 days' exposure. $\times$ 25

The date from this study and earlier higher dose studies (CLARKE & BAIR, 1964) are combined in Figure 5 to show the relationship between the quantity of alveolarly deposited PuO_2 and the survival time of dogs, as related to pulmonary pathology. Those dogs dying within 3 years all exhibited severe pulmonary fibrosis, bronchiolar and alveolar metaplasia, succumbing to respiratory insufficiency. Of those dogs

TABLE II. PATHOLOGICAL RESPONSE TO ISOLATED POCKETS OF PLUTONIUM
PARTICLES IN THE LUNG

Time after injection of plutonium (Days)	Pathological Response		
	Fibrosis	Metaplasia	Neoplasia
27	*	—	—
48	‡	—	—
87	‡	—	—
185	‡	*	—
283	†	—	Endothelioma
314	†	*	—
380	‡	‡	—
380	‡	†	—
380	‡	†	Adenocarcinoma
380	‡	—	—
400	‡	‡	—
400	‡	*	Adenocarcinoma
400	‡	—	—
400	‡	‡	—
400	‡	†	Squamous cell carcinoma
400	‡	‡	Squamous cell carcinoma Adenocarcinoma

* (minimal).   † (intermediate).   ‡ (marked).

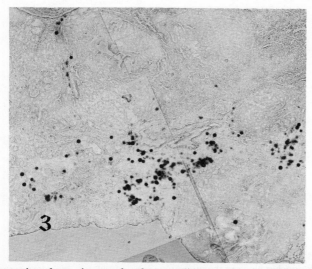

FIGURE 3. Composite photomicrograph of autoradiogram showing localization of $^{239}PuO_2$ particles in rat lung, sandwiched between two different carcinomas; 400 days after injection. × 25

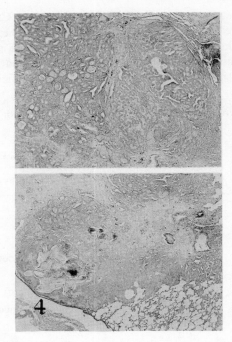

FIGURE 4. Same area as shown in Figure 3, but adjacent section without autoradiogram. Two types of tumors are seen developing from the fibrotic area containing PuO₂ particles; the top photomicrograph depicts a developing adenocarcinoma and the bottom a squamous cell carcinoma. × 25

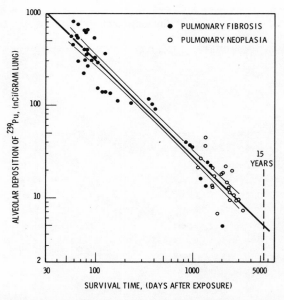

FIGURE 5. The relationship between the quantity of inhaled ²³⁹PuO₂ deposited in the lungs and the survival time of exposed dogs.

surviving longer than 3 years, 22/27 or 80% exhibited pulmonary neoplasia as well as marked fibrosis and metaplasia in the lung. The initial alveolar deposition of PuO_2 ranged from 7 nCi/g to 45 nCi/g of lung for dogs developing lung neoplasms. Extrapolation of the survival curve to 15 years postexposure, the maximum expected lifespan of these dogs, suggests that alveolar deposition of 5 nCi/g of lung might be expected to cause premature death due to pulmonary fibrosis, metaplasia and neoplasia.

Approximately 10% of the alveolar deposited plutonium was retained in the lungs 8 to 9 years postexposure. The accumulated average radiation dose to the lungs of the tumor-bearing dogs was 2500 to 12,000 rads. PuO_2 was slowly accumulated in the thoracic (tracheobronchial and mediastinal) lymph nodes such that after a few years, more PuO_2 was found in these lymph nodes than was found in the lung itself (Figure 6). In dogs developing lung neoplasms, about 15% of the ^{239}Pu was found in the liver and about 5% in the skeleton.

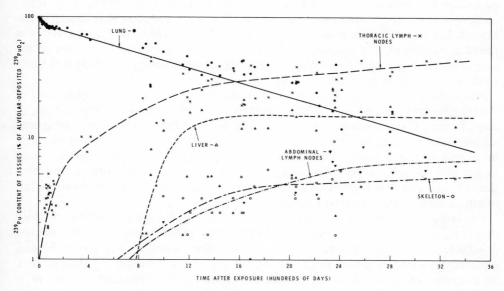

FIGURE 6. Retention and translocation of inhaled, alveolarly deposited $^{239}PuO_2$ in the dog.

Although the tracheobronchial and mediastinal lymph nodes were severely damaged and contained the highest concentration of PuO_2, the lungs were the site of primary neoplasia, with pathology in the lungs being the usual cause of death. The pathologic effects seen in the lungs consisted of an inflammatory hyperplasia, extensive fibrosis particularly in subpleural or peripheral areas of the lung, followed by alveolar cell hyperplasia, bronchiolar and alveolar types of squamous metaplasia. The lung tumors in all dogs were classified as bronchiolar adenocarcinomas. In addition to having bronchiolar adenocarcinomas, three dogs had epidermoid carcinomas, one dog a bronchial carcinoma, one dog a capillary hemangioma and another dog a lymphangiosarcoma in the lungs. Metastases were found in the tracheobronchial and mediastinal lymph nodes, liver, kidney, diaphragm, bone marrow, adrenal, brain and mesenteric lymph nodes. One dog also showed a lymphangiosarcoma which appeared to originate in the vicinity of a mediastinal lymph node. Two dogs had benign-appearing lesions of endothelial origin associated with mediastinal lymph nodes and classified as hemangiomas. One dog also showed lymphoma in the mesenteric and mandibular lymph nodes.

DISCUSSION

The development of pulmonary neoplasms in dogs inhaling $^{239}PuO_2$ has been described by CLARKE et al. (1966a, 1966b). The particles accumulate peripherally resulting in early fibrosis, particularly in areas of high particle concentration. Squamous cell alveolar and bronchiolar types of metaplasia develop in these fibrotic areas. Most of the PuO_2-induced lung neoplasms in dogs originate in these peripheral areas. The conclusion from these studies with dogs was that fibrotic areas associated with PuO_2 particle concentration in peripheral regions of the lung serve as the nidus for future neoplastic development with metaplasia in these areas being a preneoplastic, inter- mediate stage in the formation of neoplasms. Few PuO_2 particles were found in the metaplastic areas at time of death. PuO_2 was not seen within neoplasms, but was found concentrated in areas adjacent to the neoplasms. Unfortunately, most of the neoplasms in dogs had grown to large sizes at the time of autopsy, making it difficult to demonstrate their precise point of origin.

Our experience with rats where PuO_2 is localized in comparatively small pockets of the lung parenchyma, appear to bear out the validity of these earlier observations in dogs. In rats, fibrosis was associated only with areas of PuO_2 deposition. Metaplasia was seen early in the experiment, prior to the development of neoplasms, and was seen in all rats with neoplasms. The inference is that metaplasia is a preneoplastic state in the pathogenesis of Pu-induced lung tumors. The type of metaplasia and neo- plasia in rats and dogs argues strongly for the epithelial, either alveolar or bronchiolar, origin of most of the observed tumors.

DOLPHIN (1964), BEVAN & HAQUE (1968) and DEAN & LANGHAM (1969) propose that there is a volume or number of cells which must receive some minimal radiation dose before induction of lung neoplasms from alpha emitters will occur. Studies reported here and examination of the literature (SANDERS et al., 1970) indicate that lung tumors are most effectively produced by limiting the irradiated volume to a small fraction of the lung.

RICHMOND et al. (1970) have described the development of lesions in the lungs of rats from intravenously injected $^{238}PuO_2$ microspheres, which subsequently lodged in the pulmonary vasculature. These lesions were very similar to the early changes seen in the lung following transthoracic injection of $^{239}PuO_2$ particles. No metaplastic areas or neoplasms were observed in their rats up to 600 days after microsphere administration. The extremely high alpha doses, of about 10^8 rads/hour, and the high surface temperature of the microspheres of about 350°C (HSIEH et al., 1968), would be expected to preclude any direct cellular, carcinogenic role for alpha particles since viable cells within the range of alpha particles from the microspheres will be literally "fried".

The critical questions as to how small the amount of lung mass being irradiated by alpha particles and how little PuO_2 in that mass is required for induction of lung neoplasms, remain unanswered. These questions must be answered before realistic recommendations can be developed concerning the hazard of plutonium particles in the lung.

REFERENCES

BEVAN, J. S. & HAQUE, A. K. M. N. (1968). *Physics Med. Biol.* **13,** 105–112.

CLARKE, W. J. & BAIR, W. J. (1964). *Hlth Phys.* **10,** 391–398.

CLARKE, W. J., PARK, J. F., PALOTAY, J. L. & BAIR, W. J. (1964). *Am. Rev. resp. Dis.* **90,** 963–967.

CLARKE, W. J., PARK, J. F. & BAIR, W. J. (1966). *Lung tumors in animals.* Italy, University of Perugia, Division of Cancer Research. pp. 345–355.

CLARKE, W. J., PARK, J. F., PALOTAY, J. L. & BAIR, W. J. (1966a). *Hlth Phys.* **12,** 609–613.

DEAN, P. N. & LANGHAM, W. H. (1969). *Hlth Phys.* **16,** 79–84.

DOLPHIN, G. W. (1964). *Assessment of radioactivity in man,* Vol. 2. Vienna, I.A.E.A., pp. 589–602.

GEESAMAN, D. P. (1968). *Analysis of the carcinogenic risk from an insoluble alpha-emitting aerosol deposited in deep respiratory tissues.* Addendum. Livermore, University of California. UCRL–50387.

HSIEH, J. J. C., HUNTGATE, F. P. & ROESH, W. C. (1968). Pacific Northwest Laboratory Annual Report for 1967, *BNWL*–714. pp. 4.23–4.24.

KEOUGH, R. F. & POWERS, G. J. (1970). *Analyt. Chem.* **42,** 419–421.

LISCO, H. (1959). *Lab. Invest.* **8,** 162–170.

PARK, J. F., BLAIR, W. J., HOWARD, E. B. & CLARKE, W. J. (1970). Pacific Northwest Laboratory Annual Report for 1968, *BNWL*–1050. pp. 3.3–3.5.

PARK, J. F., CLARKE, W. J. & BAIR, W. J. (1964). *Hlth Phys.* **10,** 1211–1217.

PARK, J. F., WILLARD, D. H., MARKS, S., WEST, J. E., VOGT, G. S. & BAIR, W. J. (1962). *Hlth Phys.* **8,** 651–657.

RICHMOND, C. R., LANGHAM, J. & STONE, R. S. (1970). *Hlth Phys.* **18,** 293–295.

SANDERS, C. L. (1969). *Archs envir. Hlth* **18,** 904–912.

SANDERS, C. L. & ADEE, R. R. (1970). *Hlth Phys.* **18,** 293–295.

SANDERS, C. L., THOMPSON, R. C. & BAIR, W. J. (1970). *Inhalation carcinogenesis.* A.E.C. Symposium Series **18,** pp. 295–303.

TASK GROUP ON SPATIAL DISTRIBUTION OF RADIATION DOSE (1969). *Int. Commn on radiolog. Prot.* Publication 14, 1–10.

TEMPLE, L. A., MARKS, S. & BLAIR, W. J. (1960). *Int. J. Radiat. Biol.* **2,** 143–156.

DISCUSSION

W. KLOSTERKÖTTER: Can you tell us anything about acute exposure to plutonium particles?

Dr. SANDERS: Yes, we exposed rats to a $^{239}PuO_2$ aerosol and killed them at 13 minutes to 55 days. From 1 to $2 \cdot 5$ μCi of Pu were deposited in the alveoli. Under the electron microscope they showed a progressive increase in number and in detachment of type II alveolar epithelial cells. Large numbers of lipid droplets were found in septal cells by 30 days. A large exudate comprised of myeloid bodies, cell debris and a protein-like material was found in the alveolar lumens at 20 days. This stage was followed by an accumulation of histiocytes, which engulfed a large part of the exudate.

Destruction of endothelium and the accumulation of septal cells, collagen and elastin were common early findings. The alveolar septa were greatly thickened by 40 days due to edema, connective tissue formation, and the accumulation of septal cells, mast cells and plasma cells. Damage to the type I alveolar epithelium was commonly seen only in the terminal phase of the radiation pneumonitis.

W. WELLER: What was the rate of spontaneous tumours among the lung tumours of rats and dogs used in your tests? What was the absorption time of these control animals? Do you use SPF animals or conventional ones?

Dr. SANDERS: The rats were conventional. The spontaneous incidence of lung cancer in dogs is about $0 \cdot 2\%$. Lung cancer is even rarer in untreated rats. No lung cancers were observed in our untreated dogs or rats.

A. M. LANGER: Have you observed any tumors in body sites other than the lungs?

Dr. SANDERS: Two control rats and one rat given tranthoracic $^{239}PuO_2$ developed subcutaneous tumors during the course of the experiment. One lymphangiosarcoma and two haemangiomas which appeared to originate from mediastinal lymph nodes, were seen in dogs inhaling $^{239}PuO_2$. One plutonium dog also exhibited a lymphoma.

A. C. JAMES: You mentioned the highly non-uniform spatial distribution of α-dose from ^{239}Pu particulate material. In this case, dose values are almost meaningless when expressed in rads averaged over a volume of tissue. Would it not be better to attempt to express the distribution of activity, say in nCi, of individual deposited particles and then to estimate the number of alveoli containing deposited particles? Perhaps useful dose-response relationships could then be pursued.

Secondly, as the effect on sensitive cells coming within range of ^{239}Pu particles of high specific activity is likely to be lethal, can you propose an indirect mechanism for the initiation of lung tumours with this particulate material?

Dr. SANDERS: In answer to your first question, I agree that better dosimetric sophistication is badly needed and that your suggestion is a good one. It would be very tedious and difficult to accomplish.

With regard to sensitive cells, I would like to refer to the work of Barendsen who demonstrated that a single hit in the nucleus from an alpha particle (Po^{210}) was all that was required to prevent mitotic division (using Puck's clonal growth technique as a test model). Perhaps α particles passing through the cytoplasm of a cell would be more carcinogenic than those hitting the nucleus.

COMPARISON BETWEEN *IN VITRO* TOXICITY OF DUSTS OF CERTAIN POLYMERS AND MINERALS AND THEIR FIBROGENICITY*

D. M. CONNING, M. J. HAYES, J. A. STYLES and J. A. NICHOLAS

Imperial Chemical Industries Limited, Industrial Hygiene Research Laboratories, Alderley Park, Near Macclesfield, Cheshire, England

Abstract — A comparison has been made of the ability of several dusts to produce progressive or persistent fibrosis after intraperitoneal or intratracheal injection in rats, and their cytotoxic activity to alveolar and peritoneal macrophages in culture. The dusts utilised were asbestos, polyurethane, polyethylene terephthalate (PEP) and acicular calcium carbonate (aragonite), which may be paired for the presence and absence of cytotoxicity (asbestos and PEP), particle shape (polyurethane and PEP: asbestos and aragonite) and nature (mineral or polymer). The results suggest that there is a direct relationship between cytotoxicity to macrophages in culture, and fibrogenicity in the living animal and that this relationship is independent of particle shape, size and concentration, or of the phagocytic potential. It is suggested that the test described might be a useful screening process for dusts of plastic materials.

INTRODUCTION

THERE is considerable evidence to relate the ability of a chemical compound to induce fibrosis to its cytotoxic activity and, in particular, its activity in this respect to macrophages. Whereas HEPPLESTON & STYLES (1967) and WEBSTER *et al*. (1967) were unable to demonstrate a fibrogenic effect in the absence of a chemical mediator, ALLISON *et al*. (1966) claimed such an effect using frozen and thawed isologous macrophages, but only after repeated inoculation. The relation of cytotoxicity to macrophages and the fibrogenic activity of silica is better established, allowing HEPPLESTON (1969) to postulate the release of a factor from macrophages damaged in this way, which stimulates hydroxyproline production by fibroblasts. He suggested that a similar mechanism might operate with other fibrogenic compounds.

The fibrogenicity of implated polymers is related not only to chemical composition, but also to the surface configuration, rough surfaces being more active than smooth. The reason for this has not been established but may be related to ability to influence contact activation of blood coagulation systems (CONNING & GARNER — unpublished). Apart from this aspect, however, cytotoxicity of a polymer is related to the contained additives and their ability to leach out (CONNING & FIRTH, 1969). With the increasing use of polymers and the possibliity of exposure to respirable dusts of these materials, it would be valuable to know which are likely to be fibrogenic and to have a means of screening for this activity.

* This paper was received too late for presentation and discussion at the Symposium.

The present work has examined the relation between cytotoxicity to macrophages *in vitro* and the fibrogenic activity when subsequently injected intraperitoneally or intratracheally, of a number of dusts of known or unknown activity.

EXPERIMENTAL

Animals

Alderley Park strain rats of both sexes and of a weight range 200–250 g were used.

Cell Cultures

The cells used were peritoneal and pulmonary macrophages from Alderley Park rats (SPF Wistar derived) weighing 150–250 g. The cells were harvested by the methods of CONNING & FIRTH (1969) and maintained in suspension cultures.

The sterile culture vessel used was a 115 mm × 22 mm centrifuge tube sealed with a foil cap. The tube was coated internally with silicone (Clay-Adams Siliclad) to prevent cells from attaching themselves to the walls. A sterile magnet coated with PTFE, 2 cm long was used in conjunction with a magnetic stirrer to maintain the cells in suspension.

The medium used for both types of macrophages was Hanks saline containing 2% heparin and 5% calf serum. The gas phase was air. The heparin (10 i.u./ml) was used to prevent aggregation of macrophages.

Dusts

The dust samples were made up into stock suspensions of 250 mg/ml in PBSA. Each dust was stirred overnight and for 5 min before use in an experiment. For injection into animals, the dusts were prepared as fine suspensions using an inert suspending agent (Dispersol OG) and rapid mixing in a M.S.E. blender. All preparations were sterilized before injection.

The dusts employed were:

Polyester Powder (PEP)

This is particulate polyethylene terephthalate of high molecular weight. The primary particles are 0·1 μm diameter, but they exist in suspension as conglomerates 0·4 to 4 μm in diameter. The material is doubly refractile and is not cytotoxic.

Asbestos (Chrysotile)

Highly purified material obtained from M.R.C. Pneumoconiosis Research Unit, Penarth, by courtesy of Dr. J. C. Gilson.

Aragonite

This is acicular calcium carbonate and consists of crystals of mean size 1 μm in diameter and 35 μm in length. It is sparingly soluble in water.

Polyurethane foam dust

This was prepared from rigid polyurethane foam and consisted of two particle sizes (Table I).

TABLE 1. CONCENTRATION AND PARTICLE SIZE OF THE EXPERIMENTAL DUSTS

Dust	No. particles in 1 ml suspension containing 0·5 mg of dust	Particle size
PEP	$12·2 \times 10^6$	1–3 μm (diam)
Asbestos	$5·88 \times 10^6$	0·5–200 μm (length)
Aragonite	$7·68 \times 10^6$	2–50 μm (length)
Polyurethane		
Fine	$1·25 \times 10^6$	1–15 μm (diam)
Coarse	$1·0 \times 10^6$	1–50 μm (diam)

The experiment consisted of two parts, *in vitro* and *in vivo*.

Suspension cultures of the cells were treated with the various dusts for a period of 2 h during which samples were taken for counting before addition of the dusts (i.e. at zero time) and at 1 h and 2 h. All of the dusts were added at the rate of 0·5 mg/million cells. The number of particles this amount contains for each dust is shown in Table I.

At the times indicated, samples were taken, stained with trypan blue (CONNING & FIRTH, 1969) and the total number of cells, of live cells (i.e. cells not stained with trypan blue), of all cells containing dust and of dead cells containing dust, were counted using a haemocytometer, and if necessary, phase contrast illumination or polaroid filters. Each experiment was repeated between three and five times.

Groups of 6–12 animals of each sex were injected intraperitoneally or intratracheally with the various dose levels (Table II) and killed at intervals up to 12 months after injection. For the intratracheal injections, the animals were lightly anaesthetized (halothane), a fine cannula inserted between the vocal cords under direct vision and

TABLE III. ROUTES OF ADMINISTRATION AND
THE AMOUNTS GIVEN

Dust	Route	Amounts (mg/kg)
PEP	ip	50
	it	10
Asbestos	ip	12·5
	it	2·5
Aragonite	ip	50, 25, 12·5
	it	10, 5, 2·5
Polyurethane (fine)	ip	50
	it	4

ip — Intraperitoneal injection
it — Intratracheal injection

the appropriate volume of suspension injected. Only if this procedure was followed by the appearance of fine crepitations on auscultation of the thoracic wall, was the animal admitted to the experimental group.

The animals, on recovery, were caged in groups of three or four and given food and water *ad libitum*. They were killed at monthly intervals and a careful autopsy performed; the following tissues were taken for histological examination.

Lungs — these were excised *in toto* and expanded with 10% buffered formal saline. Samples were processed in the usual way and sectioned at 5 μm.

Peritoneal cavity — samples were taken of omentum, spleen, liver, kidney, and pancreas to assess the fibrotic reaction, if any, in the peritoneum and organ capsules. A stain for reticulin (Gordon & Sweets, 1936) was used where indicated, and for analysis of peritoneal fibrosis by image analysis.

Assessment of the degree of fibrosis was assayed using an automated image analyser (Quantimet, Metals Research Limited) which allows measurements of the area of a given microscopic field occupied by a suitably contrasted fraction. Thus the intensity of reticulin deposition per unit area can rapidly be measured automatically in up to 50 fields, or alternatively, the amount of reticulin per nodule can be measured. In the present work, the former assay was used.

RESULTS

The results of the culture studies (Tables III and IV) show that the greatest mortality was shown by cells treated with asbestos and the least by cells treated with PEP. Intermediate levels of activity were detected with polyurethane and aragonite. With polyurethane, the fine material was almost twice as lethal as the coarse.

All dusts, except coarse polyurethane, were ingested to the same degree (Tables III

TABLE III. SUMMARY OF FINDINGS — PERITONEAL MACROPHAGES

Dust	Time (h)	No. of Results	Live cells (% of all cells) Mean	S.D.	Cells with particles (% of all cells) Mean	S.D.	Dead cells with particles (% of all dead cells) Mean	S.D.
Polyester powder	0	5	97·46	±0·87	4·97	±0·93	—	—
	1	5	96·87	±1·17	38·28	±8·83	2·44	±1·16
	2	5	95·19	±1·45	41·05	±6·5	5·1	±1·72
Asbestos	0	4	97·87	±0·67	11·27	±1·26	6·75	±1·99
	1	4	83·55	±4·22	40·57	±11·03	36·13	±4·96
	2	3	88·8	±2·7	19·5	±9·7	47·6	±5·54
Aragonite	0	4	96·7	±0·5	9·8	±2·24	7·98	±2·1
	1	4	94·35	±1·54	50·54	±8·89	7·1	±1·06
	2	3	91·96	±1·0	53·40	±6·26	9·47	±0·12
Fine polyurethane foam dust	0	3	96·77	±0·96	2·44	±1·58	—	—
	1	3	88·77	±4·34	40·97	±12·29	21·84	±2·5
	2	3	86·18	±3·31	40·36	±8·52	23·66	±2·27
Coarse polyurethane foam dust	0	3	97·24	±0·2	2·41	±1·3	4·17	±7·22
	1	3	93·13	±2·02	22·26	±6·2	15·82	±3·86
	2	3	89·2	±0·17	33·64	±12·87	19·18	±0·45

and IV). Coarse polyurethane particles showed reduced phagocytosis at 1 h, but this had achieved levels comparable to the other dusts at 2 h. Asbestos particles were ingested normally at 1 h, but showed much reduced phagocytosis at 2 h.

The percentage of dead cells which contained particles (Figures 1 and 2) show that the dusts may be divided into three groups. Aragonite and PEP were present in less

TABLE IV. SUMMARY OF FINDINGS — ALVEOLAR MACROPHAGES

Dust	Time (h)	No. of Results	Live cells (% of all cells)		Cells with particles (% of all cells)		Dead cells with particles (% of all dead cells)	
			Mean	S.D.	Mean	S.D.	Mean	S.D.
Polyester powder	0	11	89·52	±1·43	3·25	±1·45	—	—
	1	9	88·95	±1·63	25·38	±2·23	4·91	±1·49
	2	9	88·45	±1·98	31·29	±3·32	6·119	±1·81
Asbestos	0	4	87·65	±1·96	3·55	±2·3	17·5	±11·9
	1	4	78·01	±2·96	18·69	±3·97	58·1	±8·9
	2	4	78·06	±3·24	21·75	±3·12	60·34	±0·68
Aragonite	0	5	87·79	±1·16	3·12	±1·76	7·06	±6·6
	1	5	88·0	±1·52	27·95	±5·19	10·11	±2·99
	2	5	84·56	±0·66	33·35	±2·16	9·95	±2·52
Fine polyure-thane foam dust	0	5	87·67	±1·07	1·88	±0·85	9·0	±12·4
	1	5	81·7	±2·33	19·6	±7·9	27·53	±4·1
	2	5	79·69	±3·1	32·04	±3·75	25·89	±2·7
Coarse polyure-thane foam dust	0	4	86·25	±1·25	1·13	±0·94	—	—
	1	4	84·5	±6·19	10·0	±3·48	29·5	±9·5
	2	4	81·65	±4·04	11·95	±1·8	32·3	±3·79

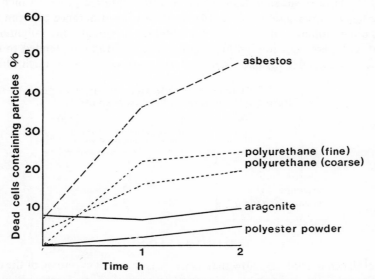

FIGURE 1. The numbers of dead peritoneal macrophages found to contain dust particles after one or two hours.

than 10% of the dead cells. Polyurethane was present in 15–25% of cells staining with trypan blue, whereas asbestos was present in more than 40% of dead cells. These values, obtained with peritoneal macrophages, were similar to results obtained with alveolar macrophages, but here the numbers of dead cells were larger.

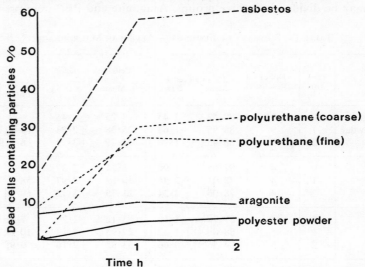

FIGURE 2. The numbers of dead alveolar macrophages found to contain dust particles after one or two hours.

The results of intraperitoneal and intratracheal inoculation show that the levels of fibrosis as measured by the degree of reticulin deposition after three months (Table V) are greatest with asbestos, least with aragonite and PEP and intermediate with fine polyurethane. Studies at 6 months and some at 12 months have confirmed these findings. (The latter results are less reliable as a proliferative process which might be neoplastic has in some cases supervened). There was no difference between the sexes. Asbestos, polyurethane and PEP were persistent dusts though only polyurethane was associated with persistent foreign body granulomata. Aragonite tended to disappear within a few weeks after injection and was never associated with much fibrosis.

TABLE V. RESULTS OF AUTOMATED ANALYSIS OF
RETICULIN DEPOSITION IN FIBROUS NODULES

Dust	Relative amounts of reticulin staining (mean of 20 fields)
PEP	28
Asbestos	90
Aragonite	12
Polyurethane (fine)	73

DISCUSSION

The overall cell mortalities show that asbestos is the most cytotoxic of the dusts, and polyester powder the least, with polyurethane occupying an intermediate position. The variation in mortality cannot be related to the concentrations of dusts; or to differing phagocytic rates, as most of the dusts were ingested to the same extent. The main exception to this was coarse polyurethane which showed a linear increase in phagocytosis as opposed to the other dusts which showed a plateau effect after 1 h. The reduced phagocytosis of coarse polyurethane at 1 h is probably related to the large particle size, thus reducing the availability of ingestible particles to much below the actual particle count. This number is probably less than the number required to achieve maximum efficiency of phagocytosis which would appear to be in the region of 1·25 particles per cell. The actual number of particles per cell was not estimated but probably does not influence the results. If, for example, it is assumed that smaller particles will be phagocytosed to a greater extent than larger particles, then small particles would show relatively greater toxicity than large particles of equal cytotoxicity. In the present study, PEP and polyurethane may be compared and as polyurethane is the more toxic and also is of greater particle size, the increase in toxicity is a real one and not related to the mechanisms of phagocytosis. It may be argued, similarly, that fibres might be ingested only with difficulty and are not likely to exhibit a true cytotoxicity in a phagocytic system because of this. In the present study, however, asbestos is the most toxic and aragonite, of similar shape, one of the least toxic.

An anomaly occurred in the experiments utilising asbestos and peritoneal macrophages. The overall phagocytic rate at 2 h appears to be much reduced compared with the rate at 1 h. This is probably due to the tendency of asbestos fibres to conglomerate in culture medium and to sediment in the culture chamber. Such conglomerations appear to include cells and these may be cells which have actually ingested fibres and not merely cells which have become entrapped in the fibrous mass. Such cells are effectively removed from examination leaving a smaller population with less material to ingest.

The alveolar macrophages tended to show less phagocytic activity than the peritoneal macrophages, but the relation of one dust to another was the same as that which pertained with the peritoneal macrophages. The altered phagocytic activity was thus not due to an effect of the dusts on the cells, but was an inherent property of the macrophages. CONNING & FIRTH (1969) noted that whereas histochemically, alveolar macrophages showed increased enzyme activity, the phagocytic ability was less than that of peritoneal macrophages and this was associated with reduced cell adhesiveness. It is possible that this reduced activity is due to the method used to obtain the cells, but the qualitatively similar response to dusts in the present work indicates the absence of a specific hindrance of phagocytic activity.

The percentage of dead cells which had undertaken phagocytosis, is an indication of the cytotoxicity of the dust after ingestion, as opposed to a cell membrane effect, or possible effects on the culture medium. Here, the dusts fall into three distinct categories of cytotoxicity and this effect is enhanced in the alveolar cells.

The intraperitoneal and intratracheal inoculations have shown that asbestos is the most fibrogenic of the dusts, whereas aragonite with PEP produce at most only transient fibrosis. Polyurethane causes moderate fibrosis associated with foreign body granuloma formation. To some extent the fibrosis was related to the persistence of the dust, but not proportionately so as there was no evidence of digestion of PEP but fibrosis was minimal.

There is thus a direct relationship between the ability of a dust to provoke fibrosis and its ability to kill phagocytosing macrophages, and this work has shown that this relationship previously demonstrated with silica, also occurs with dusts containing no silica. It is suggested, therefore, that the survival of macrophages in culture after exposure to dusts, may form a useful screening test for the fibrogenicity of these dusts, and may be particularly useful in the screening of polymers. These materials are likely to be used with increasing frequency in the constructional industries and their use may result in the release of particles of respirable size.

The present work throws little light on the mechanisms of cytotoxicity, but indicates this property is not necessarily related to particle shape. It remains most likely that the toxicity is related to additives present in the polymer, rather than the polymer itself.

REFERENCES

ALLISON, A. C., HARINGTON, J. S. & BIRBECK, M. (1966). *J. exp. Med.* **124**, 141–154.
CONNING, D. M. & FIRTH, J. (1969). *Fd Cosmetic Toxicol.* **7**, 1–7.
HEPPLESTON, A. G. (1969). *Br. med. Bull.* **25**, 282–287.
HEPPLESTON, A. G. & STYLES, J. A. (1967). *Nature, Lond.* **214**, 521–522.
GORDON, H. & SWEETS, H. H. (1936). *Am. J. Path.* **12**, 545–552.
WEBSTER, I., HENDERSON, C. I., MARASAS, L. W. & KEEGAN, D. J. (1967). In: *Inhaled particles and vapours II.* Ed. C. N. Davies. Oxford, Pergamon Press. pp. 111–120.

SECTION IV

BIOLOGICAL REACTIONS: ANCILLARY FACTORS

EXPERIMENTAL BRONCHITIS IN ANIMALS DUE TO SULPHUR DIOXIDE AND CIGARETTE SMOKE. AN AUTOMATED QUANTITATIVE STUDY

Lionel E. Mawdesley-Thomas, Peter Healey and David H. Barry

Huntingdon Research Centre, Huntingdon, England

Abstract — Increasing air pollution, both atmospheric and self-inflicted by tobacco smoking, has brought about a need for accurate quantitative bio-assays of irritation of the respiratory tract. Following preliminary anatomical studies of 12 animal species it was decided that the rat and the lamb were the most useful experimental models for studying the effects of irritation on goblet cells, alveolar macrophages (rat) and bronchial and tracheal glands (lamb). Assessments of change occurring in the tissues were made with an image analysing computer for the goblet cells and glands and a scanning microdensitometer for acid phosphatase activity in alveolar macrophages. Initial experiments using these techniques showed that it was possible to produce a dose related response to sulphur dioxide and to separate increments as low as 25 ppm. These methods have now been successfully applied to various types of cigarette smoke in order to produce an irritancy grading and thus assist in the evaluation of potentially less hazardous cigarettes.

INTRODUCTION

The terms bronchitis or chronic bronchitis have often been used in a non-specific manner implying a vague clinical condition unassociated with a defined pathological change. The suffix "itis" is often confusing in that it automatically implies some kind of bacterial infection, which, in the context of this paper, is not the case. The term bronchitis was first defined in the early 19th century (BADHAM, 1814) and emphasis was given to the acute rather than chronic aspect of the disease in keeping with medical opinion of the time. The basic physiological changes occurring in bronchitis are those associated with hypersecretion of mucus from hypertrophy or hyperplasia of mucus secreting glands and goblet cells (REID, 1954; 1968). Secondary infection may sometimes be implied but is not implicit under these particular terms of reference.

The response of a mucus secreting epithelium to a noxious influence has long been known to produce an increase in goblet cells in the gastro-intestinal tract (FLOREY & WEBB, 1931; FLOREY, 1932) and this has been investigated in great detail over the years (FLOREY, 1960; MOE, 1968). It is surprising, however, that detailed physiology of the goblet cells of the respiratory tract is virtually unknown — do they, for instance, discharge once or cycle many times; and are the underlying mechanisms nervous or humeral?

The study of goblet cells in relation to respiratory irritation goes back to Lord Florey in the early 1930's who produced goblet cell hyperplasia in cats and dogs with formol-saline (FLOREY *et al.*, 1932). Although the goblet, or chalice, cells of the respiratory tract had been a definite entity in the histology books since the 1870s they aroused but little interest. Only recently have many animal species been investigated and the effects of a variety of atmospheric irritants established (MELLORS, 1958; FALK *et al.*, 1963; ELMES & BELL, 1963; REID, 1963; FREEMAN & HAYDON, 1964; LAMB & REID, 1968; LAMB & REID, 1969).

Before an attempt could be made to extend these studies and produce a reliable bio-assay of irritation, the most suitable laboratory animal species had to be chosen. This choice was dependent on suitability of the anatomical configuration of the respiratory tract and the amount by which the animal was affected by a polluted atmosphere.

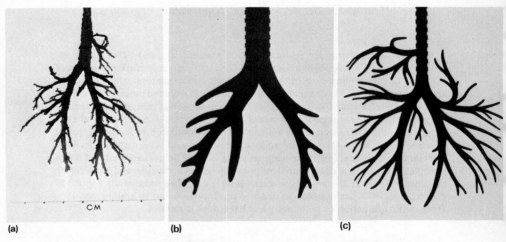

(a)   (b)   (c)

FIGURE 1. Vinylite casts of bronchial tree: (*a*) Young pig, (*b*) Rodent, (*c*) Lamb.

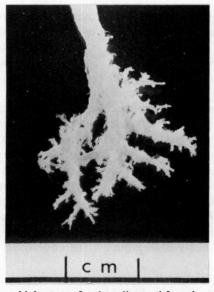

FIGURE 2. Bronchiolar tree of rodent dissected from lung parenchyma.

In order to acquire a more detailed appraisal of the suitability of the various animal species as a model for the assessment of bronchitis it was decided to study the anatomy of the bronchial tree of a number of species both macroscopically and microscopically. By such a study it was hoped to be able to map in more detail the main branches of the tracheo-bronchial tree, and also gain more knowledge of the distribution of tracheal and bronchial glands and goblet cells in the lower trachea and the lower left main bronchus or bronchiolus. After some abortive attempts to produce resin casts of the bronchial tree (TOMPSETT, 1952; 1956), Vinylite casting was used (LIEBOW et al., 1947) as it presented an easier technique with a better end product. Casts of the species examined were made and the bronchial trees were studied (Figure 1). At the same time, the bronchial tree was dissected free from lung parenchyma (Figure 2) so that positive

TABLE I. ANATOMICAL DATA: TRACHEA AND BRONCHUS OF VARIOUS SPECIES

TRACHEA

Species	Length	Internal diameter	Presence of Eparterial Bronchus	Goblet cells per cm	Glands
Dog	10 cm	15 mm	—	350	+++
Baboon	3·5 cm	5 mm	√	600	+++
Pig	13 cm	10 mm	—	150	+++
Macaca	6 cm	7 mm	—	300	++
Mouse	2 cm	2 mm	—	—	±
Rabbit	6·5 cm	10 mm	—	150	—
Guinea-pig	3·3 cm	4 mm	—	600	—
Hamster	1·5 cm	2 mm	—	6	—
Sheep	24 cm	26 mm	—	300	+++
Cat (SPF)	7 cm	7 mm	—	600	++++
Squirrel monkey	2·5 cm	3 mm	—	150	+
Rat	3·2 cm	3 mm	—	8	±
Man	11·0 cm	20 mm	—	200*	+++*

* Varies considerably.

L.L.L. BRONCHUS (AXIAL PATHWAY)

Species	Length (Carina-Periphery)	Internal diameter (measured at carina)	Cartilage extends beyond carina	Goblet cells extend to	Glands extend to
Dog	8 cm	9 mm	7·5 cm	7·5 cm	7 cm
Baboon	3·5 cm	4 mm	2·8 cm	3·5 cm	3·5 cm
Pig	13·5 cm	9 mm	11·5 cm	13 cm	13 cm
Macaca	5·5 cm	6 mm	4·5 cm	5·5 cm	3·5 cm
Mouse	2·5 cm	3 mm	—	—	—
Rabbit	5·5 cm	10 mm	0·5 cm	5·5 cm	—
Guinea-pig	3 cm	3 mm	1 cm	10 cm	—
Hamster	1·5 cm	2 mm	—	1 cm	—
Sheep	20 cm	24 mm	19 cm	19 cm	19 cm
Cat (SPF)	6 cm	6 mm	4·5 cm	5 cm	5 cm
Squirrel monkey	2·5 cm	2·5 mm	2·5 cm	2·5 cm	2·1 cm
Rat	2·3 cm	1·5 mm	0·4 cm	—	—
Man	12·0 cm	15·0 mm	12 cm	—	—

and negative impressions of the tree were obtained. Further observations and measurements were made on the comparative anatomy of the tree (Table I). In addition to these macroscopical studies, microscopical studies in relation to goblet cells and bronchial and tracheal glands were made (Figure 3).

Detailed morphological studies having been completed, an attempt was made to quantitate, in the various animal species, the response of the mucus secreting cells to a respiratory irritant. In this instance sulphur dioxide was chosen because it was easily obtainable and some background data were available (REID, 1963), although it was appreciated that this extremely soluble gas was not typical of all respiratory irritants.

The animals were exposed to an atmosphere of different concentrations of sulphur dioxide for varying times in order to establish a dose which would produce a histological response (Figure 4). The animals were exposed according to size, in one of the

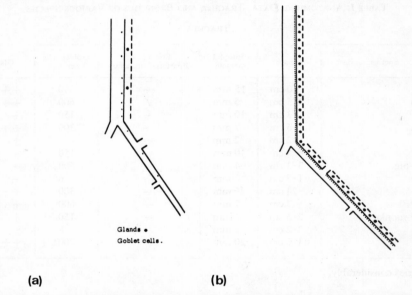

Glands •
Goblet cells.

(a)   (b)

FIGURE 3. Distribution of tracheal and bronchial glands and goblet cells: (a) Rodent, (b) Lamb.

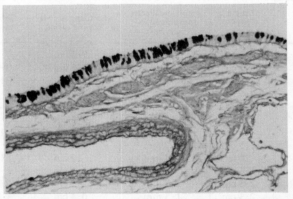

FIGURE 4. T.S. of rat lung showing a bronchiolus containing increased numbers of goblet cells. Colloidal iron/P.A.S. stain. Mag. ×60.

two types of exposure chambers (Figures 5 and 6). After a further period of experimentation it became apparent that some animals were more suitable than others as models. The problem involved two main points; those animals which possessed both goblet cells and bronchial and tracheal glands in profusion, such as the dog, sheep and pig, were more suitable for the study of glands than goblet cells, whilst the smaller animals, particularly the rodents, have virtually no glands, and were more suitable for

FIGURE 5. Chamber for exposure of small animals to sulphur dioxide.

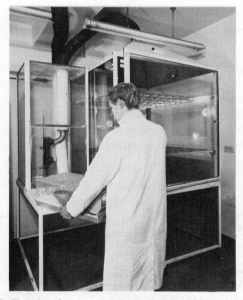

FIGURE 6. Chamber for exposure of large animals to sulphur dioxide.

the study of goblet cells. Following this investigation it was decided to use two experimental models: the rat for the study of goblet cells and sheep for the study of bronchial glands. It must be mentioned that, at this time, little information was available regarding the "cycling" of goblet cells in the respiratory tract, and it was subsequently shown that animals which were sacrificed after exposure to sulphur dioxide always had a low goblet cell count. A withdrawal study (Figure 7) showed that it was necessary to allow a period of 2–3 days to elapse before sacrifice if maximal number of goblet cells were to be seen. Because withdrawal studies were not performed on all species it is possible that the mouse, guinea pig, hamster, rabbit, wild guinea-pig and tuco-tuco, were rejected on insufficient grounds.

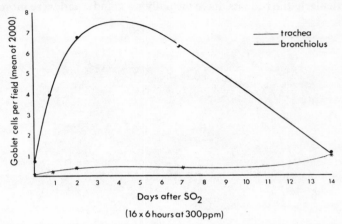

FIGURE 7. Graph showing a withdrawal curve in relation to the rat trachea and bronchiolus following exposure to high doses of sulphur dioxide.

QUANTITATIVE METHODOLOGY

Early in these investigations it was realized that if the mucus secreting cells were to be used as an "index of irritation", then it would be necessary to count large numbers of goblet cells, and area size large numbers of bronchial and tracheal glands. Current methods for doing this were all considered inadequate due to the time factor and lack of techniques suitable for measuring glandular hypertrophy, the Reid index (Figure 8) being only suited to the anatomical configuration of the human. These facts stimulated a search for some form of automatic counting which could assess certain histological features of a microscope image.

$$\text{REID INDEX} = \frac{A}{B}$$

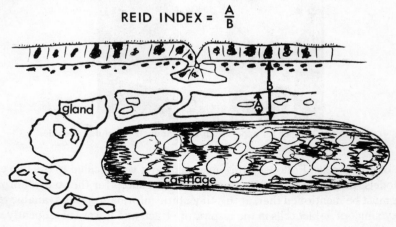

FIGURE 8. The Reid Index.

The quantitative approach to microscope images is not new. Over the past 20 years several machines for this purpose have been developed. Perhaps the best known is the "flying spot" microscope which Professor J. Z. Young and his colleagues at University College, London, developed in the 1950's. Microscopists used this instrument to count red blood cells and nerve cells, but subsequently it never received the success it deserved, due to the microscopists' failure to appreciate that a discretely differentiated specimen was required together with a precise data extraction system. However, the potential accuracy and speed had not escaped the metallurgists who subsequently developed an image analysing computer known as the Quantimet. The initial applications of this machine in relation to biological material at both light and electron microscope levels were not successful because the specimens lack sufficient contrast. Our particular quest was aided by the fact that special stains were used from the beginning. The Periodic Acid Schiff reaction and the Alcian Blue/P.A.S. reaction, produced mucopolysaccharides sufficiently deeply stained to be readily detected by the image analyser. Contrast was further enhanced by the use of a P.A.S. reaction from which the counter-stain was omitted. Counter-stains, whilst essential to the morphologist, only provide "background noise" to the image analyser (MAWDESLEY-THOMAS & HEALEY, 1969a; 1969b; 1969c). A brief word must be written about the Quantimet and the principle it employs. The Quantimet utilizes the principle of television scanning. The microscope image is projected onto a camera videcon and the output signals passed simultaneously into a television monitor and a detection circuit which selects the electrical impulses coming from the features to be measured. The computer has channels which enable information to be demonstrated by punch-tape, typewriter or digital display. Each microscope field is scanned in approximately $0 \cdot 1$ s, irrespective of the number of features measured. It is also possible to programme the machine to place features within various size groups. This facility is particularly useful in particle sizing and counting. The magnification of the optical system can be varied and calculated so that it is possible to convert Quantimet readings into square microns. The speed of the machine should be emphasized for it enables some 1–2000 fields to be assessed per hour.

The initial rat experiments involved 32 SPF Carworth female rats, which were divided into 4 groups of 8 and exposed in an exposure chamber to an atmosphere of sulphur dioxide in the following manner:

Group 1   50 ppm for 10 × 6 h exposures
Group 2   100 ppm for 10 × 6 h exposures
Group 3   200 ppm for 10 × 6 h exposures
Group 4   300 ppm for 10 × 6 h exposures.

Seventy-two hours after the last exposure all rats were killed with intraperitoneal sodium pentobarbitone and the lungs fixed in buffered formalin after expansion by the injection of fixative into the trachea. Both trachea and left bronchiolus from each lung were dissected free from lung parenchyma by blunt dissection and processed for sectioning. Sections, 5 μm thick, were taken from each block of tissue at 100 μm intervals throughout. All sections were then stained with Alcian Blue/P.A.S. technique and the P.A.S. positive areas counted and sized using a Quantimet Image Analyser. The P.A.S. positive material was considered to represent goblet cells. The effect of various concentrations of sulphur dioxide on goblet cells in rat trachea and bronchiolus (Figure 9) showed a dose related response, but at a level of 300 ppm there is considerable epithelial damage and almost complete loss of goblet cell activity. In the bronchiolus, probably due to the extreme solubility of the gas, there was a dose related response even to an atmosphere of 300 ppm. At about this time in the experimentation it was decided to compare manual counts with those obtained by the Quantimet (Figure 10). It will be seen in all cases that the manual counts are lower, but there is correlation between the results. The human operator will exclude minute P.A.S. positive droplets on the surface of the epithelium whereas the machine will not. This has not proved to be a problem in the experimental situation where relative rather than absolute values are of equal significance.

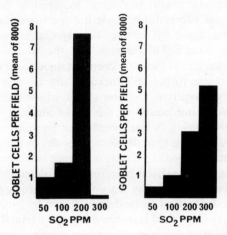

FIGURE 9. The effects of various levels of sulphur dioxide on the rat trachea (left) and bronchiolus (right).

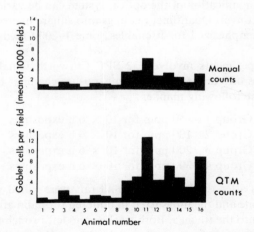

FIGURE 10. Comparative histograms of manual and machine counts of goblet cells.

It is interesting to note that following irritation with sulphur dioxide in the lamb, a large percentage of acid muco-polysaccharide was seen in both glands and goblet cells (Figure 11). The significance of this finding at the time was uncertain as it could have been due to either chemical alteration of the secreted mucopolysaccharide or direct incorporation of the sulphur dioxide into the mucus or both. Subsequent studies have shown that it was in fact due to incorporation of sulphur moeities into the mucus.

Finally, a further bioassay was applied to sulphur dioxide treated animals, this time in relation not to the bronchial tree but to the lung parenchyma, and the cells used in this case were "free alveolar cells", in all probability the alveolar macrophages.

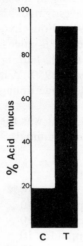

FIGURE 11. Increased incidence of acid muco-polysaccharide in the lamb following sulphur dioxide exposure.

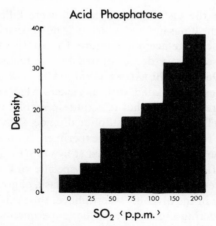

FIGURE 12. Histogram showing a dose related increase in acid phosphatase in alveolar macrophages following exposure to sulphur dioxide.

Hypersecretion of mucus, caused by sulphur dioxide and other respiratory irritants, may result in increased amounts of mucus reaching the alveolar spaces due to reduced ciliary action and subsequently altered rheology. If total airway obstruction is to be avoided this mucus must be removed. McCARTHY et al. (1964) have reported removal of mucus, by alveolar macrophages, after intra-alveolar innoculations of different mucoid substances. The phagocytosis process in macrophages has also been studied with the electron microscope (KARRER, 1958; 1960). If alveolar macrophages effected the removal of excess mucus from the alveolar spaces then a sulphur dioxide induced hypersecretion of mucus may have evoked an increase in numbers of macrophages. In short term experiments of up to 4 weeks of daily exposures to sulphur dioxide no increase in numbers of macrophages was found in rat lungs. This result suggested the possibility of increased metabolic activity in the existing macrophages.

Eighteen enzyme systems were investigated histochemically in control rat lungs (BARRY & ROBINSON, 1969a; 1969b). Four hydrolytic lysosomal enzymes — acid phosphatase, β-glucuronidase, N-acetyl β-glucosaminidase and β-galactosidase — were subsequently studied in rats which had been exposed to 300 ppm sulphur dioxide (BARRY & MAWDESLEY-THOMAS, 1970). A marked increase in acid phosphatase activity was observed in the alveolar macrophages from animals which had been exposed to sulphur dioxide.

A sulphur dioxide irritation experiment was then performed on 56 SPF Carworth female rats, divided into 7 groups of 8 animals and exposed to sulphur dioxide as follows:

Group 1   Control
Group 2   25 ppm for 10 × 6 h exposures
Group 3   50 ppm for 10 × 6 h exposures
Group 4   75 ppm for 10 × 6 h exposures
Group 5   100 ppm for 10 × 6 h exposures
Group 6   150 ppm for 10 × 6 h exposures
Group 7   200 ppm for 10 × 6 h exposures

Forty-eight hours after the last exposure the rats were killed with intraperitoneal sodium pentobarbitone, the lungs inflated with $0 \cdot 5\%$ polyethylene glycol and quenched in hexane precooled in a cardice-acetone mixture. Cryostat sections 8 μm thick, were cut and acid phosphatase activity demonstrated by the methods of GOMORI (1950) (as modified by LAKE, 1966) and BURSTONE (1961). The acid phosphatase activity in alveolar macrophages was quantitated with a Vickers M85 scanning microdensitometer. The results (Figure 12) show that it is quite possible, using this technique to differentiate the irritant effect of 25 ppm sulphur dioxide.

One of the recurring problems during this experimentation was that of a sporadic respiratory tract infection in many of the rats (MAWDESLEY-THOMAS, 1968), due to Mycoplasma pulmonis often associated with non-specific viral infection. The result of any infection is to produce in the rat a marked hyperplasia of goblet cells, and increased acid phosphatase activity in the alveolar macrophage, thus raising the base-line levels to almost 100% and rendering useless any further experimentation.

RESPONSE OF THE BRONCHIAL TREE AND ALVEOLAR MACROPHAGES TO CIGARETTE SMOKE

Rats were initially exposed to fresh whole smoke in individual smoking machines of such a design that the smoke was forced into a chamber into which the rat's nose and mouth protruded. Each rat was exposed to a 25 ml puff for 6 s each minute from a total of 8 cigarettes over a period of 4 days. The results of this experiment were inconclusive. Occasional individual exposed rats showed very high goblet cell counts raising the group means above those of the control animals (Figure 13). Statistical analysis showed these results to be only of minimal significance. Due to discrepancies in these results it was decided to consider more closely whether or not the animals in the machine were breathing similar amounts of smoke. In order to measure respiratory movement the restraining tube of a smoking machine was converted into a body

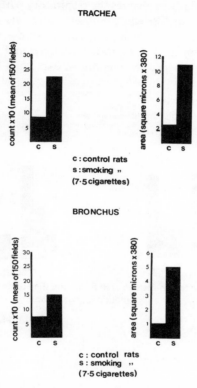

TRACHEA

c : control rats
s : smoking "
(7·5 cigarettes)

BRONCHUS

c : control rats
s : smoking "
(7·5 cigarettes)

FIGURE 13. Histograms of goblet cell count and area following preliminary experiment with cigarette smoke and the rat.

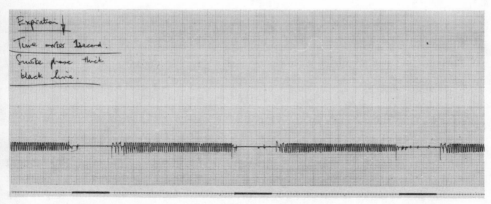

FIGURE 14. Respiratory rate recording following the exposure of rats to cigarette smoke. Note the almost absolute inhibition of respiration caused by the smoke.

plethysmograph. Recordings made with this instrument (Figure 14) showed that many rats hold their breath and refuse to breathe smoke of this concentration (Binns, 1970). It was possible that the high concentration of aldehydes caused a sensory apnoea, which was only terminated after the smoke had been flushed from the chamber with fresh air. Following this observation an attempt was made to acclimatize rats to smoke. Even after 50 consecutive daily exposures the respiratory pattern was not altered, even in animals anaesthetized with "Brietal". Subsequently rats were anaesthetized with "Brietal" and smoke administered via a polythene tube inserted into the trachea. This system caused no alteration in the respiratory pattern and further experimentation showed that a significant response to cigarette smoke could be obtained (Figure 15).

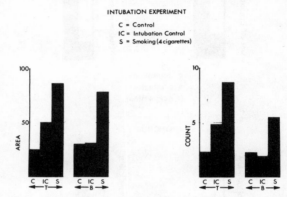

FIGURE 15. Increase in goblet cell count and area following the administration of cigarette smoke through an endo-tracheal tube.

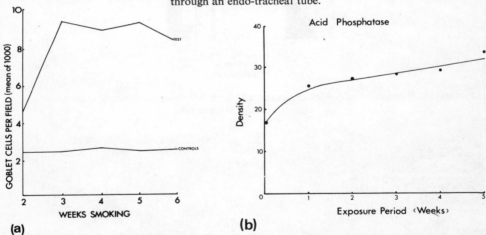

FIGURE 16. Graphs showing the effects of exposure to cigarette smoke over a period of 6 weeks: (a) goblet cell counts, (b) acid phosphatase.

However, because of technical difficulties this method was abandoned. Subsequent alterations to the smoking machine have shown that rats can be made to breathe a maximum smoke concentration of 8 % before significant alterations in their respiratory pattern occurs. A dose related response has been achieved in rats subjected to the smoke from 4 cigarettes daily for a total of 6 weeks by both evaluation of increased intracellular P.A.S. positive material and increased acid phosphatase activity in alveolar macrophages (Figure 16).

For previously described anatomical reasons, the lamb was considered to be the most suitable animal model for the study of tracheal and bronchial glands in relation to irritation (MAWDESLEY-THOMAS & HEALEY, 1970).

Practical considerations dictated that it was desirable to administer the smoke *via* a tracheostomy. The surgical technique of permanently inserting tracheostomy tubes into lambs proved quite simple, and two weeks after operation the lambs were ready for experimentation (Figure 17). Eighteen lambs were divided into 6 groups as follows:

> Group 1   Control (no smoke)
> Group 2   4 cigarettes a day for 3 weeks
> Group 3   8 cigarettes day for 3 weeks
> Group 4   Control (no smoke)
> Group 5   4 cigarettes a day for 5 weeks
> Group 6   8 cigarettes a day for 5 weeks

The lambs tolerated cigarette smoke without undue distress and subsequently one lamb smoked up to 40 cigarettes a day for over 9 months. In order to collect mucus escaping from the tracheostomy tube rubber finger cots were attached over the opening. The mean amount of mucus collected was as follows:

> Group 1   38·5 g ⎤
> Group 2   58·0 g ⎥
> Group 3   58·0 g ⎥   Over 24 h period
> Group 4   55·0 g ⎥
> Group 5   47·0 g ⎥
> Group 6   52·0 g ⎦

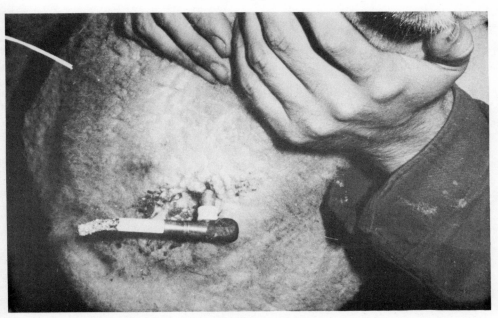

FIGURE 17. Lamb smoking a cigarette through a device attached to a tracheostomy.

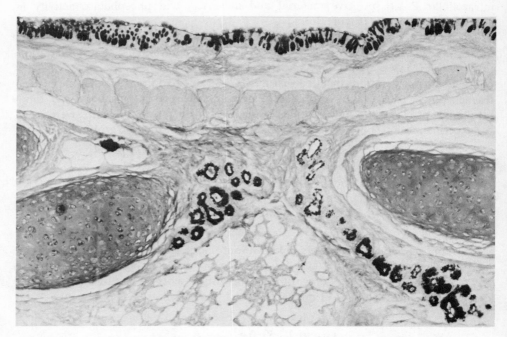

FIGURE 18. T.S. of lamb trachea showing goblet cell and glandular hyperplasia following the administration of cigarette smoke. Mag. ×90. Colloidal iron/P.A.S. stain.

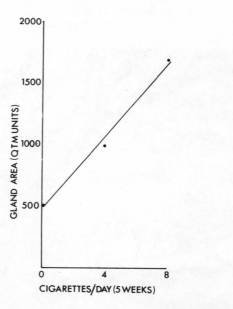

FIGURE 19. Graph showing the glandular hyperplasia following the administration of tobacco smoke.

These figures initially suggested that smoking did not cause a significant alteration to the amount of mucus produced over a 24 h period. These figures cannot be used as an indication of increased mucus production due to considerations such as the altered rheology caused by respiratory irritants (see page 516).

There was a temporary increase in mucus production in the period immediately following smoking and the mucus produced during this period appeared less viscous.

At the termination of the experiment transverse sections of trachea 5 cm proximal to the bifurcation and longitudinal sections of L.lower lobe bronchus distal to the bifurcation, were stained with Alcian Blue/P.A.S. and P.A.S. positive material in the epithelium evaluated (Figure 18). Whilst the results showed a trend towards an increase in goblet cell activity the figures could not be statistically evaluated due to the large variations and small animal group size. Measurement of areas covered by P.A.S. positive material in the tracheal glands (Figure 19) showed an increase related to the smoke exposure. This glandular hypertrophy is synonymous with an increased Reid Index although in the lamb the measurement has to be modified due to the fact that much glandular material is found deep to the cartilaginous plates.

DISCUSSION

Respiratory irritants are frequently contributory causes of chronic bronchitis or lung cancer. Epidemiological studies have been used to determine these factors mainly due to the inability of researchers to produce lung tumours in laboratory animals with carcinogenic substances. Research into the role of air pollutants as a cause of chronic bronchitis has also provided inconclusive results. A major problem in the experimental production of bronchitis has been elimination of the role played by bacterial infection allowing only the histological change caused by the noxious substance administered to be evaluated. Measurement of respiratory physiology by traditional monitoring of those changes which can be detected in the living animal provide little evidence of the more significant changes occurring in the respiratory tract. Hypertrophy of mucus secreting elements, the accepted pathological description of bronchitis, is meaningless in the context of changes produced in laboratory models unless some method of quantitation superior to the subjective assessment of the human eye can be applied. The techniques described in this paper have shown that it is possible to quantitate changes associated with bronchitis to a degree of accuracy hitherto uprecedented. It is significant that dose-response curves, as measured by mucus production and enzyme changes, can detect comparatively small increases in amounts of atmospheric sulphur dioxide even in rats which have a far more efficient barrier to the passage of substances into the respiratory tract than do humans. It is possible that the natural defence mechanisms of the body to atmospheric pollutants are able to provide some degree of protection without causing permanent damage. The stage at which permanent damage occurs is an unknown factor and any increase in sulphur dioxide in our atmosphere must contribute a considerable hazard.

Whilst it is comparatively easy to assess a cellular response to a noxious agent as deleterious, a sense of reality must be applied to this situation. The response could just as easily be assessed, initially, as an extended physiological reaction which might even be beneficial. The point at which an extended physiological reaction becomes a pathological one is not easily established. It is extremely important, however, not to consider these two reactions as similar, as misinterpretation can lead to a situation

524   LIONEL E. MAWDESLEY-THOMAS, PETER HEALY and DAVID H. BARRY

similar to that which exists in relation to liver cell enlargement, possibly due to enzyme induction and reduplication of the endoplasmic reticulum, associated with the administration of various pharmaceutical products, intentional and unintentional food additives.

The use of the sheep to demonstrate the increase in tracheal gland hypertrophy following tobacco smoke has shown that it is possible to mimic the human condition as described by Prof. Lynne Reid in patients who died of chronic bronchitis. This condition has been produced in animals being subjected to cigarette smoke for a comparatively short period of time and indicates the potential danger of cigarette smoking in relation to bronchitis. It may be that this aspect of cigarette smoking is considerably more important than the carcinogenic properties that have been the subject of so much concern. The methods have been evolved to produce bio-assays of irritation which mean it is now possible to measure exactly the irritant effect of tobacco smoke in some laboratory animals. This is the first and vitally important stage in the production of less irritant cigarettes.

Acknowledgement — The authors would like to express their appreciation to Dr. R. Binns for his help with the exposure of animals in association with this experimentation.

REFERENCES

BADHAM, C. (1814). *An essay on bronchitis: With a supplement containing remarks on simple pulmonary abscess.* 2nd ed. London, Callow. (1st Edition 1808).
BARRY, D. H. & MAWDESLEY-THOMAS, L. E. (1970). *Thorax.* **25,** 612–614.
BARRY, D. H. & ROBINSON, W. E. (1969a). *Histochem. J.* **1,** 497–504.
BARRY, D. H. & ROBINSON, W. E. (1969b). *Histochem. J.* **1,** 505–515.
BINNS, R. (1970). Personal communication.
BURSTONE, M. S. (1961). *J. Histochem. Cytochem.* **9,** 146–153.
ELMES, P. C. & BELL, D. (1963). *J. Path. Bact.* **86,** 317–327.
FALK, H. L., KOTIN, P. & ROWLETTE, W. (1963). *Ann. N.Y. Acad. Sci.* **106,** 583–608.
FLOREY, H. W. (1932). *Br. J. exp. Path.* **13,** 349–359.
FLOREY, H. W. (1960). *Q. J. exp. Physiol.* **45,** 329–336.
FLOREY, H. W. & WEBB, R. A. (1931). *Br. J. exp. Path.* **12,** 280–300.
FLOREY, H. W., CARLETON, H. M. & WELLS, A. O. (1932). *Br. J. exp. Path.* **32,** 269–284.
FREEMAN, G. & HAYDON, G. B. (1964). *Archs. envir. Hlth* **8,** 125–128.
GOMORI, G. (1950). *Stain Technol.* **25,** 81–85.
KARRER, H. E. (1958). *J. biophys. biochem. Cytol.* **4,** 693–701.
KARRER, H. E. (1960). *J. biophys. biochem. Cytol.* **7,** 357–366.
LAKE, B. D. (1966). *Jl R. microsc. Soc.* **85,** 73–75.
LAMB, D. & REID, L. (1968). *J. Path. Bact.* **96,** 97–111.
LAMB, D. & REID, L. (1969). *Br. med. J.* **1,** 33–35.
LIEBOW, A. E., HALES, M. R., LINDSKROG, G. E. & BLOOMER, W. E. (1947). *Bull. int. Ass. med. Mus.* **27,** 116–129.
MAWDESLEY-THOMAS, L. E. (1968). *Respiratory tract infections in the rat.* Carworth Europe Collected Papers 2, 37–60.
MAWDESLEY-THOMAS, L. E. & HEALEY, P. (1969a). *Science, N.Y.* **163,** 1200.
MAWDESLEY-THOMAS, L. E. & HEALEY, P. (1969b). *New Scient.* **41,** 286–287.
MAWDESLEY-THOMAS, L. E. & HEALEY, P. (1969c). *Am. Rev. resp. Dis.* **100,** 231–233.
MAWDESLEY-THOMAS, L. E. & HEALEY, P. (1970). 121st Meeting, Path. Soc. Gt. Br. & Irel., Sheffield. p. 19. (*Abstract*).
McCARTHY, C., REID, L. & GIBBONS, R. A. (1964). *J. Path. Bact.* **87,** 39–47.
MELLORS, R. C. (1958). *Proc. Am. Ass. Cancer Res.* **2,** 325.
MOE, H. (1968). *Int. Rev. gen. exp. Zool.* **3,** 254–273.

REID, L. (1954). *Lancet* **1,** 275–278.
REID, L. (1963). *Br. J. exp. Path.* **44,** 437–445.
REID, L. (1968). Bronchial mucus production in health and disease. In: *The lung. Ed.* A. A. Liebow &
    D. E. Smith Baltimore, Williams and Wilkins. pp. 87–108.
TOMPSETT, D. H. (1952). *Thorax* **7,** 78–88.
TOMPSETT, D. H. (1956). *Anatomical techniques.* Edinburgh, Livingstone.

DISCUSSION

Y. Iravani: There are well-known morphologic criteria of bronchitis. Have you ever seen signs of bronchitis in the exposed animals, other than the increase in the number of goblet cells?

Dr. Mawdesley-Thomas: The problem presented to the comparative pathologist is not an easy one, for to mimic the human condition of bronchitis one has to use more than one species. If one is interested purely in the goblet cell response then the rat, having mainly goblet cells and no tracheal or bronchial glands, is the animal of choice for study. If, however, one wants to study the effect of irritants on bronchitis affecting the bronchial and tracheal glands one has to go to an animal such as the lamb which has bronchial glands which are very similar to man. In these animals nine-tenths of the mucus produced is from the bronchial and tracheal glands and one-tenth from the goblet cells. The experimental condition induced in the lamb is very similar to that seen in non-infective bronchitis in man.

As a pathologist my definition of bronchitis is a hyper-secretion of mucus. As I am not a clinician I have not considered the clinical aspects of bronchitis.

R. B. Douglas: Using whole body plethysmography techniques we have measured changes in airways resistance due to reflex broncho-constriction after administration of SO_2 to humans.

An exponential dose response curve was obtained tailing off at 80 p.p.m. v/v SO_2 in air, which is similar to your goblet cell response curve.

Dr. Mawdesley-Thomas: I was not concerned with the physiology, but my environmental physiologist tells me he gets results very similar to those you have described.

D. C. F. Muir: Can you make use of your data on the macrophage response to indicate the circumstances under which inhaled SO_2 fails to reach the alveolus. It is such a soluble gas that I find great difficulty in understanding how any SO_2, except after exceedingly high inhaled concentrations, gets beyond the terminal bronchiole.

Dr. Mawdesley-Thomas: I was very particular to talk about the levels of sulphur dioxide in the experimental atmosphere, the amounts reaching the bronchial tree were not monitored. It is not possible at present to state whether the alveolar macrophase response is due to an altered rheology due to a hyper-secretion of mucus, or to a direct toxic effect of the sulphur dioxide, although I personally favour the former explanation. This problem is under consideration by us.

EFFECTS OF NITROGEN DIOXIDE AND TOBACCO SMOKE ON RETENTION OF INHALED BACTERIA*

MARY C. HENRY, JAMES SPANGLER, JOHN FINDLAY and RICHARD EHRLICH

Life Sciences Research Division, IIT Research Institute, Chicago, Illinois 60616, U.S.A.

Abstract — An acute 2 h exposure to 15 ppm of nitrogen dioxide followed by a 1 h exposure to 3 % (v/v) cigarette smoke significantly decreased the resistance of hamsters to bacterial pneumonia initiated by respiratory challenge with airborne *Klebsiella pneumoniae*. The change in resistance was demonstrated by enhanced mortality and decreased survival time. The effect of the combined exposures was significantly greater than that produced by exposures to either pollutant alone. The combined exposure also reduced the rate of clearance of viable bacteria from lungs to a greater extent than single exposures.

INTRODUCTION

EXPERIMENTS involving laboratory animals and epidemiological studies in human populations have emphasized that biological effects of individual air pollutants should be compared with the effects resulting from exposures to several components of the atmospheric pollution. For example, RYLANDER (1969) reported that exposure of experimental animals to sulfur dioxide alone did not affect the mechanical or bactericidal elimination of inhaled microorganisms, while exposure to coal dust reduced only the mechanical elimination of the organisms from the lungs. However, combined exposure to sulfur dioxide and coal dust appeared to have a synergistic effect since both defense mechanisms were affected. ISHIKAWA *et al.* (1969) studied the prevalence and severity of pulmonary emphysema in two cities with different levels of air pollution. The authors reported that the incidence of severe emphysema in comparable groups of cigarette smokers was four times as high in a heavily industrialized urban community as in a prairie-agricultural city. This suggested that the development of emphysema may be related to a synergistic effect of smoking and environmental pollution.

Studies in our laboratories have shown that acute exposures to either nitrogen dioxide (NO_2) (EHRLICH, 1966) or cigarette smoke (SPURGASH *et al.* 1968) reduced the resistance of experimental animals to *Klebsiella pneumoniae* infection initiated by the respiratory route. In a comparison of different laboratory animal species, hamsters were shown to be less susceptible to the effects of NO_2 than mice. Furthermore, they also have shown a high natural resistance to the experimental bacterial pneumonia.

* This study was supported by funds provided by the National Air Pollution Control Administration, Department of Health, Education and Welfare, under Contract No. PH 86–67–30.

In conducting the research reported here, the investigators adhered to "Principles of Laboratory Animal Care" as established by the National Society for Medical Research.

527

Thus it was of interest to determine the degree to which the exposure to the two pollutants, namely tobacco smoke and NO_2 would alter their resistance to infection as measured by mortality rates, survival time and retention of viable *K. pneumoniae* in the lungs.

MATERIALS AND METHODS

Male Golden hamsters, weighing 80 to 100 g, were quarantined for one week prior to being used in the experiments. Throughout the quarantine and experimental period, the hamsters were maintained on nutritionally adequate diets. Methods used for the acute exposure of experimental animals to NO_2 and to cigarette smoke and for respiratory challenge with aerosol of *K. pneumoniae* were previously described (Ehrlich, 1966: Spurgash *et al.*, 1968).

The experimental groups of hamsters used in the studies were as follows:

Control: hamsters challenged only with *K. pneumoniae* aerosol.

NO_2: hamsters exposed for 2 h to NO_2 in concentrations ranging from 5 to 35 ppm and then challenged with *K. pneumoniae* aerosol.

Smoke: hamsters exposed continuously for 1 h to 3% v/v tobacco smoke from non-filter cigarettes and then challenged with *K. pneumoniae* aerosol.

NO_2-Smoke: hamsters exposed for 2 h to NO_2 in concentrations ranging from 5 to 35 ppm, followed by 1 h continuous exposure to 3% v/v tobacco smoke from non-filtered cigarettes and then challenged with *K. pneumoniae* aerosol.

The duration of exposures were chosen to correspond to previous experiments on the effects of acute exposures to these pollutants. During tobacco smoke exposures the hamsters nose-breathed, thus no attempt was made to duplicate human smoking patterns.

During the 2-h exposure to NO_2, hamsters from the control and smoke groups were placed in an air lock of the NO_2 chamber for the same length of time. After the NO_2 exposure, hamsters from the smoke group and the NO_2-smoke group were simultaneously exposed to the tobacco smoke. Thus during the experimental exposure all hamsters were treated in identical manner with the exception of the presence of the respective pollutants. Hamsters in groups of 6 to 10 representing the various exposure conditions were challenged with airborne *K. pneumoniae* by the respiratory route. Mortality and survival time were recorded for 14 days, and the data were analyzed by the paired comparison method. The statistical significance of differences are reported at $P < 0.1$.

To determine the effect of exposures to the pollutants on the clearance rate of viable *K. pneumoniae* from lungs, hamsters in groups of 3 to 6 were killed immediately after the infectious challenge. The lungs were removed aseptically, weighed, homogenized in sterile distilled water, and assayed quantitatively on blood agar base. These initial counts (zero hour) were considered as 100% recovery of viable *K. pneumoniae* in the lungs. Thereafter groups of control hamsters not exposed to the pollutants and experimental hamsters were killed at hourly intervals up to 8 h and at 24, 48, 72 h and 7 days after the respiratory challenge. Their lungs were assayed for viable *K. pneumoniae* in identical manner.

The counts were reported as total number of viable organisms per gram lung or calculated as fraction (%) of viable organisms per gram wet weight of lung present at zero hour. The rates of bacterial clearance and multiplication in the lung were determined by the least squares method. The clearance rates are expressed as the time after challenge when 50 or 100% of the original bacterial population is present. These values were determined on a semi-logarithmic regression after conversion of the percent recovery to corresponding log values.

RESULTS

Mortality and survival time

To determine the excess deaths due to exposure to NO_2, tobacco smoke, or the combination of the two pollutants, mean mortality rate of the control hamsters challenged with the infectious aerosol only was used as the baseline. The excess death rates for the various experimental groups are shown in Figure 1. Hamsters challenged

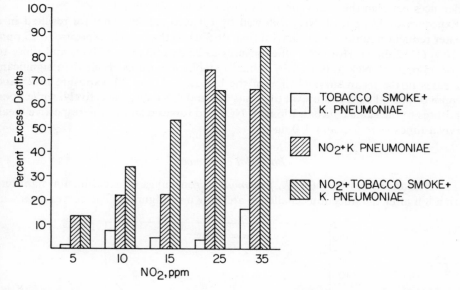

FIGURE 1. Excess mortality of infected hamsters due to exposure to NO_2 and tobacco smoke.

with *K. pneumoniae* only and those exposed for 1 h to cigarette smoke before the infectious challenge showed very similar mortality rates. Mean mortality rates and the corresponding standard deviations in the infected control group and in the group exposed to the cigarette smoke were $11\cdot4 \pm 4\cdot9\%$ and $17\cdot4 \pm 9\cdot3\%$, respectively. Thus it appeared that exposure to tobacco smoke had little effect on the mortality rates of infected hamsters.

Exposure to 10 ppm of NO_2, suggested a trend toward a reduction in resistance to bacterial infection as compared to control hamsters, the difference in death rates being significant at $P = 0\cdot14$. Exposure to 15 ppm of NO_2 produced significant excess deaths over those in control hamsters challenged with a *K. pneumoniae* aerosol only. Exposure to 25 ppm or higher produced maximum decreases in resistance to the infection, since in replicate experiments using six to ten hamsters per group the mortality ranged from 80 to 100%.

Combination of exposures to 5 ppm NO_2 and the cigarette smoke, followed by the infectious challenge did not bring about a significant increase in mortality when compared to the NO_2 exposure group. However, there was a slight excess in mortality of hamsters exposed to 10 ppm of NO_2 and tobacco smoke. At 15 ppm NO_2 the tobacco smoke appeared to have a significant effect on the resistance to bacterial infection and 67% of the hamsters died as compared to 36% of those in the NO_2 group ($P = 0·10$). Excess deaths in the 15 ppm NO_2 and the 15 ppm NO_2 and tobacco groups over those in control hamsters were 22% and 53%, respectively. Since concentrations of NO_2 of 25 and 35 ppm produced maximal reduction in resistance to infection, no additive effects of cigarette smoke could be discerned.

The mean survival time of control hamsters, calculated on the basis of a maximum 14-day survival was $13·2 \pm 0·5$ days. Upon exposure to tobacco smoke the mean survival time was reduced to $12·3 \pm 1·3$ days. A similar decrease to 12·5, 11·7, and 11·2 days was observed upon exposure to 5, 10, and 15 ppm of NO_2, respectively. The differences between the mean survival times were not significant.

Exposure to 15 ppm of NO_2 followed by tobacco smoke exposure resulted in a greater reduction in the mean survival time (9·3 days) than single exposure to 15 ppm of NO_2 (11·2 days). However, all exposures to 25 and 35 ppm of NO_2 and those to 25 or 35 ppm of NO_2 followed by tobacco smoke exposures resulted in significant decreases in the mean survival time of the hamsters. Upon 2-h exposure to 25 and 35 ppm of NO_2 the mean survival time was 6·0 and 4·8 days, respectively, while upon exposures to the same concentrations of NO_2 and tobacco smoke the respective mean survival times were 6·5 and 3·0 days.

Bacterial clearance

The clearance rates of viable *K. pneumoniae* from lungs of experimental hamsters during 8 h after the infectious challenge are shown in Figure 2. The curves represent

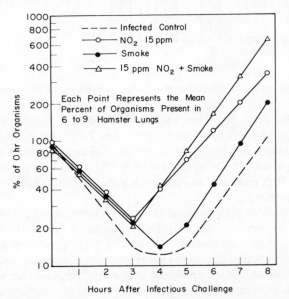

Figure 2. Viable bacteria in hamster lung 0 to 8 h after challenge.

the rates of bacterial clearance and multiplication. They were calculated separately by the least squares method and show the logarithmic progress for both rates.

Infected control hamsters showed the most rapid clearance of bacteria and 50% of the viable organisms ($t_{\frac{1}{2}}$) were cleared in $1\cdot0$ h. The lowest levels of bacteria in controls ($< 20\%$) were present between 3 and 5 h after the infectious challenge. Thereafter, the bacterial population increased and reached the initial concentration after $7\cdot98$ h.

The $t_{\frac{1}{2}}$ clearance values for experimental hamsters exposed to 15 ppm of NO_2, cigarette smoke, and those exposed to both pollutants were $1\cdot44$, $1\cdot28$, and $1\cdot17$ h, respectively. Lungs of hamsters exposed to the tobacco smoke showed the lowest bacterial population at 4 h after the infectious challenge, and the 100% concentration was reached at $7\cdot06$ h. Hamsters exposed to 15 ppm of NO_2 and those exposed to the combined stresses cleared less than 80% of the viable bacteria by 4 h, and a marked increase in bacterial population occurred over the next 4 h. Bacterial count equal to the initial inhaled population was present at $5\cdot63$ h and $5\cdot25$ h in hamsters exposed to 15 ppm of NO_2 and to the combination of NO_2 and cigarette smoke, respectively. At the end of the eight-hour period, the latter group had over 600%, while the former group had approximately 350% of the initial bacterial population. In contrast, lungs of hamsters exposed to cigarette smoke contained twice the original inhaled dose while the bacterial population in the infected control was only slightly higher than at the zero time.

In order to determine changes in bacterial population occurring over longer periods, hamsters were sacrificed at 1, 2, 3, and 7 days after the infectious challenge and their lungs were assayed for viable *K. pneumoniae*. The median value for each group of hamsters was determined and expressed as the number of bacteria per gram wet weight of lung (Figure 3). However, the concentrations of bacteria may be in error by a factor of 10. This was due to a relatively wide variability in bacterial populations observed in individual hamsters at the sampling times and the mortalities occurring in the hamsters exposed to 15 ppm of NO_2 or NO_2 and smoke combination. Nevertheless, certain trends are apparent. At 1 day after the infectious challenge lungs of all three experimental groups of hamsters had larger populations of viable bacteria than the control group. During the next seven-day period a gradual reduction in bacterial population was observed in lungs of hamsters exposed to smoke. Lungs of hamsters exposed to 15 ppm of NO_2 or NO_2 and tobacco smoke had large numbers of viable bacteria present up to three days after the respiratory challenge. At seven days after the challenge, hamsters exposed to the combined stresses still had large populations of viable *K. pneumoniae* while the hamsters exposed to NO_2 had markedly reduced bacterial counts. The results correlate favorably with the survival time data since the majority of deaths after the exposure to NO_2 or the combined stresses occurred between the third and fifth day after the infectious challenge.

COMMENT

Cigarette smoke is a pulmonary irritant which inhibits the activity of the mucociliary apparatus and the alveolar macrophage system. Mucociliary transport is important in the initial phase of lung clearance and acute as well as chronic exposures to cigarette smoke have been shown to inhibit this system (HOLMA, 1969). Phagocyte-depressing action of cigarette smoke in an *in vitro* system has also been demonstrated

(Green & Carolin, 1967). Thus this irritant appears to affect both phases of pulmonary clearance. Furthermore, it was reported that a single exposure to cigarette smoke reduces the resistance of mice to both bacterial and viral respiratory infections. This debilitating effect of cigarette smoke on resistance to respiratory infection was shown to be transitory, lasting less than 48 h (Spurgash, *et al.*, 1968).

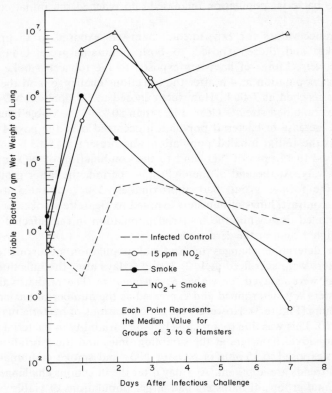

FIGURE 3. Viable bacteria in hamster lung 1 to 7 days after challenge.

Single 2-h exposures to NO_2 also reduced the resistance of mice and hamsters to infection as shown by an increased mortality and increased retention of bacteria in lungs. The effect of the acute exposure was not persistent and a return to normal resistance to infection was observed within 24 h after the NO_2 exposure (Ehrlich, 1966).

In this study, 2-h exposure to 15 ppm NO_2 followed by 1-h exposure to 3% v/v cigarette smoke were shown to significantly reduce the resistance of hamsters to bacterial pneumonia. This was demonstrated by excess deaths over those observed in infected control hamsters and hamsters exposed to 15 ppm of NO_2 or the cigarette smoke only. At lower concentrations of NO_2 (< 10 ppm) and the same smoke concentration, there was only a slight increase in death rates. The mean survival time of hamsters exposed to the combined stress of 15 ppm NO_2 and cigarette smoke was also reduced as compared to controls, and hamsters exposed to NO_2 or cigarette smoke. These results are of special interest since hamsters have a high natural resistance to *K. pneumoniae* infection initiated by the respiratory route. Estimated inhaled respiratory dose of 10^4 organisms produced mortalities of only 11% in control hamsters.

Retention of viable bacteria in lung was also affected to a greater extent by the combination of exposures to 15 ppm of NO_2 and tobacco smoke. Lung clearance during the first 3 h after challenge was slower in all three experimental groups as compared to the infected controls. Similarly after the initial clearance multiplication of bacteria was more rapid in the experimental groups. Hamsters exposed to smoke showed a slight increase in number of organisms in lungs between 5 and 8 h after the challenge as compared to controls. Hamsters exposed to 15 ppm NO_2 only or NO_2 and smoke showed a rapid bacterial multiplication and at 8 h after the infectious challenge three to six times the original population was present, respectively. This large population was maintained for at least 3 days in the hamsters exposed to NO_2, but by the seventh day the population was markedly reduced. Hamsters exposed to both 15 ppm NO_2 and cigarette smoke showed a markedly increased bacterial population up to 7 days after challenge. These results are in accord with the observations on survival time since the greatest number of deaths for this group and the NO_2 group are recorded between 3 and 5 days after challenge.

Reports of other investigators on the effect of cigarette smoke would indicate that the decreased resistance to bacterial infection noted in our studies could be due to inhibition of the mucociliary apparatus or the reduction of phagocytic capacity of the alveolar macrophages. Nitrogen dioxide has been shown to have an effect on the viability of lung macrophage (WEISSBECKER et al., 1969) and also causes macrophage congregation in tissue culture (SHERWIN et al., 1968). The effect of this gas on the mucociliary apparatus has not been accurately determined. The exact site of the synergistic effect of the two stresses has not been determined although recent studies in our laboratories indicate a profound effect on the integrity of the bronchial epithelium.

REFERENCES

EHRLICH, R. (1966). *Bact. Rev.* **30**, 604–614.
GREEN, G. M. & CAROLIN, D. (1967). *New Engl. J. Med.* **276**, 421–427.
HOLMA, B. (1969). *Archs envir. Hlth* **18**, 171–173.
ISHIKAWA, S., BOWDEN, D. H., FISHER, V. & WYATT, J. P. (1969). *Archs envir. Hlth* **18**, 660–666.
RYLANDER, R. (1969). *Archs envir. Hlth* **18**, 551–555.
SHERWIN, R. P., RICHTERS, V., BROOKS, M. & BUCKLEY, R. D. (1968). *Lab. Inves.* **18**, 269–277.
SPURGASH, A., EHRLICH, R. & PETZOLD, R. (1968). *Archs envir. Hlth* **16**, 385–391.
WEISSBECKER, L., CARPENTER, R. D., LUCHSINGER, P. C. & OSDENE, T. S. (1969). *Archs envir. Hlth* **18**, 756–759.

SO$_2$ AND PARTICLES — SYNERGISTIC EFFECTS ON GUINEA-PIG LUNGS

Ragnar Rylander, Maj Öhrström, Per Åke Hellström
and Richard Bergström

*Institute of Hygiene, Karolinska Institute and Department of
Environmental Hygiene, National Institute of Public Health, S-104 01
Stockholm 60, Sweden*

Abstract — The pulmonary clearance of viable non-pathogenic bacteria (*E. coli*) and inert particles (radioactive, killed *E. coli*) was determined in inhalation experiments where guinea-pigs were exposed to manganese dioxide, sulphur dioxide, and a combination thereof. The animals were exposed 6 h daily, 5 days a week for 4 weeks. Ninety per cent of the particles in the aerosol were less than 0·5 μm. In another experiment the addition of sulphur dioxide to manganese dioxide on a filter was found to lower the pH from 4·3 to 3·8.

The ability of the lung to clear inert particles was found to be decreased in animals exposed to MnO$_2$ + SO$_2$ as compared to control animals, or animals exposed to either of the two agents alone. A decreased clearance of viable bacteria was noted in the same group. The results indicate the importance of synergistic effects in the evaluation of airborne pollutants and point to the possible influence of pH of particulate matter for the development of biological effects.

INTRODUCTION

THE synergistic effect between particles and vapours has received increasing attention in studies on the relation between exposure to air pollutants and development of pulmonary disease. Earlier studies (RYLANDER, 1969) have demonstrated that simultaneous exposure to sulphur dioxide and carbon black particles causes the development of effects not present when either of the two pollutants are given separately. In the following presentation this synergistic effect will be further explored in experiments where manganese dioxide dust has been administered to guinea-pigs with and without simultaneous administration of sulphur dioxide.

METHODS

Exposures

Young male guinea-pigs obtained from ordinary dealer's stock were exposed for 6 h per day, 5 days weekly during 4 weeks in stainless steel exposure chambers with a volume of 1·5 m^3. The temperature and humidity in the chambers was kept constant throughout the exposures (23°C, 50% r.h.) and the chamber air was changed 4–5 times per h. The manganese dioxide aerosol (MnO$_2$) was generated in a RagPe aerosol generation unit. A block diagram of the unit is given in Figure 1.

535

By means of a centrifugal fan (F), manganese dioxide powder is circulated in the lower loop (L). An aerosol tower (T) with a volume of around 5 l is placed above the fan and connected to the loop by means of a small tube from the middle of the tower (U).

During operation, dust is thrown into the lower loop by means of the fan. When air is introduced through the inlet channel (I), a corresponding volume will be discharged through the exit (E), into the exposure chamber. By varying the air volume passing through the inlet, an appropriate amount of aerosol can be introduced into the exposure chamber. Larger particles will be recirculated via tube U into the lower loop L. By varying the height of the tower and the position of the exposure chamber inlet

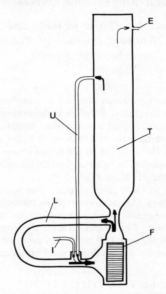

FIGURE 1. Block diagram of RagPe aerosol generator. For function see text.

the particle size of the aerosol can be varied. The amount of MnO_2 in the exposure chamber was determined by filtering chamber air through Millipore filters, which were then weighed. The sampling period was 1 h to achieve stable conditions in the chamber with reference to the volume of air withdrawn for sampling. Samples were taken 3–5 times daily. Size determinations of the aerosol were made with an ordinary light microscope. Control filters were prepared by sampling from exposure chambers in which animals were exposed to ordinary air only. Thus the influence of humidity and chamber-created dust was reduced.

Sulphur dioxide was added to the chambers from pressure bottles containing 1 % of SO_2 in air and diluted as appropriate. The analysis was made using the method of West & Gaeke (1956) with the modification that para-roseaneline base (Merck) was used instead of parafuchsinchloride.

pH determinations were performed in subsequent experiments. Thin layers of manganese dioxide or carbon black were placed on absolute filters. Sulphur dioxide was drawn through the filters, after which the dust was shaken into distilled water to which 0·2 % Tergitol (wetting agent) had been added. pH measurements were made on an ordinary pH meter after 1 min.

Effect Evaluation

The exposure effect in the experiments was evaluated using a method described by RYLANDER (1968) for determining the clearance of viable and killed bacteria. The method involves the exposure of animals to a mixed aerosol of viable and killed radioisotope-marked *Escherichia coli*. The number of viable and radioactive killed bacteria in the lung is determined at various times after the exposure.

The clearance of viable bacteria during the first hours after exposure has been shown to be due mainly to phagocytosis. The clearance of killed, radioactive *E. coli* which here serve as inert particles is carried out by mucus transport.

A strain of *E. coli* originally isolated from guinea-pigs' mouths was used. For the preparation of radioactive bacteria the culture was grown overnight in a synthetic medium containing 15 mCi ^{35}S/100 ml, then centrifuged and suspended in 15% formaldehyde. From this stock suspension samples were taken for each experiment, washed in buffer and suspended together with viable *E. coli* in phosphate buffer for aerosolization.

The guinea-pigs were exposed for 10 min in a stainless steel exposure chamber to the aerosol containing killed radioactive and viable *E. coli*. Animals were killed immediately after exposure and at 3 h thereafter. Homogenates were prepared of the lungs and the numbers of killed radioactive and viable bacteria were determined.

For determination of viable bacteria, samples of lung homogenates were incubated in endoagar pour plates and the number of colonies counted after incubation at 37°C overnight.

The number of radioactive bacteria was determined by filtering lung samples through Millipore filters (HA 0·45 μm). The filters were then applied to X-ray film, which was exposed for about 2 weeks. After development, the radioactive bacteria appeared on the film as black dots and were easily counted ($\times$30). Control experiments showed that disintegration of bacteria or dissolution of the radioactive isotope was not present to a degree which influenced the results.

RESULTS

The measurements of the MnO$_2$ aerosol and SO$_2$ show a mean concentration of 5·9 mg/m^3 (s.d. = 1·6) and 5·0 ppm (s.d. = 1·8). The size distribution of the aerosol was such that about 90% of the particles were smaller than 0·5 μm.

The pH measurements of simulated chamber aerosols showed that the pH of manganese dioxide and carbon black particles were around 4·3 and 4·6 respectively. When SO$_2$ was added, the pH decreased to 3·8 and 2·3.

The results of the bacterial clearance measurements are reported in Table I. As there was no appreciable difference between the control animals from the two exposure groups, the controls have been reported in one single group. For comparison, data from the earlier similar experiment have been included in the table (RYLANDER, 1969).

It is seen in the Table, that in 20 control animals, an average of 75% ($\pm$ 25 s.d.) radioactive bacteria remained in the lungs 3 h after exposure. In the same group an average of 16 $\pm$7% of viable bacteria remained.

The 10 animals which had been exposed to MnO$_2$ showed no significant changes in their particulate or bacterial clearance capacity as compared to the control group, (remaining in lung 79$\pm$24% radioactive bacteria and 19$\pm$10% viable bacteria).

The 9 animals which had been exposed to SO_2 did not differ significantly from the control animals in the clearance of particles or viable bacteria (remaining in lung $88 \pm 15\%$ radioactive bacteria and $10 \pm 2\%$ viable bacteria).

The group of 6 animals which had received $MnO_2 + SO_2$, however, showed a lower clearance of radioactive bacteria (remaining in lung $118 \pm 49\%$) and a lower clearance of viable bacteria ($28 \pm 16\%$). Those values were statistically significant from the control values (a $= 0 \cdot 01$, one sided t-test).

TABLE I. KILLED RADIOACTIVE AND VIABLE *E. coli* REMAINING IN GUINEA-PIG
LUNGS 3 h AFTER EXPOSURE. EXPRESSED AS PER CENT OF 0-HOUR VALUE

Treatment	Amount	Radioactive	Viable
Control	—	75	16
MnO_2	$5 \cdot 9$ mg/m^3	79	19
SO_2	6 ppm	88	10
$MnO_2 + SO_2$	$5 \cdot 9$ mg/m^3 + 5 ppm	118	28
1969			
Coal	15 mg/m^3	74	43
SO_2	$10 \cdot 4$ ppm	64	21
Coal + SO_2	15 mg/m^3 + $10 \cdot 4$ ppm	102	44

In comparison to data earlier reported it is seen that the lower concentration of particulate aerosol in this experiment ($5 \cdot 9$ mg/m^3) did not affect the capacity of the lung to reduce the number of viable bacteria as compared to the higher levels earlier used (15 mg/m^3). The finding that addition of SO_2 to the dust aerosol increased the deleterious effect on the mucus clearance is consistent with the earlier finding.

DISCUSSION

Methods

The technique for determining the reduction of radioactive and viable bacteria from the lungs is essentially similar to techniques used by CRALLEY (1942), BARNES (1947) and later by LAURENZI et al. (1963) and GREEN & KASS (1964). In comparison with other authors, the reduction of non-pathogenic *E. coli* 3 h after exposure as reported in these experiments is consistent with other authors' findings on non-pathogenic bacteria such as *S. aureus* and others. Also the reduction of inert particles corresponding in size to the radioactive *E. coli* used here is in agreement with earlier reports.

The finding that exposure to environmental agents epidemiologically connected to the development of upper respiratory disease, causes a decrease in the clearance of viable bacteria and particles is also consistent with earlier experiments. Among the agents tested are NO_2 and ozone (GARDNER et al., 1969), and cigarette smoke (RYLANDER, 1971).

Although a statistically significant effect is present in all those cases, it is of interest to note that even a prolonged exposure to high levels of pollutants has relatively little effect on the total clearance of particles and bacteria. This finding indicates that the reserve capacity for clearing the type of particles (organisms) used in these experiments is very large, and also that the development of pulmonary disease after exposure to pollutants is probably a multi-stage process involving successive alterations in several biological systems.

In accordance with this, a more sensitive method of detecting changes in bacterial clearance could be the use of pathogenic bacteria as in experiments by EHRLICH & HENRY (1968) and others. Here the animals are exposed to pathogenic bacteria and the number of deaths is recorded. In this way effects have been found after fairly low levels of exposure indicating that it is a sensitive tool for recording exposure effects. The relative merits of different experimental techniques for studying the bacterial defence of the lungs have been discussed by RYLANDER (1970). At this stage no final conclusion can be made concerning the relevance of changes demonstrated with the various experimental models for the development of human disease.

An increased biological effect with decreasing pH of the particulate phase, as noted in the experiments reported here, has also been demonstrated in experiments where the tracheal ciliary activity has been measured after administration of tobacco smoke (DALHAMN & RYLANDER, 1970), and in experiments where the number of free lung cells has been determined after the administration of cigarette smoke of varying pH levels. (RYLANDER, unpublished.)

The results presented in this study indicate that the synergistic effect between particles and SO$_2$ is of importance in the development of biological effects after exposure to air pollutants. Somewhat contradictory results have been reported for inert particles by other researchers (AMDUR & UNDERHILL, 1968) but different experimental models were used. This discrepancy demonstrates that exposure effects are different for different types of biological reaction in the lungs.

The significance of any one studied effect in animal exposure in relation to the development of human disease is a factor of great importance and should be taken into consideration when exposure effects are evaluated. At a recent workshop (KILBURN & RYLANDER, 1970) suggestions were put forward as to the preference of available experimental models for inhalation toxicity experiments. The experiments reported here and discrepancies from other experiments concerning the synergistic effect of aerosol and particulate matter further underline the necessity to evaluate several different biological models in animal inhalation experiments.

REFERENCES

AMDUR, M. O. & UNDERHILL, D. (1968). The effect of various aerosols on the response of guinea-pigs to sulfur dioxide. *Archs envir. Hlth* **19**, 460–468.

BARNES, J. M. (1947). The development of anthrax following the administration of spores by inhalation. *Br. J. exp. Path.* **28**, 385–394.

CRALLEY, L. J. (1942). Factors affecting retention and rate of removal of bacteria from the tracheal tree and lungs. *Am. J. Hyg.* **36**, 303–310.

DALHAMN, T. & RYLANDER, R. (1970). Ciliotoxicity of cigar and cigarette smoke. *Archs envir. Hlth* **20**, 252–253.

EHRLICH, R. & HENRY, M. C. (1968). Chronic toxicity of nitrogen dioxide: I. Effect on resistance to bacterial pneumonia. *Archs envir. Hlth* **17**, 860–865.

GARDNER, D. E., HOLZMAN, R. S. & COFFIN, D. L. (1969). Effects of nitrogen dioxide on pulmonary cell population. *J. Bact.* **98**, 1041–1043.

GREEN, G. M. & KASS, E. H. (1964). Factors influencing the clearance of bacteria by the lung. *J. clin. Invest.* **43**, 769–776.

KILBURN, K. & RYLANDER, R. *Editors* (1970). Pulmonary responses to inhaled materials. Workshop, Bermuda Oct. 23–25, 1969. Symposium 2425. *Archs intern. Med.* **126**, 415–511.

540   RAGNAR RYLANDER, MAJ ÖHRSTRÖM, PER ÅKE HELLSTRÖM and RICHARD BERGSTRÖM

LAURENZI, G. A., GUARNERI, J. J., ENDRIGA, R. B. & CAREY, J. P. (1963). Clearance of bacteria by the lower respiratory tract. *Science* **142**, 1572–1573.
RYLANDER, R. (1968). Pulmonary defence mechanisms to airborne bacteria. *Acta physiol. scand.* **72**, Suppl. 306. pp. 1–89.
RYLANDER, R. (1969). Alterations of lung defense mechanisms against airborne bacteria. *Archs envir. Hlth* **18**, 551–555.
RYLANDER, R. (1970). Studies on lung defense to infections in inhalation toxicology. *Archs intern. Med.* **126**, 796–799.
RYLANDER, R. (1971). The effect of cigarette smoke exposure on lung clearance of particles and bacteria. *Archs envir. Hlth*. To be published.
WEST, P. W. & GAEKE, G. C. (1956). Fixation of sulfur dioxide as disulfitomercurate (11) and subsequent colorimetric estimation. *Analyt. Chem.* **28**, 1816–1819.

DISCUSSION

S. LAHAM: The following remarks apply not only to Dr. Rylander's paper but also to the negative results shown in Dr. MacFarland's paper (p. 313). In this kind of work, I would suggest that toxicologists should not kill the animals immediately after their experiment, but let them survive for a few days or months before making their observations. We should let Lady Nature act her own way. I would also like to emphasize that toxicologists should expose animals to different and perhaps random concentrations, not necessarily every day, but at certain intervals which may simulate actual human exposure.

Dr. RYLANDER: I think this type of exposure is really needed, but if such an experiment is to be carried out successfully one has to use SPF animals. This has so far only been done to a very limited stage. In normal animal colonies about 20% of the animals die for other reasons than the exposure, which will naturally invalidate the results.

H. N. MACFARLAND: A tracing of actually measured concentrations could be used as a template to reproduce the pattern in an exposure chamber experiment.

A. SPITZER: What was your rationale in using such very low levels of SO$_2$?

Dr. RYLANDER: In earlier preliminary experiments we obtained an effect on the number of goblet cells by exposing to 15 p.p.m., but were not able to find this at levels of 10 and 5 p.p.m. We were just curious to see what happened to the particulate and bacterial clearance at this rather low level, including, of course, a side look at the TLV value.

J. FERIN: I am concerned with your use of the term "inert particles" for "killed bacteria". Under inert particles, I understand particles like TiO$_2$. Would you comment on this please? Secondly, do you have any preference for using guinea pigs in experiments of this type.

Dr. RYLANDER: I chose to identify the killed bacteria as inert particles. They were grown on a synthetic medium and are thereafter killed in formalin. Furthermore, the strain used was originally derived from guinea pigs so it is essentially not alien to the animal.

We used guinea pigs because we had found that the globlet cell structure of the guinea pig was very good to work with in other inhalation experiments, and we did not want to change the animal species. I would add that it is essential to repeat this type of experiment with other kinds of animals.

M. CORN: The standard deviation of the MnO$_2$ + SO$_2$ responses was very high. Would you comment on the concept of sensitive members of the exposed groups, or "reactants" as referred to in human or other animal (cat) studies? Is it proper to express the data in grouped form if a few animals are responsible for the bulk of the mean change?

Dr. RYLANDER: I agree that we do have reactants, and clearly you would get a larger effect if only this group was studied. At the present time, however, we have no means of distinguishing between the reactants and other animals so I feel we have to work with the whole group and evaluate the results accordingly.

D. C. F. MUIR: Does it matter whether the gaseous irritants and particulate irritants are given simultaneously? As you know, there have been suggestions that the SO$_2$ might be carried down to the small lung airways after adsorption on the particles?

Dr. RYLANDER: Yes, I think that this is the reason behind the effect. The preliminary data on pH of particulates indicates that the effect is probably associated with the low pH of the particle. We have seen the same effect in cigarette smoking, studying 12 different brands of cigarettes.

STUDIES OF INHALED RADON DAUGHTERS, URANIUM ORE DUST, DIESEL EXHAUST, AND CIGARETTE SMOKE IN DOGS AND HAMSTERS*

Bruce O. Stuart, Donald H. Willard and Edwin B. Howard

Pacific Northwest Laboratory, Battelle Memorial Institute, Richland, Washington, U.S.A.

Abstract — The incidence of lung cancer in uranium ore miners on the Colorado Plateau has risen to six times that of non-miners. Although the primary carcinogenic agent is generally accepted to be the inhaled short-lived radioactive decay products of radon, the miners are routinely exposed to several other hazardous air-borne contaminants, including ore dust and diesel-engine exhaust fumes. In addition, 97% of those uranium miners who have developed lung cancer have histories of cigarette smoking.

A program involving inhalation exposures of experimental animals was undertaken to determine the relative effectiveness of the principal mine air contaminants in the production of pulmonary fibrosis, emphysema or neoplastic changes. Six groups of 100 hamsters each are being exposed in life-span studies for 6 h daily to radon daughters, ore dust, and/or diesel exhaust fumes.

The possible synergistic action of radon daughters and cigarette smoking in the development of lung cancer in uranium miners is being studied using beagle dogs. Three groups of 20 dogs each are receiving daily exposures to 4 h of 600 Working Levels of radon daughters plus ore dust, exposure to cigarette smoking over 16 h periods, 7 days per week, and exposure to both radon daughters and cigarette smoking; 9 dogs serve as controls for hematology, physical examination and radiographic examination. Two dogs in each group receive lung washings for lung exfoliative cytology studies.

The current results of these long-term multiple exposure studies with experimental animals are discussed.

INTRODUCTION

THERE is critical need for quantitative biological data to determine cause and effect relationships between uranium mine air contaminants and respiratory tract pathology. LUNDIN *et al.* (1969) described 62 cases of lung cancer found among 3414 miners, an incidence 6 times greater than that of non-miners, and discussed the radon daughter exposures, prior hard-rock mining and cigarette smoking histories of these men. Today, the total lung cancer incidence appears to be over 140 cases among uranium miners of the Colorado plateau (SACCOMANNO, 1969). Forecasts of uranium ore production indicate nearly 20 million tons needed annually by 1980 (FEDERAL RADIATION

* This work performed under Contract AT(45–1)–1830 between the Atomic Energy Commission and Pacific Northwest Laboratory, Battelle Memorial Institute, on behalf of the Division of Biology and Medicine, Atomic Energy Commission, and the National Institute of Environmental Health Sciences, Department of Health, Education and Welfare.

Council, 1967); this will require several times the current underground mining rate with greatly increased numbers of miners. National concern for the health of these men has resulted in a new standard for an annual permissible exposure of 4 cumulative working level months (WLM*) that may be in effect by the end of this calendar year (Archer, 1970).

Several recent reports emphasize the difficulty in establishing reliable cause and effect relationships between radiological and chemical hazards in the mine air and lung pathology. Epidemiological studies show lung cancer occurring at progressively lower exposures to mine environments and after increasingly longer latent periods (Lundin et al., 1969). The finding of additional cases of lung cancer among miners who have received less than 120 WLM of estimated radon daughter exposure in uranium mines but with 7 to 30 years of prior hard-rock mining complicates the dose-response relationship at lower exposure levels (National Academy of Sciences, 1968), and suggests that other mine air contaminants such as ore dusts, diesel engine exhaust, or blasting gases could have contributed to the observed respiratory tract pathology. Drilling, blasting, and haulage of ore in uranium and hard-rock mines frequently raise opaque clouds of silica-bearing dusts (McDaniel, 1968). The continuing use of diesel engine powered equipment in these mines (Davis et al., 1964) causes a repeated daily exposure of the miners to the NO_2, SO_2, aldehydes (Linnell & Scott, 1962), and polycyclic aromatic hydrocarbons present in diesel exhaust fumes (Kotin et al., 1955). The vast quantity of condensation nuclei produced by such internal combustion engines may markedly affect the percentage of unattached radon daughters (Craft et al., 1966) and thus alter "absorbed dose/Working Level" relationships in a manner undetectable by routine sampling methods.

The possible contributory or synergistic effects of cigarette smoking among the majority of uranium miners in the initiation or development of lung cancer continues to receive a great deal of attention. The recent report by Lundin et al. (1969) indicates a similar 4-fold increase in lung cancer risk for smoking miners versus smoking non-miners as for corresponding non-smoking groups. The much higher risk for cigarette-smoking miners is similar to that described for other smoking groups (U.S. Dept. H.E.W., 1964; Terry, 1970). The more recent cases of lung cancer among present or former uranium miners seem to be those types generally associated with cigarette smoking (Saccomanno, 1970), rather than the small cell, undifferentiated tumors described previously (Saccomanno et al., 1964). An extremely high incidence of lung cancer (30 times expected levels) has also been observed among fluorspar miners in Newfoundland who received significant exposures to radon daughters arising from radon dissolved in the ground water present in these mines (De Villiers & Windish, 1964; Parsons et al., 1964). In addition to receiving daily exposures to radon daughters and concentrations of silicate-bearing fluorspar ore dust reaching 85 million particles per cubic foot, almost all of these men were smokers. Because of the highly elevated lung cancer rates among these men who also received exposures to radon daughters and heavy cigarette smoking, a contributory or synergistic action by these two agents has been suggested for both populations of miners (Evans, 1968). Both groups also received concomitant inhalation exposures to fibrinogenic siliceous ores.

The problem of determining a meaningful relationship between exposure history and the absorbed dose to critical regions of the respiratory tract, which may be

---

* One working level month (WLM) is defined as 170 h of exposure to an atmosphere containing $1 \cdot 3 \times 10^5$ MeV of potential radon daughter alpha energy per liter of air.

necessary to induce or promote lung cancer, is essential for evaluation of uranium mine inhalation hazards, and continues to be the subject of extensive review. Expert opinion as to the effective dose to selected areas of the epithelial basement membrane (NELSON *et al.*, 1969; PARKER, 1969; WALSH, 1970) ranges from <1 to 10 rads per working level month. The identification of most frequent site (or sites) of tumor origin and the characterization of the degree of attachment and size distribution of the vector aerosol for radon daughters is crucial to such evaluations. Such information can be directly obtained only from a program of chronic inhalation exposure of laboratory animals to controlled levels of uranium mine air contaminants under conditions similar to those of human exposures.

The demonstration of the presence or absence of a synergistic role of concomitant inhalation hazards present in uranium mine air in the development of respiratory tract pathology, including lung cancer, also requires the detailed observation of laboratory animals that receive lifespan daily exposures to single and combined uranium mine air constituents. In order to determine the relative effectiveness of the major mine air inhalation hazards, groups of 100 Syrian hamsters each were placed on daily exposures to two levels of radon daughters, radon daughters plus uranium ore dust, and diesel exhaust fumes as described below. These animals are resistant to respiratory tract infection and are sensitive biological models for lung cancer in man.

Auerbach has recently described the appearance of bronchiolo-alveolar tumors in dogs after $2\frac{1}{2}$ years of daily intratracheal administration of smoke from 7 to 9 cigarettes (REPORT ON MEDICINE, 1970). The present paper describes studies in our laboratory using beagle dogs that have been trained to receive daily exposures to inhaled cigarette smoke and/or radon daughters to determine the possible synergistic effects of these agents in causing respiratory tract pathology. Techniques have been developed to cause an oral inhalation of cigarette smoke followed by nose or mouth exhalation to provide a realistic simulation of human cigarette smoking patterns (BAIR *et al.*, 1969). FALK (1970) has recently reviewed the toxic actions of a variety of gas-phase constituents of cigarette smoke, including the inhibition of ciliary activity. GASTINEAU (1969) suggests that areas of hyperplasia or metaplasia in the human respiratory tract may cause thinning of the bronchial epithelium, which would expose increased numbers of basal cells to the interior environment of the respiratory passages. These changes, plus the inhibition of ciliary action during cigarette smoking, may increase the absorbed dose of alpha radiation from deposited radon daughters.

The work described below is a progress report on a continuing long-term program of daily lifespan inhalation exposures of dogs and hamsters to provide basic information on cause and effect relationships between uranium mine air contaminants and lung cancer.

INHALATION EXPOSURE OF HAMSTERS TO URANIUM MINE AIR CONTAMINANTS

Recent investigations involving the use of hamsters as a test animal for carcinogenesis studies have shown that this species can be used as a model for a variety of human pulmonary diseases (MONTESANO *et al.*, 1970). For this reason hamsters have become the species of choice for small animal experimentation sponsored by several governmental agencies (SAFFIOTTI & BAKER, 1970), as well as for the studies described below.

The current experiments are described in Table I, and involve the daily exposure for 6 h per day, 5 days per week, of groups of hamsters on lifespan studies to test the effects of two levels of radon daughters and the possible co-carcinogenic action of uranium ore dust (Groups 1 through 4). Groups 5 and 6 have begun daily exposures to determine the nature and extent of respiratory tract pathology caused by inhalation of diesel exhaust constituents, and to explore the possible additive or synergistic action of three mine air pollutants (diesel exhaust, radon daughters, and carnotite ore dust) in causing respiratory and systemic organ pathology and neoplastic changes.

TABLE I. EXPERIMENTAL DESIGN FOR HAMSTER STUDIES

Group	Number of animals	Exposure
1	100	Controls (laboratory air)
2	100	30 WL radon daughters
3	100	600 WL radon daughters
4	100	600 WL radon daughters with uranium ore dust (carnotite) 15 mg/m³
5	100	Diesel engine exhaust
6	100	Diesel engine exhaust plus 600 WL radon daughters with uranium ore dust

TECHNIQUES OF DAILY INHALATION EXPOSURES

Radon Daughter with Uranium Ore Dust Exposures

The first 4 groups of 100 hamsters each were placed on a regimen of daily 6 h exposures 19–23 months ago, using the spherical, 6 ft diameter, chambers designed for these studies. The group exposed 5 days per week to 30 WL of radon daughters and the control group inhaling laboratory air under the same conditions are now in their 23rd month of exposures. The group receiving 600 WL of radon daughters and 600 WL plus 15 mg/m³ of uranium ore dust (carnotite) have undergone daily exposures, 5 days per week, for 19 months. Radon concentrations in each chamber are recorded automatically once every hour during exposure, and each chamber is sampled daily for determination of individual radon daughter concentration using a solid state surface barrier detector designed for these studies. Fractional equilibrium levels of daughter radioactivity relative to radon (120 nCi/l) are approximately 0·9, 0·5 and 0·25–0·3 for RaA, RaB, and RaC-C[1], respectively. Aerosol exposure and sampling systems have been described in detail in a previous report (STUART et al., 1970). Daily samples of carnotite ore dust concentrations are taken, and periodic determinations of the particle size distribution of the dust are made using thermal and electrostatic precipitators followed by electron microscopic examination. Count median diameters of the ore used in these studies vary from 0·2 to 0·4 μm. The dominant role of condensation nuclei in determining respiratory tract radon daughter deposition has emphasized the necessity of measuring their concentrations in these chambers as well as attached and unattached fractions of radon daughters. Chambers receiving 15 mg/m³ ore dust show condensation nuclei concentrations of 5 to 10 × 10⁴/cm³; levels in chambers receiving laboratory air plus radon are of the order of 1 × 10⁴/cm³.

FIGURE 1. Three-cylinder 43 bhp diesel engine coupled to a 25 kW generator, designed to produce diesel exhaust fumes for inhalation studies using hamsters.

FIGURE 2. Diesel exhaust regulation and hamster exposure systems, including automatic CO monitoring and control system.

Diesel Exhaust Exposure System

Daily exposure of Groups 5 and 6 required the development, fabrication, testing and calibration of a system for the controlled exposure of groups of 100 hamsters each to diesel exhaust limited to 50 ppm of carbon monoxide, and to the same exposure plus 600 WL radon daughters with 15 mg/m³ of uranium ore dust. Figure 1 shows a 43 bhp diesel engine coupled to a 25 kW generator and resister banks that has been fitted with an automatic load cycle control programmer to simulate operation in uranium mines. Figure 2 shows two hamster exposure chambers that maintain automatic pressure control and carbon monoxide level regulation during the daily 6 h exposure period. The diesel engine exhaust passes through a muffler and enters a stainless steel surge tank (upper right corner of Figure 2). A regulated portion of the exhaust fumes then passes downwards through an orifice meter and flow regulator, and is diluted with automatically controlled inputs of fresh air before entry into the exposure chambers. The levels of diluting air for each chamber are electronically adjusted in response to the CO monitoring and control systems. Total chamber flows are set at 50 l/min by means of by-pass valves. In addition to periodic chamber sampling for particulate size and concentration, NO_x, SO_2, total hydrocarbons and limited numbers of samples for specific hydrocarbon analyses are also taken. Groups 5 and 6 with appropriate controls have recently begun exposures.

RESULTS OF INHALATION EXPOSURE OF HAMSTERS TO URANIUM MINE AIR CONTAMINANTS

Mortality Patterns

The Syrian hamsters used in the present studies were obtained from a colony maintained in our laboratories. Daily exposures were started at 3 months of age in each group of hamsters. Figure 3 shows that relatively few deaths occurred during the

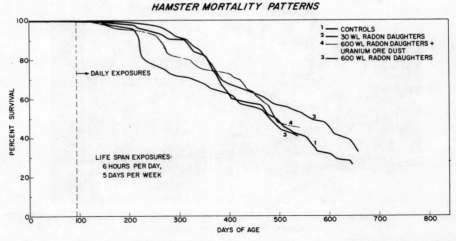

FIGURE 3. Comparative hamster mortality curves. Survival percentages are functions of age and exposure histories.

first 7 months of life. Thereafter, occasional animals in each exposure group as well as controls developed "wet tail" syndrome. These animals seemed to be affected at random and tests failed to implicate a specific etiological agent. Fourteen animals were lost from the 600 WL group at 220 days due to accidental water shortage. The exposure levels of 600 WL and 600 WL with ore dust were chosen based on the results of previous work with mice in another laboratory (MORKEN & SCOTT, 1966) in order to allow significant inhalation exposures without lifespan shortening. It is apparent that none of the exposure groups to date have shown higher mortality than controls that inhaled laboratory air under identical conditions.

Body Weights

The effects of continuing daily 6 h exposures of animals individually housed in wire cages are shown in Figure 4. Following a 2-month period of decreasing weight, a gradual acclimatization appears to have taken place; all groups at present have reached fairly stable mean body weight levels of 110 to 120 g, with little difference due to specific exposure regimens.

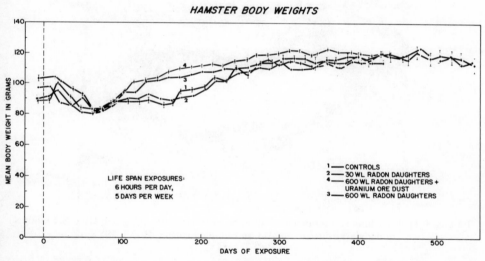

FIGURE 4. Mean hamster body weights with standard errors for controls and experimental groups.

Hematology

Other studies (MORKEN & SCOTT, 1966) have shown that mice exposed to 1750 WL of radon daughters for 150 h per week suffered a significant depression in leucocyte levels in the peripheral blood, due primarily to a reduction in lymphocytes; neutrophil levels in exposed animals were similar to or higher than levels in controls. Erythrocyte levels were slightly depressed. In the present study 10 animals were selected from each group to follow the hematological changes caused by daily exposure to 30 WL and 600 WL of radon daughters with and without uranium ore dust. Peripheral blood samples were drawn from the venus orbital plexus. To date, both red and white blood cell counts have shown essentially no change between groups or with accumulated exposure time.

Pathology

Individual animals are killed from each group when moribund. A severe weight loss usually precedes death by a few days. Sections from the trachea, lungs, liver, kidneys, spleen and gastrointestinal tract are taken for histopathological examination. After 7 weeks of exposures to 30 WL, there was some flattening of epithelial cells and a slight loss of cellularity with increased collagen in the lamina propria of the trachea. After 6 to 9 months of exposures, tracheal changes were minimal, but lungs showed a slight degree of edema and early hyalinization of the interalveolar septa. Some emphysema was found in the subplural areas. After 6 months of daily exposures to 600 WL, hamster lungs showed some edema and areas of peripheral emphysema with inflammatory reactions involving mononuclear and polymorphonuclear cells. The same animals occasionally showed evidence of bronchiolar epithelial hyperplasia (Figure 5).

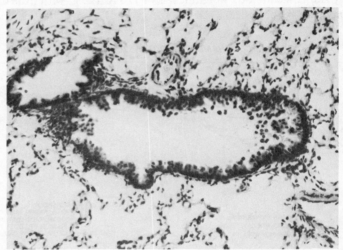

Figure 5. Hamster lung section demonstrating bronchiolar epithelial hyperplasia. Six months of daily exposures to 600 WL of radon daughters. H & F 195 ×

The lungs of animals exposed to 600 WL with carnotite ore dust (15 mg/m³) for 6 months frequently contained marked areas of alveolar septal breakdown and emphysema, with congestion of the vasculature system. Many of the medium-sized bronchioles in the lungs of animals from the 600 WL with ore group contained epithelial hyperplasia and early metaplasia, as shown in Figure 6. Many hamsters in this group showed a chronic granulomatous pneumonitis with extensive fibrosis (Figure 7). Less severe pneumonitis has been found in some animals from all groups, including controls. At 14 months, several of the hamsters receiving daily exposure to 600 WL with uranium ore dust seem to have developed changes in the bronchiolar epithelium suggestive of early tumor formation (Figure 8). These findings must be regarded as preliminary; final evaluation of these changes and their relationships to exposure history will be made after complete histopathological examination of all animals.

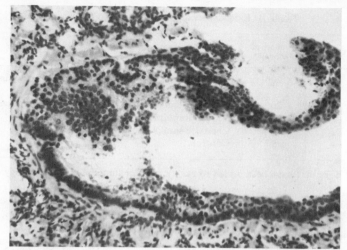

FIGURE 6. Hamster lung section demonstrating bronchiolar epithelial hyperplasia and early metaplasia. Six months of daily exposures to 600 WL of radon daughters with uranium ore dust. H & E 195×

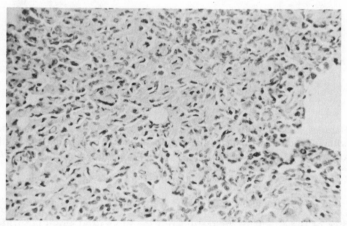

FIGURE 7. Hamster lung section showing chronic granulomatous pneumonitis with fibrosis following chronic exposure to 600 WL of radon daughters with uranium ore dust. H & E 122×

INHALATION EXPOSURE OF BEAGLE DOGS TO CIGARETTE SMOKE AND RADON DAUGHTERS WITH URANIUM ORE DUST

The continuing experiments described in this report were designed to study the cause and effect relationships in the development of pulmonary and systemic pathology resulting from daily inhalation exposures of dogs to radon daughters and cigarette smoke, both combined and separately, under carefully controlled conditions, over the lifespan of the animals. Sixty-nine beagle dogs raised in our laboratory were trained and placed on exposure regimens outlined in Table II.

Table II. Experimental Design for Dog Studies

Group	Number of animals	Exposure
1	20*	600 WL radon daughters with uranium ore dust (15 mg/m^3)
2	20*	Cigarette smoke plus 600 WL radon daughters with uranium ore dust
3	20*	Cigarette smoke
4	9*	Controls

* Includes 2 dogs that have been added to each group for lung exfoliative cytology studies.

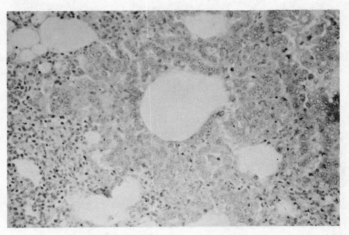

Figure 8. Hamster lung showing changes suggestive of early bronchiolar epithelial tumor formation, with invasion of stroma by neoplastic epithelial cells after 14 months of daily exposures to 600 WL of radon daughters with uranium ore dust. H & E 76×

CIGARETTE SMOKE EXPOSURES

Many studies of the effects of cigarette smoking have used small laboratory animals having relatively short lifespans. Deposition and absorption of cigarette smoke constituents in the respiratory tracts of rodents may be quite different from that in humans because of smaller air passages, different respiration volumes and rates, and the practice of whole-body or nose-inhalation exposures. Few studies have been performed using an exposure regimen similar to that of humans, i.e. intermittent smoking over 16 h per day, 7 days per week. The present studies employ the techniques developed in our laboratory for allowing dogs to smoke 3 or 4 cigarettes per hour by oral inhalation and nose plus mouth exhalation closely simulating the cigarette smoking patterns of humans. Using these techniques and head-only exposures to radon daughters with uranium ore dust, the dogs receive respiratory tract exposures similar to man. Continuing daily exposures over the lifespan of the animals may permit tumors to develop, if a long latent period similar to that in man is required. Recent work by Auerbach et al. (1970), (Report on Medicine, 1970), describes acute and chronic histopathological changes similar to those observed in human smokers in the lungs of dogs exposed to cigarette smoke through tracheal fistulas.

A total of 40 dogs in Groups 2 and 3 are currently smoking 10 cigarettes per day. One technician is able to simultaneously smoke 9 animals as shown in Figure 9, so that each dog receives a daily total of 10 cigarettes in 3 smoking periods over 16 h, 7 days

FIGURE 9. One of two modules allowing 9 beagle dogs to smoke cigarettes simultaneously.

per week. Two 10-section modules are used for simultaneous inhalation exposure of trained beagle dogs to cigarette smoke. Inhalation negative pressure sensors and electro-mechanical stepper-switch systems regulate the ratio of fresh air to smoke-filled breaths (10 : 1) for each animal individually. The IRI Reference Cigarette of the University of Kentucky is being used in these studies. Groups 1 and 4 are sham-exposed using unlighted cigarettes.

RADON DAUGHTERS WITH URANIUM ORE DUST EXPOSURES

Two exposure systems, consisting of parallel radon and uranium ore dust generation systems, aerosol dispersion units, 3000 l exposure chambers, individually ventilated dog-holding boxes, exhaust control and filtration systems, and continuous radon monitoring instrumentation, were fabricated for daily exposures of beagle dogs to aerosols of radon daughters and uranium ore dust. These facilities permit 20 dogs each of Groups 1 and 2 to receive simultaneous head-only exposures to 600 WL of radon daughters with 15 mg/m³ carnotite (uranium) ore dust for a period of 4 h daily on continuing lifespan studies. Figure 10 shows individual magnetically-closing doors that were developed to ensure an absolute seal between chamber and room during aerosol concentration build-up periods. Instrumentation for hourly radon sampling has been installed to monitor these chambers. Radon daughter and uranium ore dust concentrations are sampled daily. The chamber aerosols are also periodically monitored for particle size, condensation nuclei concentrations, and per cent unattached radon daughters.

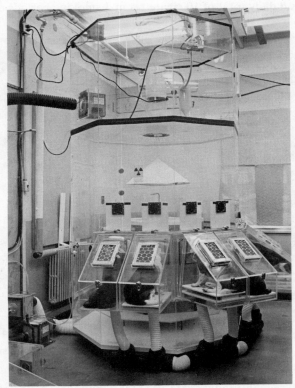

FIGURE 10. Multiple-dog chamber allowing head-only exposure to radon daughters with uranium ore dust.

BIOLOGICAL EFFECTS

Biological effects from these daily exposures are being evaluated by means of physical examination, measurements of respiratory rate and volume, body weight changes, hematology, clinical chemistry, and thoracic radiography of all dogs. Histopathologic examinations are being made following sacrifice of one dog from each group after the first 6 months of exposures. Pathology in these animals will be compared with the effects observed by Auerbach in previous smoking studies using dogs and with the pathology of lesions in uranium miners observed by Saccomanno. Excretion and blood samples are collected and analysed for thiocyanate, carboxyhemoglobin or other biochemical indices of cigarette exposure, and for ^{210}Pb and ^{210}Po to determine whether these radionuclides can be used for bioassay purposes. Tissues obtained at sacrifice are analysed for trace elements, silica, and long-lived alpha emitters. Distribution of such materials as ^{210}Po will be compared in smoking and non-smoking dogs. This information will be incorporated into a dynamic simulation model to predict long-term buildup and removal of all radon daughters, to assist in radiological dose calculations necessary for the evaluation of the hazards of chronic inhalation of uranium mine atmospheres. Two additional dogs in each group were added to study the cytology of cells obtained by lung lavage and for comparison with cells obtained from uranium miners. Possible alterations in lipids related to alveolar surfactant composition due to inhalation of cigarette smoke and/or radon daughter with uranium ore dust will also be measured in these lung washing samples from the dogs.

Respiratory rate, tidal volume and minute volume are measured on each dog once per month. Table III shows the mean values for each group. No significant changes were observed in the exposure groups compared to the controls. Mean values have generally decreased in all groups during the 6-month period of observation. This is probably due to the dogs becoming accustomed to the testing procedures. The body weights of each animal are determined monthly. No significant changes in the mean

TABLE III. MINUTE VOLUMES, TIDAL VOLUMES AND RESPIRATION RATES IN BEAGLE DOGS*

Time Post-exposure (Days)†	Group 1 Radon Daughters with Ore	Group 2 Radon Daughters with Ore + Cigarette Smoke	Group 3 Cigarette smoke	Group 4 Controls
I. Minute Volumes (liters)				
−19†	$4·8\pm1·3$	$5·4\pm1·1$	$5·1\pm1·4$	$4·9\pm1·2$
4	$4·8\pm2·0$	$4·7\pm1·3$	$4·8\pm1·5$	$4·1\pm1·1$
42	$4·8\pm1·5$	$4·7\pm1·7$	$4·1\pm1·6$	$4·2\pm1·5$
58	$3·5\pm0·7$	$4·3\pm0·9$	$3·5\pm0·7$	$4·5\pm1·5$
89	$3·0\pm0·7$	$3·0\pm0·8$	$2·8\pm1·0$	$3·1\pm1·1$
120	$3·7\pm1·1$	$3·4\pm1·3$	$3·2\pm0·8$	$2·9\pm0·9$
148	$3·8\pm1·4‡$	$3·6\pm1·3$	$2·7\pm0·8$	$2·8\pm0·6$
179	$3·2\pm1·1$	$2·9\pm0·8§$	$3·1\pm0·8$	$3·0\pm0·4$
II. Tidal Volumes (liters)				
−19†	$0·15\pm0·05$	$0·17\pm0·04$	$0·17\pm0·04$	$0·19\pm0·03$
4	$0·16\pm0·04$	$0·20\pm0·04$	$0·08\pm0·04$	$0·17\pm0·04$
42	$0·15\pm0·04$	$0·16\pm0·04$	$0·14\pm0·03$	$0·17\pm0·04$
58	$0·14\pm0·03$	$0·16\pm0·03$	$0·15\pm0·02$	$0·17\pm0·04$
89	$0·13\pm0·04$	$0·15\pm0·04$	$0·13\pm0·04$	$0·14\pm0·02$
120	$0·17\pm0·03$	$0·17\pm0·04$	$0·16\pm0·03$	$0·16\pm0·04$
148	$0·13\pm0·02‡$	$0·14\pm0·01$	$0·12\pm0·03$	$0·13\pm0·05$
179	$0·14\pm0·03$	$0·12\pm0·04§$	$0·12\pm0·03$	$0·17\pm0·03$
III. Respiration Rates (respirations/minute)				
−19†	37 ± 20	32 ± 6	30 ± 10	26 ± 4
4	29 ± 11	24 ± 6	27 ± 7	24 ± 3
42	35 ± 17	31 ± 13	29 ± 13	25 ± 6
58	21 ± 4	26 ± 4	24 ± 6	26 ± 8
89	20 ± 9	21 ± 7	26 ± 15	21 ± 5
120	22 ± 6	21 ± 7	21 ± 8	18 ± 4
148	$24\pm10‡$	28 ± 13	23 ± 9	24 ± 12
179	22 ± 5	$24\pm4§$	26 ± 6	18 ± 3

* All values include 95% confidence intervals.
† Days since beginning of smoking and sham-smoking exposures. (10–6–69).
‡ Began 4 h exposures to radon daughters with ore on 2–25–70.
§ Began 4 h exposures to radon daughters with ore on 4–21–70.

body weights have been observed in any of the exposure groups compared to the controls.

Table IV shows the mean hematology values for each group. No significant changes were observed in the exposure groups compared to the controls. No changes from controls were observed in serum chemistry studies, including analyses of blood urea nitrogen, albumin, globulins, and alkaline phosphatase. Physical examinations and thoracic radiographs, 6 months after exposure to cigarette smoke began, showed no changes for the exposure groups compared to the controls.

TABLE IV. HEMATOLOGY STUDIES IN BEAGLE DOGS*

Time Post-exposure (Dates)†	RBC§	WBC‡	Lymphocytes‡	Segmented Neutrophils‡
Group I. *Radon Daughters with Ore*				
–18	7·09±0·12	9·20±0·91	2·65±0·23	5·63±0·61
4	7·33±0·20	7·84±0·45	2·26±0·17	4·70±0·30
39	7·08±0·02	10·40±0·90	2·66±0·67	5·88±0·63
92	7·54±0·14	9·29±0·31	2·74±0·11	5·65±0·26
179‖	7·39±0·07	11·97±0·50	3·20±0·15	7·58±0·47
Group 2. *Radon Daughters with Ore + Cigarette Smoke*				
–18	7·19±0·14	10·82±3·11	2·35±0·24	7·33±2·66
4	7·38±0·18	9·12±0·64	2·64±0·61	5·72±0·75
39	6·93±0·18	9·46±0·67	2·40±0·34	5·89±0·37
94	7·46±0·23	10·50±0·42	2·98±0·13	6·76±0·39
185¶	7·01±0·11	12·43±0·62	3·60±0·19	7·50±0·34
Group 3. *Cigarette Smoke*				
–18	7·14±0·08	10·16±0·88	3·04±0·35	6·09±0·65
4	7·31±0·11	10·27±1·20	2·17±0·13	6·98±0·93
39	7·06±0·18	9·50±0·61	2·38±0·15	6·33±0·48
93	7·45±0·13	9·66±0·43	2·70±0·14	5·93±0·37
184	7·22±0·12	11·12±0·31	3·87±0·22	6·68±0·28
Group 4. *Controls*				
–18	7·36±0·25	8·82±1·06	2·66±0·38	5·31±1·04
4	7·29±0·36	8·47±0·75	2·33±0·56	5·34±0·28
39	6·97±0·20	8·27±1·27	2·18±0·60	5·36±0·87
95	7·16±0·12	9·91±0·32	3·07±0·26	5·90±0·22
186	7·42±0·17	10·50±0·76	3·33±0·34	6·18±0·45

* All values include standard error of the mean.
† Days since beginning of smoking and sham-smoking exposures (10–6–69).
‡ Thousands/mm³ ± standard error of the mean.
§ Millions/mm³ ± standard error of the mean.
‖ Thirty-seven days after beginning 4 h daily exposures to radon daughters.
¶ Twelve days before beginning 4 h daily exposures to radon daughters.

DISCUSSION

The high incidence of lung cancer found among uranium miners in the region of Schneeburg and Joachimstal, and more recently in the Colorado plateau, has emphasized the need for experimental studies to examine the possible causative agents, the relationship between exposure levels and response, and the pathogenesis of this disease.

In 1939, HUECK found a 5% incidence of malignant lung tumors in mice exposed for 2 years to a mine atmosphere containing $0\cdot03$ μCi/l of radon. More recently, MORKEN & SCOTT (1966) exposed mice continuously to $0\cdot4$ μCi/l of radon plus fractional equilibrium levels of $0\cdot9$, $0\cdot46$ and $0\cdot3$ for RaA, RaB, RaC-C', respectively, or approximately 1750 WL. These exposures reduced the life span of these animals from 90 to 35 weeks, but no tumors were found. KUSHNEVA (1959) found that rats exposed to silica and radon developed more severe pathology, including emphysema and malignant tumors than animals exposed to either agent singly, but it is not clear whether radon daughters were present. These studies suggest that other factors present in the uranium mine atmosphere may be involved in the initiation and progression of respiratory tract pathology, perhaps acting in conjunction with inhaled radon daughters.

In the present continuing experiments, daily 6 h exposures of groups of 100 hamsters to either 30 WL of radon daughters, 600 WL of radon daughters, 600 WL of radon daughters with 15 mg/m^3 uranium ore dust (carnotite), or laboratory air (controls) have been underway for 19 to 23 months. After 6 months or more of exposures, hamsters receiving 600 WL radon daughters or 600 WL radon daughters with 15 mg/m^3 uranium ore dust showed lung changes including edema, emphysema, and occasionally hyperplasia and metaplasia of the bronchiolar epithelium. Several of the animals exposed to 600 WL radon daughters with the uranium ore dust seem to have developed changes in the bronchiolar epithelium suggestive of early tumor formation after 14 months of exposures. Mortality, body weight and hematology studies have shown no significant differences between experimental groups and controls. These findings suggest that other mine air contaminants, in this case carnotite ore dust, may contribute to the development of several types of respiratory tract pathology, including neoplasia, and that an experimental protocol of daily long-term exposures at levels that do not produce lifespan shortening may be necessary to produce these effects. Continuing experiments also involve lifespan exposure of hamsters to diesel exhaust with and without 600 WL radon daughters plus ore dust, to determine whether this agent is capable of a contributory or synergistic action in the observed precancerous and possible cancerous lung pathology.

Sixty-nine beagle dogs have been placed on daily life-span exposures. Forty dogs in two groups are smoking 10 cigarettes over a 16 h period daily 7 days per week. Forty dogs are receiving daily 4 h head-only exposures to 600 WL of radon daughters with 15 mg/m^3 of uranium ore dust. No significant biological effects of these exposures have been observed after 6 months of exposures, although transient changes have been observed in respiratory rates and volumes of individual exposed animals. Physical and radiological examinations and hematology studies on all dogs are continuing on a program of life-time daily exposures.

REFERENCES

ARCHER, V. E. (1970). Occupational Health Program, Salt Lake City, Utah. Personal communication.
AUERBACH, O., HAMMOND, E. C., KIRMAN, D. & GARFINKEL, L. (1970). Emphysema produced in dogs by cigarette smoking. In: *Inhalation carcinogenesis*. A.E.C. Symposium Series 18. pp. 375–388.
BAIR, W. J., PORTER, N. S., BROWN, D. P. & WEHNER, A. P. (1969). Apparatus for direct inhalation of cigarette smoke by dogs. *J. appl. Physiol.* **26,** 847–850.

CRAFT, R. C., OSER, J. L. & NORRIS, F. W. (1966). A method for determining relative amounts of combined and uncombined radon daughter activity in underground uranium mines. *Am. ind. Hyg. Ass. J.* **27**, 154–159.

DAVIS, R. F., SEMAN, J. J., HINDMAN, G. A. & O'NEILL, W. E. (1964). Mobile diesel-powered equipment for non-coal mines approved by the Bureau of Mines, 1951–62. U.S. Bur. Mines Circ. 8183.

DE VILLIERS, A. J. & WINDISH, J. P. (1964). Lung cancer in a fluorspar community. I. Radiation, dust and mortality experience. *Br. J. ind. Med.* **21**, 94–109.

EVANS, R. D. (1968). Massachusetts Institute of Technology. Personal communication.

FALK, H. L. (1970). Chemical definitions of inhalation hazards. In: *Inhalation carcinogenesis*. A.E.C. Symposium Series 18. pp. 13–26.

FEDERAL RADIATION COUNCIL (1967). Guidance for the control of radiation hazards in uranium mining. Staff Rep. (8) (Rev.).

GASTINEAU, R. M. (1969). Investigation of the thickness of bronchial epithelium. Univ. of N. Carolina, Master's Thesis.

HUECK, W. (1939). Kurzer Bericht über Ergebnisse anatomischer Untersuchungen in Schneeberg. *Z. Krebsforschung* **49**, 312–315.

KOTIN, P., FALK, H. L. & THOMAS, M. (1955). Aromatic hydrocarbons. III. Presence in the particulate phase of diesel-engine exhausts and the carcinogenicity of exhaust extracts. *A.M.A. Archs ind. Hlth* **11**, 113–120.

KUSHNEVA, V. S. (1959). On the problem of long-term effects of combined injury to animals of silicon dioxide and radon. AEC-Tr-4473. p. 22.

LINNELL, R. H. & SCOTT, W. E. (1962). Diesel exhaust analysis. *Archs envir. Hlth* **5**, 102–111.

LUNDIN, F. R., LLOYD, J. W., SMITH, E. M., ARCHER, V. E. & HOLADAY, D. A. (1969). Mortality of uranium miners in relation to radon exposure, hard-rock mining and cigarette smoking — 1950 through September 1967. *Hlth Phys.* **16**, 571–578.

McDANIEL, P. W. (1968). New York City Health and Toxicity Department. Personal communication.

MONTESANO, R., SAFFIOTTI, U. & SHUBIK, P. (1970). The role of topical and systemic factors in experimental respiratory carcinogenesis. In: *Inhalation carcinogenesis*, A.E.C. Symposium Series 18. pp. 353–371.

MORKEN, D. A. & SCOTT, J. K. (1966). The effects on mice of continual exposure to radon and its decay products. Rep. Univ. Rochester, N.Y. (669)

NATIONAL ACADEMY OF SCIENCES: NATIONAL RESEARCH COUNCIL, NATIONAL ACADEMY OF ENGINEERING. (1968). Radiation exposure of uranium miners. Rep. Advisory Comm., Washington D.C.

NELSON, I. C., PARKER, H. M., CROSS, F. T., CRAIG, D. K. & STUART, B. O. (1969). A further appraisal of dosimetry related to uranium mining hazards. Res. Rep. Publ. Hlth Serv. Contrast No. CPE59–131.

PARKER, H. M. (1969). The dilema of lung desimetry. *Hlth Phys.* **16**, 533–561.

PARSONS, W. D., DE VILLIERS, A. J., BARTLETT, L. S. & BECKLAKE, M. R. (1964). Lung cancer in a fluorspar community. II. Prevalence of respiratory symptoms and disability. *Br. J. ind. Med.* **21**, 110–116.

REPORT ON MEDICINE (1970). Smoking and cancer—in dogs. *Time* (16 Feb.), 48.

SACCOMANNO, G. (1969). St. Mary's & Veteran's Administration Hospitals, Grand Junction (Colorado). Personal communication.

SACCOMANNO, G. (1970). St. Mary's & Veteran's Administration Hospitals, Grand Junction (Colorado). Personal communication.

SACCOMANNO, G., ARCHER, V. E., SAUNDERS, R. F., JAMES, L. A. & BECKLER, P. A. (1964). Lung cancer of uranium miners on the Colorado Plateau. *Hlth Phys.* **10**, 1195–1202.

SAFFIOTTI, U. & BAKER, C. G. (1970). Program planning in inhalation carcinogenesis. In: *Inhalation carcinogenesis*. A.E.C. Symposium Series 18. pp. 467–481.

STUART, B. O., WILLARD, D. H. & HOWARD, E. B. (1970). Uranium mine air contaminants in dogs and hamsters. In: *Inhalation carcinogenesis*. A.E.C. Symposium Series 18. pp. 413–428.

TERRY, L. L. (1970). Cigarette smoking and respiratory disease. *Inhalation Therapy* **15**, 1–8.

UNITED STATES DEPARTMENT OF HEALTH, EDUCATION & WELFARE (1964). *Smoking and health.* Rep. Advisory Comm. to the Surgeon General of the Public Health Service. Washington, U.S. Govt. Printing Office.

WALSH, P. J. (1970). Radiation dose to the respiratory tract of uranium miners — a review of the literature. *Envir. Res.* **3**, 14–36.

DISCUSSION

P. GROSS: In making the diagnosis of emphysema it is very important to have two criteria in mind: (1) that there is unquestionable destruction of alveolar septa and (2) that there is overdistension of air spaces. It goes without saying that the pressence of these criteria can be determined only if the lungs have been distended under a pressure which does not cause artefactual changes.

The distinction between a typical hyperplasia and early neoplasia is a very difficult one in any tissue and it is doubly so in the lung. The criteria for making the diagnosis of early neoplasia should be spelled out. I have used the destruction of alveolar reticulin as one criterion for making the diagnosis of an early alveolar carcinoma.

Dr. STUART:* Before arriving at a diagnosis of emphysema we considered the possibility that the changes could have been due to pressure alterations at the time of sacrifice. Although not shown specifically in the Figures presented here, organization and evidence of healing in these tissues indicate that the majority of the observed changes occurred prior to death and are pathologic.

The difference between hyperplasia and neoplasia can be very difficult, as can the separation of benign and malignant tumors at an early stage of development. Invasion of the stroma by proliferating epithelial cells, while probably not the earliest indication of malignancy, is one criterion that we insist upon before classifying the lession as bronchiolo-alveolar carcinoma. When data have been collected over the entire experimental period, we will be able to determine whether "tumorlets" present at some earlier time were precancerous or not.

R. PERRAUD: I should like to describe the results of an experiment made in the laboratory of a mining division of the Commissariat à l'Energie Atomique. We are investigating the action of radon, associated or not with different dusts, on the lungs of rats.

In a preliminary experiment made last year, we exposed 12 rats to an aerosol of non-radioactive cerium hydroxide and afterwards to inhalations of a strong dose of radon over a period of 10 months.

10–18 months after the start of the experiment we obtained a malignant tumour of the nasal passages and seven pulmonary tumours — the degree of evolution and the differentiation of these tumours was variable.

D. A. HOLADAY: I consider Dr. Stuart's study to be quite important to the uranium mining industry. The question of the importance of atmospheric contamination by agents other than radon daughters in development of lung cancer is one which requires an answer if the risks to the miners are to be minimized.

L. CRALLEY: Carnotite ore has a number of minerals present in addition to uranium. Some of these may be biologically active and also behave synergistically with radon or diesel exhaust in producing cancer. Has the carnotite used in the experiment been analysed for these other minerals?

A. M. LANGER: What is the vanadium content of the ore? This may be far more important than the free-silica content, and may be considerable.

Dr. STUART: Carnotite ore does indeed contain a number of minerals, in addition to the radioactive members of the uranium chain, which may be biologically active. The carnotite ore used in our current studies was obtained from the Colorado plateau, and contains about 70% SiO_2, 4·1% U_3O_8, 3·4% V_2O_5 by weight, plus lead, iron, aluminum and selenium oxides. We plan to study the effects of the inhaled ore *per se* in greater detail.

Prof. SELIKOFF (Chairman): This question of ancillary factors is of some importance in view of the growing body of data concerning the lung cancer rate in other mining situations in which there is also a higher radioactivity level than we would expect.

K. ROBOCK: What is your opinion about the combined action of radon and dust? Is it possible that this stronger effect is due to adsorption of radon on the dust particle surface causing a higher activity and longer duration of radiation in the lung, or does the radiation excite electrons in the particles and thereby influence electron transfer reactions between the dust particles and biological material? I remember also the papers of Kasha and Eley and Szent Gyorgyi (*Horizons in Biochemistry*, New York, 1962).

Dr. STUART: At this stage in these continuing experiments one can only guess at the combined action of radon daughters and the ore dust. The particle size of the dust to which the daughters are attached, and the much greater availability of condensation nuclei for attachment when dust is present, will strongly influence deposition patterns of the radon daughters in the respiratory tract.

* Dr. Stuart, who was not present at the Symposium, replied in writing.

Attachment of these alpha-emitting radionuclides to insoluble ore particles may alter *in vivo* translocation kinetics.

G. KNIGHT: High levels, up to 2 mg/m^3, of particulate matter apparently from diesel exhaust, have been measured in the general atmosphere of a uranium mine, and thus may be of considerable importance in the development of some uranium miners' pneumoconiosis as well as lung cancer.

Dr. STUART: We collected high volume air samples in operating uranium mines on the Colorado plateau, and found heavy deposits of soot from diesel-powered equipment on all filter samples. Radon daughters were apparently attached predominantly to submicronic soot nuclei.

J. E. M. HUTCHINSON: Is there any evidence of a difference in the site of origin of lung cancer from cigarette smoking compared with exposure to radioactive inhaled particles. Specifically — following the work of Faulds on haematite workers — are peripheral lung cancers more likely to be due to radioactive inhaled particles and cancers in main bronchi more likely to be due to cigarette smoke?

D. A. HOLADAY (at the request of the Chairman): The site of origin of the tumors is sometimes difficult to determine. The majority of the cancers are in the hilar area. This is logical as dosimetric models indicate that the bronchial areas should receive the greatest dose.

Prof. SELIKOFF (Chairman): Cigarette smoking may so overwhelm all other effects that you might not be able to tell the effect of diesel fume, for example, if there should be one. This is true in humans. It might be true in the experimental animal.

Dr. STUART: The majority of the miners who have developed lung cancer have had histories of cigarette smoking. We are using large experimental animals to test the possible contributory or synergistic action of cigarette smoking in conjunction with radon daughter inhalation. The combined and separate effects of inhaled radon daughters, diesel exhaust, and carnotite ore dust are being studied with the shorter-lived hamsters.

THE ROLE OF SOME PHYSICAL AND CHEMICAL PROPERTIES OF MINE DUST IN THE DEVELOPMENT OF PNEUMOCONIOSIS

A. M. Shevchenko

Research Institution for Occupational Safety and Health, Krivoi Rog, USSR

The study of the relationship between the fibrogenicity of dust, its physical and chemical characteristics and the conditions of dust formation is one of the most important medical and biological aspects of pneumoconiosis. Investigations in this field are necessary for a number of reasons: to ascertain the dust hazard of specific occupations; to develop and establish dust control in relation to the fibrogenicity of dust; to plan the medical service for workers in dusty occupations and to interpret the symptoms resulting from adverse work conditions. Knowledge of the physical and chemical characteristics of the dust influencing fibrogenicity of dust particles is also of great importance in solving the problem of the pathogenesis of pneumoconiosis.

Our hygiene investigations in the Mining Industry have helped to show that the fibrogenicity of the dust differed in various working places even though the dust content in the air was approximately the same and there were only small differences in chemical and dispersed content of the dust. For instance, drillers were found to fall ill with pneumoconiosis 3 times as often as scraper workers though the mean content, size distribution and composition of the dust in the air while drilling and scraping were practically the same. In the mines where blasting operations are carried out more frequently (due to the mining and geological conditions), the number of pneumoconiosis cases is much greater. Our studies of underground ore mining show that the larger number of pneumoconiosis cases is due to the influence of the dust formed as a result of intensive rock disintegration. When crushing various minerals, especially the crystalline forms of silicon dioxide, the freshly formed dust possesses greatly increased physical and chemical activity, tends to accumulate electrostatic charges on the particle surfaces, and has the ability to adsorb toxic gases on the surfaces. We suggest that the electric charge and the ability to adsorb toxic explosive gases on the surfaces greatly influence fibrogenicity of dust particles.

ELECTRIC CHARGE OF DUST PARTICLES AND ITS INFLUENCE UPON FIBROGENICITY OF THE DUST

We have established that from 92 to 100% of dust particles entering the air of underground and surface works, and influencing workers' health, carry electrostatic charges. The number of positively and negatively charged particles is approximately the same (Table I).

TABLE I. ELECTRIC CHARGE OF DUST PARTICLES UNDER VARIOUS PRODUCTION PROCESSES IN MINING INDUSTRY

Production process	No. of particles observed (in absolute numbers)	Percent neutral	Percent positive	Percent negative	Distribution of charge on particles					
					1–40	41–80	81–120	121–160	161–300	above 300
Dry Drilling										
Mine No. 1	324	4·32	47·60	48·08	66·96	14·81	6·67	3·69	2·76	0·80
Mine No. 2	345	1·73	43·20	55·07	7·19	11·01	9·84	15·93	32·73	21·45
Quarry	706	0·0	52·40	47·60	57·19	23·79	4·73	4·67	5·72	3·97
Wet Drilling										
Mine No. 1	342	4·90	43·80	51·3	68·10	17·40	4·68	2·04	1·74	0·87
Mine No. 2	313	3·15	52·30	44·55	58·05	20·77	7·34	3·18	4·77	2·23
Mine No. 3	385	0·51	51·00	48·49	44·00	16·08	13·46	6·22	15·83	3·89
Scraping										
Mine No. 1	328	7·62	46·10	46·28	83·83	6·06	0·91	1·20	0·30	—
Mine No. 2	327	6·72	50·50	42·78	70·94	11·61	3·35	3·66	2·75	0·91
Loading										
Mine No. 1	375	5·86	41·60	52·54	86·74	4·79	0·34	0·26	0·53	—
Mine No. 2	327	4·89	42·20	52·91	56·07	14·47	8·55	6·41	7·09	2·44
Crushing										
Crusher 1	305	4·59	42·80	52·61	62·95	10·48	10·81	5·56	3·26	2·29
Crusher 2	305	2·29	44·30	53·41	56·38	18·02	9·17	4·91	8·18	0·98
Crusher 3	320	2·81	36·90	60·29	30·93	18·43	16·86	8·12	11·24	11·56

The number of electric charges on dust particles varies greatly. Along with particles carrying 1–5 elementary electrostatic charges there are particles with up to 2000 or more. The greatest number of charged particles and the highest charges are produced by the intensive mechanical disintegration of rock. In this case hardness of rock is of great importance. Increasing the humidity of rock, decreases the number of charged particles.

The experimental investigations we have made to study the influence of electrostatic charges of dust particles on their retention in lungs, showed that electric charges do not influence the retention of quartz dust particles in deep respiratory tract. Chemical determination of silica in lungs of experimental animals did not show a significant difference in its content when dusted with electro-charged and electro-neutral dust. The mean content of silica in animals which inhaled bipolar charged dust was $11·18 \pm 0·5$ mg/lung, and in animals inhaling electro-neutral dust, $11·19 \pm 0·8$ mg/lung.

The study of lung tissue from experimental animals by morphological and bio-chemical methods showed that inhalation of all kinds of dust was followed by the development of silicotic changes. But their severity depended upon the electric charge on the particles. The exposure of albino rats to unipolar (positive) and bipolar charged quartz dusts for 6 months was followed by more collagen in the lungs of animals in the second group; $47 \cdot 36 \pm 1 \cdot 6$ mg and $61 \cdot 98 \pm 3 \cdot 1$ mg (P $< 0 \cdot 01$) respectively. Analogous correlations were found when analysing weight indices of lungs; the dry weight of lung tissue and lung index were great in animals exposed to bipolar charged quartz dust. The difference was statistically significant (P $< 0 \cdot 05$).

Morphological changes in animals of this series differed slightly. The development of cell-dust nodules 150–200 μm diameter took place against the background of moderately thickened alveolar septa. Catarrhal bronchitis cases were noted. In animals inhaling bipolar charged dust there were more nodules but they did not differ by the degree of their maturity. Stained sections (van Giesen) showed single thin collagenous fibres in nodules; after silver impregnation a dense net of argyrophil fibres.

We noted that dusting of animals with bipolar charged dust was followed by more marked development of fibrosis in tracheobronchial lymphatic nodules in comparison with dusting with positively charged dust. A prolonged experiment (10·5 months) showed a decrease in the differences found in the shorter experiment. In animals inhaling bipolar charged dust for this period, only dry weight of lungs showed a marked increase; $648 \cdot 12 \pm 72 \cdot 0$ mg compared with $590 \cdot 56 \pm 47 \cdot 07$ mg for the positively charged dust, but this difference is not statistically significant (P $> 0 \cdot 05$). Difference in the content of collagen was less marked.

In animals dusted with bipolar charged and electro-neutral dust it is possible to establish that the most marked increase in collagenous proteins occurs in those animals dusted with bipolar charged dust (Table 2). The mean content of collagen in lungs of animals of this group was $66 \cdot 48 \pm 3 \cdot 8$ mg/lung; in animals inhaling electro-neutral dust — $47 \cdot 36 \pm 1 \cdot 6$ mg/lung. In lungs of animals of a control group (without dust exposure) the amount of collagenous proteins was $37 \cdot 71 \pm 1 \cdot 9$ mg/lung. The difference in the amount of collagenous proteins was statistically significant among all groups of animals (P $< 0 \cdot 001$). Differences of a similar kind also take place in indices of dry weight of lungs which show the degree of pulmonary fibrosis. The mean dry weight of rats' lungs dusted with electro-charged dust was the highest, $374 \cdot 5 \pm 20 \cdot 2$ mg/lung; when dusted with electro-neutral dust it was significantly less, $275 \cdot 9 \pm 23 \cdot 4$ mg/lung; in control groups of animals, $233 \cdot 5 \pm 17 \cdot 3$ mg/lung.

While investigating morphological changes in lungs of experimental animals, we have found that after exposing animals to electro-charged dust the number of silicotic nodules in lung parenchyma was considerably greater, nodules were more mature and larger and they were more often combined into conglomerates. Along with the facts mentioned above, this group of animals had rather marked development of connective tissue in thickened interalveolar septa. Our results indicate a more marked injurious effect of electro-charged dust particles in comparison with neutral ones.

A study of the functional state of dust phagocytes by the method of vital staining showed that of the animals dusted with electro-charged dust, more dust phagocytes were in the state of partial necrosis. Irreversible degenerative changes, destruction and dissolution of cells were more often found. Changes of this kind were also observed when studying the functional state of macrophages histochemically. We noted suppression of alkaline phosphatase activity in macrophages of lungs of animals who had inhaled electro-charged dust. We believe electric charges of dust particles intensify their injurious effect upon the phagocytizing cells. The most likely mechanism of the injurious action of electrically charged dust particles upon macrophage is the destruction of the biopotential and ionic equilibrium of a cell. It is

TABLE II. QUANTITATIVE INDICES CHARACTERIZING THE DEVELOPMENT OF SILICOSIS PROCESS UNDER EXPOSURE OF ANIMALS TO ELECTRO-CHARGED AND ELECTRO-NEUTRAL QUARTZ DUST

	Number of animals	Duration of exposure (months)	Dry weight of lungs (mg)	P	Lung index	P	Collagen content (mg/lung)	P	Silica content (mg/lung)	P
Bipolar-charged dust exposure	15	6	374·48 ± 20·20		6·50 ± 0·20		66·48 ± 3·80		11·18 ± 0·50	
Electro-neutral dust exposure	15	6	275·92 ± 23·44	<0·01	7·14 ± 0·31	>0·05	47·36 ± 1·60	<0·01	11·19 ± 0·80	>0·05
Control	5	5	233·52 ± 17·27		5·60 ± 0·36		37·71 ± 1·90		0·62 ± 0·03	

TABLE IV. QUANTITATIVE INDICES OF SILICOSIS FOLLOWING EXPOSURE OF ANIMALS TO QUARTZ DUST WITH AND WITHOUT ADSORBED CARBON MONOXIDE AND NITRIC OXIDES

	Number of animals	Duration of exposure (months)	Dry weight of lungs (mg)	P	Lung index	P	Collagen content (mg/lung)	P	Silica content (mg/lung)	P
Quartz dust	10	8	358·9 ± 16·5		4·52 ± 0·1		70·43 ± 2·7		8·09 ± 0·8	
Quartz dust +CO	10	8	447·1 ± 20·3	<0·01	5·31 ± 0·1	<0·01	82·68 ± 5·9	<0·01	8·10 ± 0·2	<0·05
Quartz dust +NO$_2$	10	8	376·2 ± 22·7	>0·05	4·78 ± 0·2	<0·05	93·19 ± 4·4	<0·05	6·50 ± 0·7	<0·25
Control	7		290·0 ± 11·05		4·10 ± 0·1		51·24 ± 2·4		1·28 ± 0·12	

believed that cellular membrane is semi-permeable and its electrostatic potential is maintained by difference of ionic concentration inside and outside the cell. In a normally functioning cell the outside surface is charged positively, the inside — negatively. The change of potential may exert great influence upon metabolism between the cell and surrounding tissue fluid.

The results of our investigations add to the proof that the electric charges on dust particles affect the development of pneumoconiosis by intensification of injurious action of dust particles on dust phagocytes, but we do not consider that the injurious effect of the dust is by the electrostatic potentials only. Dust particles are characterized by a number of physical and chemical properties and their combination determines the degree of dust fibrogenicity.

ADSORPTION OF EXPLOSIVE GASES BY DUST PARTICLES AND THE INFLUENCE OF ADSORBED GASES ON FIBROGENICITY OF THE DUST

The working of mineral deposits in the form of hard ores and rocks is effected, in the present state of technology, by drilling and blasting. While carrying out blasting operations, a large amount of gas and dust is formed ($1 \cdot 6$ to $3 \cdot 2$ kg/m³ blasted rock). Toxic gases — carbon monoxide and nitric oxides — are formed as a result of the use of ammoniacal-saltpetre explosives. At the moment of explosion there exist conditions which favour the intensive adsorption of gases on dust particles.

The investigations we have made showed that dust particles formed as a result of main production processes contain a large amount of carbon monoxide and nitrogen dioxide. These gases are on dust particles which are formed in surface mining as well.

With the help of experimental investigations we have determined the dependence of explosion-gases adsorption on temperature and gas concentration (Table III). From the gas mixture, which contains nitrogen, oxygen, carbonic acid and the explosion-gases (CO or NO_2), carbon monoxide is adsorbed in small quantities and nitrogen dioxide to a much greater extent. In addition to this, the presence of water vapour with the gas mixture prevents gas adsorption as water vapour is preferentially adsorbed.

TABLE 3. THE MEAN CONTENT OF ADSORBED EXPLOSIVE GASES ON DUST PARTICLES IN UNDERGROUND ORE MINING

Type of works	Investigated object	Number of samples	Explosive gases (mg per g of dust)	
			CO	NO₂
Horizontal working	Dust-gas cloud	90	0·0070	0·1836
	Dust on the blasted rock	70	0·0052	0·1093
	Dust from the walls of mine workings	70	0·0016	0·1526
Excavation	Dust-gas cloud	90	traces	0·2260
	Dust from the walls of mine workings	90	traces	0·1163
	Dust on the let out ore	90	0·0024	0·0115
	Weighted dust	90	0·0018	0·0086

A question of great interest is how quickly the process of gas desorption takes place. In normal conditions ($t = 20$ to $30°$ C, $p = 748$ to 770 mm Hg, relative humidity 60 to 70%) release of nitric oxides occur very slowly (up to 200 days). Explosion-gases are desorbed from quartz dust more slowly than from the dust of iron oxides. In the solutions of Ringer–Lock or Ringer–Tirode, desorption occurs more quickly. Thus, there are conditions for the adsorbed gases to penetrate into the respiratory tract along with the dust particles, and be taken up by macrophages, and desorbed within the phagocytes.

To study the influence of carbon monoxide and nitric oxides, adsorbed on particles, on the fibrogenicity of quartz dust and dusts containing mainly ore oxides, animals were dusted in special chambers. Albino rats 3 to 4 months of age and weight 180 to 220 g were used. Animals similar in age and weight were selected for two series of experiments. In the first series rats were dusted with quartz dust with adsorbed carbon monoxide, quartz dust with adsorbed nitric oxides, and with quartz dust free from the adsorbed gases (three groups). In the second series, iron-ore dust was used, with adsorbed carbon monoxide, with adsorbed nitric oxides, and free from the adsorbed gases. The adsorbed gas content on dust particles was controlled continuously. The mean content of the adsorbed gases was: carbon monoxide $0·0185 \pm 0·0028$ mg/g, nitrogen dioxide $0·3580 \pm 0·0026$ mg/g.

These experiments showed that silicosis occurred both when animals were dusted with quartz dust free from carbon monoxide and nitric oxides and when dusted with quartz dust on which these gases were adsorbed. The severity of the fibrotic process differed noticeably (Table 4). The mean content of collagen in animals dusted with quartz dust with adsorbed CO and NO_2 was greater than in animals dusted with "clean" quartz dust — $82·68 \pm 5·9$ mg/lung; $93·19 \pm 4·4$ mg/lung and $70·43 \pm 2·7$ mg/lung respectively. The difference in collagen content in animals dusted with "clean" quartz dust and dust with the adsorbed gases was statistically significant ($P < 0·01$).

By determining SiO_2 in lung tissue of animals dusted with quartz dust with the adsorbed nitric oxides, we have established that the amount of SiO_2 in them is less than that in animals of the other two groups. In animals with quartz dust with the adsorbed carbon monoxide, SiO_2 content in tissue is a little greater than in animals dusted with "clean" quartz dust and with dust with the adsorbed nitric oxides. The adsorption of carbon monoxide on dust particles favours retention of the dust in the lungs of experimental animals.

Lung weight and the lung index in animals which inhaled the dust with the adsorbed carbon monoxide was the highest. Thus, on the basis of quantitative evaluation of fibrotic process, SiO_2 content in lungs, and morphological changes in lung tissue, we may conclude that carbon monoxide, adsorbed on quartz dust, intensifies the fibrogenicity of the dust.

The content of collagen in animals dusted with the dust with the adsorbed carbon monoxide showed some intensification of fibrogenicity compared with the "clean" dust. Along with this the quartz content in lungs indicates that the adsorbed nitrogen dioxide favours elimination of dust particles from lungs.

When dusting animals for the period of one year with iron-ore dust with small content of SiO_2 (up to 1 %) free from the adsorbed CO and NO_2, a small, statistically unreliable amount of hydroxyproline is noted. So, the dust of ore oxides which we used in experiment is weakly fibrogenous. The small increase in the content of hydroxyproline in lung tissue we ascribe to the foreign body response of the lungs to the dust.

When dusting animals with iron-ore dust with adsorbed carbon monoxide, no intensification of dust particles fibrogenicity is noted. The hydroxyproline content, lung weights (dry and wet), and lung index were practically the same. There were no differences in morphological picture of lungs of animals dusted with "clean" iron-ore dust and iron-ore dust with the adsorbed carbon monoxide. Nitric oxides, adsorbed on iron-ore dust, even lower the aggressive action of the latter. The hydroxyproline content in lungs of animals of this series is lower than in animals dusted with "clean" iron-ore dust and dust adsorbed carbon monoxide. This is explained by more intensive elimination of iron oxides and quartz particles from lungs. Quartz particles, though in small quantity, exist in iron-ore dust. The data on accumulation of SiO_2 in lungs of experimental animals show this. SiO_2 content in lungs of animals dusted with iron-ore dust with adsorbed nitric oxides, is lower than that in animals dusted with iron-ore dust with the adsorbed carbon monoxide.

It is of interest to find out the mechanism of the intensifying action of the adsorbed carbon monoxide on dust particles upon the fibrogenicity of quartz dust. Our findings and the literature on the action of this toxic gas on organisms suggest the following mechanism. As it is known, carbon monoxide, independent of its effect in producing carboxyhaemoglobin, exerts a direct toxic action on cells by reducing tissue respiration and hence oxygen uptake. Investigations made by some authors indicate that carbon monoxide combines with not only haemoglobin but also hemin enzymes — cytochrome, cytochrome oxidase and myoglobin. This is why chronic carbon-monoxide-poisoning may occur without anoxemia (GADASKINA, 1966; GADASKINA et al., 1961).

The occurrence of the cyto-toxic action of carbon monoxide conclusively explains numerous examples of the toxic effect (in many cases poisoning by small concentration) with a normal content of carboxyhaemoglobin. V. I. SOBOLEVA (1957) gives data which show that under acute carbon monoxide poisoning, death came at a relatively small content of carboxyhaemoglobin (45–55%).

When penetrating into cell cytoplasm, crystals of SiO_2 also damage oxidizing processes in the Krebs cycle and in the chain of tissue respiration (SCHNEIDMAN, 1967). This author observed the marked fall of the activity of dehydrogenesis, diaphorases and cytochromoxidase in cells of silicotic nodules 8 weeks after intratracheal administration of quartz dust. Thus, the effect of the intensification of quartz dust fibrogenicity may be considered to be the result of summation of cytotoxic action of quartz particles and desorbing carbon monoxide.

Our results show that the fibrogenicity of dust particles is determined by a number of their physico-chemical properties, to a great extent depending upon the character of dust formation process and the factors accompanying dust formation. This fact should be taken into account while evaluating the pneumoconiosis hazard of various dust-producing processes and when working out measures for pneumoconiosis prevention.

Preventive measures on the control of dust electric charge and adsorption of explosive gases on dust particles in the Mining Industry will help in the lowering of fibrogenicity of industrial aerosols.

REFERENCES

GADASKINA, I. D. (1960). *Promyshlennaya toksikologiya.* MOSCOW. pp. 249–255.

GADASKINA, I. D., LYUBLINA, E. I., LIPKINA, N. A. & RYLOVA, M. L. (1961). *Gigiena truda i profza-bolevaniya.* **2,** 13–18.

SHNEIDMAN, I. M. (1967). *Tezicy dokladov nauchnoï konferentsii po voprosam gigieny truda i profza-bolevaniï, Karaganda.*

SOBOLEVA, V. I. (1957). *Patologicheskaya fisiologiya i eksperimental'naya terapiya* **1,** 12–19.

DISCUSSION

O. G. RAABE: By neutral aerosols you may mean aerosols whose charge distribution had been brought to Boltzman equilibrium since it is not possible to have for long neutral aerosol particles of diameters larger than $0 \cdot 5$ μm. What were the charge characteristics of the aerosol which you reported had a higher probability for silicosis because of higher charge?

What do you think is the mechanism of the effect of aerosol charge causing a higher probability of silicosis?

Prof. SCHEVCHENKO: We measured the polarity and charge of separate particles, not the total aerosol charge. By neutral dust, therefore, we mean particles not transported in an electric field.

Electric charges in our experiments seemed to appear on dust particles due to emission of electrons from the surface of hard material (quartz) at the moment of its disintegration (Kramer's effect) because the dust was produced in the ball mill just before feeding into the chamber.

Dust particles that have passed through the upper respiratory tract were shown by I. B. Shagan (1969) to retain the electric charge. This suggests that the particles at the moment of their contact with phagocytes are electrically charged.

K. ROBOCK: We have published in 1964 (*Naturwissenschaften* **51**, 385 (1964)) results about the action of X-ray excitations on the cytoxicity of quartz. We got a greater cytotoxicity of quartz after excitation by about 20%. The explanation is that there is an increase of electron-transfer by the interaction between the electron-excited quartz and the cells in connection with the electron-theory of catalysis. What is your opinion about electron-transfer reactions in relation to the cytotoxic action of quartz?

Prof. SCHEVCHENKO: We consider that the role of electric charges in the mechanism of harmful effect of dust particles upon the phagocytes consists in a change of the normal polarization of cell membrane where it comes into close contact with the charged dust particle. As a result of membrane potential disturbance, an alteration of ion-exchange processes in the system "section-cell" takes place with all ensuing consequences. The experimental data of Kramer (1950) and Bohun (1955) point to a direct relation between the emission of electrons from the surfaces of mineral dust particles and the development of pneumoconiosis. It is the harmful effect of the emitting electrons of quartz particles upon the phagocytes that appear to explain this relation.

W. H. WALTON: We have wondered whether electric charge affects the respirability of mine dust, either by promoting coagulation or by electrostatic forces of attraction or repulsion causing particles to be differently deposited in the lungs, but we have done little research into this apart from examining whether there is any upwards deposition of dust on to the plates of a horizontal elutriator (with negative results). Do you consider that the effects you have observed are due to such factors or to a different biological reaction to charged particles?

The size distribution (particularly as affected by the presence of aggregate particles) of airborne dusts in mines varies with the type of mining operation. Violent processes such as percussive drilling of hard rock tend to produce fine unaggregated particles whereas scraping or shovelling tend to raise coarse aggregated dusts. These differences in airborne size distribution would not be shown by Andreasen size analysis of bulk samples. Could this have been a factor in your work?

Prof. SCHEVCHENKO: We have not carried out direct experiments on the influence of electric charges of dust particles upon their retention in respiratory tracts. The silica content in lungs of animals exposed to electrocharged and electroneutral dust during 6–10 months was measured chemically. At the end of the experiment (under the same conditions) the silica content in all animals almost did not differ.

We believe that the higher fibrogenous activity of the electro-charged quartz dust is related to its more noticeable influence upon substratum.

On the supposed mechanism of this effect I dwelled above. As for dispersity of the dust in various production processes we have not found significant difference in size of the weighed particles.

J. DODGSON: Do you consider it likely that coal and mineral particles (quartz, kaolin or mica) will adsorb sufficient quantities of CO or NO_2 during shotfiring (blasting) operations in coalmines to appreciably increase the dust hazard? Will coal particles adsorb relatively large amounts of toxic gas because of their high internal surface area?

The relative humidities in British coalmines are commonly near 90%. What effect will this have on the absorption process? Will methane de-sorption prevent adsorption of toxic gases?

I would also like to know how you measured the adsorption of CO and NO_2 on the dust particles.

Prof. Schevchenko: Carbon monoxide and nitric oxides adsorbed during blasting operations on quartz particles exert statistically reliable influence on the elimination of these particles from lungs. In this case carbon monoxide inhibits and nitric oxides stimulate the elimination of the dust. In animals which inhaled quartz dust with adsorbed carbon monoxide the fibrogenic process was more noticeable.

We have no data about the adsorption of toxic gases on coal particles.

High relative humidity may appear to prevent to some extent the adsorption of gases on dust particles as the adsorption activity of water vapour is the highest. The use of polyethylene sacks with water in blasting operations practically completely prevented adsorption of toxic gases on particles. Adsorption activity of methane is higher than that of carbon monoxide and less than that of nitric oxides but it should be taken into account that at the moment of explosion the gas cloud contains mainly toxic gases (CO and NO_2).

The carbon monoxide adsorption was measured on the conductiometric set after the dust had been held in vacuum during 4 hours at 100° C and residual pressure 10^{-2} mm Hg.

In order to measure nitrogen dioxide a certain quantity of dust was put into a test-tube filled with a ground-in stopper, a capillary and a tap. The test-tube was evacuated to 10^{-2} mm Hg and heated at a temperature of 250° C for 60 min. After cooling, 10 ml of 0·1 N NaOH solution was injected into the test tube. 24 hours later the concentration of nitrogen dioxide was measured by means of the Griess reagent in the photocolorimeter FEK-4.

J. C. Gilson: What were the concentrations, size distributions and quartz contents of the dusts used in your animal experiments? Were these the same in all experiments? How did you measure the electrostatic charge on the particles and was there any variation of charge distribution with particle size during the experiments? Can you explain the effect of electrostatic charge on the phago-cytes? Would the charge not be neutralized immediately the dust particle makes contact with the conducting surface of the alveolus?

Prof. Schevchenko: While studying the role of electrostatic charges of dust particles in the development of pneumoconiosis the same conditions have been kept in all test series except for the character of aerosol electric charge. The level of exposure in chambers varied within the range 75–100 mg/m³, the dispersity of dust particles was close to the dispersity of dust in mine conditions: 84–97% dust particles were not larger than 1·5 μm. For the exposure fine α-quartz including 96–98% of free SiO_2 was used.

Electrostatic charge on particles was measured by ultra-microscopy of them in an electric field. By the motion of particles to the positive or negative electrode we judged the polarity of the charge, and the quantity of the charge by the velocity of motion.

We have not investigated the relation of electric charge to size of aerosol particles. Our hypothesis about the effect of electric charges of dust particles is presented in the previous answers.